dynamic earth
AN INTRODUCTION TO EARTH SCIENCE

**McGRAW-HILL
BOOK COMPANY**
New York
St. Louis
San Francisco
Düsseldorf
Johannesburg
Kuala Lumpur
London
Mexico
Montreal
New Delhi
Panama
Rio de Janeiro
Singapore
Sydney
Toronto

dynamic earth

AN INTRODUCTION TO EARTH SCIENCE

HENRY LEPP
Professor of Geology
Macalester College

dynamic earth
AN INTRODUCTION TO EARTH SCIENCE

34567890MURM79876543

Library of Congress Cataloging in Publication Data

Lepp, Henry.
  Dynamic earth.

  Includes bibliographies.
  1. Earth sciences.   I. Title.
QE26.2.L47   551   72-8787
ISBN 0-07-037204-7

This book was set in Helvetica by Textbook Services, Inc.
The editors were Jack L. Farnsworth and Laura Warner;
the designer was Barbara Ellwood;
and the production supervisor was Joe Campanella.
The drawings were done by Danmark & Michaels, Inc.
The printer was The Murray Printing Company;
the binder, Rand McNally & Company.

Cover: Section of the Juneau Ice Field, Alaska. *D. A. Rahm, "Slides for Geology," 1971. Used with permission of McGraw-Hill Book Company.*

CONTENTS

PREFACE

In this era of exploding populations, of increasing pressures upon the environment, of intensifying demands upon the earth's resources, and of growing opportunities for global and even space travel, it becomes increasingly important for students to learn more about the earth and its neighbors in space. The purpose of this book is to help fill this need. Designed as an introduction to the earth sciences for the general college student, the book does not address itself specifically to the problems of pollution, population, or earth resources; instead, by exploring such topics as the earth's size, composition, structure, processes, relationship to other planets, and history, it attempts to provide a background for understanding some of the current environmental problems. The aim is to provide an understanding of how scientists go about studying an object as large as the earth—to convey how we know about the earth rather than what is known.

The traditional college introduction to earth study is through courses in physical and historical geology. A few decades ago physical geology, as presented in most textbooks, was chiefly a survey of the processes that slowly act to change the landscapes. More recently, with the rapid expansion of knowledge in such earth-centered disciplines as geophysics, geochemistry, meteorology, oceanography, and planetary geology, there has been a move to decrease the space devoted to the evolution of landforms in physical geology books and to provide a more balanced view of the entire planet. Physical geology has thus tended to become more like earth science as presented in textbooks that began to appear about 10 years ago. Although existing introductory courses in earth science differ widely in their coverage, they are related in that all contain some astronomy, meteorology, and oceanography in addition to geology. In other words, most earth science courses tend to cover a complete spectrum of the earth-related sciences. I have tried to follow that pattern in this book.

It was difficult to decide what to include in a first look at so diverse a subject as the earth. No doubt my choice of topics reflects the fact that I have been teaching introductory geology for some 20 years, an experience that has showed me that most college students in introductory geology or earth science courses have only minimal science backgrounds and most will take no further work in the sciences. Consequently, one of my goals has been to convey the interdependence of the earth sciences and the pervading roles of the fundamental sciences of physics and chemistry in the study of the earth. The organization of the book reflects this goal. Instead of arranging the subject matter according to discipline, I have kept the earth as the central theme. Although there is a chapter on oceans, for example, material that might normally be considered in the realm of oceanography appears in other chapters where it is pertinent to the subject being explored.

The book is loosely arranged into three major units. Chapters 1 to 6 examine the earth as a planet, covering its size, shape, motion, composition, internal structure, and relationships to other planets in the solar system. Chapters 7 to 12 deal with the processes acting on and near the surface of the earth and with the energy conversions involved in these processes. They explore such topics as the movements of the atmosphere and oceans, the hydrologic cycle, weathering and soil formation, and the evolution of landscapes. The last unit (Chaps. 13 to 18) is concerned with the earth's internal processes, its history, its environment in space, and its probable origin. No attempt is made to outline earth history; the emphasis is on how history is read from sedimentary rocks and from other earth features.

I became involved with earth science teaching and resource materials in two programs sponsored by the American Geological Institute and supported by the National Science Foundation. The first of these was the 1959 Duluth Conference, charged with developing source materials for use in the rapidly expanding elementary and secondary school earth science programs. Continued growth of earth science in the secondary schools resulted in the organization of the Earth Science Curriculum Project, and I was fortunate to be able to serve as a writer and coordinator during several of the ESCP writing conferences in 1965 and 1966. I am grateful to the above organizations, and particularly to the dozens of earth scientists with whom I was associated in these programs, for broadening my view of planet earth. So many people were involved in these projects that it is impossible to list them all or to identify individual contributions. I am particularly indebted to Robert L. Heller, who was Director of the Duluth Conference and also the first director of ESCP, and to Ramon E. Bisque, Director of ESCP from 1965 to 1967, for inviting me to participate in these ventures.

Whereas the responsibility for errors and omissions in this book is solely mine, several persons have helped to eliminate mistakes and generally to make the book better than it would otherwise have been. Much credit for the text goes to the McGraw-Hill editorial staff, in particular David Beckwith, whose red pencil helped materially in changing my original drafts to a more readable form. Dr. Robert Heller read the entire manuscript, and Dr. Samuel Goldich commented on Chap. 13. Several of the chapters were used by some of my undergraduate students, whose comments and suggestions proved to be most helpful.

Credit for the illustrative materials is given in the figure captions. When I started this project, I was almost as awed by the prospect of assembling the illustrations as I was of writing the text. The courtesy of organizations such as NASA, the U.S. Geological Survey, and the Geological Survey of Canada, together with that of many individuals, made the task much easier than I had anticipated.

Finally, I am indebted to my family for their continued encouragement and help.

Henry Lepp

dynamic earth

AN INTRODUCTION TO EARTH SCIENCE

EARTH SCIENCE

1-1 THE EARTH SCIENCES

The study of the earth—its rocks and waters, its clouds, its size and shape, its place among the stars—doubtless began soon after man evolved into a thinking being. From our vantage point in the twentieth century, however, we would scarcely consider the earliest written speculations about our planet science. Certainly such works bear little resemblance to the modern earth sciences of geology, geochemistry, geophysics, hydrology, meteorology, pedology, and oceanography, most of which are little more than a century old.

To see how the various disciplines that form earth science evolved we must recognize that the earth has become an increasingly complicated subject for study. The naturalist of 200 years ago could undertake a general approach. His work might have included the investigation of such diverse topics as the nature of certain plants or animals, medicine, the origin of rocks, and the cause of inclement weather. He was able to work on all these topics because so little was known then about any of them. But new discoveries depend on the accumulation of knowledge. Even Sir Isaac Newton, one of the greatest scientists of all time, attributed his success to the fact that he "stood on the shoulders of giants." As information about the earth increased by leaps and bounds, it became increasingly difficult for any one man to master it all. Specialties evolved. The naturalist was replaced by biologists, whose concern is the earth's living things; by physicians, who focus on man's health; by geologists, who work chiefly with the rocks of the earth's crust in attempting to unravel the earth's history; and by meteorologists, whose chief concern is to explain the activity and structure of the atmosphere.

Specialization did not stop there. Today it is much sharper. For example, mineralogy (study of minerals), petrology (study of rocks), paleontology (study of fossils), geomorphology (study of landforms), and structural geology (study of earth structures) are but a few of the many special subdivisions of geology. Other disciplines like oceanography or geophysics are also subdivided. Earth science is a blanket name for all the sciences that collectively strive to understand the earth and its space neighbors. Besides having a common goal, the disciplines and subdisciplines of earth science all apply the same fundamental laws of physics and chemistry to earth study. These are the laws that describe how matter and energy behave.

This book makes no attempt to identify the specific contributions of any particular earth science, but it is important to recognize that this survey of the earth and its place in space represents the work of many specialists.

1-2 MAN'S CHANGING VIEW OF THE EARTH

The photograph taken by a telecommunications satellite in November 1967 (Fig. 1-1) shows almost a full hemisphere. South America is visible in its entirety, as well as large parts of Africa, North America, and Europe. The spiral cloud patterns reflect the earth's major wind systems, and the vastness of its oceans is apparent.

This photograph is truly amazing when we think how long and how hard men worked to get the information it displays. Some 2,000 years ago, Eratosthenes, a

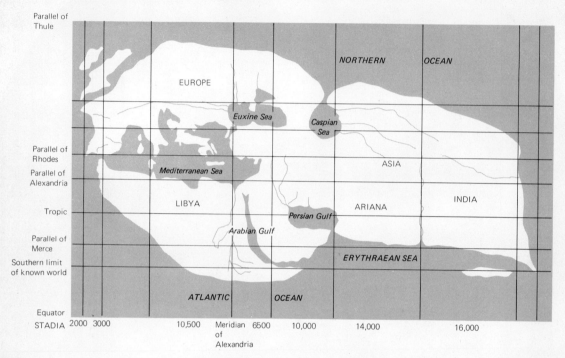

Parallel of Thule

Parallel of Rhodes

Parallel of Alexandria

Tropic

Parallel of Merce

Southern limit of known world

Equator
STADIA 2000 3000   10,500   Meridian 6500   10,000   14,000   16,000
                               of
                               Alexandria

EUROPE

NORTHERN   OCEAN

Euxine Sea   Caspian Sea

ASIA

Mediterranean Sea

LIBYA   ARIANA   INDIA

Persian Gulf

Arabian Gulf

ERYTHRAEAN SEA

ATLANTIC   OCEAN

FIGURE 1-2

The world of about 250 B.C. **according to Eratosthenes.** *M. R. Cohen and R. E. Drabkin, "A Sourcebook in Greek Science," Harvard University Press, 1948.*

Greek geographer, produced the map of the then known world shown in Fig. 1-2. The advance from this crude and incomplete map to modern world maps required centuries of exploration and thousands of man-years of measurement. Now a single photograph provides almost as much information as many centuries of work.

Little was known about the winds and weather until about 200 years ago, which, in view of the complexity and the changing nature of weather is hardly surprising. To discover patterns in the continually changing flow of air, man had to be able to make observations simultaneously at widely scattered places. Early theories about the weather were speculative. For example, the Greek philosopher Aristotle (383–322 B.C.) proposed a causal relationship between weather and earthquakes. He taught that all things were made of air, water, earth, and fire. According to him, violent weather and earthquakes resulted when air entering the body of the earth reacted with the internal fire to escape explosively into the atmosphere. As we now know, earthquakes have little or nothing to do with the weather (they result from internal earth processes). It is the uneven heating of the earth by the sun that drives the global circulation causing weather.

Aristotle's theory of a relationship between earthquakes and weather is typical of much early "science," which lacked the benefit of experiment and continued observation. After centuries of observation some of the details of atmospheric circulation were finally unraveled. Again, the achievement of many centuries of

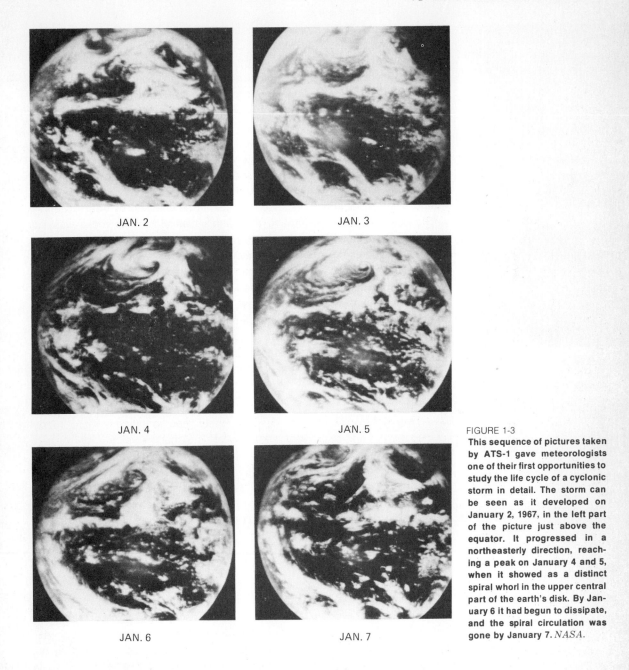

JAN. 2

JAN. 3

JAN. 4

JAN. 5

JAN. 6

JAN. 7

FIGURE 1-3
This sequence of pictures taken by ATS-1 gave meteorologists one of their first opportunities to study the life cycle of a cyclonic storm in detail. The storm can be seen as it developed on January 2, 1967, in the left part of the picture just above the equator. It progressed in a northeasterly direction, reaching a peak on January 4 and 5, when it showed as a distinct spiral whorl in the upper central part of the earth's disk. By January 6 it had begun to dissipate, and the spiral circulation was gone by January 7. *NASA.*

work is captured in the few space photographs of Fig. 1-3, which show the earth on several consecutive days. The birth and death of a cyclonic storm is clearly visible in the Northern Hemisphere. The overall cloud patterns mark the general global circulation pattern.

FIGURE 1-4
The 1967 eruption of Kilauea in Hawaii. *U.S. Geological Survey.*

Spectacular earth changes like volcanic eruptions (Fig. 1-4) or earthquakes (Fig. 1-5) always make a vivid impression. They are so terrifying and so outside the realm of everyday experience that they were long considered supernatural. This sort of thinking extended to other earth processes as well, the eighteenth-century explanation for mountain formation being that they were the product of a single cataclysmic event that occurred when the earth was made.

Clearly there could be no geology as long as the idea of mystic, capricious, and cataclysmic earth processes prevailed. Geology seeks to decipher the history of the earth. Interpreting earth history in terms of events never experienced by man is like playing a game without rules. One supernatural explanation for features like mountains is as good as the next, and it is impossible to argue against such explanations because they cannot be checked by observation.

The basic rule for interpreting the earth's history from its rocks was established late in the eighteenth century by the Scottish geologist James Hutton. His idea, known as the *principle of uniformitarianism*, was simply that the record in the rocks can and must be interpreted in terms of known processes. In other words, present processes are the key to interpreting the past.

This principle of uniformity of process soon changed man's view of the earth. Early in the nineteenth century many learned men believed the earth to be only a few thousand years old. So long as the mountains and valleys were considered to have been formed by a great catastrophe, this small figure for the earth's age presented no problem. When it became clear that the past could not logically be

FIGURE 1-5
In the Alaskan earthquake of March 27, 1964, the first-floor level of this theater in Anchorage dropped below the street. *U.S. Coast and Geodetic Survey.*

FIGURE 1-6
**The Grand Canyon of the Co-
lorado River. How long did it
take the river to carve this
chasm?** *N. W. Carkhuff, U.S.
Geological Survey.*

explained by upheavals never experienced by man and required slow but continuous known processes, it was obvious that the earth must be very much older.

Many generations of Americans have observed and photographed the apparently changeless scene of the Grand Canyon (Fig. 1-6). An examination of the
Colorado River, at the base of the canyon, shows it to be continuously carrying
sand and silt to the Gulf of California. According to Hutton's principle, the slow
erosion by the river must have created the canyon. Since the canyon has not
changed visibly during the past century, we are forced to conclude that for the
river to carve out the great chasm tens of thousands of years were needed.

The walls of the Grand Canyon consist of layers, or beds, of hardened sands,
mudstones, and limestones. How could such layers of rock have formed? A look
at the present shows that similar sheets of sand, mud, and lime are accumulating
in shallow seas at the rate of a few centimeters per century. According to the principle of uniformity, the lithified (hardened) sediments in the walls of the Grand
Canyon represent similar accumulations; since these walls are several thousand
meters high, it gradually became apparent that the earth must be millions of
years old.

The uniformitarian view of the rock record indirectly influenced the formulation of the theory of evolution. Although Charles Darwin's own studies were con-

FIGURE 1-7
Limestone with many marine fossils. Rocks of this sort were once thought to have formed during the great flood of Noah. *E. C. Hardin, U.S. Geological Survey.*

cerned chiefly with similarities among living organisms, he probably would not have proposed his bold theory if he had not been familiar with the uniformitarian view of the rock record. Before Hutton, layered sedimentary rocks of the type shown in Fig. 1-7 were usually considered products of the great flood of Noah's time. Uniformitarianists observed rivers carrying sands to the sea and noted the similarities between modern beach sands and the sandstones of the continents. The conclusion was clear: the sedimentary rocks on the continents were not the product of a single cataclysmic flood but represented material that had accumulated over many eons during periods of slow transgression and regression of the seas. This, of course, is exactly the sort of earth history Darwin needed for his theory of organic evolution.

The very long periods of time suggested by the rock record and required by the theory of evolution were not immediately accepted. With the discovery of radioactivity in the 1890s, man found a clock which could measure long periods of time. At first measuring techniques and instruments were both too crude to give accurate results. As a consequence the accepted age of the earth as measured by radioactive clocks changed by about a billion years per decade between 1920 and 1950. New technology and refined theories finally resulted in the age presently agreed upon for our planet of about 4.5 billion years.

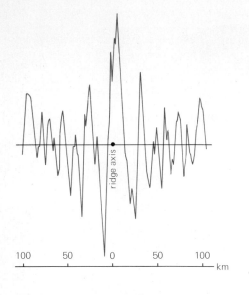

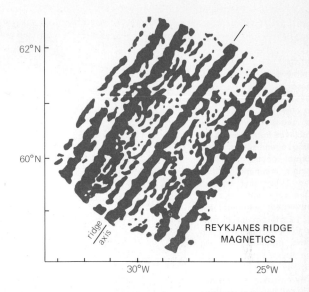

REYKJANES RIDGE
MAGNETICS

A

B

FIGURE 1-8
(*A*) **Observed profile of magnetic intensity across the Reykjanes ridge, southwest of Iceland. The bar graph at the bottom is the magnetic-reversal time scale determined by studies of magnetic polarity in lava flows formed during the past few million years, with color indicating normal and white reversed magnetic polarity.(*B*) A summary of a number of magnetic intensity profiles across the Reykjanes ridge; the peaks (positive magnetic anomalies) are color; the central positive anomaly corresponds to the ridge axis. See Fig. 1-9 for an explanation of how the symmetrical magnetic pattern over the ocean ridge systems is related to periods of reversal of the earth's magnetic field.** *From J. R. Heirtzler, X. Le Pichon, and J. G. Baron, Deep-Sea Res., vol. 13, pp. 427-443, 1966.*

1-3 DISCOVERING THE EARTH'S SECRETS

How are new discoveries in the earth sciences made? Although there is no simple answer to such a question, analyzing some of the significant advances in the earth sciences demonstrates that two factors are usually involved: (*1*) the overall expansion of scientific knowledge and (*2*) the development of instruments to extend man's senses.

Let us see how these factors are interrelated in a recent significant discovery. During the 1960s sufficient evidence had accumulated to convince most earth scientists that the floors of the oceans are spreading apart (since this process is discussed in Chap. 16, we omit the details here). The most powerful evidence that new crust is continually being generated along the ocean ridge systems comes from magnetic measurements made at sea and on land. Figure 1-8 shows a typical magnetic-intensity profile across the mid-Atlantic ridge and a graph demonstrating how the earth's magnetic field has reversed in the recent past. The humps and valleys of the Atlantic magnetic profile have the same spacing, or pattern, as the normal and reversed-polarity periods of the magnetic-reversal time scale. This is just what one would expect if the sea floor is spreading apart with new basaltic lava filling in the gap. Lava that erupts during a period of normal magnetic polarity retains this polarity. On the other hand, lava that crys-

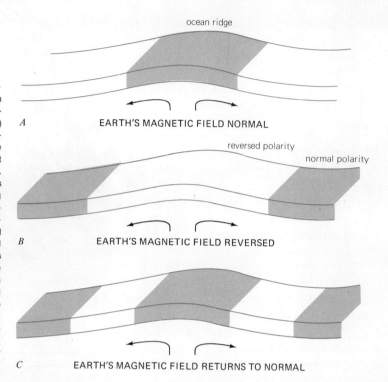

ocean ridge

A EARTH'S MAGNETIC FIELD NORMAL

reversed polarity

normal polarity

B EARTH'S MAGNETIC FIELD REVERSED

C EARTH'S MAGNETIC FIELD RETURNS TO NORMAL

FIGURE 1-9
The symmetrical magnetic patterns associated with the ocean ridge systems can best be explained by this model. (*A*) Earth's magnetic field is normal, and lavas formed along the spreading ocean ridge adopt this normal magnetic polarity. (*B*) Earth's magnetic field is reversed; lavas now erupting along the spreading ridge exhibit reversed magnetic polarity. (*C*) Earth's magnetic field returns to normal. The striped symmetric magnetic patterns over the ocean ridges must be due to the spreading of the sea floors. By matching the normal and reversed bands along ridge axes with the magnetic-reversal time scale, it is possible to determine spreading rates, which turn out to be of the order of a few centimeters per year.

tallized during a period of reversed polarity would have the reversed magnetism (Fig. 1-9).

Let us trace the background of this startling discovery. Early in this century it was found that the magnetic directions in recent lava flows are parallel to the direction of the earth's magnetic field where the flows formed. Further magnetic work during the 1920s disclosed groups of lava flows where some had normal and others reversed magnetic polarity. There are only two logical explanations for such observations: (*1*) the earth's magnetic field was reversed when the lavas with reversed polarity were formed, or (*2*) something caused a reversal of the magnetic direction of these lavas after they were formed. The first investigators naturally favored the second interpretation because the idea of the earth's north and south magnetic poles switching places seemed too drastic.

After a method was devised to compare periods of normal and reversed polarity on a worldwide basis, it became evident that the magnetic reversals in lava really do reflect reversals of the earth's poles. Such a comparison could be made only by measuring polarity in lavas of known age in different parts of the world. Thus the data of Fig. 1-8 depended upon the availability of a method for accurately dating rocks and specifically for dating lavas that erupted during the past 10 million years.

It should be evident that a great deal of prior knowledge in physics, chemistry, geology, and oceanography was needed before sea-floor spreading could be discovered. A knowledge of magnetism, a branch of physics, was fundamental. The earth's magnetic field had to be known. The magnetic properties of rocks had to be studied. Much work on the theory of radioactive decay and the establishment of decay constants had to be accomplished before radioactive dating became possible. This had to be followed by extensive experiments on techniques for detecting radioactive elements and measuring their abundance. Geological work was needed to apply the radiometric-dating techniques to minerals and rocks. Finally, the discovery of the ocean ridge systems was the result of extensive exploratory work on the oceans using sophisticated instruments developed since the beginning of World War II.

The role of instruments in this scientific discovery is equally obvious. Magnetic measurements are made by *magnetometers*, which, of course, had to be perfected before the oceanographic data of Fig. 1-8 could be acquired. New navigational instruments for locating ship positions accurately were necessary before meaningful data could be gathered at sea. Many instruments perform the chemical analysis connected with the radioactive dating of rocks. Of special importance in radioactive dating are *mass spectrometers*, which measure the relative abundance of isotopes in a sample. In fact, except for a few samples dredged from the ocean bottom, most of the present information on the topography and composition of the sea floor comes from measurements made at the surface of the water with a variety of instruments. They permit man to explore the hidden sea floor, to measure its depth, to determine its composition, and to "see" its topography.

Prior knowledge and instruments are important for discoveries in all the sciences. Are the earth sciences in any way unique? Yes, in that their subjects are so large and so complex that direct experiment is usually impossible. The earth scientist must work like a detective. His reasoning is mainly inductive; he puts together a picture or model of the earth from particular information from many of its parts. The earth is too large, the energy involved in earth changes too great, and the time needed for such changes too long to allow full-scale tests.

This does not mean that experiment is not a part of earth science. Many earth scientists work solely in the laboratory, concentrating on parts of the earth rather than the whole. During the 1960s, in preparation for the Apollo lunar landings, many earth scientists focused their attention on the moon and particularly on the problem of the origin of the lunar craters. Heated debates ensued between proponents of a volcanic origin for the craters and those who maintained that the craters are chiefly the result of meteorite impact. How do such structures differ? What criteria positively distinguish a volcanic crater from an impact crater?

The approach of examining known volcanic and impact structures on earth is a limited one because the impact origin of some earth craters is itself an interpretation. Experiment proved more valuable. Studying artificially produced impact and explosion craters and performing laboratory experiments on the behavior of

A

FIGURE 1-10
(*A*) **The SEDAN nuclear crater produced by the detonation of a 100-kiloton nuclear device 200 meters below the surface in Nevada. Crater diameter is about 350 meters. (*B*) The Barringer Meteor Crater in Arizona, diameter about 1,300 meters.** *N. M. Short, J. Geol. Educ., vol. 14, p. 154, 1966.*

B

materials under the high pressures accompanying impact led to the identification of certain materials and structures characteristic of impact. Figure 1-10 illustrates the resemblance between a nuclear-explosion crater and a meteorite-impact crater. Scientists expected such a similarity because experiment and theory indicated that meteorites with high kinetic energies should explode as they hit the earth's surface.

The knowledge of impact materials and structures gained from experiment and simulation has proved useful in other ways. Many previously unexplained circular earth structures are now positively identified as impact craters. The new information is also being applied in interpreting materials brought back from the moon.

1-4   THE PRACTICAL VALUE OF EARTH SCIENCE

In addition to studying the earth for the sheer pleasure of learning, there are a number of practical applications of earth science, the most obvious being the search for mineral resources and their intelligent exploitation. Petroleum and mining companies employ large numbers of geologists, geophysicists, geochemists, and (more recently) oceanographers in their search for oil and mineral deposits. Many earth scientists work with federal and state governments to find new resources of minerals, water, or energy.

Mining geology is the branch of earth science devoted to the study of mineral deposits. Petroleum geology deals with oil and gas accumulations in the crust. The relevance of these branches of geology to man's search for mineral raw materials is obvious. Every mineral-exploration venture is based upon some theory. If we knew exactly how mineral deposits formed, they would not be difficult to find. On the other hand, if we were completely unfamiliar with the processes that act to enrich the earth's crust with metals and wanted to look for nickel, say, we would have no reason to narrow the search to specific localities. The whole world would be the target, and the probability of discovery would be very small. Geologists have learned that all significant nickel deposits found to date are somehow associated with dark-colored igneous rocks called *gabbros*. There are several theories to explain this association, but whether the theories are right or wrong, the knowledge of the association is important. By narrowing the search to those small areas of the globe which contain this favorable rock the chances for discovery are markedly increased.

The importance of the earth sciences in supplying man's mineral needs is increasing. Once prospectors combed the countryside looking for surface indications of mineralization and dug trenches or blasted tunnels to expose veins. Most of the earth has now been explored, and the probability of finding a significant mineral deposit exposed at the surface is rapidly approaching zero; but there are still vast stretches of the continents where potential mineral-bearing rocks are hidden under soil or layers of barren rock. Moreover, the ocean floor, particularly on the continental shelves, is likely to contain mineral wealth.

These hidden deposits are the chief hope for our future mineral supply. Since they may be buried hundreds or even thousands of feet beneath the surface, their discovery depends upon the development of remote-sensing techniques. Geophysicists have perfected many methods of "looking" into the hidden parts of the crust. Magnetic measurements made from aircraft flying over the land have helped discover deeply buried iron deposits. Seismology is used to detect buried structures that may be potential traps for oil and gas. Surface and airborne electromagnetic devices have proved useful in detecting buried conductors such as metal deposits.

A broader and less conventional concern of the earth scientist is man's effect on planet earth. The earth is very large by human standards, but with exploding populations and increasing industrialization, man has become a significant

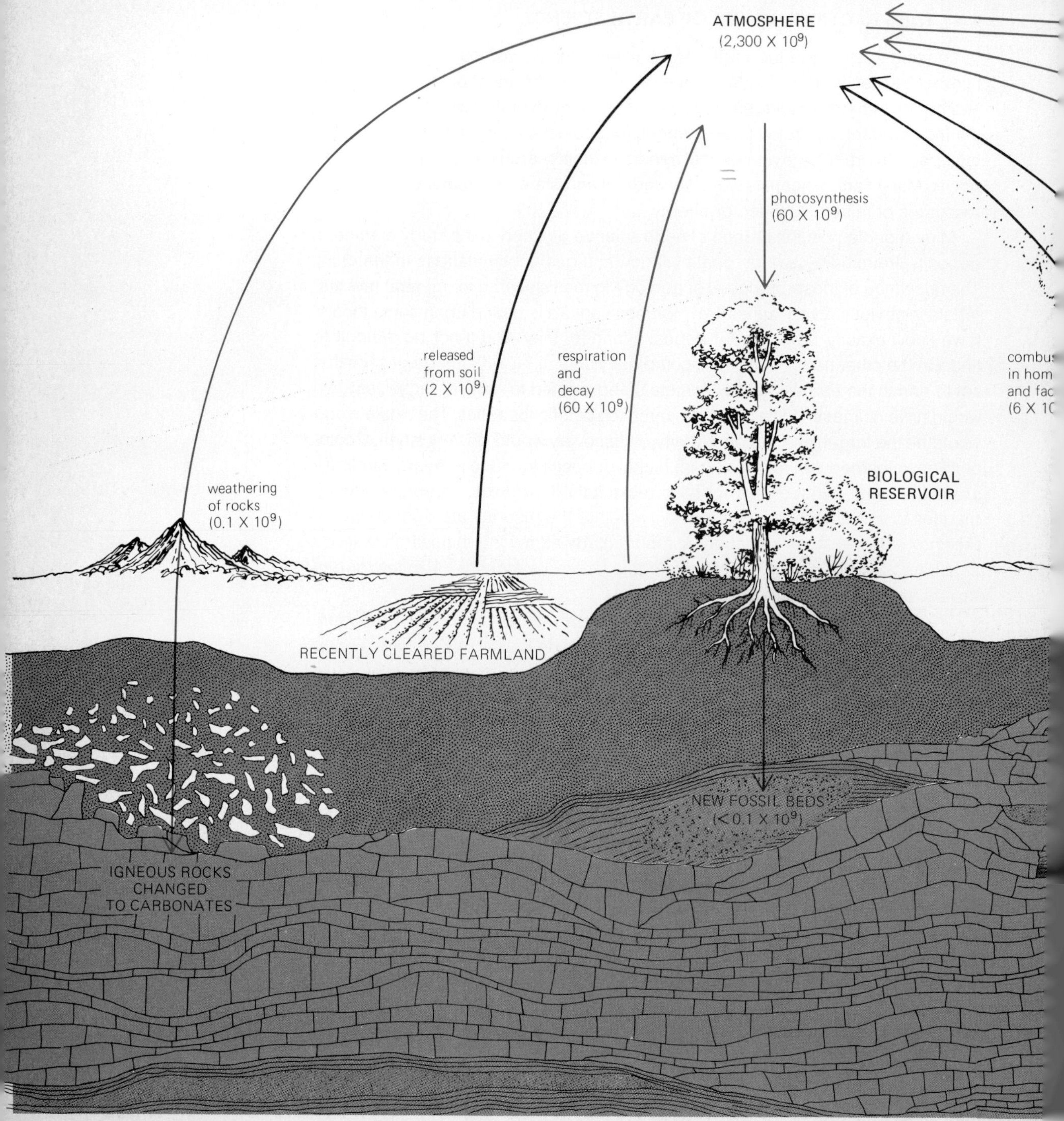

ATMOSPHERE
$(2,300 \times 10^9)$

photosynthesis
(60×10^9)

released
from soil
(2×10^9)

respiration
and
decay
(60×10^9)

combus
in hom
and fac
$(6 \times 10$

weathering
of rocks
(0.1×10^9)

BIOLOGICAL
RESERVOIR

RECENTLY CLEARED FARMLAND

NEW FOSSIL BEDS
$(< 0.1 \times 10^9)$

IGNEOUS ROCKS
CHANGED
TO CARBONATES

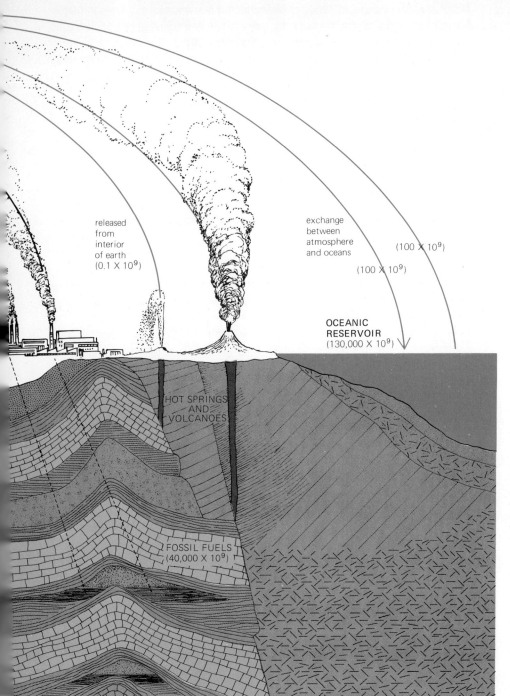

released
from
interior
of earth
(0.1 X 10⁹)

exchange
between
atmosphere
and oceans
                    (100 X 10⁹)

(100 X 10⁹)

OCEANIC
RESERVOIR
(130,000 X 10⁹)

HOT SPRINGS
AND
VOLCANOES

FOSSIL FUELS
(40,000 X 10⁹)

FIGURE 1-11
The cycle of carbon dioxide in nature. The numbers in parentheses after the name of a process indicate the number of tons of CO_2 being used in that process each year. Many factors influence the concentration of CO_2 in the air. Much of the CO_2 added to the atmosphere by artificial processes (dark arrows) is ultimately stored in the three great natural reservoirs: the earth, the oceans, and the biosphere. *Modified from G. N. Plass, Carbon Dioxide and Climate. Copyright © Scientific American Inc., July 1959. All rights reserved.*

factor in earth change. In 1960, for example, the burning of fossil fuels in factories, aircraft, cars, ships, homes, etc., resulted in the transfer of about 10,000 billion kilograms of carbon dioxide into the atmosphere. This amounts to about 1.3 parts of carbon dioxide per million parts of air, a fraction which seems small until we consider that the total amount of carbon dioxide in the atmosphere is only 315 parts per million. What will such an annual increase in the carbon dioxide content of the atmosphere do to our planet?

As with most questions involving the earth, the answer to this one is neither simple nor even known with certainty. Carbon dioxide in the atmosphere acts rather like glass in a greenhouse; i.e., it is transparent to the sun's radiation but tends to seal in the longer-wavelength radiation emanating from the earth. An increasing carbon dioxide content in the atmosphere should thus produce a gradual warming of the earth. But, as we shall see, the problem is complicated.

What temperature will we have to face in a hundred years? As we can see by Fig. 1-11, this complex question involves many facets of earth science. To predict the carbon dioxide content of the atmosphere a century from now involves much more than merely estimating man's use of fossil fuels. As new carbon dioxide moves into the atmosphere, the amount removed by plants in photosynthesis will change. The balance of carbon dioxide between the oceans and atmosphere will be altered. Predicting the amount of new carbon dioxide the seas can absorb requires an accurate knowledge of the mixing rates of ocean-water masses. The total influence of the sea in buffering the carbon dioxide content depends also upon reactions between carbon dioxide in seawater and the carbonates in the bottom sediments. Since carbon dioxide in the atmosphere is instrumental in weathering rock, it is clear that the rate of rock weathering should increase with increasing amounts of carbon dioxide in the air. Some of the carbon dioxide will be removed from the air by the increased weathering. Many other earth changes are equally complicated, in that a change in one variable affects many others.

Even if we could predict the carbon dioxide content of our atmosphere 100 years from now, we still would be far from determining the earth's surface temperature then. A slight rise in temperature would result in an increase in evaporation and cloudiness. Clouds reflect the sun's energy more effectively than land or sea and hence act to cool the earth.

Moreover, besides adding carbon dioxide to the atmosphere, burning fossil fuels also sends much smoke and fine dust into the air. These tiny particles reflect the sun's rays and work to decrease the earth's surface temperatures. With so many interacting variables it is small wonder that scientists do not agree in their predictions for the earth's temperature in the future.

This book does not address itself specifically to such practical problems of earth science as mineral supply and environmental control, but to understand these questions properly a person must first know something about the earth. He must have some knowledge of its constituent parts, its solid body, its atmosphere, and its hydrosphere. He must be aware of the size of the earth and of its relation to the sun and other space neighbors. Above all he must recognize that the earth is a changing body.

A few centuries ago prevailing opinion favored a static earth. The mountains and their rocks were thought to be changeless. Today we realize that the most constant feature of the earth is change. Water evaporates from sea and land into the atmosphere, whence it returns to its starting place as rain or snow. On a much slower scale rocks are worn away to form new rocks somewhere else. Mountains that have been worn flat are uplifted, and new mountains are born of the sea. These cyclical changes have been going on for at least 3 billion years.

In the pages to follow we shall look at some of the features and cycles of the earth, surveying its position in the universe, its motions, its size and shape, its composition, its constituent parts, and its "physiology" and noting its relationship to other celestial bodies. With this background we shall be in a better position to understand how the earth was formed and what its future is likely to be.

REFERENCES

Adams, Frank D.: "The Birth and Development of the Geological Sciences," Dover Publications, Inc., New York, 1954.

Bates, D. R.: "The Planet Earth," Pergamon Press, New York, 1964.

Cailleux, A.: "Anatomy of the Earth," McGraw-Hill Book Company, New York, 1968.

Cloud, Preston: "Adventures in Earth History," W. H. Freeman and Company, San Francisco, 1971.

Gass, I. G., P. J. Smith, and R. C. L. Wilson: "Understanding the Earth: A Reader in the Earth Sciences," M. I. T. Press, Cambridge, Mass., 1971.

Gilluly, J., A. C. Waters, and A. O. Woodford: "Principles of Physical Geology," 3d ed., W. H. Freeman and Company, San Francisco, 1968.

Holmes, Arthur: "Principles of Physical Geology," The Ronald Press, New York, 1965.

Leet, L. D., and Sheldon Judson: "Physical Geology," 3d ed., Prentice-Hall, Inc., Englewood Cliffs, N.J., 1970.

Longwell, C. R., R. F. Flint, and J. E. Sanders: "Physical Geology," John Wiley & Sons, Inc., New York, 1970.

Ordway, Richard J.: "Earth Science," D. Van Nostrand Company, Inc., Princeton, N.J., 1966.

Spencer, Edgar Winston: "Geology: A Survey of Earth Science," Thomas Y. Crowell Company, New York, 1965.

Spur, Jerome: "Earth, Sea and Air: A Survey of the Geophysical Sciences," Addison-Wesley Publishing Company, Inc., Reading, Mass., 1965.

Strahler, Arthur N.: "The Earth Sciences," 2d ed., Harper & Row, Publishers, Incorporated, New York, 1971.

Verhoogen, F. J., F. J. Turner, L. E. Weiss, C. Wahrhaftig, and W. S. Fyfe: "The Earth: An Introduction to Physical Geology," Holt, Rinehart and Winston, Inc., New York, 1970.

THE SATELLITE EARTH

The earth is a satellite of the sun. Like the manned spacecraft of our era, it carries its own life-support systems as it travels through millions of miles of space around the sun each year. Its systems are so vast and so adjustable that they have been able to maintain the conditions necessary for life for several billion years despite continuous change on earth.

Our study of the planet earth begins with an outward look into space, for two reasons. Since historically man solved many of the problems related to the earth's motions and its position in space before he learned to see what was underfoot, in beginning our investigation this way we are following the lead of history. It is also important to realize that the earth is influenced by the other bodies around it, particularly the sun. The general view of our planet will be particularly helpful when we later focus on details.

Man's interpretation of the motions he observed in the stars, planets, sun, and moon as he looked out from the earth changed markedly with time. For thousands of years most men believed that the earth was fixed and unmoving at the center of the universe. The observed motions in the sky were thought to be actual motions of the celestial bodies. Continued observation and careful measurements eventually showed this interpretation to be wrong. Early in the seventeenth century Kepler demonstrated that the earth and planets travel in elliptical orbits about the sun. Some 80 years later, Sir Isaac Newton showed that gravity controls the earth's motion, its tides, and its own satellites. Indeed, Newton's law of gravity was the basis for the computations that directed the satellite of Fig. 2-1 to a pinpoint landing on the moon.

2-1   THE SKYWARD VIEW

On a clear dark night the sky overhead looks like a great dome or half sphere, called the *celestial sphere*. The stars, the moon, and (in the daytime) the sun seem like patches or points of light on this sphere. Close observation of the celestial sphere reveals patterns in the star groups like Ursa Major (Big Dipper), Ursa Minor (Little Dipper), Cassiopeia, Cepheus, and others. These star groups, called *constellations*, were recognized by the ancients and are used to define areas of the celestial sphere.

If we watched the northern sky long enough on a starry night, we would see that the stars rotate, as shown by the time exposure in Fig 2-2. The position of the stars relative to each other does not change, but the entire sphere rotates around a point very close to Polaris, the North Star, known as the *north celestial pole* (NCP). Two stars at one end of the bowl of the Big Dipper act as pointers to

FIGURE 2-1
Astronaut Conrad inspects $Surveyor$**, which landed on the moon some 2½ years before the lunar module** $Intrepid$**, seen in the background.** $NSSDC$.

Polaris. Figure 2-3 illustrates how they can be used to locate Polaris regardless of the season or the time of night.

Closer inspection of the celestial sphere revealed "stars" that are not fixed in position. The Greeks called them *planetes*, planets, which means "wanderers." They move from month to month relative to the fixed stars in roughly the same paths among the constellations followed by the sun and moon. If we observed the planet Mars every evening for several months, we would recognize a motion rela-

FIGURE 2-2
Paths of the stars in the northern sky photographed by leaving the shutter open in a camera pointed at the polestar for 8 hours. *Lick Observatory photograph.*

tive to the fixed stars like that in Fig. 2-4. The planet first appears to move in one direction relative to the fixed stars; then it develops a reverse, or retrograde, motion, only to loop back to its original direction.

These motions in and of the celestial sphere, which have been known for millennia, can be interpreted in two ways: (*1*) as absolute motions of the stars and planets viewed from a stationary earth or (*2*) as relative motions of the celestial bodies seen from a spinning and moving earth.

2-2 THE PTOLEMAIC INTERPRETATION

The Greek astronomer Ptolemy developed an explanation for the motions of the heavens about A.D. 150. He reasoned first that the earth could not possibly be moving or things would be thrown skyward and moreover it would break apart. Furthermore, he believed that the motions of the celestial bodies must trace out circles because circles were considered to be perfect forms. From these premises Ptolemy developed a system of the universe that dominated thinking on the subject for over 1,000 years.

He first supposed the stars to be fixed lights on a huge rotating transparent sphere completely surrounding the sun and planets. At the center of all was the

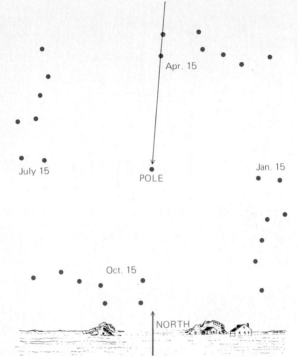

FIGURE 2-3
The Big Dipper as it appears at 9 P.M. in different seasons. The pointer stars of the Dipper always line up with the polestar.

earth. Thus an earthbound observer would expect the stars to trace circles in the night sky. The sun's motion offered no difficulty, as it was assumed to be in a circular orbit around an immobile earth. The occasional backward, or looping, motions of the planets proved more complicated. To account for them Ptolemy envisioned the planets as moving around central points in small circles

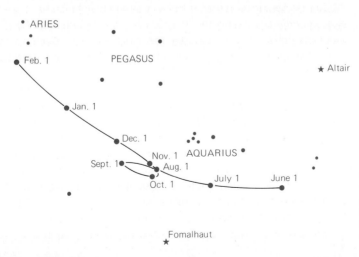

FIGURE 2-4
The path of Mars among the fixed stars. Although its general motion is from right to left, between early September and early October of the year shown the motion was reversed.

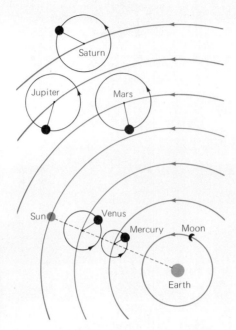

FIGURE 2-5
Ptolemy's interpretation of planetary motions. The smaller circles are epicycles within the larger circular orbits.

(epicycles) while these centers themselves were carried in large circular orbits, or cycles (Fig. 2-5).

For an acute observer, however, the Ptolemaic system was not ideal because it could not predict the positions of the planets accurately. In the sixteenth century the Polish astronomer Nicolaus Copernicus developed a sun-centered theory of planetary motion. Although the idea was not new, having been proposed by the Greeks centuries earlier, it met with strong resistance because it ran squarely against common opinion and religious dogma. According to Copernicus, the apparent motions of the stars are the result of the rotation of the earth on its axis. In his system the earth becomes one of the planets orbiting the sun, and, as we can see from Fig. 2-6, the occasional looping motions of the planets are explained without Ptolemy's cumbersome epicycles. The Copernican theory, however, was little better in predicting future positions of the planets. Its main advantage lay in its simplicity, which made it more palatable to the scientist.

The Italian astronomer and physicist Galileo added strong support to the Copernican theory in 1610, when, with the newly invented telescope, he discovered four moons revolving about the planet Jupiter (Fig. 2-7), thus providing visual proof that the earth is not the only center of revolution in the heavens. Moreover, Galileo's telescope also revealed the moonlike phases of Venus, which fitted the Copernican system but not the Ptolemaic one.

Using instruments capable of measuring to as close as 0.01°, Tycho Brahe, a

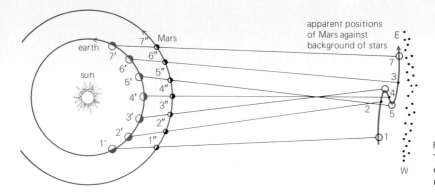

FIGURE 2-6
The real and apparent motions of Mars according to the Copernican system.

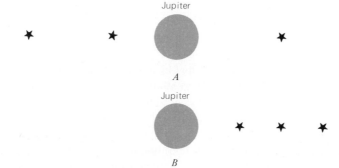

FIGURE 2-7
(*A*) On January 7, 1610, Galileo observed what appeared to be three stars lined up with the planet Jupiter. (*B*) The arrangement of these "stars" the next night. By January 13 it became clear that there were four starry objects near Jupiter and that they were indeed orbiting around that planet.

Danish nobleman and astronomer, spent most of his life carefully charting the positions of the planets. Although he failed to settle the problem of celestial motion, his measurements were effectively used to establish a new understanding of planetary motion by his student Johannes Kepler.

2-3 KEPLER'S LAWS OF PLANETARY MOTION

Kepler had worked with Brahe and had access to his voluminous data. After Brahe's death, in 1601, Kepler painstakingly plotted the results of many years of measurement of planetary positions (see Fig. 2-8). In 1609 he finally proposed the first two of his three laws of planetary motion. After more study and observation he published his third empirical law in 1619. His laws may be stated as follows:

1 All planets move in the same direction around the sun, following elliptical orbits with the sun at one focus of the ellipse.

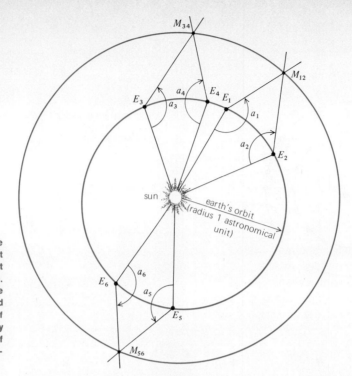

FIGURE 2-8
Kepler's method of plotting the orbit of Mars. With the earth at position E_1, Mars is seen at angle a_1 to the line of the sun. Mars returns to the same place 688 days later (its period), and at that time it makes an angle of a_2 with the line of the sun. By plotting other similar pairs of points the orbit of Mars was established.

2 Each planet moves so that its radius vector sweeps out equal areas in equal periods of time. This is illustrated in Fig. 2-9, which shows that when a planet is closest to the sun in its orbit (perihelion), it must move faster than when it is farthest from the sun (aphelion) in order for this rule to hold.

3 The ratio between the square of the time required to make a complete revolution around the sun (period) and the cube of the average distance from the sun is a constant for all the planets. For any two planets a and b this means

$$\frac{(P_a)^2}{(D_a)^3} = \frac{(P_b)^2}{(D_b)^3}$$

where P is the period and D the average distance from the sun. Thus if the period and distance from the sun for one planet are known, the distance of any other planet from the sun can be calculated from its period.

Unlike the earlier schemes of planetary motions, Kepler's empirical laws proved successful in predicting future positions of the planets. These laws, based on observations made with instruments we would now consider crude, have since been checked many times with modern telescopic measuring devices and are still accepted. The orbits of the planets are almost circular. Kepler's data were sufficiently accurate to reveal the slight ellipticity in their orbits. Not only did Kepler follow Copernicus in displacing the earth from its central position in the solar system, but his measurements also eliminated that supposedly perfect form, the circle.

Let us examine the apparent motions of the celestial sphere according to Kepler's view of the universe. The observed rotation of the stars around the poles becomes the result of the rotation of the earth on its axis. Similarly the daily rising

FIGURE 2-9
The earth's orbit is nearly circular, but the eccentricity has been greatly exaggerated here to illustrate Kepler's second law: the radius vectors blocks out equal areas in equal periods of time. Area ASB = area CDS, where AB and CD represent distances traveled by the earth in the same length of time and S is the sun.

and setting of the sun and moon are the result of the earth's spin. The apparent motion of the sun and planets against the background of the fixed stars is explained by the earth's yearly revolution around the sun. Because all planets move with different speeds around the sun, their motions should sometimes appear retrograde to an earthbound observer, as shown in Fig. 2-4.

2-4   WHAT KEEPS THE SOLAR SYSTEM TURNING?

Kepler's laws describe the observed motions of the planets but make no attempt to explain the cause of the motions. Why do the planets speed up when they are closest to the sun? Why do the inner planets travel faster in their orbits than those farther away? What keeps the whole system turning? The answers to these questions were found, not from a closer study of planetary motion but by examining the greater question of motion in general.

Just as the idea of an earth-centered universe dominated the world until the sixteenth century, so too did the idea that rest rather than motion was the natural state and that objects of different size or composition fell at different speeds. Galileo was among the first to challenge these beliefs. Legend says he dropped a bullet and a cannonball from the leaning tower of Pisa to demonstrate that objects of different size fall with equal acceleration. While there is no record that he actually made this test, he did conduct experiments with spheres rolling down inclined planes, and the germ of the idea that uniform motion is as natural a state as rest is found in his work.

In the seventeenth century Newton studied the question of motion and formulated scientific laws of motion that are still valid. His first law states that every body continues in a state of rest or uniform motion in a straight line unless a force acts upon it. Imagine a ball on a rough surface. If we give this ball a small push, it will move a short distance and stop. Now make the ball and the surface on which it moves smoother and smoother. The ball moves farther and farther in response to our slight push. If we could eliminate friction completely, the ball would move in a straight line forever. Some outside force would be required to turn it from its straight path or to stop its motion.

How does this tie in with our problem of planetary motion? The planets are always in motion but not in straight lines. Their curved paths mean that some force is constantly working to move them from a straight path. Newton called this force *gravity.* Although even today no one knows how gravity arises, Newton was able to demonstrate that the magnitude of the force of gravitational attraction is directly proportional to the product of the masses involved and inversely proportional to the square of the distance between them. Expressed as a formula, his universal law of gravitation becomes

$$F = \frac{Gm_1m_2}{d^2}$$

where F = force of gravitational attraction
G = universal numerical constant
m_1, m_2 = mass of objects 1 and 2
d = distance between objects 1 and 2

2-5 APPLICATION OF THE UNIVERSAL LAW OF GRAVITATION

Before showing how Newton's law of gravitation can be applied to provide new insight into the motions and properties of the planets, we must look at his second law of motion, which relates force and change of motion. We all have some familiarity with the second law of motion although we may not be able to put it into words. For example, no one is likely to kick a large ball of lead, but no one would hesitate to kick a football. The choice does not depend on a lead ball's having less resiliency than a ball filled with air: a lead ball somehow resists being put into motion.

The rate of change of motion of an object, called *acceleration,* may be an increase or decrease in speed in a given direction or a change in the direction of motion with no change in speed. Acceleration is measured in such units as kilometers per hour per second or centimeters per second per second. Figure 2-10 shows three accelerating objects; two are changing speed, and one is moving at a constant speed but changing its direction. Since all are accelerating, all are being acted upon by some force. The directions of the three forces causing these accelerations are, of course, all different.

Newton's second law of motion relates force F, mass m, and acceleration a according to the formula $F = ma$. Mass may be defined as the quantity of matter in an object. It is different from weight, which is the force of the earth's gravitational attraction on a body. As we shall see in Chap. 3, the weight of an object on a high mountain is different from its weight at sea level, but its mass remains the same whether it is on the earth, on the moon, or floating in space.

Now we can see that a bullet and a cannonball dropped from the leaning tower of Pisa should indeed accelerate equally. The acceleration in both cases is due to the force of gravity. According to the universal law of gravitation, this force for the cannonball of mass m would be

$$F = \frac{GM_{earth}m}{d^2}$$

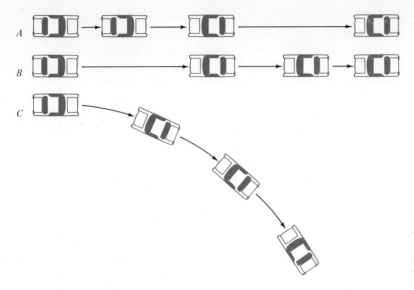

FIGURE 2-10
Three vehicles undergoing uniform acceleration. The drawings show positions at equal time intervals.

The value of d, the distance between the two masses, is equal to the radius of the earth for any object at the earth's surface because Newton showed that the mass of a sphere can be considered as being concentrated at its center. We also know that the force F necessary to produce an acceleration a in a cannonball of mass m is $F = ma$. Substituting for F in the previous equation, we get

$$ma = \frac{GM_{earth}\,m}{d^2} \qquad \text{or} \qquad a = \frac{GM_{earth}}{d^2}$$

The value for the mass m of the cannonball cancels out, and so would that of a bullet or any other object.

If the law of gravitation is truly universal, it should apply as well to the moon and planets as to objects falling near the earth's surface. Since the moon does not fall toward the earth, it may not be easy at first glance to see how the motion of the moon and an apple falling from a tree are related. Objects released near the earth's surface fall (accelerate) toward the earth's center. Let us now imagine ourselves on a tall building from which we simultaneously drop a stone and throw one horizontally (Fig. 2-11). Both stones accelerate earthward at the same rate because both are drawn by the force of gravity. The stone thrown horizontally will cover a greater distance, but if there were no air resistance, it would hit the earth at the same time as the one that dropped straight down. If we imagine progressively greater initial speeds for the stone thrown horizontally, the arc of its trajectory becomes flatter and flatter until it becomes parallel to the earth's surface. At this initial velocity the stone would continue to circle the earth forever if there were no air resistance to slow it down. It still deviates earthward from a

FIGURE 2-11
Two stones, one dropped vertically and the other thrown horizontally, will reach the ground at the same time because both are accelerated downward by the same constant force.

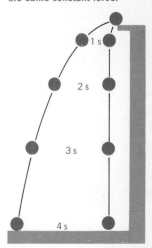

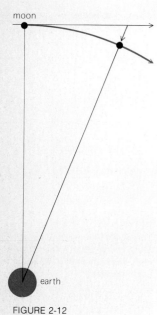

moon

earth

FIGURE 2-12
The moon accelerates toward the earth from the straight path that it would follow if no force were acting on it. The observed deviation from the straight path is equal to that predicted by Newton's law of gravitation.

straight path at the same rate that a stone falling vertically does because of the pull of gravity.

We know, of course, that the principle described above is used in launching an orbiting satellite. The moon too must have had an initial velocity, and it is the earth's gravitational attraction that bends its otherwise straight path into a nearly circular orbit. Experiments with falling bodies at the earth's surface in Newton's day had already shown them to accelerate at 9.8 meters per second per second (written m/s^2). Objects at the earth's surface are about 6,400 kilometers from its center. If an object is lifted 12,800 kilometers above the surface of the earth (twice the distance from the center), its initial acceleration should be 1/2^2, or $\frac{1}{4}$(9.8 m/s^2), because the force varies inversely as the square of the distance $(F = Gm_1m_2/d^2)$ and the acceleration is directly proportional to the force $(F = ma)$.

The moon is about 60 earth radii (384,000 kilometers) from the earth, and thus it should be falling earthward with an acceleration of 1/(60)^2, or $\frac{1}{3,600}$ (9.8 m/s^2). This works out to 0.0027 m/s^2, which corresponds to the moon's observed acceleration (Fig. 2-12). The law of gravitation is indeed universal because it applies equally to the moon and planets and a stone falling near the earth.

The law of gravitation differs from Kepler's empirical laws of planetary motion because it permits scientists to calculate the effect of one planet on another accurately. In fact, the planets Neptune and Pluto were discovered by the application of the law of gravitation. Uranus was discovered in 1781. Until about 1800 the motions of the new planet seemed perfectly regular and in accord with those predicted for it by the law of gravitation. By 1840, however, it had become clear that Uranus was not moving as it should; it was then 1.5 minutes of arc from its predicted position.

Some astronomers attributed the difference between the predicted and observed positions of Uranus to departures from the inverse-square law of gravitation at great distances. Others, however, held to the universality of gravitation, suggesting that the minor deviations of the orbit might be due to the gravitational effect of an undiscovered planet. In 1841, John C. Adams, an undergraduate at Cambridge University, set himself the task of attempting to calculate the position of an unknown planet that could account for the slight irregularities in the orbit of Uranus. After 4 years of work he obtained a solution, but his contemporaries unfortunately paid little attention to the work and did not even bother to turn their telescopes toward the position.

In 1845 the French astronomer Le Verrier, not knowing of Adam's work, made similar calculations, and a year later he published the predicted position of the unknown planet, which agreed almost exactly with that proposed by Adams. Astronomers in Berlin used Le Verrier's figures, looked into that region of the sky where he had calculated the new planet to be, and immediately found it. It was named Neptune.

After Neptune became better known, small irregularities in its orbit suggested that there might be yet another planet still farther out. Early in this century the

American astronomers Percival Lowell and William Pickering calculated the probable position of the suspected planet. It was so small and so distant that many years elapsed before it was finally discovered by Clyde Tombaugh, of the Lowell Observatory, in 1930. Figure 2-13 shows photographic plates of the type which led to the discovery of Pluto. Although the planet turned out to be about where Lowell and Pickering predicted, it is small wonder that years were needed to pin down this tiny wanderer.

2-6 THE MASS OF THE EARTH

According to the law of gravitation, a spherical body may be considered to act as though its mass were concentrated at its center. Consequently the force on a mass m at the earth's surface is

$$F = \frac{GM_{earth}\,m}{d^2}$$

Also according to the second law of motion, the acceleration due to gravity g at the earth's surface is related to force F by the relation $F = mg$. We have seen that the acceleration of gravity at the surface of the earth is 9.8 m/s². Substituting the term mg for force in the earlier equation, we get

$$mg = \frac{GM_{earth}\,m}{d^2} \qquad \text{or} \qquad M_{earth} = \frac{gd^2}{G}$$

As we noted earlier the distance d is the earth's radius. In Chap. 3 we shall see how the radius is measured. Since the acceleration of gravity g and the radius of the earth are known, the only figure needed to determine the earth's mass from the preceding equation is G, the universal constant of gravitation.

This constant was first measured by Henry Cavendish in 1798; later it was measured independently by the German scientist Philipp von Jolly, whose method (Fig. 2-14) is the easier of the two to describe. He first weighed a mass m_1 and then reweighed the same mass with a second large mass m_2 placed directly under it. In this case the force of gravitational attraction between the masses m_1 and m_2 is the difference between the two weighings. The distances between the two masses were carefully measured, leaving G as the only unknown in the relation

$$F = \frac{Gm_1 m_2}{d^2}$$

The constant G could thus be calculated from the data.

The presently accepted value of G is 6.67 × 10⁻⁸ cubic centimeter per gram-second per second. When this number is inserted in the earlier equation $M_{earth} = gd^2/G$, the mass of the earth is found to be 6 × 10²⁷ grams, or 6 × 10²¹ metric tons. (Students not familiar with scientific notation, i.e., numbers like 6 × 10²¹ and 6 × 10⁻⁸, should refer to the explanation in Appendix A.)

MAR. 10, 1934

MAR. 11, 1934

FIGURE 2-13
Two photographs of Pluto showing its change in position among the fixed stars in 1 day. *Yerkes Observatory photograph.*

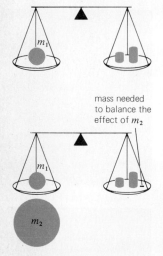

mass needed
to balance the
effect of m_2

FIGURE 2-14
Jolly's method of determining the gravitational constant.

2-7 DIRECT EVIDENCE OF ROTATION AND REVOLUTION

We have seen how the interpretation of the observed motions of the celestial sphere has changed in time. According to Kepler's explanation, the observed daily motions of the stars in the celestial sphere are the result of the daily rotation of the earth. Moreover, the yearly revolution of the earth around the sun and the similar revolutions of the other planets, each in its own orbit, explain the observed planetary motions as viewed from earth. This interpretation of the planetary motions seems correct both because it is simple and because it permits relatively accurate prediction of the positions of celestial bodies. Moreover, it is the type of motion to be expected from Newton's laws. The fact remains, however, that Ptolemy's system, although much more complicated, could with modifications also account for the celestial motions. Is there any direct evidence—internal evidence, so to speak, which does not depend upon observations of extraterrestrial bodies—that the earth is spinning on its axis?

A method of demonstrating earth rotation was devised by the French scientist Jean Foucault (1819–1868). He suspended a cannonball from a 219-foot wire fastened to a freely rotating swivel in the dome of the Pantheon in Paris. Scientists had demonstrated that a pendulum of this sort should continue to swing in the same plane in space. When Foucault's pendulum was set in motion, it appeared to rotate slowly at the rate of 360° in about 31 hours.

Foucault pendulums are now displayed in many museums and science buildings. The significance of the apparent motion of the pendulum is best understood by visualizing one swinging at the North Pole (Fig. 2-15), where it would appear

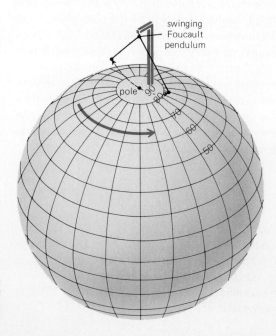

swinging
Foucault
pendulum

pole

FIGURE 2-15
At the North Pole a Foucault pendulum swinging in a fixed plane appears to turn 360° in a day because of the earth's spin.

to rotate through 360° in 24 hours. Since the plane of the pendulum's swing is fixed, the observed rotation must be due to the daily rotation of the earth beneath the pendulum. Away from the poles the observed rotation of the Foucault pendulum is not a simple 360° in 24 hours. What would such a pendulum do at the equator?

Supporting evidence for rotation of the earth is furnished by the distances between the earth and the sun or stars. The distance from the earth to the moon, the sun, and even to a few of the closest stars can be measured by triangulation, a common technique of surveyors. For example, in Fig. 2-16 the distance AB across the river is found by measuring the length of the line AC on one side of the river and determining the angles ACB and CAB. With these two angles and the length of one side it is an easy matter to plot the triangle and thus to scale the lengths of the unknown sides. The distances represented by the unmeasured sides can also be calculated trigonometrically.

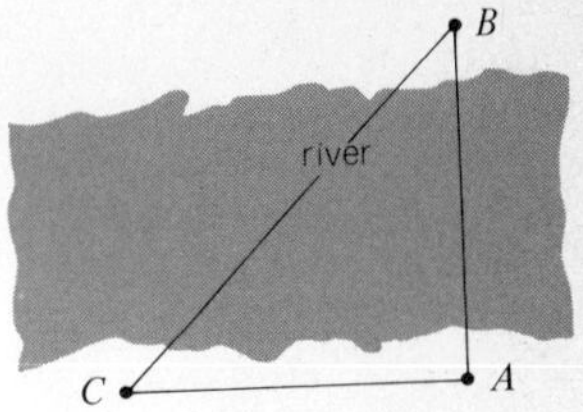

This method is used by astronomers to measure distances from the earth to the moon or other planets. Figure 2-17 shows two observatories separated by a known distance of several thousand miles. If measurements of the angle between each observatory and the moon, for example, are made at the same time, we have the same information as in Fig. 2-16. Actually, in this case, it is the small angle at P that is measured by noting how far the moon appears to shift against the background of the fixed stars when viewed from two positions. One-half of the angle at the apex (angle P) is called the *parallax* of the object being measured. Note that triangle LOP is an equilateral triangle; thus if we know the angle at P, we also know the other two angles of the triangle. The distance to the moon can be calculated from these data. The sun's parallax determined from two stations separated by a distance equal to the earth's diameter is only 8.8 seconds of arc (0.0025°). Its distance turns out to be 150×10^6 kilometers, or 93 million miles. Recently more refined measurements of distances to the sun and planets have been made by radar.

To see how the distance to the sun is related to the problem of earth-sun motions suppose that the sun were actually moving around the earth on a path with a radius of 1.5×10^8 kilometers. It would then have to travel 10,900 kilometers per second in order to complete the trip in 24 hours. The more distant stars would have to travel millions and even billions of times as fast to make their daily circles. Because such speeds are completely unreasonable, it is much more log-

FIGURE 2-16
By measuring the length of the side AC and the angles BCA and BAC the distance AB across the river can be calculated or determined graphically. Astronomers use a similar technique to measure distances in space.

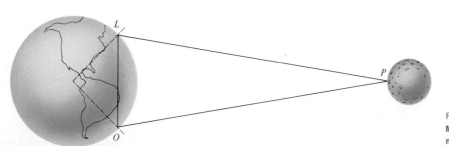

FIGURE 2-17
Measuring the distance to the moon.

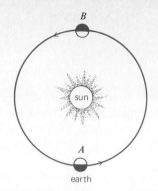

fixed stars

ical to assume that the apparent daily motions of the sun and stars result from the daily rotation of the earth.

The stars are so far away that no parallax can be detected when the same star is viewed from two points on earth at the same time, but distances to some of the closest stars can be determined by the parallax method when the base line is lengthened from one earth diameter to the diameter of the earth's orbit about the sun. We return to the question of stellar parallax in Chap. 17, where we shall see that even with a base line of some 180 million miles the near stars exhibit only tiny parallactic shifts. That they do show parallax, however, is proof of the earth's yearly rotation about the sun.

At position A in Fig. 2-18 the earth is moving away from the stars shown, whereas at point B it moves toward them. Most of us are aware that the sound of an approaching train or aircraft changes pitch as it approaches the listener or moves away from him. This change in pitch, or frequency, is known as the *Doppler effect*. Light is affected by relative motion in the same way: its frequency, or color, is changed. A light source moving toward an observer should appear bluer than a stationary source, whereas light from a receding source should appear redder. Objects cannot be seen to change color as they pass, because very elaborate instruments are needed to register the Doppler effect for light. Careful spectral analysis of starlight reveals that the light from a given star is bluer at one time of the year and redder 6 months later, thus confirming the conclusion that the earth revolves around the sun.

2-8   TIDES AND SEASONS

Next to the rising and setting of the sun, the most obvious effects of the earth's rotation and revolution are the daily tides and the yearly seasons. Man has long known of the relationship between tides and phases of the moon, but the reason for the tides has not been so obvious. Kepler attributed them to "some kind of magnetic attraction between the moon and the earth's waters." It was Newton's law of gravitation that finally explained the tide-causing forces.

We all know that the tides are somehow related to the moon's gravitational attraction, but the story does not end there. According to the law of universal gravitation, the force of gravity exerted by the moon on a unit mass of water at the earth's surface is

$$F = \frac{GM_{\text{moon}}}{(d_{\text{moon}})^2}$$

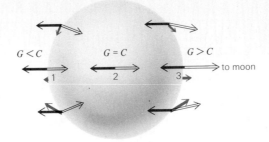

FIGURE 2-19
The tide-producing forces.
Open arrows represent gravitational attractive force G; dark
arrows are centrifugal force C
arising from rotation of the
earth-moon system; color
arrows are the tide-producing
resultants.

The force exerted by the sun on the same unit of mass would of course be

$$F = \frac{GM_{\text{sun}}}{(d_{\text{sun}})^2}$$

Even though the sun is almost 400 times as far away as the moon, it exerts the
greater force because it is about 27 million times as massive. In fact we can see
that the sun's attraction should be about $27,000,000/(400)^2 = 170$ times as great
as the moon's. How then can the moon be the primary cause of the tides?

The tide-raising forces at points on the earth's surface are the result of differences in gravitational attraction. To illustrate let us consider points 1, 2, and 3
in Fig. 2-19. Point 2 is at the center of the earth. The magnitude and direction of
the moon's gravitational attraction on a unit mass there is displayed by the open
arrow. If this were the only force acting on this unit mass, it should be falling
toward the moon. Because this is not happening, there must be an equal and opposite force acting upon the unit of mass. This counterbalancing force is the centrifugal force arising from the rotation of the earth-moon system.

At points 1 and 3 the centrifugal component remains the same as it does everywhere on earth, but the attractive forces due to the moon's gravitational influence are different. Point 3 is at an average distance of 236,000 miles from the
moon's center, whereas point 1 is 244,000 miles away. The gravity component is
thus larger at 3. Subtracting the centrifugal component from the moon's gravity at
1, 2, and 3 leaves us with small outward components at both 1 and 2. These are
the tide-producing forces which cause tidal bulges on both sides of the earth.
The rotation of the earth makes them sweep across the globe, so that most har-
bors experience two high tides and two low tides every day (semidiurnal tides).

It should be clear that the tides occur because of the differences in the moon's
gravitational attraction at various places on earth. We can now see why the sun is
not as big a tide producer as the moon even though its force on a unit of matter is
much greater. The difference between 236,000 and 244,000, the distances
in miles from the center of the moon to the two sides of the earth, is much more
significant than the difference between 93,004,000 and 92,996,000, the same distances for the sun.

Actual tides are much more complicated than those predicted by this simple
model, as we can see from Fig. 2-20. These complications arise from the influence of other tide-producing factors. The sun accounts for tidal forces about 46

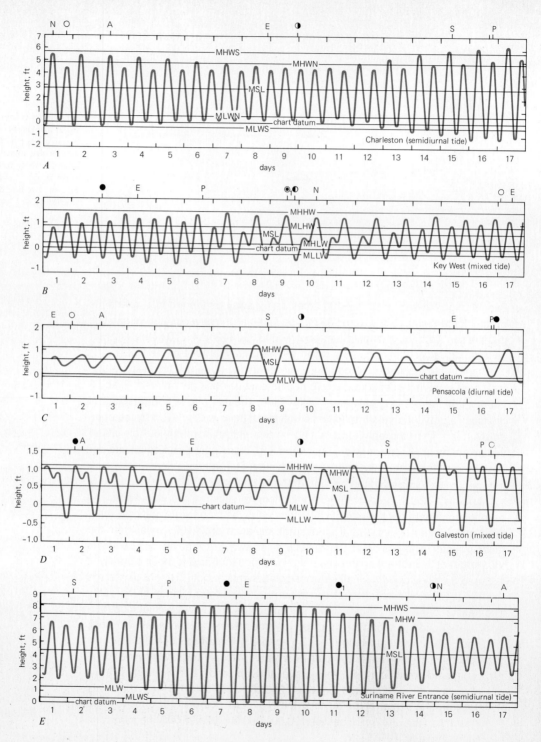

FIGURE 2-20

Tidal variations at several ports. For the stations shown, the height of maximum tide above and below mean sea level (MSL) ranges from 0.6 ft at C to 4.2 ft at E. Periods vary from semidiurnal (A and E) through mixed (B and D) to diurnal (C). *U.S. Navy Hydrographic Office.*

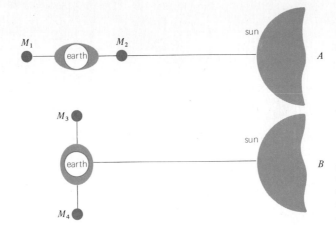

FIGURE 2-21

(*A*) **Spring tides occur when the moon is at** M_1 **or** M_2 **(moon and sun reinforce).** (*B*) **Neap tides arise when the moon is at** M_3 **or** M_4 **(moon and sun counteract).**

percent as strong as those of the moon. Figure 2-21 shows that higher tides occur when the sun and moon act together (spring tides) and lower tides (neap tides) occur when they act in opposition. Moreover, the moon's orbit is not circular, nor does it lie exactly in the plane of the earth's orbit about the sun (ecliptic plane). At perigee, the nearest point, the moon is some 15,000 miles closer than its average distance, whereas it is an equal distance farther away at apogee, the greatest distance. These various components combine to produce the tidal bulges.

Actual tides measured on a given stretch of coastline are further affected by the configuration of the coast. Exceptionally high and low tides are found in narrowing bays (Fig. 2-22). The irregular shapes of the continents exert a braking effect on the moving tidal bulge, thus throwing the arrival of high tide further out of phase with the moon's passage. These factors plus the fact that the earth's axis is

FIGURE 2-22

Exceptionally high tides are experienced in long narrow bays where the advancing tide becomes confined in an increasingly narrower space. Photographs taken near Sackville, N.B. *New Brunswick Travel Bureau.*

FIGURE 2-23
The earth's axis maintains a constant orientation as the planet orbits the sun. The seasons result from the unequal distribution of the sun's energy over the globe. Only at the vernal and autumnal equinoxes are both hemispheres illuminated equally. At summer solstice the Northern Hemisphere receives more of the sun's radiant energy than the Southern Hemisphere, whereas at winter solstice the reverse is true. The earth is closer to the sun (perihelion) during northern winters.

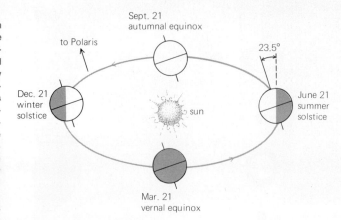

inclined to the plane of the moon's orbit, act together to determine the tides graphed in Fig. 2-20.

The seasons of the year are the combined effect of the earth's revolution around the sun and the tilt of the earth's axis. As the earth travels around the sun, its axis maintains a fixed orientation in space, as shown in Fig. 2-23, being inclined 23.5° from a line perpendicular to the plane of its orbit (plane of the ecliptic). Consequently the sun favors the Northern Hemisphere during half a revolution and the Southern Hemisphere during the other half. Only at the vernal and autumnal equinoxes is the sun directly over the equator.

Figure 2-24 shows the apparent path of the sun during one rotation of the earth

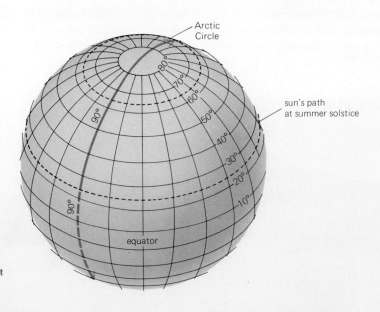

FIGURE 2-24
Apparent path of the sun at summer solstice.

FIGURE 2-25
**Eight exposures at 20-minute
intervals taken in late July near
Etah, Greenland, show the mid-
night sun.** *Courtesy of the
American Museum of Natural
History.*

at summer solstice, which is the longest day of the year for the Northern Hemisphere. On that day, June 21 or 22, the sun is directly overhead at 23.5°N, and, as
the earth turns, traces a circle at that latitude. Because the sun illuminates half
the globe (90° north and south of 23.5°N), it does not set at any point north of the
Arctic Circle at summer solstice. An observer north of the Arctic Circle would see
the sun move as illustrated in Fig. 2-25.

From its position at the summer solstice the sun seems to move gradually
southward, and about September 22 it appears directly above the earth's equator. The sun's crossing over the equator is called the *autumnal equinox.* By
December 21 or 22 the sun is 23.5° south of the equator; then it moves northward
to cross the equator again at the vernal equinox on March 20 or 21.

This apparent motion of the sun around the earth in the plane of the ecliptic affects the distribution of the sun's energy over the earth. The sun is so far away that
its rays may be considered parallel. Thus a fixed amount of the sun's radiant
energy is spread over a greater area where the rays strike the earth's surface
obliquely than where they strike vertically (Fig. 2-26). It is easy to see from Fig.
2-23 that during summer solstice the sun shines more directly on the Northern
Hemisphere and also that a greater proportion of this hemisphere is illuminated
compared to the Southern Hemisphere. The reverse is true at winter solstice. This
variation in the distribution of the sun's energy over the earth accounts for the
seasons.

Only at the equinoxes is the circle of the sun's illumination a great circle
through the poles of the earth, so that both hemispheres are equally illuminated
(Fig. 2-23). Except for the poles, all points on earth experience 12 hours of
daylight and 12 of night at equinox. In fact, the word equinox comes from the
Latin *aequi,* meaning "equal," and *nox,* "night." At other times of the year the
days and nights are of unequal length.

Since the distribution of the sun's energy determines the seasons, we might
expect to find the hottest days of the year around the time of the summer solstice
June 21 or 22. It is then that the Northern Hemisphere receives the most radiant

FIGURE 2-26
**A unit of the sun's radiant en-
ergy is spread over a greater
area wherever it strikes the
earth obliquely.**

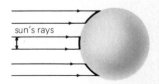

sun's rays

energy from the sun. Instead the warmest days of summer usually occur in July or August, the delay being related to the storage of the sun's heat energy in the earth's crust, waters, and atmosphere. Some of this stored energy is released in winter, so that the coldest days appear a month or more after the shortest day, December 21.

2-9 THE EARTH AS A TIMEKEEPER

At night the apparent movement of the stars around the north celestial pole is like a giant clock. An observer can clearly mark the passage of time by watching the stars trace out their circles. This star clock fades with the rising of the sun, but then the sun's motion provides a means of marking the passage of time, as we know from the sundial. Do these two celestial clocks, known and used for thousands of years, keep the same time?

Let us use our knowledge of planetary motions to answer this question. Both clocks are clearly the result of the earth's rotation. For the sun clock, however, the revolution of the earth also comes into play. If an observer sights the sun at its highest point (noon) on one day, he will have to wait slightly longer than one turn of the earth to see the sun in the same position again. The reason for this delay is that the earth itself has moved through $\frac{1}{365}$ of its orbit from the starting place (Fig. 2-27). The stars, on the other hand, are so far away that their positions are unaffected by the earth's orbital motion.

Time measured by the stars is called *sidereal time*, and time measured by the sun is called *solar time*. It is easy to see from Fig. 2-27 that the difference between sidereal and solar time is 1 day per year because in 1 year the earth moves completely around the sun or, conversely, the sun appears to move completely around the celestial sphere.

Of the two, sidereal time is more constant. A sidereal day, the time between successive passages of a given star over an observer's meridian (north-south line), marks the true period of the earth's rotation. Not only is the sun day a little longer ($\frac{1}{365} \times 24$ hours = 3 minutes 56 seconds) than the sidereal day, but it also varies slightly in length with time of year. This is because the earth travels in an elliptical orbit and speeds up or slows down at different positions in that orbit (Kepler's second law). Although sidereal time is more constant and reliable than solar time, we rely chiefly on the sun clock because our activities are governed by the position of the sun. If our timepieces were set by the stars, 12 o'clock would correspond with the high or low position of the sun only once a year. To get around the problem of slight variations in the length of the solar day with time of year, astronomers invented *mean solar time*, or time measured against a imaginary sun that moves regularly throughout the year. The daily motion of the imaginary sun is the average or mean daily motion of the actual sun. Mean solar time is set to make each day 24 hours long. Time measured by the real sun shows some

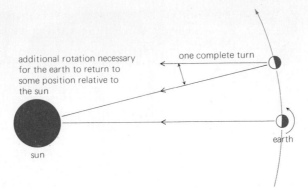

additional rotation necessary for the earth to return to some position relative to the sun

one complete turn

sun

earth

FIGURE 2-27
Because the earth moves around the sun, an observer must wait slightly longer than one earth rotation between successive passings of the sun over his meridian.

days to be slightly longer and some slightly shorter than 24 hours. Over a period of a year, however, the average day marked off by the sun works out at 24 hours.

With the development of watches and clocks that can be regulated to keep mean solar time, the average man rarely if ever has occasion to tell time by the sun or stars. If the need should arise, the simplest time of day for the layman to determine from the sun is local noon, which occurs at the instant when the sun is highest in the sky for an observer.

The rotation of the earth makes it appear that the sun moves completely around the earth in a day (24 hours). It moves at the rate of 360° per 24 hours = 15° per hour. Since the sun moves from east to west, a person located 15° west of an observer who has just noted local noon must wait 1 hour before he sees the sun at its maximum height. Sun time is obviously different for observers in different positions. Only persons situated on the same north-south line have exactly the same time.

With the advent of the telegraph and fast trains in the mid-nineteenth century, local timekeeping became troublesome. Some large American cities had to keep track of as many as five local times because of transportation links. To overcome this difficulty the entire world was ultimately subdivided into time zones, each about 15°, or 1 hour, wide. This reduced the number of different local times to 24, one for each 15° zone. As shown in Fig. 2-28, the zones are irregular where necessary to correspond to political boundaries or follow prominent topographical features. In addition, scientific work uses a single, worldwide standard, Greenwich mean time. It is the time measured by the mean sun along the zero meridian of longitude, which was set to pass through Greenwich, England, formerly the site of the Royal observatory.

Because the sun appears to move 360° from east to west in 24 hours (15° per hour), the meridian opposite Greenwich has some unusual characteristics; it can be both 12 hours ahead of Greenwich time and 12 hours behind it. For example, if it is 3 P.M., March 4, at Greenwich, it will be 12 hours later 180° east of Greenwich,

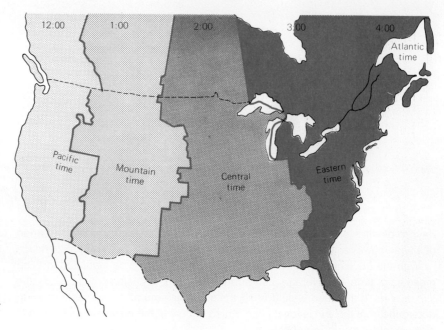

FIGURE 2-28
Standard time zones of the United States.

which would make it 3 A.M., March 5, on the antemeridian. But if we look west of Greenwich at the same instant, we find the time at the 180° meridian to be 12 hours earlier, or 3 A.M., March 4.

The 180° meridian thus functions as the international date line. It is fortunate that Greenwich was chosen as the reference meridian for timekeeping because the antemeridian 180° from it falls mainly over water. As it is, the date line is locally deflected by international agreement in order to bypass certain land areas.

SUMMARY

Anyone who has experienced the sensation of motion in a standing vehicle because he was watching an object that was moving realizes that motion must be described relative to some reference system. The celestial objects all move when viewed from the earth, and centuries ago man had no intuitive way of knowing that he was looking at the heavens from a moving platform. Consequently, Ptolemy's interpreta-

tion, which envisioned a fixed earth at the center of a universe of moving objects, was accepted for over 1,000 years.

Ptolemy's system eventually proved too complicated to explain observed planetary and stellar positions. Gradually the simpler sun-centered planetary systems of Copernicus and later Kepler were accepted. Kepler's laws of planetary motion are still valid today, some 300 years after they were first proposed.

More fundamental investigations

of the whole question of motion ultimately led to Newton's laws of motion and his universal law of gravitation. Newton's laws did more than explain planetary motions. The masses of the earth, sun, and planets were determined by the application of these laws. Tides arise because the effects of gravitational attraction of the moon and sun differ over the earth.

The sun's radiant energy is distributed equally between the Northern and Southern Hemispheres only when the sun is directly over the equator. Because the earth's inclined axis maintains a constant orientation in space as the planet revolves about the sun, this equal heating of the hemispheres occurs only two days out of the year. Throughout the remainder of the year either the Northern or the Southern Hemisphere receives more radiant energy, thus accounting for the seasons.

The earth's spin provides the reference for the measurement of time. Because the sun moves at slightly different speeds during the year, an imaginary sun that travels at the average rate of the real sun provides the reference for mean solar time. The earth is divided into 24 time zones. Universal time is the time along the 0° meridian of longitude, which passes through Greenwich, England.

QUESTIONS

1 Suppose that you observed the Big Dipper at 9 P.M. on January 1 and then again on March 1. Both observations are made from the same place. Would the constellation appear in the same part of the sky on both nights? Why?

2 How did Ptolemy account for the apparent looping motions of the planets?

3 Kepler found that the planets revolve in elliptical rather than circular orbits. An ellipse is a variable form in that the dimensions of the major and minor axes are not fixed. Look up the characteristics of the earth's elliptical orbit. Is it almost circular (major and minor axes nearly equal), or are the two axes markedly different?

4 What does Kepler's second law say about the speed of a planet in its orbit?

5 The moon's period of revolution around the earth is about 27 days, and it is about 240,000 miles from the earth. An artificial satellite is observed to circle the earth once each day. According to Kepler's third law, what is the average distance of this satellite from the earth?

6 Why does the sun have less influence than the moon in producing tides when its mass is thousands of times that of the moon?

7 What effect would there be on the seasons if the earth's axis were perpendicular to the plane of its orbit?

8 If an object were lifted 8,000 miles above the surface of the earth, how much would it weigh there compared to its surface weight? How much change would there be in its mass?

9 When it is 11 A.M. mean solar time at Greenwich, England, what time is it in New York, 75°W?

10 If the earth could be temporarily stopped in its orbit and released, how would it move?

11 If the sun's gravitational attraction could be suddenly turned off, how would the earth and other planets move?

12 If the sun attracts the earth and planets, why don't they fall into the sun?

13 What is the difference (in minutes) between the sidereal and the mean solar day?

14 Using Newton's laws, show why two objects dropped near the earth's surface accelerate at the same rate.

15 How was the earth's mass determined?

REFERENCES

Abel, George: "Exploration of the Universe," Holt, Rinehart and Winston, Inc., New York, 1969.

Clancy, Edward P.: "The Tides: Pulse of the Earth," Doubleday Company, Inc., Garden City, N.Y., 1968.

Gamow, George: "Gravity," Doubleday Company, Inc., Garden City, N.Y., 1962 (Anchor Paperback).

Howell, B. F., Jr.: "Introduction to Geophysics," McGraw-Hill Book Company, New York, 1959.

Mehlin, Theodore G.: "Astronomy and the Origin of the Earth," Wm. C. Brown Company Publishers, Dubuque, Iowa, 1968.

Odishaw, Hugh: "The Earth in Space," Basic Books, Inc., Publishers, New York, 1967.

Stumpff, K.: "Planet Earth," University of Michigan Press, Ann Arbor, 1959.

FINDING THE EARTH'S DIMENSIONS

The earth is not a lifeless ball of matter hurtling year after year around the sun. Rain, rivers, wind, and ice interact with its solid surface to produce change. Fiery volcanoes and earthquakes are evidence of an internal cycle, less well known than the surface cycle of weathering, erosion, and deposition. Together these internal and external processes make the earth a dynamic planet. Like a living thing, the earth has a characteristic physiology. Its major cycles, their causes, their effects, their histories, and their energy sources are subjects of great interest.

Before studying the earth processes, however, it is important to ask: How big is the earth? What is its shape? What determines this shape and that of other celestial bodies? These are some of the questions to be considered in this chapter.

As we investigate the dimensions of the earth, we shall see that man's knowledge of the size and shape of our planet has increased by steps, by a series of approximations. Early observations led to the conclusion that the earth is a

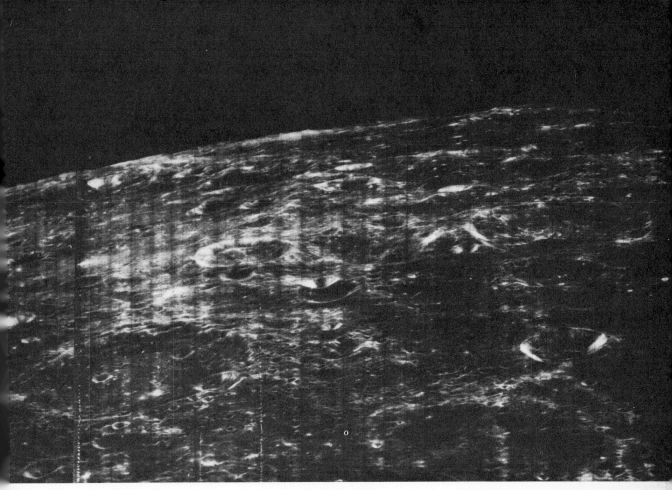

sphere. More refined measurements revealed a polar flattening and a corresponding equatorial bulge. Still more sophisticated measurements uncovered other minor irregularities. The exact shape of the earth remains a subject for future research, and it is, in fact, not a constant to be fixed at the ultimate level even by the most sophisticated methods of measurement because our dynamic, living planet changes continually.

3-1 EVIDENCE FOR A SPHERICAL EARTH

A look at Fig. 3-1 should convince even the greatest skeptic that the earth is round. Yet for centuries men thought of the earth as being flat. The change from a flat to a spherical concept was not sudden. Several thousand years ago a few Greeks thought the earth was round and (as we shall see later in this section) even calculated its circumference using this premise. However, they failed to convince others. Even when Columbus made his famous first voyage, some 500 years ago, many people believed him in great danger of falling off the edge of a flat earth. What evidence and what sort of reasoning finally convinced men before the space age that the earth must be round?

FIGURE 3-2
The hull of a tall ship sailing away from land disappears before the mast does, suggesting that the earth's surface must be curved.

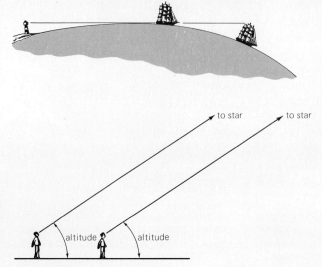

FIGURE 3-3
Because the stars are so far away that lines of sight to them from any place on earth are parallel, the altitude of a given star would be the same everywhere if the earth were flat.

For the moment let us put ourselves in the position of someone who lived several hundred years ago. How would we have been led to suspect that the earth, which seems flat except for irregularities in hills and valleys, might actually be spherical? The fact that the sun, moon, and planets look round would have influenced our thinking. Moreover, the curvature of the earth's shadow on the moon during a lunar eclipse is strong evidence for a rounded shape. Figure 3-2 shows how a tall ship appears to an observer at a distance. The very top of a

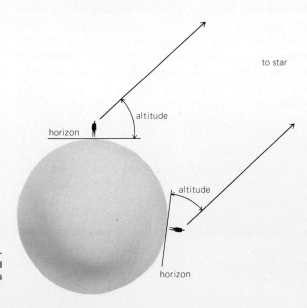

FIGURE 3-4
On a sphere an observer's horizon changes with position, and thus the altitude of a star varies with position.

receding ship disappears last and suggests that it is moving on a curved surface. Together these bits of evidence might have convinced someone that the
earth's overall shape is curved rather than flat.

Further evidence for a curved (and more specifically spherical) shape was
discovered in the stars. Once it was recognized that the stars are almost infinitely
distant from the earth, it became clear that the lines of sight to a given star from
any two points on earth separated by a few hundreds or even thousands of miles
should be essentially parallel. This being so, the altitude of a given star should
be the same everywhere on a flat earth (Fig. 3-3), where altitude means the angular height of the star above the observer's horizon. Actual measurements, however showed that the altitude of a star varies with the observer's position. This is
just what should happen if the earth is round, because on a globe the horizon
changes with position (Fig. 3-4).

Related to the evidence found in determining the altitudes of specific stars
from various positions on earth is the general appearance of the nighttime celestial sphere. Travelers to the far north observe that most stars do not rise and set
but merely circle the north celestial pole (Fig. 3-5). On the other hand, observers
at the equator see the stars rise abruptly and move straight up from the horizon.
This difference in the apparent motions of the stars also points to a spherical
shape for the earth.

Around 300 B.C. the Greek scholar Eratosthenes made an ingenious deduc-
tion from the variation in the altitude of a star, in this case our sun. Eratosthenes
was in charge of the library in Alexandria, a center of knowledge in the ancient
world. Learning that a deep vertical well near Syene, in southern Egypt, was entirely lit by the sun at noon every June 21, and knowing that in Alexandria, almost
due north of Syene, the sun cast a shadow at noon that day, he put these facts
together and by assuming that the earth was indeed spherical measured its circumference.

His measurements and assumptions are diagrammed in Fig. 3-6. Because the
sun shone directly down the vertical well at noon on June 21 in Syene, the sun
must have been directly overhead there. At Alexandria, at the same exact time,
the length of the shadow cast by a vertical pole indicated that the sun's rays were
inclined 7°12' from the vertical. From Fig. 3-6 we can see that the angle of inclination at Alexandria must equal the angle at the center of the earth subtended by

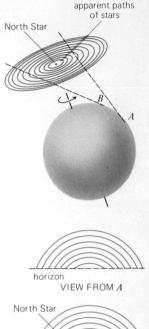

FIGURE 3-5
At high latitudes more stars remain above the horizon all night than at low latitudes. This is evidence of the earth's sphericity. *From K. B. Kraus-kopf and A. Beiser, "Fundamentals of Physical Science," 5th ed. Copyright © 1966 by McGraw-Hill, Inc. Used with permission of McGraw-Hill Book Company.*

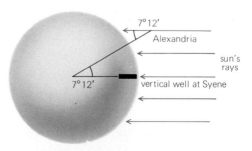

FIGURE 3-6
Eratosthenes' method of measuring the earth's circumference.

FIGURE 3-7
An object at the equator moves at about 1,000 miles per hour around the axis due to the earth's rotation.

the arc between the two cities if the sun's rays are indeed parallel. Knowing the distance between Alexandria and Syene to be about 5,000 stadia, Eratosthenes computed the circumference of the earth from the relation

$$\frac{\text{Earth circumference}}{5,000} = \frac{360°00'}{7°12'}$$

or

$$\text{Earth circumference} = \frac{360}{7.2} \times 5,000 = 250,000 \text{ stadia}$$

This value converts to about 28,000 miles, or 46,000 kilometers, which is suprisingly close to the presently accepted value of 24,860 miles, or 40,009 kilometers.

In order to measure the earth's circumference Eratosthenes assumed that our planet is spherical. Indeed the earth is very nearly a sphere. Modern measurements reveal that the deviations from sphericity, including all surface irregularities such as mountains and ocean deeps, amount to about only $\frac{1}{300}$ of the earth's radius. This is so small that it cannot be shown on the small-scale drawings of the earth that appear in this book.

With the formulation of Newton's law of universal gravitation the reason for the spherical shape of the earth and other celestial bodies became clear. All particles of an object like the earth are pulled toward the center of gravity. The natural response to this force is the formation of a sphere, which represents the greatest possible concentration of matter with the smallest possible surface.

Whereas a sphere is the shape expected for a nonrotating body, this prediction does not hold exactly for our planet, which rotates on its polar axis. Newton was the first to suggest that the earth should have a slight equatorial bulge because the centrifugal force arising from the rotation should make the equatorial region distend.

To see why Newton predicted that the earth's shape should be that of a slightly flattened sphere, known as an *oblate spheroid*, let us consider several points on a rotating earth. An object at the earth's poles has no velocity, whereas one at the equator is moving around the earth's axis at about 1,000 miles per hour

FIGURE 3-8
The centrifugal force (CF) due to the rotation of the earth has a component opposite in direction to the force of gravity and a horizontal component directed toward the equator.

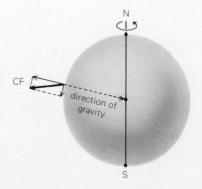

(Fig. 3-7). The object at the equator (and to a lesser degree any object away from the poles) experiences a centrifugal force perpendicular to the axis of rotation. As Fig. 3-8 shows this centrifugal force can be resolved into a radial component, which is opposite in direction to the force of gravity, and a tangential component, which points toward the earth's equator. The centrifugal force thus tends to reduce the force of gravity slightly, the maximum reduction occurring at the equator. The lower gravitational force at the equator and the tangential component elsewhere on the earth (Fig. 3-8) work to produce a slight equatorial bulge.

How can Newton's prediction of an equatorial bulge be checked? One way is to refine the method of Eratosthenes. If the earth were a perfect sphere, as shown in Fig. 3-9, the arc subtended by a fixed angle (for instance 5°) should be the same everywhere. This is an inherent property of a sphere. On the other hand, if the earth is an oblate spheroid, its cross section can be visualized as consisting of many intersecting circles of varying radius, as pictured in Fig. 3-10. Careful measurements show that the length of arc for 1° of latitude is 69.407 miles at the poles and only 68.704 miles at the equator. When the earth's shape is determined from such measurements, it is found to have a polar radius of 3,949.99 miles and an equatorial radius of 3,963.34 miles. The flattening is very slight; if the arcs subtended by 1° of latitude at the equator and poles are measured to the nearest mile, both are 69 miles. Much more precise measurements than were possible in Eratosthenes' day—or even Newton's—were required to reveal the flattening.

Other measurements made in Newton's time actually prompted his prediction of an equatorial bulge. We noted earlier that the centrifugal force arising from the earth's daily rotation is greatest at the equator. Since the centrifugal force acts in a direction opposite to the force of gravity, the acceleration of gravi-

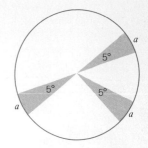

FIGURE 3-9
The cross section of a sphere is a circle. In such a figure the length of arc a subtended by a fixed angle at the center is the same everywhere.

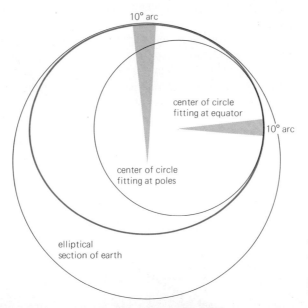

FIGURE 3-10
The cross section of a flattened sphere is an ellipse, which can be visualized as being composed of the arcs of many circles of differing radius.

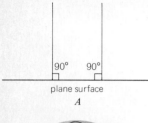

plane surface
A

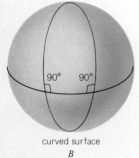

curved surface
B

FIGURE 3-11
(*A*) **On a plane surface two lines perpendicular to a third line are parallel to each other.** (*B*) **This is not so on a curved surface, where the interior angles of a triangle add up to more than 180°.**

ty should be least at the equator. It was because of the lowered measured gravity at the equator that Newton predicted the equatorial bulge. One of the means of measuring the acceleration of gravity is the pendulum. The period of a pendulum is the time required for one complete swing; it depends upon the length of the pendulum and upon the acceleration of gravity, according to the relation $P = 2\pi\sqrt{D/g}$ where P is the period, D the length of the pendulum, and g the acceleration of gravity. Experiments made by Jean Richer (1630-1696) in France and equatorial South America showed that the same pendulum clock oscillated slower in South America than in France, indicating that the acceleration of gravity is indeed lower near the equator.

The results of earth measurement made over the years are summarized in Table 3-1. We shall see in Sec. 3-4 that besides the slight flattening there are other irregularities in the earth's shape. However, they are even smaller than the flattening, which amounts to only 13 miles in 3,950 miles, or 1 part in about 300. Thus for most purposes we can think of the earth as a sphere with a radius of about 4,000 miles, or 6,400 kilometers.

3-2 LATITUDE AND LONGITUDE

Surveyors engaged in mapping the earth need some sort of reference system. When mapping is to be carried out in a small area, the reference system may be nothing more than one point and a reference direction. With this as a start, a second point can be located by measuring its direction and distance from the reference point. A third point is located from the second one by a similar procedure, and so forth, until all the features to be mapped are located.

This system of referencing would be too cumbersome to use for the entire earth because errors arising from measurements between points are cumulative, and checking back to the starting point over long distances would be burdensome. Moreover, the system of plane surveying used in relatively small areas on the earth (which for such purposes may be considered flat, i.e., plane) does not work on a sphere. Herein lies an independent approach to establishing the earth's shape. The evidence we considered earlier for a spherical earth was mainly related to celestial observations. If the sky had always been cloud-covered,would man have discovered the earth's spherical shape? He would have if he had extended plane surveys over very large areas.

For a flat, or plane, triangle the interior angles always add up to 180°, but this relationship does not hold for a three-sided figure drawn on a sphere (Fig. 3-11). On a curved surface two lines each 90° from a common line converge to form a

TABLE 3-1
The earth's major dimensions

	Kilometers	*Miles*
Polar radius	6,356	3,950
Equatorial radius	6,378	3,963
Polar circumference	40,009	24,860
Equatorial circumference	40,074	24,900

spherical triangle whose interior angles add up to more than 180°. The shape of
the earth can be determined from the rate of convergence of such lines.

Returning to an earthwide reference system, almost everyone is familiar with
the circles drawn on most globes as lines of latitude and longitude. These imaginary lines form a grid system that can be used to locate points on the earth. The
lines of latitude are based on the equator, which lies in a plane through the
center of the earth and perpendicular to its axis. The latitude of any point is
measured in degrees north or south of this plane. It is a comparatively easy matter to get an approximate value for latitude at any place in the Northern Hemisphere by measuring the altitude of Polaris, the polestar. Lines of sight to this
very distant star from any point on earth are parallel. Therefore, as drawn in Fig.
3-12, the altitude of Polaris is approximately the latitude of the observer. Someone at the North Pole would see the star directly overhead, or 90° above his horizon. The latitude of the North Pole is 90°. An observer at the equator would see
the star on the horizon (0° above the horizon), and his latitude is 0°. For someone
between the equator and the pole the altitude of the polestar is roughly equal to
the angle at the earth's center between the observer and the equator, which is the
latitude.

The latitude determined by measuring the altitude of Polaris would be exact if
Polaris were situated precisely at the north celestial pole and if the earth were a
featureless sphere. But as neither of these conditions is met, an *ephemeris*, or
star table, must be consulted to relate the star's observed position to the north
celestial pole, and a small correction must be made to account for the spheroidal
shape of the earth

Lines of latitude, called *parallels*, form circles which become progressively
smaller toward the poles. All circles of latitude are parallel to the equatorial
plane. The imaginary lines of longitude, which are used to fix positions in the
east-west direction, converge toward the poles. Lines of longitude are *meridi-
ans*, i.e., great circles passing through the earth's poles; they form planes perpendicular to the equatorial plane.

We have already encountered the lines of longitude in Chap. 2, where we saw
that 1 hour's difference in time is equivalent to a 15° difference in longitude and
noted that the reference meridian traverses Greenwich, England. Thus the longitude of a place can be determined by measuring the local time and by simultaneously comparing it with local time at Greenwich. To illustrate, suppose that we
have a sun that keeps mean solar time. One time of day easily determined from
the sun is noon, the time when the sun is highest in the sky. If at the instant of
noon at an unknown location it is 6 hours past noon (6 **P.M.**) at Greenwich, the difference in longitude between the two places must be 6 hours times 15° per hour,
or 90°. This would be 90°W longitude because Greenwich must be east of the
location if it experienced noon 6 hours earlier.

Not just solar noon, but the "noon" of any star can be used to determine longitude: one observes the time at which the star crosses directly overhead at the
location in question. Because both latitude and longitude can be determined

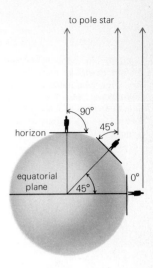

FIGURE 3-12
The altitude of the polestar
gives the approximate latitude
at any place in the Northern
Hemisphere.

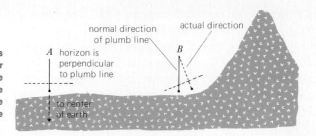

FIGURE 3-13
A plumb line normally points straight down, as at A**. Near very large mountains at** B **the gravitational attraction of the mountain mass should pull the plumb line very slightly off the vertical.**

from celestial measurements at any place on earth, they form an ideal system of reference for locating points on our globe.

3-3 ISOSTASY AND THE HEIGHT OF THE EARTH'S SURFACE

Over a century ago Sir George Everest (1790–1866) Surveyor General of India, discovered a puzzling discrepancy in a land survey conducted south of the Himalaya. The surveyors established the latitude and longitude of a station near the town of Kalianpur and made similar measurements at Kaliana, about 375 miles north in the shadow of the Himalaya. From the differences in latitude and longitude of two points the distance between them can be computed. For example, two points on the same meridian that are 5° apart in latitude must be separated by a distance equal to $\frac{5}{360}$ of the earth's circumference. When the surveyors calculated the distance between the two stations from their values for latitude and longitude (taking into account a correction for polar flattening), it did not correspond with the distance they had actually measured along the ground between Kalianpur and Kaliana. The difference was small but greater than the limits of error of their instruments.

In seeking an explanation of this discrepancy it was recognized that the Himalaya might have affected the astronomical measurements used to determine latitude and longitude. The mountains rise high above the survey area, and thus their combined mass might attract the plumb bob away from the vertical (Fig. 3-13). This influence would be greatest at Kaliana, which is closest to the mountain range. The resulting difference in gravitational attraction would throw off the latitude measurements because latitude is determined by measuring the altitude of a star above the horizon, which in turn is set by the plumb bob. The gravitational attraction of the mountains, however, would in no way influence the results determined by ground measurements.

In 1855, J. H. Pratt, archdeacon of Calcutta and a mathematician, made an estimate of the mass of the Himalaya in the survey region. Using the law of gravitation, he calculated the effect the mountains should exert on the plumb lines at both stations and found to his surprise that they should have introduced an error three times as great as that actually found. At first glance it appears he might

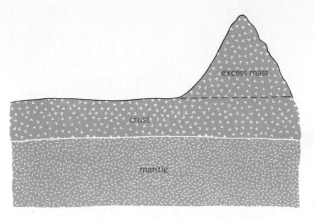

FIGURE 3-14
In his initial calculations on the effect of the Himalaya on the plumb line Pratt assumed that the mountains represent an excess of mass above the average crust. He subsequently developed an interpretation involving flotational balance of the mountains.

have overestimated the mass of the mountains, but it is not difficult to determine the masses of such mountains from their height and area, and Pratt had used a very conservative estimate. Thus the puzzle of the measurement error became even more of a mystery.

Somehow the mountains were not exerting the gravitational force they should on the plumb lines. Since there was no reason to question the law of gravitation, some other physical explanation was needed. The answer was not long in coming. About 4 months after Pratt published his calculations, G. B. Airy, the Astronomer Royal of England, came up with the hypothesis that just as the height of an iceberg is determined by the thickness of ice beneath the water, so too is the height of a mountain related to the total thickness of light crustal rock floating in the denser mantle.

In his initial calculations Pratt had assumed the mountains to be masses of crustal rock lying above the mean level of the region, as pictured in Fig. 3-14. Airy questioned this interpretation because the rocks at the base of such high mountains as the Himalaya are under sufficient pressure from the weight of overlying rock to cause them to flow. He proposed instead that the mountains are buoyed up by deep roots of lighter crustal rock floating in a denser fluid substrate (Fig. 3-15).

We can see how Airy's interpretation explains why the Himalaya do not exert the gravitational pull Pratt first calculated. If the mountains do indeed have large roots, the deficiency of mass underneath would oppose the northward attraction of the mountains themselves.

In 1889 C. E. Dutton, an American geologist, introduced the term *isostasy* for the condition of flotational balance that appeared to control the heights of continents and mountains and the depths of the ocean floors. As we can see from Fig. 3-16, if the mountains are high because, like icebergs, they are buoyed up by deep roots in a fluid substrate, then their heights and the levels of the continents and ocean basins should be determined by the thickness of crustal rock. The

FIGURE 3-15
Airy's hypothesis (isostasy). He considered the segments of the crust to be floating on the denser mantle like blocks of wood in water. The highest mountains then must be buoyed up by the greatest thickness of light crustal material.

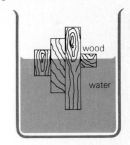

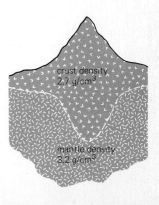

crust density 2.7 g/cm³

mantle density 3.2 g/cm³

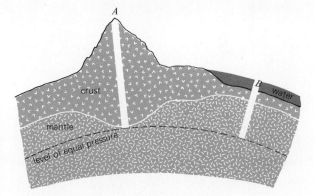

FIGURE 3-16
If isostasy is established, columns A and B, although different in length, would have equal masses because A contains more low-density crustal material and B has more of the high-density mantle.

condition of isostasy implies a level of uniform pressure (Fig. 3-16). Since the pressure in the earth is determined by the weight of the overlying rock, this means that rock columns A and B in Fig. 3-16 must have equal masses.

Today there is ample evidence for isostasy, or balance, in the earth's crust. Although we know from earthquake evidence that the material beneath the crust is not liquid in the ordinary sense of the word, this does not mean that the crust cannot be thought of as floating on the material beneath it. The rocks of the upper mantle are under high temperatures and pressures and behave rather like liquids in being able to flow or deform plastically. Unlike the liquids that we are most familiar with, they do possess some tensile strength. Hence, although the earth tends toward the condition of isostasy, adjustment to changing loads is very much slower than for the simple case of ice or wood floating on water.

3-4 THE EARTH'S GRAVITY FIELD AND THE GEOID

Observation first led scientists to the conclusion that the earth is spherical rather than flat. Refined measurement and the application of theory (the law of gravitation) subsequently showed that the shape is not exactly spherical but more nearly that of an oblate spheroid. Both the sphere and the spheroid are regular figures which can be expressed mathematically. Does still closer examination reveal further irregularities in the earth's shape?

Before we explore this question, it should be clear that we are considering an average shape and that such surface irregularities as mountains and valleys are disregarded. They appear large to us but are insignificant compared to the overall dimensions of our planet.

The specialized science concerned with mapping and measuring the earth is called *geodesy*. Geodeticists have found that the earth's shape differs slightly from an idealized oblate spheroid. The actual shape, which includes the minor elevations and depressions which depart from the ideal spheroid, is called the

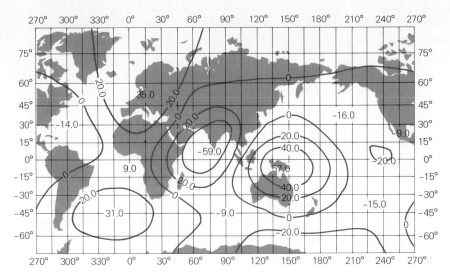

FIGURE 3-17
Geoid heights in meters above and below a reference ellipsoid with a flattening of 1/298.3. *After G. J. F. MacDonald, "The Use of Artificial Satellites for Geodesy," Interscience Publishers, 1964.*

geoid. The geoid, unlike the spheroid, is not determined by measuring lengths along the earth's surface; instead it is defined as the surface which is everywhere perpendicular to the direction of the earth's gravitational attraction. To visualize this surface, imagine the continents crisscrossed with canals interconnecting all the oceans and lakes. The top of the resulting single body of water would be the geoid.

One way to find the slope of the geoid at any place on the earth's surface is to use the plumb line, which automatically follows the direction of gravitational force and thus is always perpendicular to the geoid. In discussing the concept of isostasy we saw that the unequal distribution of mass in the earth's crust causes a plumb line to be pulled away from the direction it would take for a uniform spherical earth or even a spheroidal one. Thus the geoid coincides with neither of these simpler shapes and is a highly irregular figure which cannot be described by any single mathematical formula.

In recent years important information about the shape of the geoid has been obtained from satellite observations. This is not surprising, since the earth's gravity field, which defines the geoid, controls the motions of the satellites. If the earth were a sphere, a satellite would travel in a fixed elliptical orbit. The excess of mass in the equatorial regions causes the orbits of satellites whose paths are inclined to the equator to shift slowly as the satellites are attracted by the excess mass. Other irregularities in mass distribution on earth also cause minor but measurable perturbations in the orbits of artificial satellites. The shape of the geoid has been determined from the analysis of such motions coupled with gravity readings taken on the ground. Note that the geoid shown in Fig. 3-17 departs by only a few meters to a few tens of meters from the idealized spheroid.

3-5 GRAVITY ANOMALIES AND ISOSTASY

The correspondence between the irregularities in the earth's shape and composition and irregularities in its gravitational field is worth discussing in further detail. We recall that the gravitational attraction between two bodies is proportional to the product of their masses and inversely proportional to the square of the distance between them. Moreover, the force of gravitational attraction may be considered as originating at the centers of the masses. For one unit of mass on the surface of the earth this relation can be written

$$F = \frac{GM_{\text{earth}}}{r^2}$$

where G is the universal constant and r is the radius of the earth. Moreover, Newton's second law of motion tells us that acceleration g due to gravity of the unit mass equals the force F, or $g = F$. Substituting for F, we get

$$g = \frac{GM_{\text{earth}}}{r^2}$$

The acceleration due to gravity can be accurately measured by a sensitive pendulum because, as we saw earlier, the period of a pendulum is determined by its length and by g, the acceleration of gravity. Suppose that measurements of g had been made at many points on the surface of the earth; how could we interpret the data?

Looking critically at the relation $g = GM_{\text{earth}}/r^2$, we see that G and the mass of the earth are fixed and that only r varies with changing values of g. Such measurements of the gravity field intensity thus provide information about the shape of the earth. Before we can use the measurements in this way, however, a number of corrections must be made. For example, we must account for the centrifugal force arising from the earth's rotation, which is greatest at the equator and decreases to zero at the poles. The effects of topography and of unequal mass distributions within the crust must also be evaluated before gravity readings can be accurately converted into distance from the earth's center.

Because of the many factors which influence the acceleration of gravity at any place, it is usually not possible to use values of g directly as a measure of the earth's radius. Gravity measurements are usually made for another purpose, namely, to detect differences in mass distribution in the crust. Mining companies, for example, make use of gravity surveys to detect large buried metal deposits. Because metallic minerals usually have densities that are twice or more as great as those of ordinary crustal materials, gravity measurements made over large buried metal deposits should be anomalously high. The effect of even an immense buried metal deposit on the absolute value of the acceleration of gravity is very slight, however, because it must be measured as a deviation from the force attributable to the entire earth.

It is much easier to measure differences in the force of gravity than to obtain

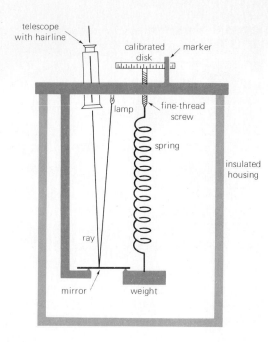

FIGURE 3-18
Schematic diagram of a spring gravimeter. *After B. F. Howell, Jr., "Introduction to Geophysics," p. 212. Copyright © 1959 by McGraw-Hill, Inc. Used with permission of McGraw-Hill Book Company.*

absolute values for the acceleration of gravity. *Gravimeters*, instruments consisting of a mass on a delicate spring (Fig. 3-18), can be used to reveal differences in gravitational attraction to as close as 1 part in 100 million. The gravimeter is basically an ultrasensitive spring balance. To compare gravity at two places the operator simply reads the weight of the gravimeter mass at the locations. Although the gravimeter has made the job of measuring differences in the gravity field intensity easy, interpreting these differences may be difficult, particularly in surveys covering large areas, where corrections for the rotation of the earth and for its oblateness must be made before the raw readings become meaningful.

Still other corrections must be made in order to detect density differences in the crust. Figure 3-19 shows in cross section the situation that should exist beneath a mountain area if isostasy has been achieved. The only part of this area that is visible, of course, is the surface. How can the presence of a buried root of low-density material beneath the mountain be established by gravity measurements?

From Fig. 3-19 it is obvious that a gravity reading at point A should be less than one at point B because A is farther from the center of the earth. Therefore, to compare the two readings they must be reduced to a common elevation, as shown by the dashed line in the cross section. Even with a correction to compensate for the difference in elevation between the two points, the readings are not equivalent because the reading at point A was also influenced by the mass of

FIGURE 3-19
Will measurements of the gravity field intensity in a region such as this disclose the presence of the buried and hidden mountain root?

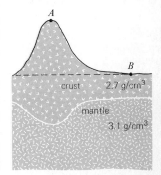

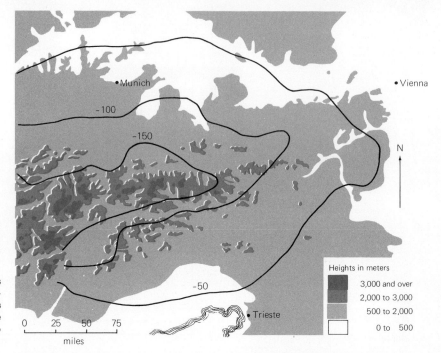

FIGURE 3-20
Bouguer anomalies of the Alps and their relation to topography. The negative anomalies are greatest in the areas of the highest mountains. *After Paavo Holopainen.*

rock lying above the level line. The effect of this extra rock can be computed from the law of gravitation, and a further correction can thus be made to the reading at point A. After both corrections have been made, the readings at A and B should be the same if the densities of the rocks underlying the two points are the same. If the reading at A is still lower than that at B, it suggests that point A must have a higher proportion of low-density material underlying it. In Fig. 3-19 a lower adjusted value at A would be evidence for the existence of a low-density root.

In practice hundreds of gravity readings are taken in an area instead of only two. Such work shows that, for the most part, values of corrected gravity are lower under mountainous areas than under plains regions or ocean basins. This is additional evidence for the conclusion that isostasy, or balance, is the normal state. Since a French mathematician and geodeticist, Pierre Bouguer (1698–1758), first suggested these corrections, maps showing corrected gravity readings are referred to as Bouguer gravity maps. Figure 3-20 shows a Bouguer map of the Alps. Note that the low values of gravity (negative anomalies) coincide with the topographical highs.

Gravity measurements are reported in terms of the acceleration of gravity. An acceleration of 1 centimeter per second per second is called a *gal*, after Galileo. Because most gravity anomalies are only a small fraction of a gal, the unit in common use in gravity work is the milligal (0.001 gal), representing an acceleration of 0.001 centimeter per second per second. Figure 3-21 is a gravity map of

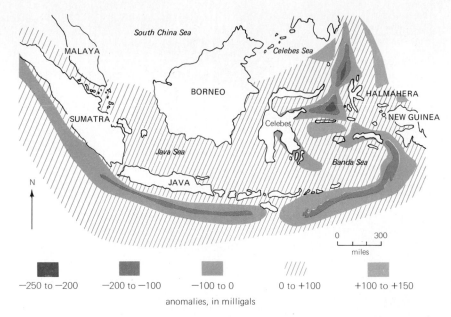

FIGURE 3-21
Gravity map of part of Indonesia. Values in milligals. The negative gravity anomalies here cannot be related to mountain roots of light rock because they occur over deep ocean trenches. *After W. A. Heiskanen and F. A. Vening Meinesz, "The Earth and Its Gravity Field." Copyright © 1958 by McGraw-Hill, Inc. Used with permission of McGraw-Hill Book Company.*

−250 to −200   −200 to −100   −100 to 0   0 to +100   +100 to +150

anomalies, in milligals

part of Indonesia. Note the long and narrow negative anomalies, obviously not mountain roots because they are along deep ocean trenches. What causes such anomalies? How are they related to isostasy?

To answer these questions requires a closer look at some of the implications of isostasy. We have used mountains and their roots to illustrate this concept, but isostasy should not be confused with a mountain-building process or force. It is merely a state of balance or equilibrium. If the earth were able to adjust quickly to changes in load, and if there were no other forces acting, isostasy would prevail and there would be no regions of anomalous gravity field intensity. For example, visualize the erosion of a mountain range. As material is removed from its top, the mountain root should rise (Fig. 3-22). The material eroded from mountains is

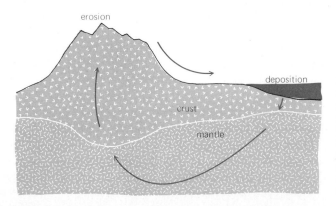

FIGURE 3-22
If balance (isostasy) is to be maintained, a mountain root must rise as material is eroded from the mountaintop and the depositional basin must sink as water is displaced by denser sediment. This balance is accomplished by the slow transfer of material in the mantle.

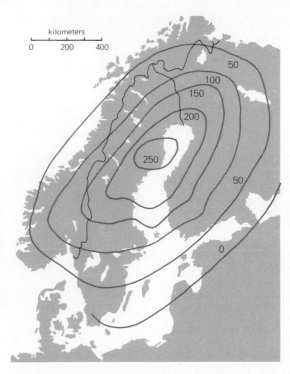

FIGURE 3-23
During the Pleistocene Epoch, Fennoscandia, like northern North America, was covered by a continental ice sheet estimated to have reached 3,000 meters in thickness. When this great load was released with the melting of the ice, the land slowly rose. The map shows the amount of uplift (in meters) that has taken place since glacial times as reconstructed from raised shorelines, marine fossils, and other evidence. The greatest rise (250 meters) corresponds approximately to the region of thickest ice. This is an example of isostatic adjustment. *After R. A. Daly, "The Changing World of the Ice Age," Yale University Press, 1934.*

FIGURE 3-24
If it were possible to measure very minute gravity differences, a small-scale gravity survey would reveal a negative anomaly where the less dense wood is forcibly held under water.

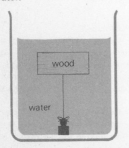

deposited in the oceans, where it represents an excess of mass. Therefore the depositional area must sink if isostasy is to be preserved. This rising and sinking of the surface must be balanced by a transfer of material in the depths of the earth.

Evidence for isostatic adjustments of this type is found in parts of the earth covered by thousands of feet of ice during the Pleistocene Epoch, which ended some 12,000 years ago. Raised beaches and changes in the elevations of survey reference points in the Baltic region (Fig. 3-23) show this part of the earth to be rising. Studies of the glacial geology of the area reveal that the center of the ice sheet was in the area of the most rapid rise. When this region was covered by thousands of feet of ice for many millennia, it must have been depressed in order to achieve balance. The present rise then represents a move to reestablish isostasy.

Getting back to Fig. 3-21, how can the negative anomalies over the ocean deeps be accounted for? They obviously represent a departure from isostasy, like that resulting if we pushed a light block of wood into water (Fig. 3-24). It is equally clear that the ocean anomalies cannot be due to some force from above because they occur over ocean deeps that contain very little sediment. Some force from within the earth must be pulling downward on the crust at the trenches. When we consider mountain building and continental drift in Chaps. 15 and 16, we shall find that such forces do indeed arise within the earth.

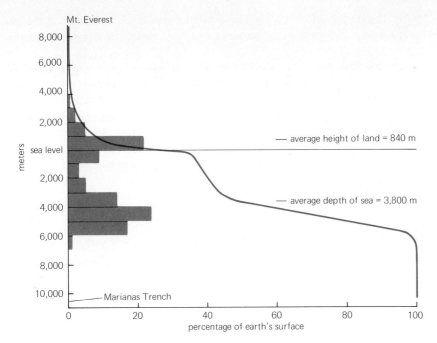

FIGURE 3-25
Percentages of the earth's surface at various levels above and below sea level. From the hypsographic curve, showing cumulative percentages, we can see that about 30 percent of the surface is above sea level and most of that is only a few hundred meters higher than the sea.

3-6 SURFACE FEATURES OF THE EARTH

In discussing the size and shape of the earth we neglected the surface features. Let us now briefly explore the surface of our planet.

One of the most obvious features of the outer part of the earth is the division between land, water, and air. The rocky crust of the earth is referred to as the *lithosphere*. The waters of the oceans, glaciers, and snowfields and the waters of the lands together make up the *hydrosphere*. Surrounding them is the enclosing envelope of air, the *atmosphere*.

Mapping the earth has shown that the oceans account for about 71 percent of the total surface area, the continents making up the remaining 29 percent. Sea level is used as the datum or reference level for elevation. Maps of land areas that exhibit elevations are called *topographic maps*. Those showing the depths of the sea are called *bathymetric maps*. Much of the surface of the continents has been topographically mapped, and preliminary bathymetric charts showing the depths to the ocean floors are available for most parts of the world. When such elevation data are plotted on a histogram (Fig. 3-25), we can see that the distribution of elevations is bimodal: two peaks in the histogram represent two dominant levels on earth, one being the average height of land at about 840 meters above sea level and the other the average depth of the oceans at about 3,800 meters below sea level. Some places on the land rise high above the average, and similarly some deeps in the sea sink far below the average. These extremes, however, account for only a very small fraction of the total area of the globe. The portion of land lying above 4,000 meters and the portion of the sea lying below 7,000 meters are so small that they cannot be shown on the histogram of Fig. 3-25.

Why are there two main levels? If we traveled over all the continents and examined the rock types, we would find great diversity. Extensive mapping and drilling have revealed, however, that by far the most abundant rock on the continents is *granite*. It is a coarse-grained crystalline rock originating deep in the crust and composed of feldspar, quartz, and minor amounts of dark minerals such as biotite or hornblende. The continental crust is thus referred to as the *granitic crust* or the *sial*, a word coined from syllables of silica and alumina to indicate the major constituents of these rocks.

Rocks that make up the ocean islands and the ocean floors are composed chiefly of basalt. Like granite, basalt contains silicate minerals, but it has more dark-colored magnesium- and iron-rich silicates, such as olivine, augite, and hornblende. The oceanic crust is often called the *basaltic crust* or the *sima*, another coined word reflecting the fact that these silicate rocks are rich in magnesium.

The two main levels of the earth appear to be related to the differences in composition of the continents and ocean basins. The sima, of the oceanic crust, has a slightly higher density than the sial, of the continents. According to Airy's interpretation of isostasy (Fig. 3-15), the lighter material should form the higher levels. We shall see in Chap. 16 that the crust is much thicker under the continents than it is under the oceans. It appears, therefore, that the two prominent levels are in fact the result of a tendency toward balance, or isostasy, on the earth. The exceptionally high or low places represent unusual density distributions or rare deviations from isostasy.

Figure 3-25 shows the average height of land to be about $\frac{1}{2}$ mile above sea level and the average depth of the seas to be about $2\frac{1}{2}$ miles below sea level. How much does the lithosphere deviate from these average values? The highest point on the land is the peak of Mount Everest, with an altitude of 29,028 feet, or about 5.5 miles. The lowest point in the oceans is in the Marianas Trench, at about 36,198 feet, or 6.9 miles, below sea level. The maximum relief is thus about 12.5 miles. A relief like this sounds tremendous to an earthbound traveler, but it is not so great when viewed in proper perspective. In Fig. 3-26, a scale drawing of the highest mountain and the deepest borehole, these mighty features lose their immensity, as well they should, since 12 miles is only about $\frac{1}{330}$ of the earth's radius.

The atmosphere is the subject of Chap. 8, but it is relevant here to look briefly at its size. Its mass is reasonably well known: it accounts for only 0.00009 percent of the total mass of the planet. The thickness of the atmosphere is much more difficult to define than the dimensions of the crust or of the hydrosphere. Whereas the boundaries, or interfaces, between the rocky crust and the hydrosphere and between the crust and the atmosphere and the hydrosphere

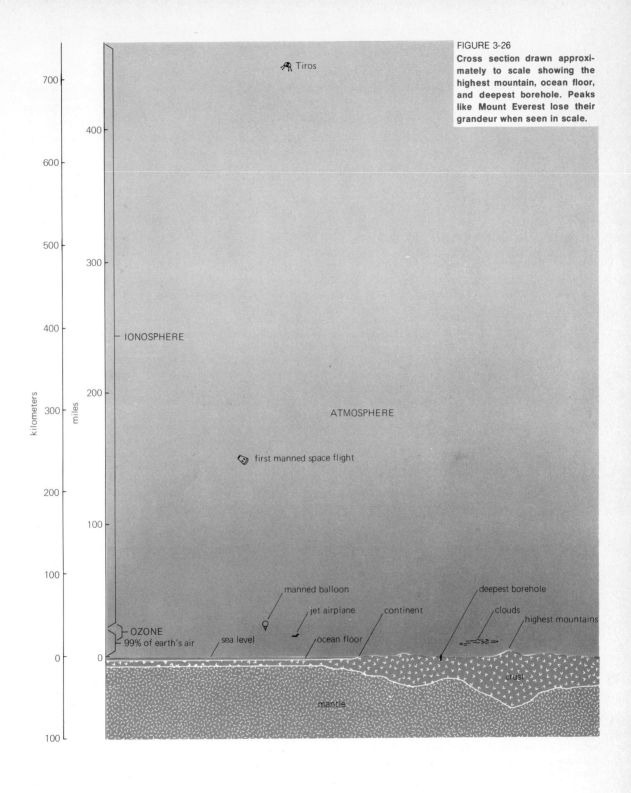

FIGURE 3-26
**Cross section drawn approxi-
mately to scale showing the
highest mountain, ocean floor,
and deepest borehole. Peaks
like Mount Everest lose their
grandeur when seen in scale.**

and the atmosphere are all reasonably sharp, the interface between the atmosphere and space beyond is diffuse. Although some extremely thin air exists for hundreds of miles above the earth's surface, a climber on the peak of Mount Everest is already above more than half the total material in the atmosphere. At an altitude of about 30 miles the atmospheric pressure is only 1 millibar, which is one-thousandth the pressure on the earth's surface.

SUMMARY

With the creation of artificial satellites man could look at the earth from space for the first time and see its overall shape and its major surface features. Previously most information on the size and shape of the earth had come from observations directed in the opposite way—outward from the earth toward celestial objects. Beginning with Eratosthenes, some 2,000 years ago, earth measurement involved determining the angular height, or altitude, of the sun or a star at different points on the earth.

In establishing the latitude of a place from solar or stellar observations the geodeticist uses his horizon as a reference. The local horizon is the plane everywhere perpendicular to the plumb line, which represents the direction of gravity. If the earth were perfectly spherical, and if it had a spherically symmetrical distribution of mass, the plumb line would always point toward its center. These conditions, however, do not hold, and the plumb line does not always point toward the same central point. Thus the problem of determining the exact shape of the earth becomes a matter of establishing departures of its gravity field from a strictly radial direction.

The main deviation of the earth shape from sphericity is the polar flattening and the corresponding equatorial bulge, resulting from decreased gravity toward the equator because of the earth's spin. The ideal figure of the earth accounting for the 13-mile difference between the polar and equatorial radii is called the spheroid. Density variations within the crust cause further minor variations in the direction of gravity and hence in the shape of the earth. The name geoid is given to the earth shape that is everywhere perpendicular to the plumb line. The geoidal shape deviates by only a few tens of meters from the idealized spheroid, but it is an irregular and nonmathematical shape.

Gravity measurements and other evidence suggest that the major segments of the earth's crust are in balance. This condition is called isostasy. Many mountainous regions are known to be elevated because, like icebergs, they are buoyed up by roots of lighter rock floating in a dense subcrust. The analogy with icebergs is only a rough one because the plastic rocks of the earth are not liquid and a long time is required for balance to be restored once it has been disturbed.

About 71 percent of the surface of the earth is covered by water. The greater portion of the ocean basins lies at a depth of about $2\frac{1}{2}$ miles below sea level; most of the land areas are about $\frac{1}{2}$ mile above sea level. These major levels probably represent an approach toward isostasy because continental materials are less dense than those of the ocean basins. The difference between the highest point on land and the greatest ocean deep is about $12\frac{1}{2}$ miles, which is only about $\frac{1}{330}$ of the earth's radius.

QUESTIONS

1 List three or four independent kinds of evidence for the conclusion that the earth is not flat.

2 A man standing 100 feet south of an east-west wall 50 feet high sees Polaris at the top of the wall. What is his approximate latitude?

3 How many places on earth do each of the following describe: (a) latitude 40°, longitude 30°, (b) latitude 90°, (c) latitude 50°N, longitude 20°W?

4 Venus is known to have a diameter of about 12,200 kilometers. Assuming a spherical shape for the planet, how far apart would two points on Venus have to be for the sun's shadow at the two places to differ by 30°?

5 When a surveyor sights along a level line, which of the earth's figures is he sighting along (sphere, spheroid, geoid)?

6 Keeping in mind that the period of a pendulum clock is proportional to $\sqrt{D/g}$, how much faster or slower would a pendulum clock run on the moon, where the acceleration of gravity is about one-sixth that of the earth?

7 An object at the equator moves through a distance equal to the earth's circumference in 24 hours. It thus has a velocity of about 1,000 miles per hour. Would an object at 45° latitude have half the velocity? Give reasons for your answer.

8 Would measurement of the gravity field intensity provide unam-

biguous proof for Airy's interpretation of isostasy?

9 Where on the earth is a circle of latitude a great circle?

10 The earth is sometimes said to be pear-shaped because of depressions in the geoid surface in parts of the middle Northern Hemisphere. Looking at the geoid map of Fig. 3-17, do you think that you would see the pear shape from a spaceship? Explain.

11 Saturn has a radius about 9.5 times the earth's radius and a mass 95 times the earth's mass.

How would its surface gravity compare with that on earth?

12 What must happen in order for isostasy to be preserved during the erosion of a high mountain with a deep root of light rock?

13 How do the oceanic and continental crusts differ?

14 How would you go about establishing the longitude of a place?

15 Do you think that the atmosphere is as thick at the equator as at the poles? Why?

REFERENCES

Beiser, Arthur: "The Earth," Time-Life Books, New York, 1964.

Greenwood, David: "Mapping," rev. ed., The University of Chicago Press, Chicago, 1963.

Strahler, Arthur N.: "The Earth Sciences," 2d ed., Harper & Row, Publishers, Incorporated, New York, 1971.

Stumpff, K.: "Planet Earth," University of Michigan Press, Ann Arbor, 1959.

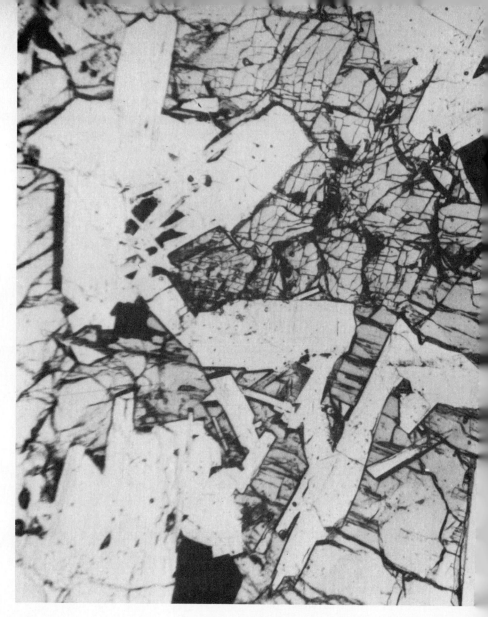

4 EARTH CHEMISTRY AND MINERALOGY

In the preceding chapters we looked at our planet as a whole; we saw how advances in astronomy and physics made it possible to determine the mass and size of the earth; we noted how gravity measurements disclosed the existence of flotational balance among major units of the earth's crust and contributed to our knowledge of the exact shape of our planet. In this chapter we shift our scale drastically from planets and stars to atoms. We examine the materials of the earth to see what they are made of, how they are distributed, and what they can tell us about the history of the earth.

FIGURE 4-1
Microscopic view of a lunar rock. The photograph illustrates that lunar rocks, like earth rocks, are composed of several minerals—naturally occurring inorganic crystalline substances. *NASA*.

The laws of motion and gravitation are laws of physics. As far as these laws are concerned, a gram of material behaves the same whether it is gold or lead or chocolate cake. Here we examine the earth from a chemist's and mineralogist's viewpoint. Instead of looking at the earth as a planet, we take a microscopic view of its materials.

Although this chapter is chiefly about the earth materials, the ideas we discuss apply equally well to other terrestrial planets. So far the only other body man has explored directly is the moon. Its rocks and minerals are much the same as some we find on earth. One difference is that in the absence of air and water moon rocks are usually remarkably fresh, as Fig. 4-1 illustrates.

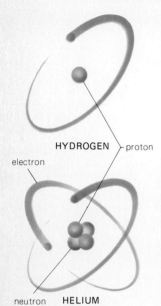

HYDROGEN — proton

electron

neutron HELIUM

FIGURE 4-2
Schematic drawing of the two simplest atoms, hydrogen and helium.

4-1 ATOMS AND THEIR PARTS

The science of chemistry evolved from alchemy, the search for a way to change common materials into gold and other precious substances. The ancient Greeks thought that matter consisted of four principles, earth, air, fire, and water. Alchemy arose from the belief that any material could be derived from the proper combination of these four basic substances. This was not a blind assumption because experience at that time seemed to show that magical things happened when several of these ingredients were mixed. For example, when reddish earth (which we now know contains iron oxide) was heated in a strong fire, the ash was found to contain gray, malleable metallic iron. It was natural to conclude that iron was a mixture of earth and fire.

For centuries alchemists experimented with different combinations of materials, trying ro change them into precious metals. We may think that the work of the alchemists was worthless and foolish because they were operating under a false premise, and we would be right in a sense; however, in the trial-and-error approach of alchemy lay the seed of the scientific method. In fact, the science of chemistry grew out of alchemy in the eighteenth century. By then experiment had shown that some substances simply cannot be further broken down by chemical means. Such substances are called *elements*.

Today, some 92 naturally occurring elements are recognized, and still others have been produced in the laboratory. Elements differ from each other in the structure of their atoms, which are made up of still more basic particles—protons, neutrons, and electrons. Each element has a characteristic number of protons. These structural differences are also responsible for the physical and chemical properties of elements.

The hydrogen atom, the simplest, has one electron revolving around a nucleus that consists of a single proton. Helium has two electrons and a nucleus consisting of two protons and two neutrons. The drawings of these two atoms in Fig. 4-2 are entirely schematic. No one has seen an atom, but there are methods of measuring the mass and size of atoms. Such experiments show that the atoms of all elements are mostly space; i.e., most of the mass of an atom is concentrated in the nucleus, consisting primarily of protons and neutrons. A proton has one unit of positive electric charge, whereas a neutron has no charge. Both neutrons and protons have about the same mass, called one mass unit. The nucleus, consisting of protons and neutrons, is surrounded by shells, or clouds, of rapidly moving electrons. An electron has one unit of negative charge and only about $\frac{1}{1,836}$ the mass of a proton.

The number of protons in the nucleus of any atom, i.e., its positive charge, is balanced by the number of electrons, i.e., negative charge. One element differs from another in the number of protons in the nucleus, called its *atomic number*. Hydrogen has an atomic number of 1; helium, 2; lithium, 3; and so on up to uranium, with an atomic number of 92.

If the atoms of all elements are composed of the same subatomic particles, and if most of the mass of an atom is contained in protons and neutrons, which have about the same mass, one would expect the atomic weights to be whole-number multiples of one mass unit. The atomic weights of the elements determined by various chemical means at the beginning of this century did not show such a relationship. In 1913 the physicist J. J. Thomson discovered why the atomic weights are not simple multiples. His experiments with neon showed it to be made up of two kinds of neon atoms, of atomic weights 20 and 22, occurring in the proportion that gives an *average* atomic weight of 20.2. Since we know that the atoms of any given element must contain the same number of protons, the difference between the two types of neon atoms must lie in the number of neutrons in the nucleus.

Atoms of the same element (same atomic number) that differ in mass are called *isotopes*. Thomson found two isotopes for neon. Hydrogen has three isotopes: ordinary hydrogen, with one proton alone in its nucleus; deuterium, with one proton and one neutron; and tritium, with one proton and two neutrons. The combined number of neutrons and protons in the nucleus is the *mass number* of an element or isotope. Thus hydrogen has three mass numbers, namely 1, 2, and 3. ^{235}U stands for a uranium isotope with a mass number of 235 or, in other terms, with a combined total of 235 protons and neutrons in its nucleus.

4-2   COMPOUNDS AND BONDING

Only a few chemical elements are found in the native, or uncombined, state in the natural environment. Most elements are sufficiently active chemically to combine with other elements, forming *compounds*, like sodium chloride, NaCl, or calcium carbonate, $CaCO_3$. Atoms bind together in several different ways, the most important being ionic, covalent, and metallic bonding.

Ionic bonding

This is an electrical type of bonding that results when atoms of an element gain or lose electrons and become ions. Atoms have a strong tendency to bring the number of electrons in their outer shells up to eight. An atom of sodium has one electron in its outermost shell, whereas a chlorine atom has seven. If the sodium atom loses an electron to the chlorine atom, both will end up with eight electrons in the outer shells (Fig. 4-3). The sodium atom in losing an electron (one unit of negative charge) becomes a positive ion, with one plus charge, whereas the chlorine, in capturing the electron, becomes a negative ion, with one minus charge. These oppositely charged ions attract each other and may unite to form the compound sodium chloride, NaCl, in which the positively charged sodium ions are balanced by the negatively charged chloride ions. The charge of an ion is called its *valence*. Metallic ions have positive valences; the valences of most nonmetallic ions are negative.

Covalent bonding

The bonding in some compounds cannot be explained on the basis of ionic attraction. For example, chlorine gas consists of molecules each containing two

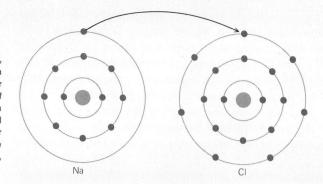

FIGURE 4-3
Schematic drawings of sodium, Na, and chlorine, Cl, atoms. Na has one electron in its outer shell, whereas Cl has seven. If the outer electron from the Na is captured by the Cl, both will have completely filled outer shells but both atoms will be charged electrically (Na = 1$^+$, Cl = 1$^-$) to become ions.

chlorine atoms, Cl_2. What holds the two atoms together? Obviously if these atoms were ionized, they would have the same charge and thus would not attract each other. Figure 4-4 illustrates schematically how two atoms of chlorine can share electrons so that both appear to have eight electrons in their outer shell. The chlorine atoms in chlorine gas are held together by a form of electron sharing called a *covalent bond*.

Metallic bonding

Ionic and covalent bonds are by far the most common types, but the atoms in native metals such as gold, silver, and copper are held together by a third type, known as the *metallic bond*. Each atom in a metal is surrounded by many similar atoms. Each metal atom has a few electrons in its outer shell, not enough to share with an adjoining atom to form the stable configuration of eight. Thus the outer electrons are completely shared as a kind of *electron gas* free to move among the metal ions. It is these free electrons that make metals such good conductors of electricity and heat.

4-3   MINERALS AND CRYSTALS

By definition minerals are naturally occurring inorganic crystalline substances. Let us examine each part of this definition.

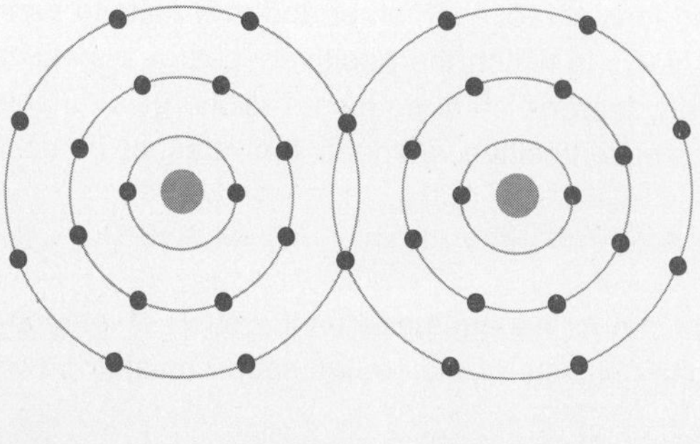

FIGURE 4-4
Two chlorine atoms can unite to form a chlorine molecule, Cl_2, by sharing electrons, so that both appear to have eight electrons in the outer shell.

FIGURE 4-5
Crystals of galena, PbS. The cubic crystals reflect the cubic pattern of Pb and S atoms. *Ward's Natural Science Establishment, Inc.*

Naturally occurring substances

There are only about 2,000 minerals, and of these fewer than 100 exist in important quantities. In contrast, tens of thousands of compounds are produced in chemical laboratories. Most of these synthesized chemicals, however, are far too reactive to exist unaltered on or within the earth. The same may be said of many pure elements. Minerals, on the other hand, are those elements and compounds which form naturally in the outdoors. In a later section we shall learn how the relationship between minerals and natural environments is used to reconstruct past conditions on earth.

Inorganic substances

The restriction of minerals to inorganic materials is a minor qualification, since well over 99 percent of the materials of the crust are inorganic anyway. The name *mineraloids* is sometimes used to refer to naturally occurring organic compounds such as those found in coal.

Crystalline substances

A crystal is a solid bounded by naturally formed plane (flat) faces (Fig. 4-5). The faces and symmetry of crystals of any substance are a reflection of an ordered internal atomic pattern. If we break a crystal with a hammer, we destroy the crystal faces but do not change the internal atomic pattern that led to the formation of the crystal faces in the first place. Any substance with an ordered internal atomic pattern is said to be crystalline. All crystalline substances are capable of forming crystals, but they do not necessarily exhibit crystal faces.

FIGURE 4-6
Diamond and graphite have the same chemical composition but vastly different physical properties. Diamond is the hardest natural substance known, whereas graphite is so soft it is used in pencils and lubricants. This difference in properties reflects a difference in internal atomic patterns and bonding.

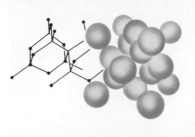

diamond

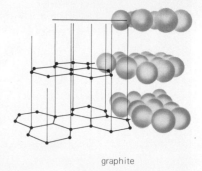

graphite

Glassy solids such as opal do not have the regular atomic arrangement of crystalline solids. A glass is amorphous: its atoms have a rather scrambled pattern, like the molecules of a liquid. The name *mineraloid* is also given to natural amorphous solids. In time all glasses crystallize, so that there are no very old natural glasses.

We cannot speak of molecules in the world of crystalline solids because the term loses its significance. The mineral galena, for example, is composed of lead and sulfur in the ratio of 1:1. Yet one lead and one sulfur atom could not possibly combine in a form that would have the four-sided symmetry shown by the galena crystals in Fig. 4-5. A galena crystal or fragment thereof is a continuum of lead and sulfur atoms arranged so that they give galena its symmetry and physical properties. No one part of this continuum can be said to be different from another, and thus there is no place for the term molecule unless the whole is called a molecule.

The crystalline nature of minerals is their most important property. Many pairs or groups of minerals have the same chemical composition. Diamond and graphite, for example, are both pure carbon, yet one is the hardest natural substance

A

B

C

FIGURE 4-7
Crystals of several different minerals. The shapes result from different atomic arrangements: (*A*) pyrite, FeS$_2$, crystals; (*B*) orthoclase, KAlSi$_3$O$_8$, crystals; (*C*) corundum, Al$_2$O$_3$, crystals. *Filer's.*

known whereas the other is used as a lubricant. The difference between these two minerals is in the internal atomic patterns, as shown in Fig. 4-6.

Although methods for determining the internal atomic patterns of minerals were not discovered until early in the twentieth century, previous studies of natural crystals had strongly suggested that such patterns exist. A Danish physician, Nicolaus Steno (1638-1687), is credited with the discovery of what is now known as the law of constancy of interfacial angles. Figure 4-7 shows photographs of a number of natural crystals; each group appears different, as they should because they are crystals of different materials. The drawings in Fig. 4-8, on the other hand, are all cross sections of quartz, SiO_2, crystals, and even these, despite a family resemblance, do not all look the same.

Steno discovered that in any two crystals of the same substance corresponding faces make the same angle, regardless of the sizes or gross shapes of the crystals. We can see this relationship for quartz in Fig. 4-8. Certainly a constancy of angle between corresponding faces suggests some governing internal pattern. At the beginning of the nineteenth century Abbé Haüy's experiments on breaking calcite, $CaCO_3$, crystals led him to conclude that an ultimate building block accounted for the crystal properties. Calcite always cleaves into rhombohedrons (Fig. 4-9). Haüy reasoned that all the faces exhibited by crystals of calcite could be formed by assuming the rhombohedron as the ultimate unit of pattern, as shown in Fig. 4-10. Other minerals had other unit forms to account for the shapes of their crystals.

FIGURE 4-8
How individual quartz crystals vary in cross section. The outlines look different, but the angles between corresponding faces are always the same.

FIGURE 4-9
Calcite always breaks into six-sided fragments called rhombohedrons. This mineral has three directions of perfect cleavage.

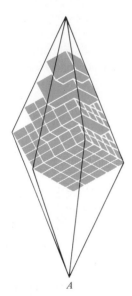

rhombohedron

scalenohedron

A

B

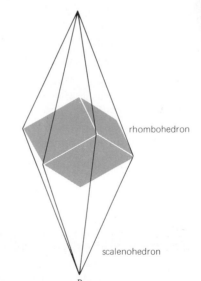

FIGURE 4-10
Hauy's conception of the internal structure of crystals. He found that although calcite always breaks into rhombohedrons (*A*), it usually crystallizes into a form called a *scalenohedron*. He reasoned that the basic building block of calcite must be tiny rhombohedrons that could be stacked together to produce either rhombohedrons or scalenohedrons (*B*).

FIGURE 4-11
The lattice pattern of calcite. The atoms are not shown to scale because if they were, the carbon would be completely hidden by the large oxygen ions and the atoms would all be touching, so that we could not look inside the structure. Note that the basic atomic pattern is rhombohedral.

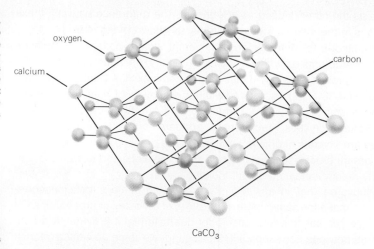

CaCO₃

FIGURE 4-12
Wave interference. (I) Waves started along stretched strings *AC* and *BC* will interfere at *C*. (II) Crest meets crest, and the interference is constructive. (III) Crests and troughs line up, and the interference is destructive. (IV) A mixture of constructive and destructive interference. *From K. B. Krauskopf and A. Beiser, "Fundamentals of Physical Science," 5th ed. Copyright © 1966 by McGraw-Hill, Inc. Used with permission of McGraw-Hill Book Company.*

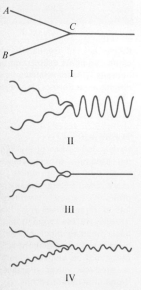

Although there was a germ of truth in Haüy's picture of crystal structure, we know today that the ultimate building units of crystalline materials are atoms and not tiny solid blocks. Figure 4-11 shows the basic unit of pattern exhibited by the ions in calcite, which turns out to be a rhombohedron.

How do we know the arrangement of atoms in crystalline substances? The solution to this problem began early in this century, shortly after x-rays had been discovered in 1895. As we know, x-rays are very penetrating, and it was soon realized that they must be a type of electromagnetic radiation of very short wavelength. In fact, it became clear that their wavelengths are of the same order of magnitude as the diameters of individual atoms. Thus x-rays were recognized as a potential yardstick for measuring distances between atoms.

Sir Lawrence Bragg, of England, was a pioneer investigator of internal atomic structure by x-rays. His work led to the formulation of the *Bragg relation*

$$n\lambda = 2d \sin \theta$$

where n = an integer
λ = wavelength of incident x-rays
d = spacing between atomic planes
θ = angle of incidence = angle of reflection of x-rays

The main idea behind the Bragg equation is that when two waves — x-rays, sound waves, or water waves — come together, they destroy each other unless the crests of one coincide with the crests of the other (see Fig. 4-12). Suppose then that an x-ray beam of wavelength λ strikes a crystal, as in Fig. 4-13. The part of the beam reflected from the lower atomic plane travels farther than the part reflected from the upper plane, the difference in distance being $AB + BC$. This path difference must be equal to a whole number of wavelengths $n\lambda$ if the two

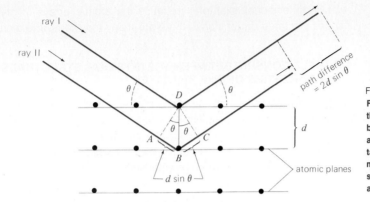

FIGURE 4-13

For constructive interference of the reflections of this x-ray beam from the atomic planes of a crystalline substance the distance ABC must be some whole multiple n of a wavelength. The small dark circles represent atoms.

sets of crests are to coincide. The diagram shows that $AB + BC = 2d \sin \theta$. Thus the condition for a reinforced reflection is $n\lambda = 2d \sin \theta$, which is just Bragg's relation.

The Bragg equation contains three variables, incident angle θ, x-ray wavelength λ, and the spacing between atomic planes d. If the wavelength of the x-rays is known and the angle θ is measured, then d, the spacing between atomic planes, can be calculated. Every crystalline substance has many d values, as is illustrated for some two-dimensional arrays in Fig. 4-14. The crystallographer measures all the d values displayed by a crystalline material. He then proceeds to develop an atomic arrangement that would produce the measured spacings. For example, from the d values of Fig. 4-14 we could tell whether the unit pattern was a square or a rectangle. His job is, of course, very much more difficult than

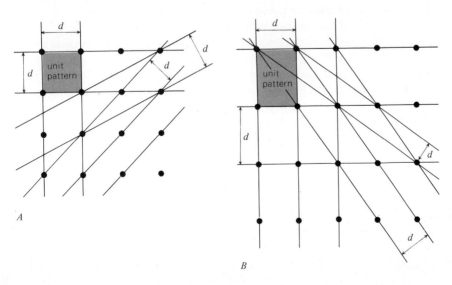

FIGURE 4-14

Some possible atomic planes in two-dimensional arrays. The relationship between the interplanar spacing d is different when the unit of pattern is a square (A) and when it is a rectangle (B). Each three-dimensional crystal lattice has many possible values of d. It is from the measured d values that the crystallographer reconstructs a model of the unit atomic pattern.

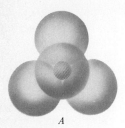

A

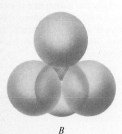

B

FIGURE 4-15
The silicon-oxygen tetrahedron, SiO_4^{4-}. The silicon ion is just the right size to fit into the hole left when four oxygen ions touch. (A) View from above; (B) from the side.

our two-dimensional example; because the atomic arrays in crystalline substances are three-dimensional, there are many more possible atomic planes.

4-4 RELATIONSHIP BETWEEN THE INTERNAL STRUCTURES AND PROPERTIES OF THE SILICATES

Minerals are classified on the basis of their chemical composition into major groups such as elements, sulfides, oxides, carbonates, sulfates, phosphates, and silicates. Of all the mineral groups the silicates are by far the most abundant. Because they make up over 90 percent of the crust, we shall use them to demonstrate the relationship between internal structure and the physical and chemical properties of minerals.

The silicon ion, with a charge of 4+, is very small compared to the oxygen ion, with a charge of 2−. In fact, it is just large enough to fit perfectly into the hole left when four oxygen ions touch each other (Fig. 4-15). In all silicate minerals each silicon atom is surrounded by four oxygen atoms, as shown, and this basic unit is known as the *silicon-oxygen tetrahedron*. In minerals, the tetrahedrons form a variety of configurations by sharing oxygen ions (Fig. 4-16).

A single tetrahedron has a residual charge of 4− (silicon = 4+; 4 oxygens = $4 \times 2 = 8-$). When all the oxygens are shared, as in the mineral quartz, the structure is balanced electrically because only one-half the charge of an oxygen ion is directed toward any one silicon ion. Where there is no sharing or only partial sharing of oxygen ions, the individual tetrahedrons or rings, chains, or sheets of tetrahedrons must occur with other positive ions such as Mg^{2+}, Fe^{2+}, Ca^{2+}, or K^+ in order to achieve electrical balance.

We can see from Fig. 4-16 that the formula of a silicate mineral tells us which type of skeletal silicate structure it has. For example, a mineral in which the tetrahedrons do not share any oxygens should have a silicon/oxygen ratio of 1:4, which is the ratio of a single tetrahedron. The mineral olivine, $(Mg, Fe)_2 SiO_4$, contains isolated tetrahedrons which are held together by positively charged ions of magnesium and iron. In beryl, $Be_3Al_2 \cdot Si_6O_{18}$, the Si_6O_{18} tells us that the tetrahedrons share oxygens to form rings. Where each tetrahedron shares two oxygens ($2 \times \frac{1}{2} = 1$) and has two unshared oxygens ($2 \times 1 = 2$) the silicon/oxygen ratio is 1:3. The formula of diopside, one of the pyroxenes which exhibit this single-chain structure, is $CaMg(SiO_3)_2$.

In double chains the silicon tetrahedrons alternately share two and three oxygens. The silicon/oxygen ratio in tetrahedrons sharing two oxygens again must be 1:3, and in those sharing three oxygens ($3 \times \frac{1}{2} = 1\frac{1}{2}$) with only one oxygen unshared ($1 \times 1 = 1$) the ratio becomes $1:2\frac{1}{2}$. The overall ratio thus is $2:5\frac{1}{2}$, or 4:11, which is reflected in the formula of tremolite, $Ca_2Mg_5(Si_4O_{11})_2(OH)_2$, one of the amphibole family of minerals, all of which possess the double-chain configuration. Where each tetrahedron shares three oxygens, the oxygen/silicon ratio becomes $1:2\frac{1}{2}$, or 2:5, which is the ratio found in the micas, and where all oxygens are shared the ratio is, of course, 1:2, which is what we find in quartz, SiO_2.

	Configuration	Number of oxygens shared	Example
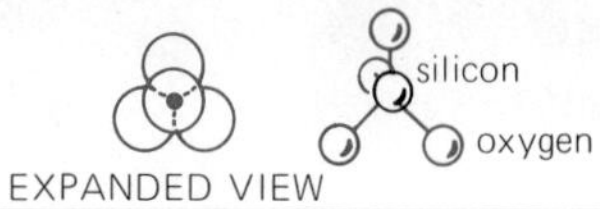 silicon / oxygen EXPANDED VIEW	Single tetrahedrons SiO_4^{4-}	0	Olivine, $(Mg, Fe)_2SiO_4$
	Rings of tetrahedrons $Si_6O_{18}^{12-}$	2	Beryl, $Be_3Al_2 \cdot Si_6O_{18}$
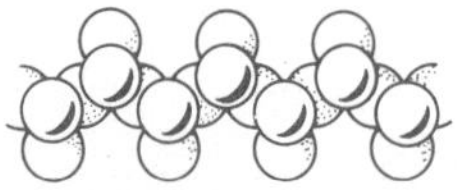	Single chains SiO_3^{2-}	2	Enstatite, $(Mg,Fe)_2Si_2O_6$
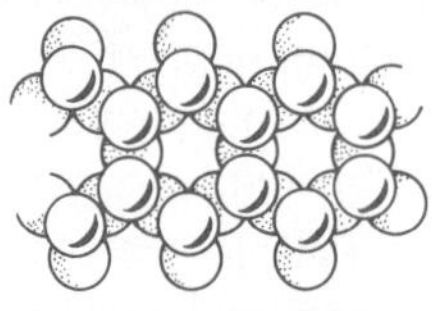	Double chains $Si_4O_{11}^{6-}$	2,3	Tremolite, $Ca_2Mg_5Si_8O_{22}(OH)_2$
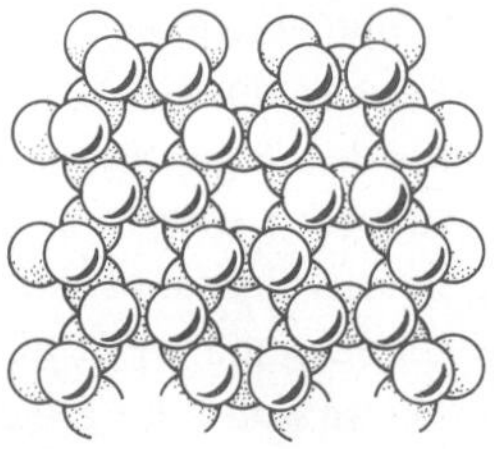	Sheets $Si_2O_5^{2-}$	3	Talc, $Mg_3Si_4O_{10}(OH)_2$
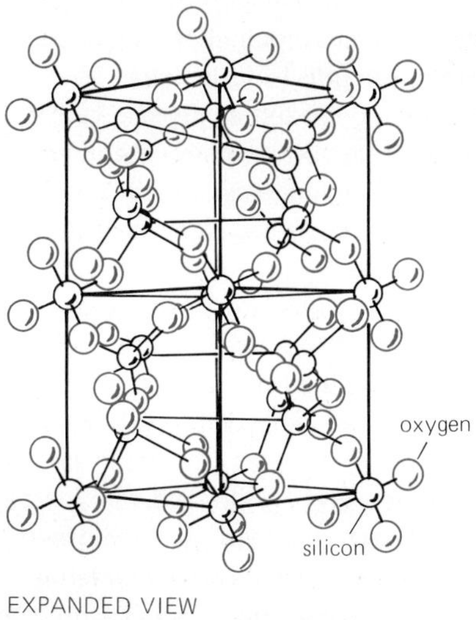 oxygen / silicon EXPANDED VIEW	Framework SiO_2	4	Quartz, SiO_2

FIGURE 4-16
The principal types of silicate structures.

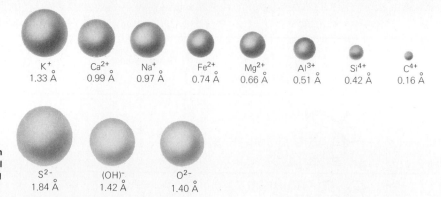

FIGURE 4-17
Relative sizes of some common ions found in minerals. Actual sizes given in angstroms (Å); 1 Å = 10^{-8} cm.

We have said that the silicates are the most abundant minerals in the earth's crust. Of the silicates, a group known as the feldspars are the most common. These silicates of sodium, calcium, potassium, and aluminum make up over 50 percent of the mineral content of the crust. One of the feldspars, orthoclase, has the formula $KAlSi_3O_8$. At first it would appear that the Si_3O_8 does not fit any of the silicate patterns of Fig. 4-16. It turns out that orthoclase (and all the feldspars for that matter) have a framework type of silicate structure, where all of the oxygens of the silicon-oxygen tetrahedrons are shared. The reason the Si/O ratio does not come out to 1:2 is that every fourth silicon position in the array of tetrahedrons in orthoclase is occupied by an aluminum ion. We could write the formula for orthoclase as $K(Si, Al)_4O_8$, which shows the expected 1:2 ratio of silicon to oxygen positions. Since Al has a charge of only $3+$ instead of the $4+$ of silicon, a singly positive ion (K^+) must be incorporated into the structure for electrical balance.

Aluminum ions are able to occupy the same structural sites as silicon ions in the feldspars because they are also small enough to fit between four oxygen ions. This characteristic of two ions competing for the same site in a mineral structure is quite common, not only in the silicates but in many other minerals as well. For instance, Mg^{2+} and Fe^{2+} occupy the same sites in the olivine structure, and it is easy to see why from Fig. 4-17. They have the same charge and are nearly identical in size. Whereas it is possible to have a magnesium olivine, Mg_2SiO_4, or an iron olivine, Fe_2SiO_4, most olivines are mixtures of the two, $(Mg, Fe)_2SiO_4$, the proportions varying from place to place and depending upon the conditions of formation and the availability of the two elements. This helps to explain why some minerals lack a constant chemical composition. Sometimes such compositional variations are easily visible. In the amphibole, $Ca_2(Mg, Fe)_5Si_8O_{22}(OH)_2$, the variety with no iron is white, and with increasing amounts of iron the mineral becomes first green and then blackish green.

Let us return to Fig. 4-16 and examine the relationship between internal structure and some physical properties. The silicon-oxygen bond is very strong. In the micas the silicon-oxygen tetrahedrons occur as continuous sheets which are

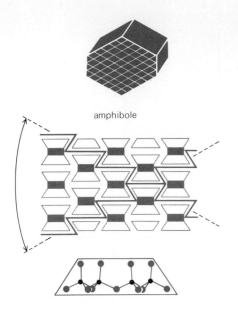

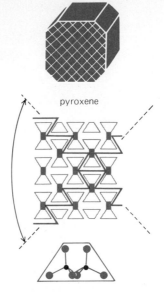

FIGURE 4-18
The cleavages of pyroxenes and amphiboles (both ferromagnesian silicates) reflect the configuration of silicon-oxygen tetrahedrons in the minerals. Color lines show that both minerals break between the silicon-oxygen chains. Because single chains and double chains differ in cross section, the cleavage angles are different.

bonded together with other positive ions such as K^+ and Mg^{2+}. When micas are broken, the breaks tend to occur between the sheets of tetrahedrons, with the result that broken pieces of mica are flat and sheetlike. The ability of a mineral to break along flat planes is called *cleavage*, and all the micas and other sheet silicates possess one direction of cleavage.

The pyroxenes and amphiboles are chain silicates of iron, magnesium, and calcium. Although these two mineral groups are similar in chemical composition, they differ in their physical properties (Fig. 4-18). Again these minerals tend to break between the silicon-oxygen chains, resulting in two cleavage directions near 90° for the single-chained pyroxenes and in two directions at 60° for the double-chained amphiboles.

Quartz, as we know, has only silicon-oxygen bonds. This explains its strength, its resistance to chemical decomposition, and its lack of cleavage. Olivine, on the other hand, can be physically broken or chemically decomposed without breaking any silicon-oxygen bonds because its tetrahedrons occur singly without oxygen sharing. This does not mean that olivine is soft and easy to break; the bonds between magnesium or iron and oxygen in olivine are strong also. Like quartz, olivine lacks cleavage, but as we shall see in Sec. 10-4, it decomposes chemically much more readily than most other silicates.

4-5 MINERALS AS INDICATORS OF PAST ENVIRONMENTS

To many of us the word mineral conjures up the sparkle of diamonds, emeralds, or rubies. The geologist too is interested in gemstones, where they occur, and

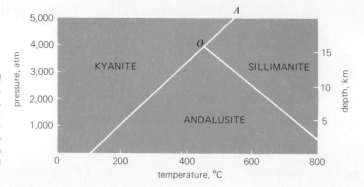

FIGURE 4-19
The fields of stability of the three aluminosilicates, Al_2OSiO_4, andalusite, kyanite, and sillimanite. Because pressure in the earth is usually determined by depth of burial, the depths at which the pressures given will be realized are noted at the right.

why they possess desirable properties; but far more precious to him are the clues which minerals provide about past conditions on earth.

To understand how minerals can be used as indicators of environment let us examine the conditions that must be met for a given mineral to form at a particular time and place. Obviously one controlling condition is the availability of the chemical elements of which the mineral is made. But this cannot be the only condition, for it would not determine the choice between minerals like diamond, C, and graphite, C, that have identical chemical compositions. Many minerals in fact have similar but not identical chemical compositions. Thus environmental factors such as temperature, pressure, acidity, alkalinity, and aridity determine whether one mineral or another of similar composition will form. Herein lies the value of minerals to the geologist in his task of reconstructing the history of the earth. If by experiment, by observing minerals forming under known conditions today, or by the application of chemical theory he can determine the conditions that control the combination of chemical elements into the form of a given mineral, he has a clue to the past.

A good many man-years have been expended, and more will be expended, by experimental and theoretical mineralogists on the job of synthesizing minerals in order to determine the conditions necessary to form them. Such work has shown that some minerals are good environment indicators because they form only under a narrow range of conditions. Others have little value as clues to the past because they grow over a broad range of conditions. Groups or associations of minerals are more valuable than single minerals in this task of reconstruction.

Minerals having the same chemical compositions but different internal structures and hence different physical properties are called *polymorphs*, from the Greek, meaning "many forms." As an example of mineralogical investigations let us look at the stability diagram for the three polymorphs of Al_2OSiO_4 shown in Fig. 4-19. The information shown there was determined experimentally by measuring the temperatures at which kyanite changes to sillimanite and vice versa. This change is very slow and can be effected within a reasonable time only by working at high temperatures. Other points on the graph were determined by mixing the components Al_2O_3 and SiO_2 and heating them to see which of the

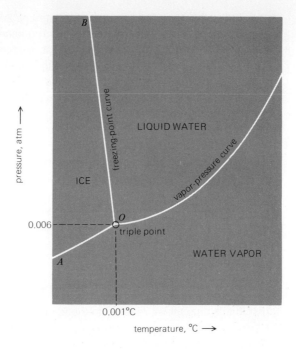

FIGURE 4-20
Stability fields of the various forms of H_2O.

polymorphs would form at various temperatures and pressures. Chemical theory was used to extend the lines into areas of the lower temperature and pressure. Although further experimental work may change the exact positions of some of the lines on this equilibrium diagram, we shall accept it for now. What does it tell us?

The important parts of the diagram are the lines showing where the stability fields of the minerals come together. Only in the temperature and pressure range indicated by the line AO can kyanite and sillimanite form together. Thus if kyanite and sillimanite occur together in a rock in such a way that suggests that they formed at the same time, it is safe to conclude that the rock formed at a pressure and temperature related by the line AO. If the temperature of formation of the rock can be established by some other means, the pressure is fixed by the line, and vice versa. If all three minerals are found together in a rock, both the temperature and the pressure would be fixed at point O on the diagram.

An example of a more familiar equilibrium situation is that of Fig. 4-20, involving the various phases of H_2O. Again any two phases such as water and ice can exist together only along the line BO. At atmospheric pressure, water and ice coexist at 0°C. If the temperature is raised slightly, only water will be stable; if it is lowered, only ice will be present. Water, ice, and vapor can coexist in equilibrium only at point O on the diagram.

The parallelism between our mineral example and the H_2O system does not hold when the fate of an equilibrium assemblage is considered. If the temperature of a vessel containing water and ice in equilibrium is lowered slightly, soon only ice will be present. On the other hand, a mixture of kyanite and sillimanite

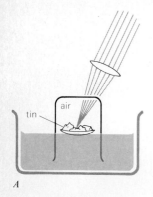

FIGURE 4-21
Lavoisier's experiment showing that air is composed of several substances. Upon heating, the tin reacts with something in the air (A), but after one-fifth of the air has been used up, the reaction stops (B).

formed under the conditions indicated by the line AO of Fig. 4-19 remains the same when cooled to surface temperatures. The minerals are a frozen record of the temperature and pressure conditions that existed when they were formed.

Some minerals are sensitive to conditions other than temperature and pressure. Halite, for example, which is ordinary table salt, is highly soluble. Consequently where halite is found as rock salt, the conditions at the time of formation must have been very dry and warm. Fine-grained pyrite, FeS_2, in sediments oxidizes quickly when exposed to the air, and when some pyrite-bearing shales are broken up at the surface, they actually burn spontaneously. Again we can be confident that rocks with pyrite must have formed in an oxygen-free environment.

We shall see other ways in which minerals are used as environment indicators in later chapters. The use of minerals as clues to the past is complicated by the diversity of the natural world. It is not yet possible to duplicate the complicated systems of nature in the laboratory exactly.

4-6 THE COMPOSITION OF THE OUTER PART OF THE EARTH

Earlier in this chapter we referred to the 92 natural elements. Now we ask: How are these elements distributed? Are they all about equally abundant, or are some much more common than others? If so, which elements are the most common? In this first look at the distribution of the elements let us take up separately each of the three spheres that meet at the surface of the earth to form our environment.

The atmosphere

The atmosphere is composed of a mixture of gases that we call air. Antoine Lavoisier (1743–1794), a great French scientist, first recognized that air is a mixture of several elements and in so doing pioneered the development of modern chemistry. He burned, or oxidized, tin in a closed vessel by focusing the sun's rays on a piece of the metal (Fig. 4-21). As the tin changed to a white powder on being heated, the water rose in the vessel, suggesting that something out of the air had combined with the metal to form the powder. In experiments with mercury he was able to isolate the gas that had combined with the metal. The gas left in the vessel at the end of such experiments was unable to support further combustion, and animals left in it quickly died. On the other hand materials burned with exceptional vigor in the gas that had combined with the metals. Although Joseph Priestley had produced this gas (which we now know as oxygen) several years earlier and others had conducted experiments similar to those just described, it was Lavoisier who first recognized their significance. He deduced that air is not a single substance or element, as previously supposed, but consists of several elements. His interpretation was a first step toward the discovery of the chemical elements as we know them today.

Many chemical analyses of samples of the atmosphere have been made since the time of Lavoisier, and, as one would expect from the mobility of gases, the composition of the atmosphere at sea level shows little variation over the globe. Table 4-1 shows the composition of the lower atmosphere.

The elements in the air are present mainly as molecules. Oxygen exists chiefly as the O_2 molecule, nitrogen as N_2, and carbon in carbon dioxide, CO_2. During the early part of the nineteenth century the Italian scientist Amadeo Avogadro hypothesized that equal volumes of gases under the same conditions of temperature and pressure contain equal numbers of molecules. This idea has since been confirmed and is now known as *Avogadro's law*. According to this law, the column in Table 4-1 showing composition of the atmosphere by volume can be interpreted as molecular abundances. For every 78 molecules of nitrogen there must be 20.9 molecules of oxygen and 1 atom of argon.

Three gases, nitrogen, oxygen, and argon, account for over 98 percent of the lower atmosphere. This does not mean that the other constituents are unimportant, however. Carbon dioxide, which makes up only about 0.03 percent of the atmosphere, is vital to the growth of all plant life. Moreover it plays a major role, along with ozone, O_3, in inhibiting the escape of radiant energy from the earth.

FIGURE 4-22
The water molecule. Because the positive hydrogen ions are not symmetrically arranged, the molecule is polar, i.e., has a positive and a negative end.

The hydrosphere

The hydrosphere is the partly discontinuous shell of water at and near the earth's surface. The great bulk of this sphere is the salty water of the oceans, but the fresh waters of lakes and rivers, the ice of snowfields and glaciers, the fresh and salt waters in the pores of rocks are also included.

The water molecule, consisting of one oxygen and two hydrogen ions, has some unusual properties. Its two hydrogen ions are covalently bonded to the oxygen ion in such a way that they make an angle of about 105° with each other, as shown in Fig. 4-22. This arrangement makes the water molecule polar; i.e., one of its sides has different properties from the other. The side of the molecule containing the two hydrogen ions is electrically positive with respect to the side without the hydrogens. Opposite sides of water molecules thus tend to attract, and this attraction in part accounts for the unusual properties of water.

For one thing, the attraction between water molecules explains why water has such a high surface tension compared to most liquids. Surface tension is what permits a needle or a razor blade to float on water and allows water to rise in capillary openings such as the pore spaces in soil or the fine spaces in a sponge. The polar nature of the water molecule also accounts for its remarkable solvent

TABLE 4-1
Average composition of dry air*

Gas	Composition	
	By volume	*By weight*
N_2	78.09	75.51
O_2	20.95	23.15
Ar	0.93	1.28
CO_2	0.03	0.05
Others		
(Ne, He, CH_4)	Less than 0.002	Less than 0.002

*The moisture content of air is usually much lower than 5 percent.

properties. In dissolving a substance like common salt, NaCl, for example, the positive ends of the water molecules become attached to negative chloride ions, and the negative sides of other water molecules are attracted to positive sodium ions.

The hydrosphere continually interacts with the materials of the earth's solid crust, with the result that natural waters contain many elements in solution. Seawater contains an average of 3.5 percent dissolved solids by weight. Although the proportions of dissolved ions in seawater are the same everywhere, the total quantity of dissolved solids varies slightly from place to place because of variations in the rates of evaporation and precipitation. The fresh waters of the land contain a much smaller dissolved load than seawater. Usually their dissolved load ranges from 20 to 200 parts per million (0.0002 to 0.02 percent). Moreover, the principal ions dissolved in fresh water are different from those found in seawater (as is shown later in Table 9-2). Chlorine and sodium are the most abundant dissolved constituents in seawater, whereas calcium and sulfate head the list for the waters of the lands. These are by no means the only dissolved constituents, however. Careful microanalyses show trace amounts of almost all the elements in the hydrosphere.

The lithosphere

The terms *crust* and *lithosphere* refer to the earth's outer rocky shell. In Chap. 5 we look deeper into the earth at the materials that underlie the crust and explore the techniques used to measure the thickness of the crust and unravel the internal structure of our planet. For now, let us accept that the crust varies in thickness from about 3 to 30 miles, the average being about 10 miles (17 kilometers).

A moment's reflection will show that determining the average composition of the crust is much more difficult than for either the hydrosphere or the atmosphere, in which both the high mobility of the molecules and ions and the convective motions of water and air make for thorough mixing and a homogeneous composition. This is not true for the solid crust, as evidenced by the diversity of materials in it. Soils, surface debris, layered rocks, massive rocks, dark rocks, and light rocks all occur in the crust; within the span of a human lifetime they show no tendency to mix.

However, the problem of estimating the average chemical composition of the crust is not as difficult as it first appears. A preliminary survey of chemical analyses of earth materials reveals that only a few of the 92 elements are common or abundant. Most of the elements are so rare, in fact, that special analytical techniques are required to detect them. Investigators of the geochemistry of the crust must have been convinced after the first few hundred rock analyses that it consists mainly of oxygen, silicon, aluminum, and iron.

A further simplification is that most of the many rock types are comparatively rare when the entire crust is viewed. We already noted (Chap. 3) that mapping earth materials showed that two rock types account for over 90 percent of all rocks. On the continents granite is the chief rock type although it is usually covered by a veneer of layered sediments. The ocean basins, on the other hand, contain basalt as the principal rock. Both granite and basalt are igneous rocks (rocks formed from molten materials), and both are composed mainly of silicate minerals. Granite contains more silica as feldspar and quartz than basalt does; basalt, on the other hand, is characterized by a greater abundance of iron and magnesium silicates.

Table 4-2 shows three independent estimates of the composition of the lithosphere by weight. The estimate by Clarke and Washington is actually an average of some 5,000 individual analyses of igneous rocks. Since the crust is composed chiefly of igneous rocks, their estimate is frequently reported as an average for the entire crust.

The Goldschmidt estimate presents a unique approach to the problem in that it is an average of some 77 analyses of glacial clays from Scandinavia. The rocks of Scandinavia are deeply eroded, old rocks, believed to be typical of the continental crust. Goldschmidt reasoned that the glaciers of the Pleistocene Epoch should have scraped off representative samples of these rocks. Instead of collecting many hundreds or thousands of samples of the rocks themselves, he collected specimens of ground-up glacial flour, each of which was a sample of the many rocks that the glacier had traversed. His estimate is surprisingly close to that of Clarke and Washington.

The Poldervaart average represents a more systematic approach. Instead of attempting to determine an overall average of many analyses, Poldervaart first considered the relative masses of the major crustal segments. For example, from information on the area of the oceans and the average thickness of the oceanic crust he was able to compute the total mass of oceanic crust. With such information he combined average analyses for the various segments of the crust so as to give appropriate weighting to the masses of the segments. One of the chief criticisms of the earlier estimates was that some rock types or crustal segments were unduly represented.

Sample weighting can be illustrated by considering the problem of determining the average concentration of salt in two beakers, one containing 1,000 grams of solution and the other 2,000 grams. If the 1,000-gram container has 2 percent salt and the 2,000-gram container has 4 percent salt, what is the salt content when the two are mixed? Obviously it would not be a simple average, $(2 + 4)/2 = 3$ percent, because there is more of one strength than of the other. In-

TABLE 4-2
Some estimates of the average composition of the earth's crust

Source	SiO_2	Al_2O_3	Fe_2O_3	FeO	MgO	CaO	Na_2O	K_2O	TiO_2	P_2O_5
Clarke and Washington	60.18	15.61	3.14	3.88	3.56	5.17	3.91	3.19	1.06	0.30
Goldschmidt	59.12	15.82	6.99		3.30	3.07	2.05	3.93	0.79	0.22
Poldervaart	55.2	15.3	2.8	5.8	5.2	8.8	2.9	1.9	1.6	0.3

stead the weighted average would be

$$2\% \times 1{,}000\ g = \quad 2{,}000\%\ g$$
$$4\% \times 2{,}000\ g = \quad \underline{8{,}000\%\ g}$$
$$\text{Total} \quad 10{,}000\%\ g$$

$$\text{Weighted average} = \frac{10{,}000\%\ g}{3{,}000\ g} = 3.3\%$$

In Table 4-2 the abundances of the chemical elements are reported in terms of oxides (SiO_2, Al_2O_3, etc.) because they are chemically analyzed in this form. Table 4-3, computed on the basis of elements, lists all the elements which occur in abundances of over 1 percent. We can see that just eight elements, oxygen, silicon, aluminum, iron, calcium, sodium, potassium, and magnesium, account for almost 99 percent of the total mass of the earth's crust.

Because ions differ in size, it is interesting to recompute the abundances on a volume basis; this shows that oxygen, which has the largest radius of all the common ions, constitutes almost 94 percent of the crust. We can thus think of the lithosphere as a tightly packed mass of oxygen ions with smaller positive metal ions occupying the interstices between the oxygen spheres and binding them together.

TABLE 4-3
The most abundant elements in the earth's crust

Element	Symbol	Weight, %	Radius, Å	Volume, %
Oxygen	O	46.6	1.40	93.8
Silicon	Si	27.7	0.42	0.86
Aluminum	Al	8.13	0.51	0.47
Iron	Fe	5.00	0.74	0.43
Calcium	Ca	3.63	0.99	1.03
Sodium	Na	2.83	0.97	1.32
Potassium	K	2.59	1.33	1.83
Magnesium	Mg	2.09	0.66	0.29

*From B. H. Mason, "Geochemistry," John Wiley & Sons, Inc., New York, 1966, by permission.

SUMMARY

The atoms of all chemical elements consist of a nucleus, made up of positively charged protons and (except for hydrogen) neutrons and surrounded by shells of rapidly vibrating electrons. Most of the mass of the atom is in the nucleus. Atoms of one element differ from those of another in the number of protons contained in the nucleus.

Minerals are naturally occurring inorganic crystalline substances. Most minerals are compounds, but a few, like gold and sulfur, consist of a single element. The atoms in minerals are arranged in regular patterns; this internal symmetry in large part determines the properties of a given mineral. The relative size of the ions in minerals contributes to their internal atomic structure. Ions of two elements having about the same size may occupy similar sites in the structure of a mineral, thus accounting for the variable compositions of some minerals.

Since some minerals or associations of minerals form only under restricted conditions of temperature, pressure, or other environmental variables, they are used by geologists as clues to past environments in reconstructing the physical history of the earth.

Of the 90-odd chemical elements

in earth materials, 8 account for almost 99 percent of the composition of the crust. Oxygen is by far the most abundant element in the crust and in the hydrosphere and is a major constituent of the atmosphere. The molecules of the atmosphere and the hydrosphere are relatively well mixed in their respective spheres. Mixing is very slow in the solid materials of the crust, where heterogeneity rather than homogeneity is the rule. The crust may be thought of as a closely packed array of oxygen ions bound together by positive metal ions like silicon, aluminum, iron, sodium, and potassium, which occupy the holes between oxygens.

QUESTIONS

1 What is the relationship between element, ion, and isotope?

2 What subatomic particles are found in the nucleus of an atom?

3 How does one element differ from another if they are all made of the same particles?

4 ^{235}U has an atomic number of 92. How many neutrons are there in its nucleus?

5 All minerals are crystalline solids, but not all mineral specimens are crystals. Why?

6 Why do the micas break into flat sheets whereas quartz breaks into irregular fragments?

7 Two specimens of the mineral olivine, $(Mg, Fe)_2SiO_4$, from different localities are analyzed chemically. Both are homogeneous, clean samples, yet one is

found to contain 10.2 percent iron and the other 15.4 percent iron. How would you account for this variability?

8 Given that the atomic weight of oxygen is 16 and the atomic weight of hydrogen is 1, what is the weight percent of oxygen in the hydrosphere?

9 Quartz has the formula SiO_2. If silicon and oxygen always combine in a tetrahedral relation, why is there no mineral with the formula SiO_4?

10 What sort of cleavage would you expect to find in the mineral lepidolite, which has the formula $K_2Li_3Al_3(AlSi_3O_{10})(OH)_2$?

11 In a few silicates the silicon-oxygen tetrahedrons share only one oxygen. What would the Si/O ratio be in these silicates?

12 Noting that the mineral goethite, $Fe_2O_3 \cdot H_2O$, dissociates into Fe_2O_3 (hematite) and H_2O at about 130°C, what can you say about the thermal history of a rock containing goethite known to have formed 100,000 years ago?

13 Which of the following ions would most likely occupy the same site in a mineral structure as Fe^{2+} (radius = 0.74 Å)? Be^{2+}, radius = 0.35 Å; Mn^{2+}, radius = 0.80 Å; Sb^{3+}, radius = 0.76 Å.

14 What are the eight most abundant elements in the lithosphere?

15 Why is the water molecule said to be polar? How does its structure affect the properties of water?

16 Keeping in mind the chemical composition of the earth's crust, what can you say about the ex-

pected abundances of the minerals galena, PbS; albite, $NaAlSi_3O_8$; quartz, SiO_2; and calcite, $CaCO_3$? Which would you expect to be the most abundant?

17 A stockpile of ore contains 10,000 tons of material with 2.0 percent copper, 50,000 tons with 2.8 percent copper, and 100,000 tons with 1.5 percent copper. What is the weighted average copper content of the entire pile?

18 What is a polymorph?

19 How does the oceanic crust differ compositionally from the continental crust?

20 What is the principal ion in seawater? In fresh water?

REFERENCES

Berry, L. G., and B. H. Mason: "Mineralogy: Concepts, Descriptions, and Determinations," W. H. Freeman and Company, San Francisco, 1959.

Ernst, W. G.: "Earth Materials," Prentice-Hall, Inc., Englewood Cliffs, N.J. 1969.

Hurlbut, C. S., Jr.: "Dana's Manual of Mineralogy," John Wiley & Sons, Inc., New York, 1959.

Kraus, E. H., W. F. Hunt, and L. S. Ramsdell: "Mineralogy," 5th ed., McGraw-Hill Book Company, New York, 1959.

Mason, B. H.: "Geochemistry," John Wiley & Sons, Inc., New York, 1966.

Sinkankas, John: "Mineralogy for Amateurs," D. Van Nostrand Company, Inc., Princeton, N.J., 1964.

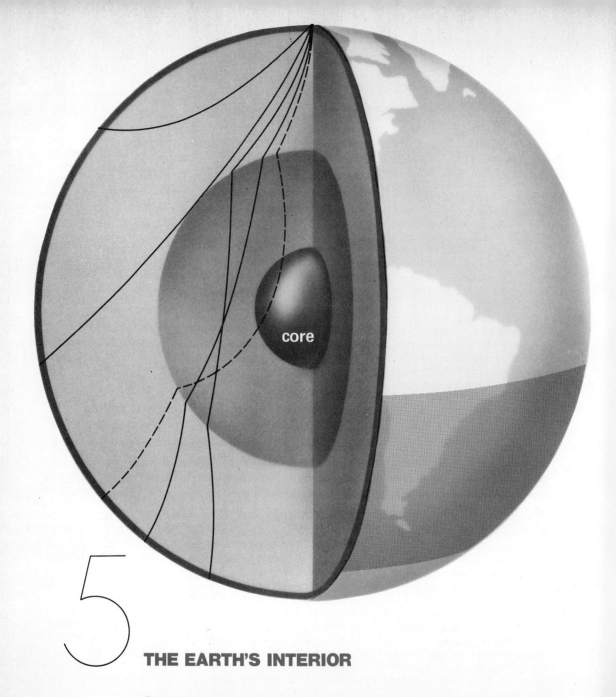

5

THE EARTH'S INTERIOR

Beneath the earth's outer crust lies a region less well known to us than the distant stars. The deepest mines extend about 10,000 feet; a hole in the Pecos oilfield of west Texas penetrates 7.7 kilometers of the crust. These man-made openings are indeed insignificant when compared with the 6,400 kilometers to the center of the earth. Thus to learn about the interior, scientists must resort to inductive reasoning from data acquired by measurements at the surface.

When one reads the original literature on the earth's interior, one frequently encounters the term *model* or *earth model*. Now, besides denoting something miniature, the word model refers to a mathematical or conceptual view of an object or process. The geophysicist uses model in the latter sense. He accumulates data from measurements of seismic activity, gravity, heat flow and other earth properties. By applying the principles of physics he then computes what these measurements should be for various earth models. Whichever model, or mental picture, best accounts for all the measured data is the best model. A geophysical model is like a hypothesis. Once a certain model has been derived, it is possible to test it with other measurements. New data are continuously added to refine the initial model. In this chapter we shall trace the development of models for the earth's interior.

5-1 CONSTRUCTING A MODEL EARTH

In Chap. 2 we found that by applying the law of gravitation it is possible to measure the mass of the earth. Also by applying certain principles of geometry, the earth's size can be determined. The term *density* refers to mass per unit of volume; the earth's overall density, obtained by dividing its total mass by its volume, is 5.52 grams per cubic centimeter. It is comparatively easy to measure the densities of rock samples, and many such measurements have been made. Most rocks have densities that are less than 3 grams per cubic centimeter, and the average density for the crust is 2.8 grams per cubic centimeter.

With this information it is already possible to construct a preliminary model of the earth's interior, namely an earth of which the interior is composed of denser material than the surface. If the overall density is 5.52 grams per cubic centimeter and the average density of surface rocks only 2.8 grams per cubic centimeter, obviously the interior materials must be denser than those on the surface. This preliminary model, however, still leaves many questions unanswered. For example, does density increase uniformly from the surface to the center? Is the crust only a thin lighter scum over an earth with a density of close to 5.5 grams per cubic centimeter? Which of the models shown in Fig. 5-1, each giving a mean density of 5.5 grams per cubic centimeter is most nearly correct? These are some of an infinite number of models that could be made to satisfy the density requirement.

The common practice of balancing automobile tires is important because a wheel out of balance creates vibrations and results in uneven wear of the tire.

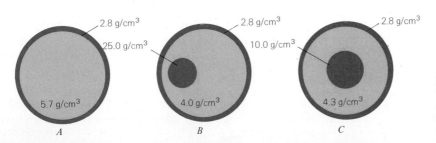

FIGURE 5-1
These are but a few of the possible earth models having a surface density of 2.8 g/cm³ and an overall density of 5.5 g/cm³.

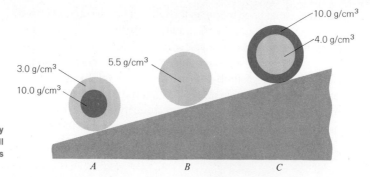

FIGURE 5-2
Each ball has an overall density of 5.5 g/cm³. In a race downhill *A* would win because of its lower moment of inertia.

Similarly, a spinning earth out of balance because of nonuniform mass distribution (Fig. 5-1*B*) would wobble. Although there are very small irregular motions of the earth's axis, major gyrations that would signal an earth out of balance are not present. Hence, all such models can be rejected.

The precession of the earth's axis gives further information about its interior. Consider three balls, each with an overall density of 5.5 grams per cubic centimeter. Ball *B* has a constant density throughout (Fig. 5-2); ball *A* has an outer shell of density 3 grams per cubic centimeter and an inner part of density 10 grams per cubic centimeter; and ball *C* has an outer shell of density 10 grams per cubic centimeter and an inner part of lower density. Even if the three balls are identical on the outside, they can still be distinguished without recourse to a direct examination of their interior.

If the balls are rolled down an inclined plane, ball *A* will roll fastest, as shown in Fig. 5-2. The explanation is that the moment of inertia, which is a measure of the degree of dispersion of mass away from the center of an object, is the lowest for ball *A*. A figure skater can increase her rate of spin by pulling in her arms and thus lowering her moment of inertia. The earth's moment of inertia can be determined by applying the theory of dynamics to the precession of the equinoxes. It turns out to be about 80 percent of the value that would be shown by an earth with a uniform distribution of mass.

Although such calculations cannot disclose the exact mass distribution within the earth, they are nevertheless valuable in setting limits to which the earth model must conform. In this case, the low moment of inertia requires some concentration of mass toward the center of the earth. Models like *B* and *C* in Fig. 5-2 are not acceptable because they require a moment of inertia appreciably higher than the measured value. The earth must be something like ball *A* in Fig. 5-2, but more information is needed about the exact distribution of mass in the interior.

5-2 EARTHQUAKES

Earthquakes have always been held in dread, and it is small wonder that the ancients accepted supernatural explanations for these disastrous events. In the six-

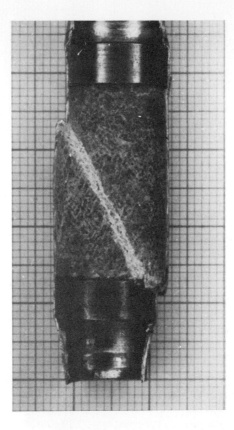

FIGURE 5-3
This cylinder of rock was compressed in a testing device. As pressure was applied, the rock shortened slightly, until at several thousand atmospheres of pressure it suddenly ruptured along the diagonal shear plane.
Courtesy of F. A. Donath.

teenth century, an earthquake in Shensi Province, China, was reported to have killed more than 800,000 people, many of whom were living in caves. On All Saints' Day (November 1) 1755, a large earthquake in Lisbon resulted in some 60,000 deaths. In December 1908, some 75,000 people lost their lives as a result of an earthquake in Messina, Italy.

What does cause the earth to quake? Figure 5-3 shows the kind of thing that happens in most earthquakes. The block of rock in this picture has been subjected to a compressive stress. As pressure was applied, the block was deformed (strained) to shorter lengths. Finally, when the applied pressure reached the breaking strength, the block ruptured along the diagonal fractures and the strain was released by slippage along the fracture plane. In the same way crustal rocks under stress occasionally are strained to their breaking point, with the resultant release of stored (potential) energy by motion along a fracture. The term *fault* is used to describe a fracture in the earth along which there has been differential movement.

All earthquakes produce waves, which radiate through the earth in every direction from the center. These vibrations, which carry the released stored energy,

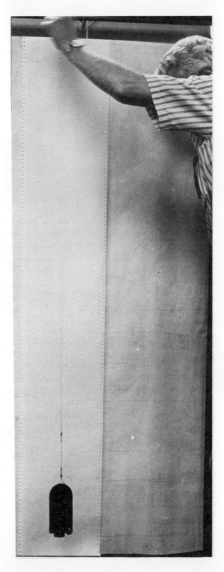

FIGURE 5-4
Although the supporting string of this pendulum is being shaken, the mass remains stationary. If such a pendulum were photographed during an earthquake, the mass would show a fuzzy image on the photo. Why?

are extremely useful to investigators of the earth's interior. Most of what we know about the internal structure and composition of the earth comes from *seismology*, the study of earthquakes. Of the 150,000 or so earthquakes that occur every year, only a very few produce waves intense enough to be felt even at moderate distances. Thus seismology became a powerful tool only after the development of sensitive instruments, called *seismographs*, that can detect and record minute earth vibrations.

Luigi Palmieri an Italian physicist and inventor, first used the term seis-

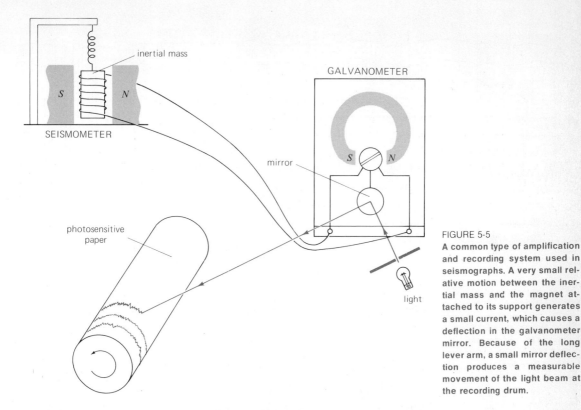

FIGURE 5-5
A common type of amplification and recording system used in seismographs. A very small relative motion between the inertial mass and the magnet attached to its support generates a small current, which causes a deflection in the galvanometer mirror. Because of the long lever arm, a small mirror deflection produces a measurable movement of the light beam at the recording drum.

mograph in 1855 to describe an instrument he had developed for detecting distant earthquakes. The first modern seismograph was built by J. Milne in Japan in 1892. Today hundreds of seismic stations throughout the world continuously monitor earth vibrations.

The detecting element of a seismograph, the *seismometer*, consists of a heavy mass supported by a spring or pendulum (Fig. 5-5). When the earth shakes, the support for the mass, which is attached to solid rock, shakes, the scale of reference shakes, and only the mass remains stationary because of its inertia, or resistance to motion. In Fig. 5-4 the supporting string of a pendulum is being rapidly shaken yet the massive bob remains stationary.

Once detected, the weak vibrations of minor earthquakes or the vibrations of very distant strong earthquakes must be amplified before being recorded. Figure 5-5 shows a common type of seismographic amplification and recording system. When a coil of wire is moved in a magnetic field, a current is generated in the coil. In Fig. 5-5 the inertial mass of the seismometer, surrounded by a coil of conduction wire, is placed between the poles of a magnet fixed to the pier, or support, of the instrument. Any external or ground vibration causes the magnet to move relative to the coil, and the current generated in the coil

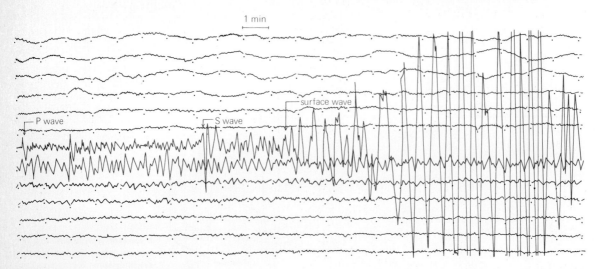

1 min

P wave

S wave

surface wave

FIGURE 5-6

The record (seismogram) made by a seismograph built to detect vertical motion of the ground shows the P, S, and surface waves. The earthquake recorded occurred about 5,400 kilometers from the seismic station at St. Louis, Missouri.

produces a deflection in a sensitive current-measuring device called a *galvanometer*. The galvanometer has a small mirror attached to it, and when the mirror moves, a light beam reaching the mirror from a point source and directed to a drum covered with photosensitive paper also moves. A very slight motion of the mirror produces a much larger motion of the light spot because of the distance from the galvanometer to the drum. Since the recording drum rotates and moves laterally along its axis, a continuous line is traced out on the paper by the light spot. Figure 5-6 shows part of such a seismogram.

In order to interpret seismograms the time of arrival of earthquake vibrations must be accurately known. Therefore, another important part of any seismograph system is a means of recording time. In Fig. 5-6, the small deflections in the trace represent time intervals of 1 minute imposed on the record by a chronometer. At the beginning and end of each day time signals from the U.S. Bureau of Standards radio station WWV are also entered on the seismograms as a check on the chronometer.

5-3   INTERPRETING SEISMIC RECORDS

At the turn of the century it was discovered that the disturbances produced by earthquakes have three phases, each corresponding to a different kind of wave. The slowest phase propagates along or close to the surface of the earth. The other two phases, known as *primary* and *secondary waves*, travel through the earth and are referred to as *body waves*. Only the primary and secondary waves are useful in investigating the earth's interior because they alone penetrate it.

The P, or primary, wave is usually the first wave to be recorded on a seis-

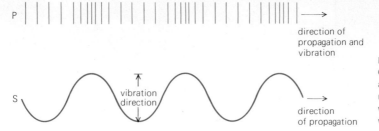

direction of
propagation and
vibration

direction
of propagation

FIGURE 5-7
Of the two body waves, P waves
are longitudinal compression-
rarefaction waves like sound; S
waves are transverse, or shear,
waves.

mogram because it travels the fastest. Primary waves are like sound waves in
that they vibrate in the direction of propagation. These compression-rarefaction
waves (see Fig. 5-7) can be transmitted through a solid, liquid, or gas.

The secondary, S, waves are shear waves, with the direction of vibration perpendicular to the direction of travel. Because liquids and gases cannot transmit
shear waves, the behavior of these waves in the body of the earth is of special interest as a source of additional information for our earth model. If all of the interior
behaves like a solid, we can expect S waves to be recorded at all seismic stations. On the other hand, if parts of the hidden interior of the earth are not solid the
S waves should be filtered out so that they do not appear at some seismic stations. We follow up these clues in Sec. 5-4; here we consider a more practical
related question, namely locating earthquakes from seismograms.

Most seismological research early in this century was concerned with determining the travel times or velocities of earthquake waves. This research by men
like Sir Harold Jeffreys (England), K. E. Bullen (Australia), and Beno Gutenberg and C. F. Richter (the United States) resulted in the establishment of
travel-time curves for the principal types of earthquake waves (Fig. 5-8). The
horizontal dimension of the graph represents the distance between the earthquake site and the recording station measured along the earth's surface. The vertical axis of the graph is a measure of the time required for the earthquake waves
to travel to recording stations at varying distances.

We learned earlier that seismologists have identified three main types of
earthquake waves, one which travels along the earth's surface and two (P and S
waves) which move through the body of the earth. We would expect the time-
distance graph for the surface waves to be a straight line if such waves move at
constant speed. Twice the distance should mean twice the time and so forth. A
look at the travel-time graph for surface waves shows that this prediction of a
straight-line relation for surface waves is confirmed by measurement.

The case of body waves is different because they travel through the interior of
our planet. Figure 5-9 shows the probable paths of P, S, and surface rays from an
earthquake to several recording stations. The reason for the curved paths will
become clear in Sec. 5-4 when we discuss wave refraction. For the moment let us
merely note that the actual distance of travel of a P or S ray is not the distance

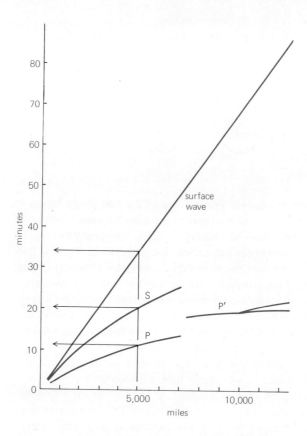

FIGURE 5-8
Time-distance (travel-time) curves for earthquake waves.

FIGURE 5-9
Paths of P, S, and surface waves.

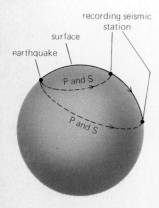

recorded in our travel-time graph, which we defined as distance measured along the earth's circumference. We can see from Fig. 5-9, however, that the depth of penetration of the body waves increases with distance measured along the earth's surface.

Figure 5-8 shows that the travel-time graphs for the body waves (P and S) are curved lines. The graphs become flatter with increasing surface distance, which we have just seen means greater depth penetration. The flatter the slope of the time-distance curve, the greater the distance covered during a fixed time interval; i.e., the body waves speed up with increasing depth.

Let us now examine how travel-time curves are used to locate earthquakes. Figure 5-8 shows that it would take the P wave about 12 minutes to arrive at a seismic station from an earthquake that occurred 5,000 miles away. For this same distance, however, the S wave would require about 21 minutes of travel time and the first surface wave around 34 minutes. There is no way of knowing the time of origin of most earthquakes. Therefore, the distance to an earthquake site cannot be determined from the arrival time of any single phase such as P at the seismic station. The difference between arrival times of P, S, and surface waves, however, does give the distance of an earthquake from the station.

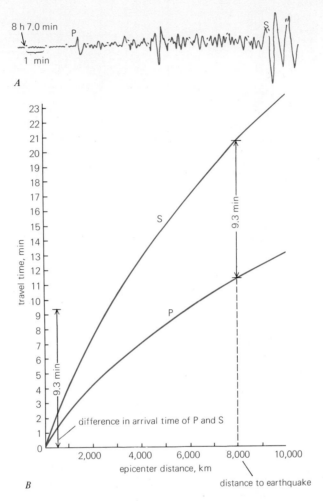

FIGURE 5-10
(*A*) **Partial seismogram showing arrival of the P and S waves.** (*B*) **By plotting the difference in arrival times on a strip of paper we can see from the travel-time curves that this earthquake must have occurred 8,000 kilometers from the recording station.**

Figure 5-10*A* is a seismogram on which the two principal body waves (P and S) have been identified. We can see from the record that the P wave arrived at 8 hours 9.6 minutes and the S wave at 8 hours 18.9 minutes. The difference in arrival time between them is 9.3 minutes. If this time is plotted on a strip of paper to the same scale as the travel-time curve, the distance to the earthquake can be determined as shown in Fig. 5-10*B*. Moreover, knowing the distance, which in the example is 8,000 kilometers, one can turn to the travel-time curves and find when the earthquake actually occurred. In our example this would be 7 hours 58.4 minutes, which we obtained by subtracting the time required for P to travel 8,000 kilometers from its actual arrival time.

Knowing the distance of an earthquake from one recording station does not provide a unique solution for its location. If the distance of the earthquake from at

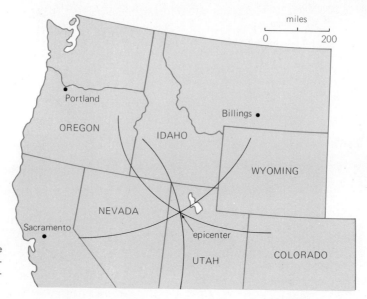

FIGURE 5-11
The location of an earthquake can be determined if its distance from at least three seismic stations is known.

least three stations is known, its location can be determined by intersection, as illustrated in Fig. 5-11. In the United States, earthquake records from stations throughout the world are processed by the U.S. National Oceanic and Atmospheric Administration. After combining records from many stations, they release information on the locations of epicenters at regular intervals.

5-4   EARTHQUAKES AND THE EARTH'S INTERIOR

Looking at the seismogram of Fig. 5-6, one may wonder about the many deflections present besides those labeled P, S, and surface. For the most part these complications in the record arise from the reflection and refraction of the principal phases at interfaces between two different media within the earth. Earthquake waves behave like the more familiar light waves. We know from experience that light from the sky is reflected from the smooth surface of a lake. Not all the light is reflected at the air-water interface, however, or the water would be perfectly dark. Some light from the sky enters the water, and in so doing it is bent, or refracted. A straight stick partly submerged in water appears bent. This is an effect of light refraction at the air-water interface.

For a better understanding of the behavior of waves within the earth we must review the laws governing reflection and refraction, which were discovered in the course of experimentation with light waves but are equally applicable to all forms of wave motion.

Consider a light source from which waves emanate in all directions, as illustrated by the circles of Fig. 5-12. Where such waves strike a reflecting surface,

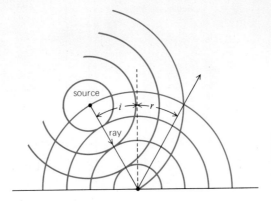

FIGURE 5-12
Successive wavefronts from a light source are reflected at an interface. A line perpendicular to the wavefront is a ray.

they set up new waves moving outward from the surface. In considering reflection and related problems it is convenient to envision light as dimensionless rays, where a ray is everywhere perpendicular to the wavefront, as illustrated in Fig. 5-12. We know, of course, that there can be no such thing as a dimensionless beam, but the idea of rays is a convenient abstraction because it allows us to draw and visualize the paths of infinitely small beams. Experiments with narrow beams of light reveal that the angle of incidence i always equals the angle of reflection r.

Let us see what happens when a narrow beam of light passes from air into a block of glass (Fig. 5-13). At the instant when ray I arrives at the air-glass interface, the line BA represents the wavefront. Light travels slower in glass than in air, and thus in the time that it takes ray II to move from A to C the new wave emanating from B will have traveled only to the position indicated by the largest hemisphere. The line CD thus represents the new wavefront, and, as we can see

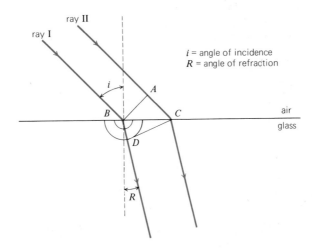

i = angle of incidence
R = angle of refraction

FIGURE 5-13
In traveling from one material to another, light is bent, or refracted.

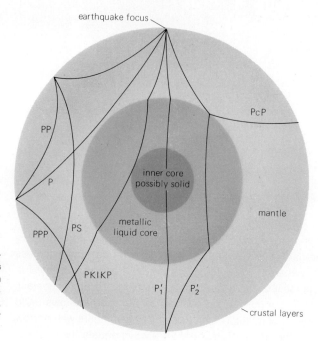

earthquake focus

PcP

PP

P

inner core
possibly solid

mantle

PPP   PS

metallic
liquid core

PKIKP

P_1' P_2'

crustal layers

FIGURE 5-14
Paths of some common earthquake waves shown on a cross
section of the earth. In addition
to the P and S waves a seismograph may record PP, SS,
PS, PPP, and many other
phases. *After K. E. Bullen.*

from the diagram, the light rays in the glass have been bent toward the line that is
normal (perpendicular) to the interface. The angle of refraction for any incident
angle is given by Snell's law

$$\sin R = \frac{V_2}{V_1} \sin i$$

where R = angle of refraction
$\quad i$ = angle of incidence
$\quad V_1$ = speed of light in medium 1
$\quad V_2$ = speed of light in medium 2

Note that a ray is bent toward the normal when it passes into a lower-velocity material and away from the normal when it moves to a higher-velocity material.

It is important to recognize that at most interfaces the incident ray is partly
reflected and partly refracted. With this background we turn to the problem of the
various unaccounted-for disturbances in the seismogram of Fig. 5-6. Figure 5-14
illustrates how reflection from the core or the base of the crust, coupled with
refraction into and out of the core, generates many other phases such as those
labeled PP, PPP, PcP, PKIKP, etc. The PP phase represents a P wave refracted to
the crust-mantle interface and thence reflected back down to reappear at the
seismic station. PcP is a P wave reflected from the core, and PKIKP is a P wave
refracted through the outer and inner core and back through the mantle to the
surface.

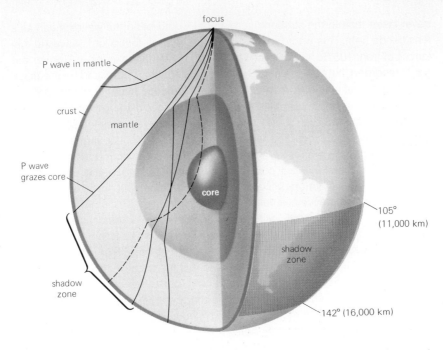

focus

P wave in mantle

crust

mantle

P wave
grazes core

core

105°
(11,000 km)

shadow
zone

shadow
zone

142° (16,000 km)

FIGURE 5-15
The absence of P waves on seismograms recorded at distances of from 105° to 142° from an earthquake is explained by the refraction of these waves at the core-mantle interface. Beyond 142° the P wave reappears, but the S wave does not. Since S waves cannot travel through fluids, this suggests that at least the outer core must be liquid.

From all these reflected and refracted earthquake waves it ought to be possible to put together a picture or a model of the earth's interior. This is just what happened historically.

We noted earlier that seismologists were concerned mainly with the establishment of travel-time curves early in this century. To determine travel times they needed records of earthquakes from many seismographs throughout the world. Seismic stations thus became more widespread, and as the amount of data increased, a curious relation concerning the arrival times of P and S waves was discovered. To illustrate, let us examine the records of a hypothetical earthquake at the southern tip of South America, near Cape Horn. A seismograph station in Rio de Janeiro, some 40° north of the quake, detects both the P and S phases. Several minutes later P and S waves are recorded on a seismograph in Miami, some 85° north of Cape Horn, and still later the same phases leave their traces on seismographs in Chicago, which is 100° north of the site. Seismographs in Canada, however, do not receive records of the P and S waves, although they do record other phases. Still farther north, in Greenland and in arctic Canada, the P wave reappears on seismograms, but the S wave is absent. Waves from other earthquakes, centered at other locations, exhibit the same kind of behavior. Evidently there is a distinct shadow zone at a distance 105° to 142° from the site of an earthquake in which P waves are somehow blocked out. Beyond 142° the P waves reappear, but they are behind their expected arrival time. S waves do not reappear after about 105°.

In 1906 R. D. Oldham, of England, found a model which accounts for these observations (Fig. 5-15). A planetary core of dense material in which seismic waves travel faster than in the surrounding material would bend the waves much as a lens bends light. This would explain the shadow zone found for P waves at distances of from 105° to 142°. Beyond 142° from the earthquake focus P waves are again recorded, but they are slightly behind schedule just as would be predicted if the first arrival was a P wave refracted by the dense material of the core.

What about the absence of the S waves at distances of more than 105° (11,000 kilometers) from the site? If only refraction were involved, they too should reappear at greater distances. The fact that they do not reappear suggests that the core apparently is composed, at least in part, of material that does not transmit shear waves. From this we conclude that the core is at least partly liquid, because, as we have already seen, liquids cannot transmit shear waves.

By 1924 the existence of a central core was firmly established when Beno Gutenberg, of the University of California, located the core boundary at about 1,800 miles (2,900 kilometers) below the surface, a value within a few miles of the best current estimate. However, the story does not end here. More sensitive seismographs developed in the 1930s revealed that the shadow zone for P waves is not so complete as originally supposed. Small amounts of energy from the P phase were in fact being transmitted to the shadow area, as shown by the dashed line in Fig. 5-15. In 1936 Inge Lehmann, of Copenhagen, proposed an explanation in terms of a core within the core. The inner core could account for phases like PKIKP being refracted back to the shadow zone. Subsequent work on travel times has confirmed this conclusion and has located the central core more precisely. The inner core (at a depth of 3,200 miles, or 5,100 kilometers) is generally thought of as being solid. We know of no compositional difference between the inner and outer cores; hence the logical conclusion is that the boundary represents a difference in state. To prove the solid character of the inner core is a subject of current research. The question would be settled if it could be shown that the inner core conducts shear waves; but since they are filtered out by the surrounding outer core, scientists must search for other evidence to confirm the solid character of the inner core.

5-5 A REFINED EARTH MODEL

We have seen how seismology has disclosed the existence of two major physical discontinuities deep within the earth. A third, much shallower discontinuity was discovered early in this century by A. Mohorovicic, who also used seismic techniques. The *Mohorovicic discontinuity* (or *Moho*) lies at a depth of only 10 to 50 miles beneath the surface; it marks the base of the earth's crust, or lithosphere. The region between the earth's crust and the outer core is called the *mantle*. Seismology reveals that the crust varies significantly in thickness, being thin in the ocean basins and thickest under the high parts of the continents, which is just what the principle of isostasy (Chap. 3) led us to believe.

On the surface of the earth a great variety of rocks are found (granite, lavas of many compositions, sandstones, fossil limestones, etc.). Do the major discontinuities within the earth divide it into regions which are also of mixed composition?

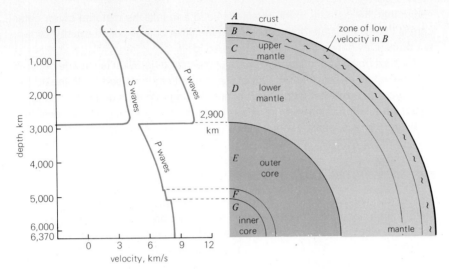

FIGURE 5-16
**Depth-velocity curves for seis-
mic waves within the earth and
a cross section of the earth
showing the layers indicated by
the varying seismic velocities.**
After K. E. Bullen.

Once again seismology gives the answer. Laboratory experiments show significant differences in the speed of seismic waves in various rock types. If the interior of the earth were heterogeneous, the travel times for body waves should
vary from area to area. This is not the case, however, and it is therefore logical to
infer that the mantle, the core, and the inner core are each homogeneous.

The establishment of major physical boundaries such as the base of the crust,
the base of the mantle, and the boundary of the inner core opened the door to a
sharper estimate of the distribution of mass within the earth. K. E. Bullen, an
Australian, undertook the job of calculating a refined model of the density distribution, using the physical boundaries revealed by seismology together with
the data on the earth's moment of inertia and the rates of travel of seismic waves.

Bullen's model for the distribution of density within the earth is shown in Fig.
5-16. On the basis of the velocity-depth curves he divided the earth into seven
zones labeled A through G in Fig. 5-16. The density of zone A, the crust, is known
from direct measurements. As we shall see in the next section, data from deep-
seated intrusive rocks give scientists a good idea of the density of the material in
the upper mantle. From this starting information, together with a knowledge of the
relationship between seismic-wave speeds and density and an understanding of
the expected relation between pressure (depth) and density, Bullen assigned
densities to the remaining zones. He then was able to compute both an overall
density and a value for the moment of inertia of the entire earth. By adjusting the
density values for the various zones he eventually arrived at an almost unique
solution, or model, for which his calculated density and moment of inertia
equalled the actual measured values for these variables.

No longer is the interior of the earth an area of complete mystery. The estimate
of density distribution within the earth is built on a sufficient amount of independent data to make any future major changes unlikely. Moreover, the evidence is

strong that the material of the mantle is solid and that the material of the outer core is liquid. The state of the material in the inner core is not so exactly known, but present evidence suggests that it is solid.

The next obvious question to ask about the interior is: What is it made of? This requires a somewhat different line of reasoning from that used to delineate the structure of the earth's interior. Much of our thinking about the chemical composition of the interior of the earth is strongly influenced by the study of objects that arrive from space, namely meteorites.

5-6   METEORITES AND THE EARTH'S INTERIOR

Most of us have read that the interior of the earth is presumed to be composed of metallic iron and nickel because some meteorites are made of these materials. Let us see what lies behind this statement, which is true enough but hardly does justice to the amount of work and thought that has gone into the problem.

The fast-moving bright objects occasionally seen in the night sky are *meteors*. A *meteorite* is a meteor that has survived the scorching trip through the earth's atmosphere. The main classes of meteorites are (*1*) those composed chiefly of metallic iron and nickel, called the *irons*; (*2*) those composed of globules of metal in a matrix of silicate minerals (*stony irons*); and (*3*) the stony meteorites, composed of dark-colored silicate minerals. Most meteorites displayed in museums are of the iron variety, and early investigators believed the irons to be the most abundant of the three groups. However, metallic iron is an unusual material among the minerals of the crust and as such attracts much more attention than a stony meteorite composed of some of the same minerals found in crustal rocks. Also iron normally decomposes slower at the surface of the earth than the silicate minerals of stony meteorites.

Table 5-1 shows the distribution of meteorites into these classes. The category labeled *finds* represents meteorites accidentally found at the surface of the earth. The *falls*, on the other hand, are meteorites that were observed to fall. The falls obviously are more nearly representative of the true distribution of meteorites, and they show that stony meteorites are far more abundant than metallic ones.

TABLE 5-1
Frequency of meteorite finds and falls*

	Finds		Falls	
Type	*Number*	*Percent*	*Number*	*Percent*
Irons	409	66	29	5
Stony irons	46	7.5	8	1.5
Stones	165	26.5	547	93.5
Total	620	100	584	100

*From F. G. Watson, "Between the Planets," rev. ed., Harvard University Press, Cambridge, Mass., 1956.

The source of meteorites is still an incompletely answered question, but there is general agreement that these are objects of the solar system. Moreover, there is evidence that many meteorites come from the belt of asteroids that revolve about the sun in the gap between the orbits of Mars and Jupiter. The distances of the planets from the sun form a geometric progression, known as *Bode's law* (Table 18-1), according to which there should be a planet between Mars and Jupiter. Instead, we find hundreds of small bodies of matter called *asteroids*. Some astronomers believe that these objects are pieces of a planet that broke up. If this interpretation is correct, and if most meteorites do indeed come from the asteroid belt, we can think of them as samples of an entire planet. Because the stony meteorites resemble some earth rocks, we conclude that they must have come from the outer parts of the disrupted planet. The iron and nickel meteorites must then be material from its hidden interior, and we infer that the earth must have similar material in its dense core.

Recently the idea that the meteorites are actually pieces of a former planet has fallen into disfavor. Even if this idea is an oversimplification, we still are driven to the conclusion of an iron-rich core for the earth from meteorite studies because there is strong evidence that the meteorites and the earth had a common origin. They are related in both space and time. Meteorites are known to come, for the most part, from our own planetary system. Radioactive dating (which we discuss in Chap. 13 in connection with the age of the earth and its rocks) reveals that many meteorites have ages of between 4 and 5 billion years, which agrees with the best estimates of the age of the earth. It thus seems reasonable to conclude that meteorites and the earth must have formed from the same original mix of elements.

We saw in Chap. 4 that eight elements—oxygen, silicon, aluminum, iron, calcium, sodium, potassium, and magnesium—account for over 98 percent by weight of the earth's crust. Chemical analyses show the average composition of meteorites to be as given in Table 5-2, with the 80 some unlisted elements together making up only 2 percent. Clearly, if we are seeking a heavy element or elements to account for the high density of the earth's core, it would be unreasonable to pick lead, copper, zinc, or gold because they are far too rare. Iron is by far the most logical choice because there seems to have been plenty of it when the planets formed.

Iron is a good choice for the core material for another reason: it has about the correct density. Recent experiments on the density of iron under high pressures suggest that an earth core composed predominantly of iron, together with some nickel and silicon, would have the density of the actual core and moreover would exhibit a seismic velocity equal to that measured in the earth's deep interior.

Although the overall evidence strongly points to an earth core composed chiefly of metallic iron, other models have been proposed. The main justification for other hypotheses lies in our lack of experience with the behavior of materials under the tremendous pressures existing within the core. It has been suggested that perhaps the silicate minerals of the mantle are changed into much denser

TABLE 5-2
Average composition of meteorites

Element	Percent
O	33.2
Fe	27.2
Si	17.1
Mg	14.3
S	1.9
Ni	1.6
Ca	1.3
Al	1.2

forms under the pressure existing at the core boundary. This sort of a phase change could account for the higher density and the increase in seismic velocities at the core. In spite of some uncertainty about the behavior of silicate minerals under tremendous pressures, however, an iron core is still the preferred model. As we shall see in Sec. 5-7, an iron core gives an overall chemical composition for the earth that is more in line with the abundances of heavy elements in the sun and stars.

There is still debate among earth scientists over the composition of the material directly beneath the earth's crust. Some investigators believe that the Mohorovicic discontinuity indicates a phase transition in which the minerals of the basalt in the lower crust change to denser forms like garnet and pyroxene to make a rock called eclogite. Others conclude that the Moho is marked by a compositional change from basalt to a more magnesium- and iron-rich rock called peridotite.

Most volcanoes have their source in the mantle, and both theory and experiment show that the common basaltic lavas could originate either by complete melting of eclogite or by partial melting of peridotite. Eclogite and peridotite also are found in the diamond-bearing rocks of Africa, which apparently originated in the mantle at depths of several hundred kilometers. The peridotite inclusions are the most abundant, which favors the change-in-composition hypothesis.

Further support for this hypothesis is provided by the variable thickness of the crust. A phase change from basalt to eclogite would depend upon pressure and hence upon depth of burial. Such a pressure-determined change should take place at nearly constant depth, but as we have seen the thickness of the crust varies considerably. Also, peridotite closely matches the material of the upper mantle in seismic velocity.

5-7 HOW DOES THE COMPOSITION OF THE WHOLE EARTH COMPARE WITH THAT OF OTHER BODIES IN THE SOLAR SYSTEM?

The chemical makeup of the crust of the earth was discussed in Chap. 3, but, as we can see from Table 5-3, the crust contains only 0.4 percent of the mass of the entire earth. To get the earth's overall chemical composition we must include the compositions of the mantle and the core according to their respective masses.

TABLE 5-3
Volumes and masses of earth shells[†]

	Thickness, km	Volume, cm³ × 10²⁷	Mean density, g/cm³	Mass g × 10²⁷	Mass %
Atmosphere				0.000005	0.00009
Hydrosphere	3.8*	0.00137	1.03	0.00141	0.024
Crust	17*	0.008	2.8	0.024	0.4
Mantle	2,883	0.899	4.5	4.075	68.1
Core	3,471	0.175	10.7	1.876	31.5

*Mean.
†Brian Mason, "Principles of Geochemistry," John Wiley & Sons, Inc., New York, 1966, by permission.

105

5-7 HOW DOES THE COMPOSITION OF THE WHOLE EARTH COMPARE WITH THAT OF OTHER BODIES IN THE SOLAR SYSTEM?

The most widely accepted earth model has a core with approximately the same composition as that of iron meteorites and a mantle composed of magnesium and iron silicates, like those found in stony meteorites and in peridotite. When the expected compositions of the core and the mantle are combined with that of the crust, we find that for the entire earth iron is the most abundant element followed by oxygen, magnesium, and silicon. When we recall that the order of abundance of the elements in the crust is oxygen, silicon, aluminum, and iron, we see that including the iron-rich core and the magnesium- and iron-rich mantle has reversed the picture.

How does the earth as a whole compare in composition with the sun and other stars? Their composition is reasonably well known from spectrographic studies; moreover, as discussed in Chap. 7, the model for the sun's interior is perhaps even more refined than that for the earth. Table 5-4 lists the chemical elements in order of abundance in the earth, sun, and meteorites. At first glance it may appear that the earth and sun must have formed from different stuff because hydrogen and helium, by far the most abundant elements in the sun, are only minor constituents of the earth. However, these light elements may originally have predominated on the earth too.

We discuss the question of escape velocities in Chap. 6; for now let us merely recognize that any object—rocket or molecule—can escape the earth's gravitational field if it has a speed greater than the earth's escape velocity. The molecules of the atmosphere are in continual motion, the lighter molecules moving faster, on the average, then the heavier ones at any given temperature. Even today the lightest molecules, hydrogen and helium, frequently attain the velocity to escape from the earth. There is reason to believe that these elements once made up a large proportion of the earth but were dissipated in the early stages of the planet's development.

Accepting the hypothesis that the volatile elements escaped from the earth early in its history, let us focus on the heavier elements. Here the check between the earth and the sun is very good. Of the nonvolatile elements, iron, magnesium, and silicon head the list for both the earth and sun. This similarity in abundance of the nonvolatile, heavier elements further supports our model earth with an iron-rich core and a mantle composed chiefly of magnesium and iron silicates.

TABLE 5-4
Relative abundances (in decreasing order) of the elements by weight*

Whole earth	Crust	Sun	Meteorites
Fe	O	H	O
O	Si	He	Fe
Mg	Al	O	Si
Si	Fe	Fe	Mg
Ni	Ca	Mg	S
S	Na	N	Ni
Ca	K	Si	Ca
Al	Mg	S	Al

*Brian Mason, "Principles of Geochemistry," John Wiley & Sons, Inc., New York, 1966, by permission.

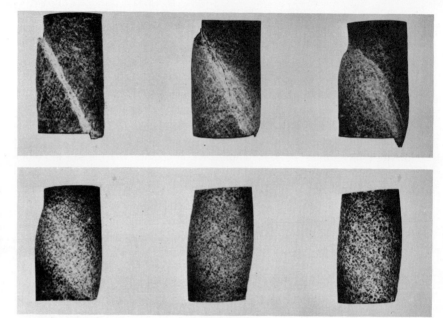

FIGURE 5-17
Specimens of limestone deformed at different confining pressures. At low confining pressures (corresponding to shallow depth) the specimen ruptures (upper left). With increasing confining pressure the deformation becomes plastic, as shown in the bottom pictures. *Courtesy of F. A. Donath.*

5-8   THE ASTHENOSPHERE

The concept of isostasy (Chap. 3) demands a plastic layer somewhere in the crust or upper mantle to allow the condition of flotational balance to become established among segments of the earth's crust. Early in this century, well before seismology was developed as an exact science, Joseph Barrell, an American geologist, predicted that such a plastic layer would be found at a depth of about 100 kilometers and called it the *asthenosphere* ("weak zone" in Greek).

Later, when seismograms seemed to show earthquakes occurring at depths as great as 700 kilometers, geologists had difficulty in accepting the idea of the plastic zone because they believed that a plastic material under stress should fail by flowage rather than rupture. An earthquake, of course, is a rupture. How then could earthquakes be found in Barrell's asthenosphere?

Today there is no doubt about the existence of earthquakes down to 700 kilometers. This does not mean, however, that there is no asthenosphere. For a number of years a play material called Silly Putty has been on sale. Under short-term stresses Silly Putty behaves like an elastic solid; e.g., it bounces like a ball. Intense short-term stresses cause it to rupture. On the other hand, a lump of Silly Putty left sitting for several hours will flow into a flat pancake. The behavior of this material illustrates what has been demonstrated with rock-forming minerals under laboratory conditions, namely that it is possible for a material to act as a brittle solid under one set of conditions while acting as a plastic solid and deforming by flowage in another environment (Fig. 5-17). Therefore the fact that

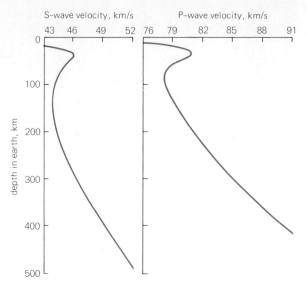

S-wave velocity, km/s

43 46   49   52 76 79   82   85   88   91

P-wave velocity, km/s

depth in earth, km

0
100
200
300
400
500

FIGURE 5-18
The velocities of both P and S waves are lower than normal at depths of from 50 to 250 kilometers. *After Don L. Anderson, The Plastic Layer of the Earth's Mantle. Copyright © 1962 by Scientific American, Inc. All rights reserved.*

earthquakes occur in the region believed to be the asthenosphere and that S waves are propagated through this region are not by themselves proof that the asthenosphere does not exist.

Don L. Anderson, an American geophysicist, recently summarized the evidence for a plastic layer. Figure 5-18 shows that both P and S waves reveal a low-velocity layer at depths of from 50 to 250 kilometers. Velocities in that part of the earth are hard to determine accurately. Only by working with seismic waves generated by accurately timed nuclear explosions could Beno Gutenberg obtain the velocity curves shown in the diagram. The low-velocity layer is interpreted as a weaker, plastic zone.

Figure 5-19 shows graphs of the projected changes of pressure and temperature with depth in the upper part of the earth. Pressure is known to increase the melting points of most substances, and the relation between pressure and the melting point of rocks was used to compute the graph of Fig. 5-19*C*. From this graph it again appears that the material at depths of from about 100 to 300 kilometers should be weaker and more plastic than the material above and below that level because it is closest to its melting point.

The principal earthquake area, the belt bordering the Pacific Ocean, is also known as the *ring of fire* because most of the world's active volcanoes are found there. Small earthquakes associated with erupting volcanoes originate at depths of from 50 to 200 kilometers, suggesting that this region is the source of the molten rock that rises to form surface lava. Again, an asthenosphere is indicated.

The overall evidence, therefore, is strong in favor of a zone of flowage in the upper part of the mantle at depths of from 50 to 250 kilometers beneath the surface. This asthenosphere is not found at the Moho, which has an average depth of

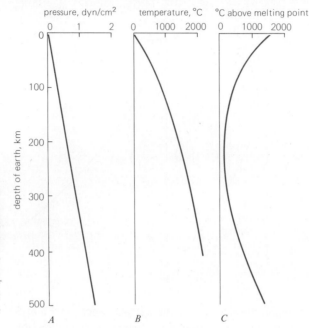

FIGURE 5-19

Calculations of melting points within the earth based upon predicted temperatures and pressures show the rocks at depths of 100 to 300 kilometers to be much closer to their melting points than those above or below that level. *After Don L. Anderson, The Plastic Layer of the Earth's Mantle. Copyright © 1962 by Scientific American, Inc. All rights reserved.*

only about 17 kilometers, but in the upper mantle and appears to be related to the fact that the rocks there are close to their melting points. The asthenosphere is the region where transfer of material to maintain isostasy takes place. It also seems likely that it is the level at which magmas develop, and its presence makes the concept of moving or drifting continents (discussed in Chap. 16) much more plausible.

SUMMARY

To gather information about the hidden interior of the earth scientists have had to rely solely on measurements and observations made at the surface. Data acquired by surface measurements form the base upon which mathematical or conceptual models of the interior are constructed.

The earth has an overall mean density of 5.52 grams per cubic centimeter, whereas the crust has a mean density of only 2.8 grams per cubic centimeter. This requires an earth model in which material be-

neath the crust is denser than the surface materials. The earth's moment of inertia is what would be expected for an almost spherical body with a distinct concentration of mass toward its center. Many earth models can be developed to account for the overall density and the measured moment of inertia.

Earthquake waves provide significant information about the internal structure of the planet. Seismology, the study of earthquakes, has disclosed three sharp and several transitional boundaries within the earth. The first sharp discontinuity, which

marks the base of the crust, is called the Mohorovicic discontinuity after its discoverer. The next and most pronounced boundary, at a depth of about 1,800 miles (2,900 kilometers), marks the top of the core. An inner core at a depth of 3,200 miles (5,100 kilometers) is the last major discontinuity.

The boundaries disclosed by seismology coupled with information on the earth's overall density and moment of inertia allow a nearly unique model of the density distribution within the earth to be calculated Because the speed of earthquake waves is related to density, they provide further information on density problems. Shear waves do not pass through the core of the earth, showing that at least the outer core has the characteristics of a liquid.

The chemical composition of the earth's interior is deduced largely from studies of element distribution in the sun, stars, and meteorites. Iron is the only common element that has the characteristics of the material in the earth's core. The mantle is believed to be composed chiefly of magnesium and iron silicates. The abundances of the heavy elements in the model earth described in this chapter correlate reasonably well with their abundances in the sun and stars as determined by spectral studies. This lends credibility to the model.

QUESTIONS

1 The earth's mean density of 5.5 grams per cubic centimeter could be accounted for by assuming a greater density in the mantle with a correspondingly lower-density core. Why is this not an acceptable earth model?

2 Why is the core of the earth thought to be partially fluid?

3 The diagram below shows part of a record of an earthquake. Using the travel-time curve of Fig. 5-10, find the distance from the earthquake site to the recording station.

4 When did the earthquake in Question 3 occur?

5 If someone at the site of the earthquake (Question 3) had telephoned to the recording station within 5 minutes of the initial shock, would the message have reached the station before or after the earthquake waves?

6 When abundances of the elements in the earth are compared with those in the sun or universe, the values for comparison are usually reported in atoms per 10.000 atoms of silicon instead of in weight percent. Can you think of a reason for this?

7 What is the evidence for the conclusion that some meteorites may once have been fragments of a much larger body?

8 The Moho is a physical boundary. Seismic velocities are measurably lower in the material above the Moho than beneath it. Can such a physical discontinuity be accounted for without a chemical change? How?

9 Where do most of the world's earthquakes occur?

10 How do you explain a phase such as PPP on a seismic record? Why does the P wave in this instance keep returning to the surface?

11 At the earth's surface rocks behave like brittle solids and rupture when they are stressed past their breaking point. Beneath the surface, because of increased temperatures and confining pressures, they are able to flow without rupture. Does the ability to flow increase continually with depth?

12 The earth's crust varies in thickness from about 3 miles to over 30 miles. Where is the crust the thinnest?

13 How do we know that the earth's mantle is homogeneous?

14 Which of the principal earthquake waves would be recorded at each of the following seismic stations: (*a*) station 45° distant from earthquake, (*b*) station 120° distant from earthquake, (*c*) station 175° distant from earthquake?

REFERENCES

Ahrens, L. H.: "Distribution of the Elements in Our Planet," McGraw-Hill Book Company, New York, 1965.

Hodgson, John H.: "Earthquakes and Earth Structure," Prentice-Hall, Inc., Englewood Cliffs, N.J., 1964.

Howell, B. F., Jr.: "Introduction to Geophysics," McGraw-Hill Book Company, New York, 1959.

Mason, Brian: "Principles of Geochemistry," John Wiley & Sons, Inc., New York, 1966.

Sumner, John S.: "Geophysics, Geologic Structures and Tectonics," Wm. C. Brown Company Publishers, Dubuque, Iowa, 1969.

14 h 6 min   P   S

1 min

THE DYNAMIC EARTH

So far we have looked at the place of our earth in the solar system, examined its overall size and weight, focused upon the materials of which it is made, and glimpsed its hidden interior. We might say that we have learned where our patient lives, determined his weight and height, and found out what he is made of; now it is time to take his pulse and check his vital functions.

That the earth is dynamic and does indeed have a pulse should be obvious to even the casual observer. To see just how active it is let us look for comparison at our neighbor the moon. Working with the rocks of the Apollo program, scientists have estimated from the degree of cosmic-ray exposures that individual samples have lain exposed on the lunar surface for 20 million to 400 million years. That is about how long we can expect the footprints of Fig. 6-1 to survive. Similar footprints on earth would be erased in days, or at the most a few months or years. Compared to the moon, the earth certainly is a dynamic and changing body.

In this chapter we shall examine the major processes at work on and in the earth to produce change. We shall also take a look at some of our nearest planetary neighbors to see how they compare with earth. The earth obviously is different from the other planets in that it has a hydrosphere. We are led to wonder, however, whether this is the only major difference. Are other change-producing processes on earth also active on our neighbors in space?

6-1 MAJOR EARTH PROCESSES: EROSION, VULCANISM, AND DIASTROPHISM

One constant feature of the earth is change. Winds come and go, blowing grains of silt for miles across the land. Rains wash soil to the rivers, which carry it to the sea. Glaciers grind up rocks and carve out deep valleys. The shoreline is an area of conflict, where beating waves wear back the land. Fiery volcanoes build new mountains on land and create islands in the oceans. Blocks of the crust move, sometimes sharply enough to cause the earth to quake. Mountains arise as a result of crustal movements.

Constructive and destructive processes clash on the battlefield of the earth's surface. Erosion by streams, wind, ice, and waves exerts a leveling effect upon the earth. Working in response to the force of gravity, these surface processes move materials from high areas to low ones. Material is moved a few meters by sliding down a hillslope or transported for thousands of kilometers by a river system. Ultimately most eroded debris is deposited in the sea by rivers. In conflict with these surface processes are the internal processes of vulcanism and diastrophism (earth movement), continuously creating new land to replace that worn away. The earth's surface at any instant represents a balance between these opposing processes.

The photographs of Fig. 6-2 illustrate some of the effects of erosional processes. Occasionally flash floods or landslides transfer material rapidly from one place to another, but erosion usually proceeds imperceptibly, and it is only by viewing its results that we realize how significant it really is.

Slow as it may be by human standards, erosion has markedly altered our planet because it has had several billion years in which to operate. Running water is the most powerful agent of erosion. Measurement of the rate of flow of the earth's major rivers and sampling of the sediment they move reveal that rivers now carry about 10 billion tons of weathered debris to the sea each year. The

A

B

C

FIGURE 6-2
Some effects of erosion. (*A*)
Stream erosion, Gulf of Aden
(*NASA*). (*B*) **Stream erosion of**
loess plain (windblown dust),
China (*U.S. Geological Survey*).
(*C*) **Wind erosion and deposi-**
tion, Saudi Arabia (*Arabian*
American Oil Company). (*D*)
Glaciated terrain in the North-
west Territory of Canada (*Divi-*
sion of Energy, Mines, and
Resources, Canada). (*E*) **Glacial**
erosion, British Columbia (*U.S.*
Geological Survey).

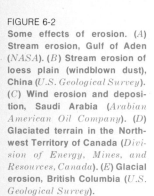

D

E

Mississippi River alone delivers about 500 million tons of sediment per year to the Gulf of Mexico. Such measurements permit us to estimate the present rate of denudation of the continents.

$$\text{Sediment brought to oceans by rivers} = 1 \times 10^{10} \text{ tons/y}$$

$$\text{Area of continents} = 57.5 \times 10^6 \text{ mi}^2$$

$$\text{Tons eroded per square mile per year} = \frac{1 \times 10^{10}}{57.5 \times 10^6}$$

$$= 200 \text{ tons/(mi}^2)(y)$$

$$\text{Mass of layer of sediment 1 ft thick spread over 1 mi}^2 = 2.5 \times 10^6 \text{ tons}$$

$$\text{Time required to remove 1 ft from the continents} = \frac{2.5 \times 10^6}{200}$$

$$= 10,000 \text{ y (approx)}$$

Furthermore, we can see that if erosion operated unopposed, slopes must once have been steeper and rivers faster than they are now, so that erosion rates were formerly even greater than the present 1 foot in 10,000 years. This being the case, the continents would long ago have been worn flat if there were not earth processes tending to build up the land. Figure 6-3 shows one of these building processes in action.

The term *vulcanism* refers to all development and movement of magma (molten rock) within the earth's crust and mantle. In Fig. 6-3 we can clearly see that vulcanism is an effective builder, but we see only part of the story. Magma originates in the upper mantle or the lower parts of the crust, and frequently it crystallizes before reaching the surface. Figure 6-4 illustrates how the movement of magma beneath the surface can elevate the overlying land. Of course, we cannot see the activity of magma underground, but erosion frequently exposes deep-seated (plutonic) igneous masses that crystallized at depth.

A survey of the rocks exposed in the present major mountain chains indicates that vulcanism is not the only builder—indeed, not even the main builder. Figure 6-5 shows a typical mountainous area in which most of the rocks are layered, or bedded, sedimentary rocks. Such rocks are the end products of the erosional processes, and we know that they originally accumulated as flat beds in the low-lying areas of the earth, particularly along the margins of the ocean basins. Closer inspection reveals that many such rocks of mountain systems are folded and frequently contain the remains of marine organisms. Somehow these rocks have been uplifted thousands of feet above the ocean basins in which they formed. This cannot be explained by a lowering of sea level. Even when much of the water of the sea was tied up in ice on the land, during the geologically recent Ice Age, calculations reveal that sea level cannot have been lowered by more than a few hundred feet. Moreover, the folded nature of the sediments of mountain chains attests to the involvement of these rocks in some type of earth movement.

Diastrophism is the general term used to describe movements of segments of the earth's crust relative to each other. Sometimes such movement take place

FIGURE 6-3
South Sister Volcano near Bend, Oregon. This 10,000-foot volcanic cone and the other cones in the background show that vulcanism is an effective builder. Several light-colored flows that have erupted from the flank of South Sister are clearly visible. *D. A. Rahm, "Slides for Geology," 1971. Used with permission of Mc-Graw-Hill Book Company.*

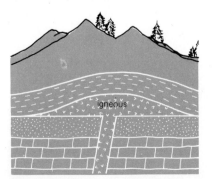

A

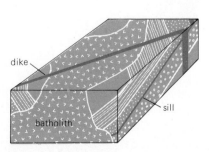

B

FIGURE 6-4
Magma, being fluid and less dense than the surrounding rock, tends to rise. The intrusion in (*A*), which has produced an upwarping of the surface, is called a *laccolith*. Erosion ultimately exposes intrusive igneous rocks as illustrated in (*B*), which shows some of the principal types of intrusions. Dikes and sills, both sheetlike intrusions, differ in that dikes cut across other layers whereas sills are squeezed between them. Batholiths are very large irregular igneous intrusions.

FIGURE 6-5
Rocky Mountains near Sullivan River, British Columbia. These Cambrian sediments, originally laid flat, have been uplifted and folded by the mountain-building processes. *R. A. Price, Geological Survey of Canada.*

as sudden displacements along faults (Fig. 6-6). Sometimes it involves folding and flowage rather than fracture (Fig. 6-7). Movement of crustal segments may also include only gentle uplifting or downwarping without significant deformation. For example, a number of the layers of rock high in the Grand Canyon contain the remains of marine organisms; although still in their original horizontal positions, these rocks have been lifted high above the level of the sea.

The definition of *work* is force times distance. Work is measured in such units

FIGURE 6-6
Aerial view of the Carrizo Plain area, California, showing displacements of stream channels caused by earth movements along the San Andreas Fault. A fault is a fracture in the crust along which movement occurs. The total movement above is the end result of many sudden shifts, each producing an earthquake. *U. S. Geological Survey.*

RECENT EARTH MOVE-
MENTS ALONG FAULT
HAVE DISPLACED
STREAM CHANNEL
FROM A TO B

REPEATED MOVEMENTS
OVER THOUSANDS OF
YEARS HAVE DISPLACED
CHANNEL FROM A TO C

B

C

500 FEET

A

• • SAN ANDREAS
FAULT

FIGURE 6-7
Deep within the earth the elevated temperatures and high confining pressures allow rocks to deform by folding and flowage rather than by rupture. The joints (cracks) in this outcrop of contorted gneiss formed only after extensive erosion had brought this deep-seated rock to the surface, where failure by rupture is the rule. *J. A. Fraser, Geological Survey of Canada.*

as newton-meters or pound-feet. $Energy$ is the ability to do work. We have often heard that a certain food is a good source of energy. This is quite accurate: to exert a force through a distance you must use some of the chemical energy stored in the food you have eaten.

Without exception, work can be done on one body only if another body loses a corresponding amount of energy. Now consider the earth's highest mountains, the Himalaya (Fig. 6-8). These mountains consist mainly of sedimentary rocks, and some layers as high as 20,000 feet above sea level contain marine fossils.

FIGURE 6-8
Two views of the mountains in the Himalaya. *Courtesy of Clyde Rice.*

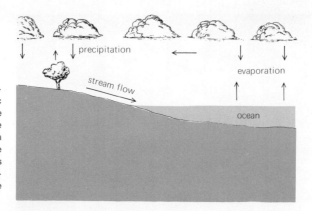

FIGURE 6-9
The hydrologic cycle. It is estimated that some 37,000 cubic kilometers of water runs off the land to the sea each year. The potential energy of this much water falling from the average height of land to sea level is tremendous. Much of this energy is spent in sculpturing the land.

Certainly a tremendous amount of work was involved in moving the billions of tons of rock in these mountains from a position below sea level to their present lofty height. This work involved the expenditure of equally large amounts of energy. Where did the energy come from?

The most obvious energy source for earth processes is the sun. Everyone has felt the sun's radiant heat, and it is this energy that powers the hydrologic cycle pictured in Fig. 6-9. Energy from the sun warms both the land and water areas of the earth, causing evaporation. Water in the clouds thus formed returns to the surface as rain, snow, or dew, to complete the cycle. It is the hydrologic cycle that keeps rivers flowing to the sea and thus continuing their work of gradation. Continued precipitation as snow feeds glaciers and allows them to grow, and the uneven distribution of solar energy causes winds to blow.

The sun-driven hydrologic cycle cannot be the only cause of erosion. On an earth completely covered by water there would still be evaporation and precipitation, but there could be no surface erosion. The erosive processes thus also depend upon uplift and mountain building brought about by diastrophism or vulcanism.

Does the energy for vulcanism and diastrophism also come from the sun? Seismic evidence around active volcanoes shows that magma reservoirs from which the lavas originate lie tens of kilometers beneath the earth's surface. In most places temperature measurements taken a few meters below the surface exhibit no seasonal fluctuations. Moreover, measurements of temperature in mines and boreholes show temperatures to increase with depth. Since heat always flows from areas of high temperature to areas of low temperature, heat must be flowing outward from the interior of the earth. This is proof that the sun's energy does not penetrate more than a meter or so. The internal building processes must largely be powered by energy from within.

6-2 ROCKS: THE BUILDING BLOCKS OF THE EARTH'S CRUST

We have seen that erosion wears down the rocks exposed at the earth's surface. Transportation and deposition of this eroded material results in the formation of

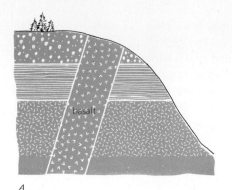

A

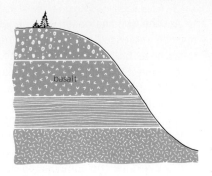

B

FIGURE 6-10
Two rock units of the same composition (basalt) but different histories. (*A*) Since the basalt cuts all other rocks, it must be the youngest unit. (*B*) Since the basalt is parallel (concordant) with the other rocks, it must either be a buried lava flow or a sill. What would you look for to determine its origin?

new rocks from old. Vulcanism forms rocks where formerly there were none. The major earth processes thus are actively involved in creating rocks. To learn more about the relation between earth processes and rocks let us briefly survey the major rock classes.

The term *rock* is used by geologists to designate aggregates of minerals sufficiently extensive to make up a significant part of the earth's crust. Most rocks are composed of several minerals, but some, like limestone, may consist of interlocking grains of only one mineral (limestone is composed chiefly of the mineral calcite, $CaCO_3$). There is no definition of how big an assemblage of minerals must be to be considered a rock; the important thing to realize is that a complete understanding of rocks can be gained only through a combination of field studies and laboratory studies. Microscopic examinations of rock specimens reveal only compositional aspects of a rock unit. We have said that rocks must be big enough to figure in the architecture of the earth's crust. As illustrated by Fig. 6-10, two rocks may have identical compositions and yet differ in their structural relations with other rocks.

Rocks are known to form on and near the earth's surface in three principal ways. We shall look separately at the three main genetic classes of rocks, igneous, sedimentary, and metamorphic, which represent these three modes of formation.

Igneous rocks

Rocks that form by the crystallization of magma are called *igneous rocks*. Because they have crystallized from liquid, igneous rocks usually consist of tightly interlocking mineral grains and are thus dense and nonporous, except for certain lavas and other volcanic materials that contain trapped gas bubbles. Moreover, large masses of igneous rocks tend to be remarkably homogeneous in composition, and, except in lava flows, layering is absent.

When magma erupts at the earth's surface, it is called *lava*. Igneous rocks that form from lava are said to be *extrusive*. By far the greatest proportion of igneous rocks, however, crystallize beneath the surface. These are called *intrusive* rocks because they intrude the rocks with which they are in contact. Some of the principal types of igneous intrusions are drawn in Fig. 6-4.

Anyone who has observed igneous-rock specimens in a geological museum must be impressed by their great variety. Although hundreds of kinds of igneous rocks have been collected, studied, and given separate names, these many types are not equally abundant. In fact, we have already found that on a global scale we do not err greatly when we say the earth's crust is composed of two igneous-rock types, granite in the continental regions and basalt in the ocean floors. Although this is an oversimplification for some purposes, certainly for many field studies the rock categories of Table 6-1 are adequate.

The classification of Table 6-1 is based upon two variables, mineral composition and texture. The composition of any related suite of igneous rocks depends upon the composition of the magma from which they formed. As we shall see in Chap. 16, however, rocks of different composition may form from the same magma because the various silicate minerals that make up igneous rocks crystallize at different temperatures. Texture refers to the size and relationship between the mineral grains of a rock. In classifications the most important textural attribute is grain size.

The grain sizes exhibited by an igneous rock depend largely upon the magma cooling rate. Once water has been cooled to 0°C, another 80 calories of heat energy must be lost per gram to convert it to ice. This is known as the *latent heat of crystallization* of water. Each mineral has its own heat of crystallization. For a mineral to crystallize, the magma must first be cooled to the freezing temperature of the mineral, and then it must lose an additional amount of heat to change from the liquid to the solid state.

For a magma crystallizing underground the only direction in which heat can be lost is up. Rocks are good insulators, as we know from the fact that rock wool and other rock products are widely used in home insulation. Consequently a large buried body of magma, which must lose many millions of calories of heat energy in order to crystallize, may require hundreds of thousands or even millions of years for this heat energy to flow to the surface. A lava erupted at the

TABLE 6-1
Simplified classification for igneous rocks

Texture	*Composition*				
	Felsic ←——————————————————→ *Mafic*				
	Orthoclase ←————————————→ *Plagioclase*				
	Quartz ←———————				
	————————*(increasing)*————————→ *Ferromagnesian minerals*				
Coarse-grained	Granite	Syenite	Diorite	Gabbro	Peridotite
*Fine-grained**	Rhyolite	Trachyte	Andesite	Basalt	(Rare)
	Felsite		Basalt		
Glassy	Obsidian	(Glasses rare or absent)			

*Because the minerals of fine-grained igneous rocks are too small to be identified without a microscope, these rocks are frequently subdivided into only two groups, the light-colored felsites and the dark-colored basalts.

surface does not face the same problem because it loses heat directly by radiation.

It is known that when a silicate melt is quenched (cooled rapidly), an amorphous glass is formed. We might say that a glass has zero grain size because it contains no crystals. Slower cooling allows crystals with ordered internal atomic arrangement to form; in general the slower the cooling the coarser the crystals. Therefore an igneous rock with large crystals must almost certainly have formed at considerable depth, where cooling was necessarily slow. Rocks with two distinct sizes of grain (Fig. 6-11) are said to be *porphyritic* and may reflect a history of slow cooling followed by rapid cooling. Thus the grain size of an igneous rock is a rough guide to the depth at which the rock crystallized. Coarse-grained rocks form well beneath the surface, whereas fine-grained and glassy rocks form on or near the surface.

We know that surface vulcanism is an active process today. Geologic mapping of igneous rocks of varying age has revealed the times and places of past igneous activity. Vulcanism has been a significant process since the earth's beginning.

Sedimentary rocks

Sedimentary rocks are formed at the surface of the earth by the accumulation of material eroded and weathered from exposed rocks. From Fig. 6-12, a microscopic view of a typical sedimentary rock, we can see how such rocks differ from igneous rocks. Most sedimentary rocks are composed of cemented fragments derived from preexisting rocks. Instead of being made up of tightly interlocked mineral grains, they are usually relatively porous. Fragments of organisms are common in many sediments, which is what one would expect of rocks formed at the surface.

FIGURE 6-11
Photomicrograph of an igneous rock exhibiting a porphyritic texture, i.e., one with two distinctly different grain sizes. *Courtesy of D. L. Southwick.*

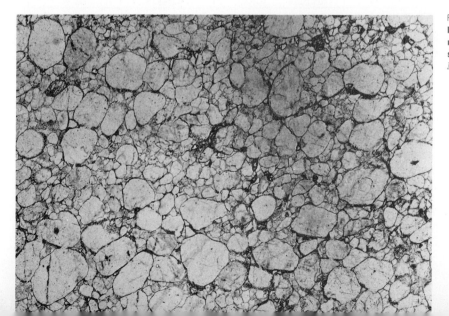

FIGURE 6-12
Photomicrograph of a slightly recrystallized quartz sandstone. *California Division of Mines.*

Some sedimentary rocks do exhibit the crystalline texture associated with igneous rocks, namely the sediments that form as precipitates from seawater. But even they are easy to distinguish from other rocks because, like all sediments, they form in beds, or layers. Moreover, the chemically precipitated sediments usually consist of only one mineral, whereas igneous rocks have two or three principal minerals. Finally, the minerals found in precipitated sediments are rare or absent in igneous rocks.

Sedimentary rocks are grouped into two broad classes, *clastic* sediments, which consist of cemented particles of minerals, rocks, and fossils, and *chemical* sediments, which consist of minerals precipitated from the water in which the rock formed. As we can see by the simplified classification chart (Table 6-2), clastic sediments are named according to their grain size, whereas the names for chemical sediments reflect their compositions.

Since some exposed sedimentary rocks are at least 3 billion years old, we know that the hydrologic cycle and the erosive processes have been operative for at least that long. Studies of ancient sedimentary rocks provide a history of the erosive processes throughout geologic time. By careful analysis the geologist can distinguish between marine and nonmarine sediments. It is sometimes possible to distinguish between sediments deposited by running water, wind, and glacial ice and thus to chart the relative importance of these erosional agents in time.

Metamorphic rocks

Metamorphism in rocks is induced by exposure to elevated temperatures and pressures. Metamorphic changes, which are aided by pore water, include recrys-

TABLE 6-2
Classification of sedimentary rocks

Type	*Texture or grain size*	*Composition*	*Name**
Clastic	Many pebbles or granules with diameters over 2 mm	Rock fragments, quartz	*Conglomerate*
	Sand-sized particles $\frac{1}{16}$ to 2 mm in diameter	Chiefly quartz: With feldspar With silt and clay	*Sandstone:* Arkose Graywacke
	Clay and silt-sized particles less than $\frac{1}{16}$ mm in diameter	Quartz, feldspar, clay minerals, iron oxides	*Shale*
Chemical	Crystalline	Calcite, $CaCO_3$	*Limestone*
		Dolomite, $CaMg(CO_3)_2$	*Dolomite*
		Gypsum, $CaSO_4 \cdot 2H_2O$	Rock gypsum
	Microcrystalline	Very fine quartz	Chert

*Most common forms in italics

FIGURE 6-13
Some typical metamorphic rocks: slate (left); garnet mica schist (center); biotite gneiss (right).

tallization of old minerals, replacement of one mineral by another, and sometimes granulation, or crushing. These changes take place without melting. Just as soft pliable clay is changed into hard brick in a kiln, so clay and other sediments are changed into dense crystalline rock when they are deeply buried and submitted to elevated temperatures and pressures for an extended time.

FIGURE 6-14
The slaty cleavage (metamorphic foliation) in these rocks clearly cuts across the original bedding. *Geological Survey of Canada.*

Like igneous rocks, metamorphic rocks are products of the depths; they are generally nonporous and dense, being composed of tightly interlocking mineral grains. Both metamorphic and sedimentary rocks are called *secondary rocks* because they are formed from preexisting rocks. Furthermore, metamorphic rocks resemble sedimentary rocks in that they are usually laminated, or banded, although the laminations are often strongly contorted.

There are many varieties of metamorphic rock because they are formed from rocks of varied composition and because conditions of metamorphism differ. In Chap. 4 we noted that minerals are sensitive to environment, which means that we would expect some minerals of metamorphic rocks formed near the melting temperature to be the same as those found in igneous rocks. This is indeed the case. Rocks metamorphosed at high temperature (high-grade metamorphism) are closely akin to their igneous cousins. On the other hand, metamorphic rocks formed at only slightly elevated temperatures and pressures are more like sedimentary rocks.

Like the rocks of Fig. 6-13, most metamorphic rocks contain parallel laminations. This property is called *foliation*. The foliation of metamorphic rocks is not the same thing as the bedding observed in sedimentary rocks. In fact, as illustrated in Fig. 6-14, metamorphic foliation frequently cuts across bedding. Meta-

morphic foliation is related to directed pressure or stress. Where shales, for example, have been folded and metamorphosed, the resulting slates and schists are usually foliated in the direction perpendicular to the compressive stress that produced the folding. The platy metamorphic minerals that impart foliation tend to form at right angles to the major stress direction.

Not all metamorphic rocks are foliated. In particular, metamorphic rocks formed from other rocks with only one mineral are usually massive. Table 6-3 gives the names of the chief varieties of foliated and nonfoliated metamorphic rocks.

6-3 THE ROCK CYCLE

We have seen how erosion, vulcanism, and diastrophism, either independently or by interaction, work to form and re-form the rocks of the earth's crust. Studies of rocks now exposed at the surface of the earth tell us that these processes have been operative for billions of years. The picture we form of the earth's crust is that rocks are continually being destroyed by weathering and erosion, by metamorphism, or by melting. At the same time, however, new rocks are formed to replace the old. The overall processes of rock formation are cyclical (see Fig. 6-15).

The earliest crustal rocks in Fig. 6-15 must have been igneous. As the earth developed an atmosphere and hydrosphere, the hydrologic cycle went into operation and with it the major surface erosional processes. Exposed igneous rocks were broken down and the eroded debris transported and deposited as sediment. Upon burial under layer upon layer, the first-formed sediments became compacted, cemented, and ultimately hardened (lithified) into sedimentary rock.

Sedimentation is a slow process. It has been estimated that on the average 1,000 to 2,000 years are required for 1 foot of sediment to accumulate. Even at

TABLE 6-3
Classification of metamorphic rocks

Type	Texture or composition	Name
Foliated	Very fine-grained; exhibits slaty cleavage	Slate
	Medium to fine-grained	Schist
	Coarse-grained; banded	Gneiss
Non-foliated	Chiefly interlocking crystals of calcite or dolomite	Marble
	Chiefly interlocking grains of quartz	Quartzite
	Feldspar and quartz, together with metamorphic minerals such as garnet and andalusite	Granofels

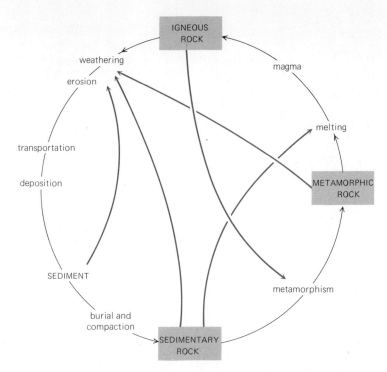

FIGURE 6-15
The rock cycle.

such slow rates, however, piles of sedimentary rocks tens of thousands of feet thick would accumulate in depressions after several hundred million years. The greatest sediment thicknesses would be expected where diastrophism was most active. At the bottoms of such thick sediment piles, pressures and temperatures far above those of the earth's surface would slowly change the sediments into metamorphic rocks. Sometimes the temperatures in such thick sediment wedges reached the melting point, and magma developed. Metamorphism would be particularly intense next to these buried magma chambers. When these magmas cooled and crystallized, they formed new igneous rocks, which brings us back to our starting point in the cycle.

This ideal cycle from igneous to sedimentary to metamorphic and back to igneous rocks rarely happens without intermediate steps. We can see why by looking at the rocks now undergoing erosion at the surface of the earth. About three-fourths of the land areas are presently covered by sedimentary rocks; they are being weathered and eroded by surface processes, and the eroded debris is building up new sediments. There is clearly a shortcut in the cycle from sedimentary rocks via erosion to sediment back to sedimentary rocks.

Similarly, since large areas of metamorphic rocks are exposed to the action of surface processes in various parts of the continents, there must be a shortcut from metamorphic rock back to sedimentary rock. Igneous rocks are known to

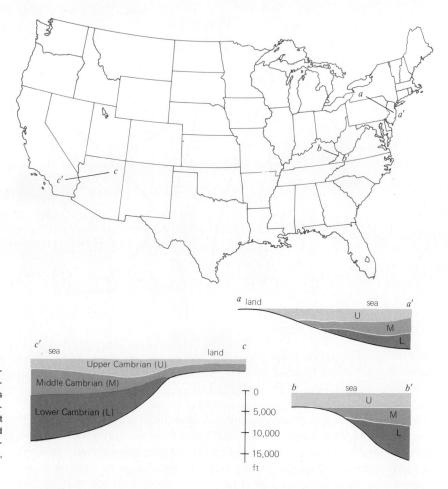

FIGURE 6-16
Restored cross sections showing the thicknesses of sediments deposited in various parts of the United States during Cambrian time. The greatest sediment thicknesses are found in areas that are now mountainous. *Adapted from M. Kay, Geol. Soc. Am. Mem. 48, 1951.*

recrystallize to new rocks by metamorphism, providing still another shortcut. And finally, deeply buried sedimentary rocks may sometimes melt to form igneous rocks.

If the rock cycle has truly been operative throughout most of the earth's long history, we might well ask: why are any very old rocks left at all? Why have the geologically ancient rocks not been changed into new ones? There are two good reasons. One, already noted, is the extreme slowness of the earth processes. In some mountain regions sedimentary-rock thicknesses up to 50,000 feet have been measured. At the present rates of sedimentation it must have taken them several hundred million years to accumulate, and it would take them even longer to be uplifted and eroded away again.

A second reason is that diastrophism and vulcanism do not occur randomly over the earth. Gravity measurements show that mountains are underlain by roots of lighter rock (Chap. 3). This evidence together with other information on the

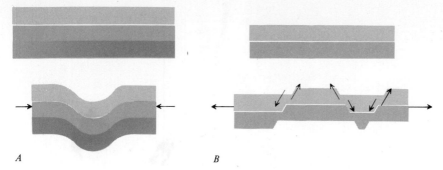

FIGURE 6-17
The layered rocks in many mountain chains are folded (Fig. 6-5). (*A*) Folding and crustal shortening are the result of compressive stresses. (*B*) Tension, on the other hand, results in faulting and lengthening.

earth's shape suggest that isostasy is partly responsible for the major levels of the earth's surface. Isostasy, however, is neither the only factor nor the controlling factor in determining where mountains form.

Closer inspection of the present mountain systems reveals that most of them contain abnormal thicknesses of sedimentary rocks. Several cross sections of parts of the United States (Fig. 6-16) show the thicknesses of sediments deposited during a given interval of geologic time. Much more sediment accumulated in areas that are now mountainous than in the plains regions. This in itself tells us that the mountain regions must once have been actively sinking basins, i.e., places where diastrophism was already working. Moreover, sedimentary beds are originally deposited flat, but those of the mountain regions are usually folded. Figure 6-17 illustrates how compressive forces are required to change a flat layer into a folded one. There seems to be no question that mountain regions are sites of diastrophism.

The type of earth movement involving folding and faulting that is associated with mountain building is called *orogeny*. Most large igneous intrusives are found in the exposed cores of mountain chains, and metamorphism is largely restricted to active belts where folding and intrusions occur. Not only that, but all active continental volcanoes are situated along young mountain chains.

The details of the development of fold mountain systems will be treated in Chap. 15. For now, let us simply recognize that mountains are not randomly distributed over the earth but occur as chains or linear belts. The Rocky Mountains, running along the west side of North America, and the Andean chain, bordering the west margin of South America, are good examples of the linear nature of these active belts. The positions of the earth's mountain belts seem to have changed in time. Witness the "dead" Appalachian chain and the still growing Rocky Mountains. Because of their height, mountains are places where erosion is most active. They also turn out to be places where igneous activity and metamorphism are most pronounced. In short, they are where the action is.

During the 1950s, some earth structures even greater in extent than the fold mountain chains were discovered, namely the ocean ridge systems (Fig. 6-18). The ocean basins are made up chiefly of the volcanic rock basalt; it is along the

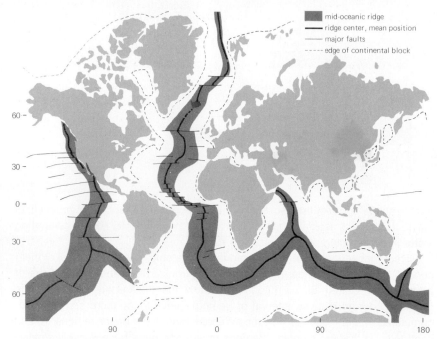

legend:
- mid-oceanic ridge
- ridge center, mean position
- major faults
- edge of continental block

FIGURE 6-18
The ocean ridge systems and the faults that offset the ridges. These major tensional structures, hidden under thousands of feet of seawater, are longer than any known fold mountain systems. *After B. C. Heezen in M. N. Hill (ed.), "The Sea," Wiley-Interscience, New York, 1963.*

ocean ridge systems that basalt magma wells its way upward from the mantle to the surface. Unlike the mountain belts, the ocean ridge systems exhibit the characteristics of structures formed by tension (Fig. 6-17).

We can now see how some very old rocks have been spared from participation in the rock cycle. The action of earth processes occurs chiefly in certain belts, and outside these active zones there is little or no igneous activity or metamorphism. Examine the rock structures of Fig. 6-19. In this region of northern Minnesota the rocks exhibit the earmarks of a fold mountain system long since worn flat by erosion. In Chap. 13 we discuss the methods used to date rocks. Radioactive dating of igneous and metamorphic rocks measures the time since the rocks were last crystallized. Dating of the rocks from the Cuyuna region of Minnesota reveals the youngest ages to be 1.7 billion years, meaning that there has been no melting or metamorphism (and hence no significant orogeny) there in the last 1.7 billion years. During that time erosion has been the dominant process, and it too came to a virtual halt with increased flattening of the region eons ago, resulting in the preservation of these old rocks.

6-4   WHAT ARE THE OTHER PLANETS LIKE?

So far naturally we have been focusing on planet Earth, but we can gain further understanding of our planet by comparing it with its neighbors in the solar system.

The motions of the planets were discussed in Chap. 3. We recall that Newton's

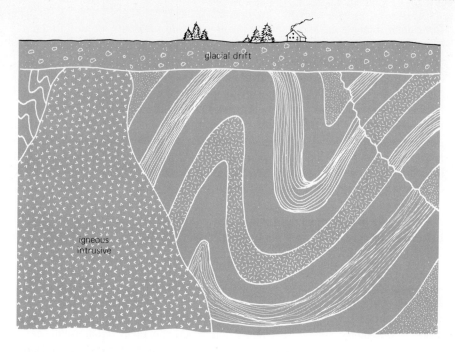

glacial drift

igneous
intrusive

FIGURE 6-19
**Diagrammatic cross section
through part of the Cuyuna iron
district of Minnesota. The iron-
bearing and related sedimentary rocks here have been explored by underground mine
workings and drilling. They are
known to be folded, intruded,
and faulted and in general to
exhibit structures typical of fold
mountains.**

law of gravitation, which can be used to predict the planetary motions, also made
it possible to determine the masses of the planets. From telescopic observations
astronomers have obtained reliable measurements of the diameters of the
planets. Knowing the planetary masses and sizes, it is an easy task to calculate
their average densities (Table 6-4).

Disregarding the outermost planet Pluto for the moment, we see from a casual
glance at Table 6-4 that the planets fall into two distinct groups on the basis of
mass and density. Jupiter, Saturn, Uranus, and Neptune all have relatively high
masses and low densities. Indeed the overall density of Saturn is less than the
density of water (1 gram per cubic centimeter) at the earth's surface. These large,

TABLE 6-4
Characteristics of the sun and
planets

	Radius	*Mass*	*Density,* g/cm^3	*Distance from sun*
Sun	109	333,000	1.41	
Mercury	0.38	0.053	5.3	0.4
Venus	0.97	0.815	4.95	0.7
Earth	1.00*	1.00*	5.52	1.0*
Mars	0.53	0.107	3.95	1.5
Jupiter	11.20	318.0	1.33	5.2
Saturn	9.47	95.2	0.69	9.5
Uranus	3.75	14.6	1.56	19.2
Neptune	3.50	17.23	2.27	30.1
Pluto	?1.1	0.9	?4	39.5

*By definition.

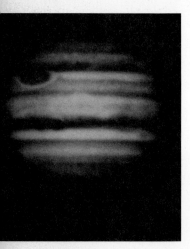

FIGURE 6-20
Jupiter, the largest of the planets. The marked polar flattening is the result of the planet's rapid rotation. *Hale Observatories photograph.*

low-density planets are known as the *major* or *Jovian planets.* Mercury, Venus, Earth, and Mars, which all exhibit relatively low masses and high densities, are known as the *minor* or *terrestrial planets.*

From Table 6-4 it is clear that the major planets must be made of much lighter materials than the earth and other minor planets. To find out just what these lighter materials may be is a more difficult matter. It is far easier to analyze the composition of the sun than that of a planet. The sun emits light, which can be analyzed spectrographically to reveal something about its constituent elements. Moreover, the sun is composed of gaseous materials, which behave more simply than the liquids and solids that make up the planets.

However, planets do reflect sunlight, and spectrographic analysis of such reflected light reveals something about the composition of the atmosphere of a planet, although little about the composition of the main body itself. We can learn about the composition of the main parts of planets, however, by fitting models to our data, just as we did for the earth in Chap. 5.

Spectral studies of the largest planet, Jupiter, show that its atmosphere consists largely of methane, CH_4, ammonia, NH_3, and molecular hydrogen, H_2. The element hydrogen appears in all these materials and must be a significant constituent of the planet. Jupiter has an overall density of 1.33 grams per cubic centimeter. Information obtained from theory and experiment on the relation between density and pressure of the common elements forces scientists to the conclusion that the main body of Jupiter consists chiefly of the light elements hydrogen and helium, because only such a composition can account for its low density. Thus Jupiter has essentially the same composition as the sun but differs from it in that the two elements must be largely in the frozen state. Figure 6-20 is a telescopic photograph of this giant planet.

The density of Saturn is even less than that of Jupiter. Spectrographic studies show that its atmosphere is also chiefly methane and ammonia, and we must conclude that it too is rich in the light elements. Figure 6-21 is a typical view of Saturn which reveals its most striking feature, the rings.

Saturn's rings are so thin that they would not be observed in an edgewise view from the earth. Observations and measurements suggest that the rings are composed of small particles. They are not solid plates, as evidenced by the fact that the inner parts of the rings rotate more rapidly than the outer ones. Since a bright star behind the rings can be seen through them, they cannot be made of dense materials; yet they are not gaseous because they yield no spectral lines of their own. It seems then that the rings must be made of solid particles that are not joined together in a solid mass. Studies of the light reflected from the rings support this conclusion because it has the characteristics of light reflected by pebble-size ice-coated fragments.

Uranus and Neptune are so far from the sun (and earth) that their surfaces cannot be observed clearly. Spectral studies suggest that methane is the dominant constituent of their atmospheres, and the interpretation is that ammonia, if present, is largely liquefied because of the low temperatures that exist so far from the sun. Their low densities lead us to conclude that they too are composed largely of the light elements.

Pluto, the outermost planet was not discovered until 1930. It is so far from the sun (40 astronomical units, or earth distances) that neither its size nor its period of rotation is accurately known. Spectral examination of Pluto does not reveal methane or ammonia, which are characteristic of the atmospheres of the major planets. Pluto is also unique in that its orbit crosses that of another planet, Neptune. It has been suggested that Pluto is not one of the original planets but a former large satellite that escaped to become captured in its present solar orbit.

Turning now to the earthlike, or terrestrial, planets, we see quite a different picture. These planets are all relatively small and dense. In Chap. 4 we found the earth to be composed chiefly of the heavier elements oxygen, silicon, iron, and aluminum. Hydrogen and helium, the chief constituents of the Jovian planets, play minor roles in the earth's overall chemical makeup. The other inner planets, Mercury, Venus, and Mars, must also be made up chiefly of heavier elements to account for their relatively high densities. Venus is nearest in size to the earth. The diameter of Mercury and Mars is roughly half that of the earth.

The atmospheres of the terrestrial planets are also very different. We already know that the earth's atmosphere consists chiefly of nitrogen, N_2, and oxygen, O_2. Venus is perennially covered by a very thick opaque cloud layer made up chiefly of carbon dioxide, CO_2. Investigations of Mars by the Mariner space probes have shown that its atmosphere is less than 1 percent as dense as the earth's. What little is there seems to consist chiefly of carbon dioxide, nitrogen, and trace amounts of oxygen. Since Mercury is never seen at night, it is not possible to study its atmosphere spectrographically, but there is strong evidence that Mercury, like the moon, has no atmosphere.

Most of the planets are either so far away or are covered by such a thick atmosphere that little or nothing is known about their solid surface. For this reason we turn next to the moon and the planet Mars, the only two bodies for which there is sufficient information to make a comparison of surface features with those of the earth.

FIGURE 6-21
Saturn and its rings. *Hale Observatories photograph.*

6-5 THE SURFACE OF THE MOON

The moon has a diameter of 3,476 kilometers, or somewhat more than one-fourth the diameter of the earth. Its mass is 1/81.6 of the earth's mass. The overall density of the moon is 3.34 grams per cubic centimeter, compared with the earth's density of 5.52 grams per cubic centimeter. The moon is unique among satellites in the solar system in being so close in size to its parent planet. Indeed, the earth-moon can be thought of as a double planet.

Figure 6-22 is a photograph of the earth side of the moon. The surface of the moon is dominated by circular structures of varying size, from small pits measuring a few meters in diameter, to large, distinct craters, to very large circular "seas," called *maria*. Because the moon lacks an atmosphere and hydrosphere,

FIGURE 6-22
The earth side of the moon.
Courtesy of Sherman Schultz.

there can be no hydrologic cycle and no erosion related to such a cycle. The moon's surface features must have formed by processes different from those responsible for the earth's surface.

Until the recent Apollo landings, the origin of the lunar craters was a subject for heated debate. The evidence now is strong for an impact origin rather than a volcanic one for most of them. It may seem unreasonable to assume that meteorite impact always forms circular features. Some of the projectiles must have hit at an angle, leading one to expect oblong or elliptical pits; however, controlled experiments with high-velocity impacts, coupled with studies of known meteorite craters on earth, have shown that circular patterns are to be expected. A high-

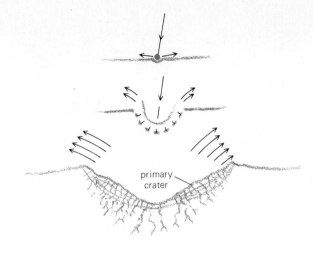

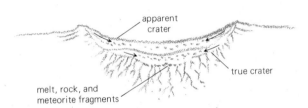

FIGURE 6-23
How a simple crater is formed by an impacting meteorite. Large craters are formed by comparatively small meteorites if the kinetic energy ($\frac{1}{2}mv^2$) is sufficiently high. *After M. Dence.*

velocity impact (greater than 2.5 kilometers per second) is like an explosion. The resulting crater is formed by shock waves, which move material and cause partial melting. A mass moving at 6 kilometers per second has a kinetic energy of about 5000 calories per gram, which is five times the specific energy of TNT. Figure 6-23 illustrates the probable steps in the development of explosion craters.

Studies of meteorite and explosion craters on earth have revealed a regular relationship between the rim height R_H or rim width R_W and crater diameter D. No other types of terrestrial craters plot along the same line. As we can see from Fig. 6-24, however, the lunar craters do exhibit the same relationship, which means that they must also have had an impact origin. If this is not enough evidence, we are assured that most lunar craters are of the impact type because their number increases with decreasing size, as is true of earth-bound meteorites.

We have made a strong case for the impact origin of lunar craters. This is not to eliminate all volcanic activity on the moon. The rocks brought back by the Apollo missions are, in fact, volcanic rocks that are very similar to earth basalts. Although the volcanic cones and collapsed cones found on the earth so far have not been positively identified on the moon, there is evidence that a type of volcanic depression called a *maar* does indeed exist on the lunar surface.

Lunar craters are visible only through a telescope, but even the naked eye can

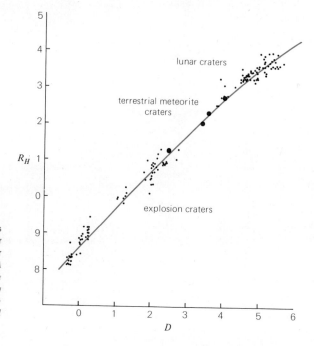

make out the maria, the remarkably flat, dark areas which contain fewer craters
than the upland regions. It seems that the dark maria material is something that
has flowed over a broad area, drowning older craters. On earth we have regions
(like the Columbia Plateau, in Washington) where outpourings of dark basaltic
lavas have formed sheets covering thousands of square miles. Even before the
manned lunar landings, many scientists believed the maria to be lava flows, but
there were difficulties with this interpretation because it seemed unreasonable
that lava flows on the moon, which has a much smaller gravitational force, should
be even flatter than similar flows on earth. Therefore some investigators
speculated that maria were flows of fine-grained ash because explosive volcanic eruptions on earth are known to have spread volcanic dust for great distances. There was some apprehension early in the lunar space program that a
thick, powdery blanket of volcanic dust might present an obstacle to landing.
The Apollo missions, however, have laid the dust-blanket hypothesis to rest. Although the immediate surface is covered by rock rubble, mechanical drills had
to be used to sample the lava flows even at shallow depth.

Lunar rilles are a type of valley that appear to have no terrestrial counterpart
(Fig. 6-25A). Rilles have steep walls and relatively flat floors, and the opposite
walls are roughly parallel. They range in width from a few meters to 3 or 4 kilometers. Some extend for hundreds of kilometers, crossing other lunar surface features. Although the regularity of shape suggests some sort of faulting, there is no
evidence of movement where a rille cuts through another structure such as a
crater. The origin of rilles is still very much an open question.

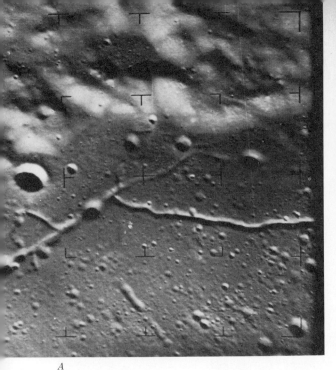

A   B

FIGURE 6-25
(A) Lunar rilles.(B) Lunar land-scape photographed by *Lunar Orbiter III*,showing the north-ern portion of Oceanus Procel-larum. The largest crater in the background is about 10 miles across and over 1 mile deep. Wrinkle ridges are evident on the mare. *NASA*.

Wrinkle ridges, a lunar structure frequently associated with maria, are usually only a few hundred feet high, but they may be several miles wide and hundreds of miles long. The relatively shallow wrinkle ridges appear to represent compres-sional structures associated with lava flows (Fig. 6-25B), but they in no way resemble the major compressional fold mountain belts of the earth.

In the absence of an atmosphere and a hydrosphere, impact craters once formed on the moon remain, while similar craters formed on earth are quickly modified, and finally destroyed, by erosion. What little leveling is observed on the moon seems to be due to the effects of overlap of craters and in particular to the bombardment by micrometeorites, coupled with a slow downslope creep of surface materials (Fig. 6-26).

Missing too from the lunar landscape are the effects of erosion's great antago-nist, diastrophism. There are no large-scale lunar structures to match the earth's fold mountain belts and ocean ridges. True, the moon has mountain ranges, but they are all related to circular and presumably impact-created features. Since diastrophic change is internally generated, the moon must be quiet inside as well as outside. Compared with the dynamic earth, the moon is a dead planet.

6-6 THE PLANET MARS

Mars has a diameter 0.52 times the earth's diameter and a mass 0.107 times the earth's mass. It falls about midway between the earth and the moon on a geomet-ric scale of mass (Earth = 1, Mars = 0.1, Moon = 0.01). How do the processes on a body of this size compare with those on earth?

Mars has long been the subject of intensive telescopic study because it is the only planet whose surface is visible from earth. The best telescopic resolution at-tainable, however, is only about 0.2 second of arc, which is about 60 kilometers

FIGURE 6-26
The trail left by a boulder rolling down this lunar slope shows that there is some leveling even on the moon. *NASA.*

on the Martian surface when the planet is closest to the earth. Visual resolution is much better than photographic resolution because of the time exposures needed, and consequently many details reported by actual observers cannot be duplicated on photographs.

Mars is generally known as the *red planet*. Actually, however, several colors are visible. About three-fourths of the surface is reddish to reddish yellow, which suggests that the surface materials may be oxidized (the reds and yellows being forms of iron oxide). The remaining one-fourth of the surface tends to be darker in color, sometimes exhibiting shades of green and blue. These darker regions, known as *maria*, change with the seasons. Seasonal changes are also evident in the growth and retreat of white polar caps (Fig. 6-27).

The exact nature of the changing polar caps is not known. Only two atmospheric constituents have been positively identified on Mars, carbon dioxide, CO_2, and water vapor. Of the two, carbon dioxide is by far the more abundant. In 1965, data relayed by the Mars probe *Mariner 4* showed the surface atmospheric pressure to be less than 1 percent that of the earth's. There may be other unidentified constituents in the Martian atmosphere (N_2, O_2), but they cannot be very abundant because of its tenuous nature and high CO_2 content. It has been proposed that the polar caps are not ice but solid CO_2. The planet has so little at-

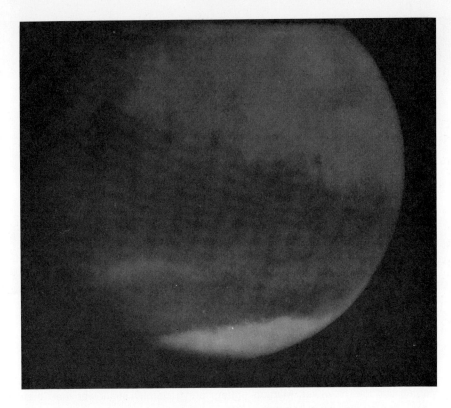

FIGURE 6-27
Mars as photographed by *Mariner 6* **in 1969. Pictures taken at different times of the year show that the white polar cap waxes and wanes with the seasons.** *NASA.*

mosphere, of which only a small fraction is H_2O, that it is difficult to imagine enough ice forming to make visible caps. Even if the caps turn out to be ice, however, there still cannot be any water as lakes or seas on the planet. The temperature at the edges of the white polar caps is estimated to be $-75°C$ and not the $0°C$ we would expect on earth. Instead of melting, ice sublimates in the thin air of Mars, i.e., changes directly from the solid to the vapor phase.

Various clouds have been observed on the surface of the planet, including large white cloud masses that sometimes last for days and weeks and move over the surface. A number of astronomers have observed yellowish clouds, believed to be dust storms, which spring up suddenly and obscure the detail over hundreds of square miles of the Martian surface. That this hypothesis is correct became evident when *Mariner 9*, launched May 30, 1971, with the goal of continuing the photographic work on Mars, arrived at the planet November 14, 1971, only to find much of the surface hidden by dust storms. Fortunately after a few weeks the dust settled, and the unmanned craft was able to relay back some excellent pictures. That the dust in such clouds takes so long to settle indicates that it must be exceedingly fine to remain suspended in so rare an atmosphere.

Mariner 4 (launched in November 1964) relayed back the first close-up photographs of Mars early in 1965. Although these pictures covered only about 1

FIGURE 6-28
Two views of the Martian surface photographed by *Mariner 6* **in 1969.** *NASA.*

percent of the total surface, they were significant because they show it to be pitted, like the surface of the moon. Subsequent pictures from *Mariner 6* and *7* (launched in 1969) confirm this discovery.

As shown by Fig. 6-28, craters of various sizes are important features of the Martian surface. However, Martian craters are generally shallower than their lunar equivalents, which, together with a relative dearth of small craters, suggests that erosion is more active on Mars than on the moon—exactly as one would expect.

The Mariner experiment has also shown that Mars, unlike the earth, lacks a magnetic field. Although the exact cause of the earth's magnetic field must await further study, scientists agree that it is related to the partially fluid metallic core. This suggests that Mars has no distinct core, a conclusion strengthened by the lower overall density of Mars compared with earth.

In summary, Mars has a tenuous atmosphere and a weak surface erosional cycle. Although only a fraction of its surface has been observed in detail, there appear to be no major mountain structures comparable to the mountain systems on earth. In fact, radar measurements show the Martian surface to be exceptionally flat. Existing evidence indicates that Mars is much quieter internally than the earth but probably more active than the moon.

6-7 WHY ARE THE PLANETS SO DIFFERENT?

The problem of the differences in the size and composition of the planets is related to the larger question of the origin of the solar system, discussed in Chap. 18. In brief, it seems reasonable to assume that the planets and the sun were

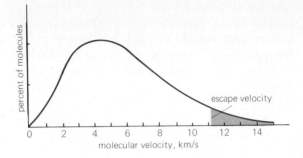

FIGURE 6-29

Velocities of hydrogen molecules at 20°C. Some 10 percent of the molecules are moving with speeds greater than the escape velocity of 11.2 km/s.

formed together from the same stuff. That the planets all lie in about the same plane and rotate in the same direction around the sun speaks for such a common origin. The uniformity of relative abundances of the heavy elements in the sun, in meteorites, and in the earth (Chap. 5) is also evidence that these bodies were formed from the same material.

If the planets all condensed from the same material at about the same time, why are they so different? As noted in Chap. 5, one property that can explain much of the diversity is escape velocity, or the speed an object must attain to escape from the planet's gravitational attraction. The same escape velocity applies to a gas molecule as to a large artificial satellite.

The mass and size of a planet determine its escape velocity. For Mercury the value is 4.3 kilometers per second, for earth it is 11.2 kilometers per second, and for Jupiter it is about 60 kilometers per second. The escape velocity for the moon is only about 2.4 kilometers per second. It is significant that planets like Jupiter and Saturn, with high escape velocities, still contain large amounts of light elements like hydrogen and helium. The earth, with an intermediate escape velocity, has an atmosphere, but it is composed chiefly of nitrogen and oxygen rather than hydrogen compounds. The moon, with a comparatively small escape velocity, has no atmosphere and no hydrosphere.

To understand how the value of the escape velocity controls the abundances of the elements we must refer to the kinetic theory of gases. According to the model used in that theory, the molecules of a gas are in continual random motion. All possible speeds are represented among the molecules, and therefore all possible molecular kinetic energies, $\frac{1}{2}mv^2$, where m is the mass of a molecule and v is its speed. A basic feature of the kinetic theory is that the absolute temperature of a gas can be identified with the average kinetic energy. This means that in a mixture of gases that have achieved a common temperature, e.g., in a planetary atmosphere, the lighter molecules (smaller m) are, on the average, moving faster (bigger v) than the heavier molecules. The lighter molecules thus have a better chance of exceeding the escape velocity and leaving the planet permanently.

For escape it is not necessary that the *average* speed of the molecules exceed the escape velocity. Figure 6-29 shows the velocities of hydrogen molecules at 20°C. The average velocity at this temperature is 4.3 kilometers per second, but 10 percent of the molecules have speeds of over 11.5 kilometers per second. At this temperature, then, hydrogen gradually escapes the earth's gravitational field (escape velocity = 11.2 kilometers per second) even though the average speed of its molecules is less than the escape velocity.

Now we can understand why the terrestrial planets are depleted of the light elements. They are all small, with relatively low escape velocities; moreover, since they are closer to the sun, their gas molecules are moving faster to begin with. In Chap. 18 we see that the temperatures of the earth and other minor planets must once have been considerably higher. These planets must then have lost hydrogen and helium and even some heavier molecules from their primordial atmospheres. What remains are the heavier elements and those lighter elements which were tied up in minerals.

By contrast, the major planets have retained a much higher proportion of the primordial materials because they are larger and much colder than the inner planets.

In the terrestrial planets there appears to be a relation between size and internal activity. The earth is active internally partly because its interior is hot, and it is differentiated into a partially fluid core and a plastic mantle. The moon and Mars lack an internal core, and available evidence suggests that both are very sluggish in internal activity compared with the earth. Venus, which has a mass about equal to earth's, may possess a comparably active interior. Unfortunately, its surface is hidden from view, and until space probes are able to explore its surface more completely we can only speculate about its volcanic and diastrophic activity.

SUMMARY

The surface of the earth is continually changing and has been doing so for several billion years. Three major processes—erosion, diastrophism, and vulcanism—interact to produce these changes. Erosion is a leveling process, which acts to wear down elevated regions and to fill in depressions on the earth's surface. Diastrophism and vulcanism are building processes. They derive their energy from within, whereas the great surface cycle is driven mainly by solar energy.

Rocks are both destroyed and created by the major earth processes. Sedimentary rocks form on the surface from eroded materials.

Metamorphic rocks result when other rocks are subjected for long periods to elevated temperatures and pressures and directed stresses beneath the surface. Melting of earth materials produces magma, which crystallizes into igneous rock upon cooling. Changes from one rock type to another proceed according to the rock cycle.

The earth's major structural features, which are the sites of most vulcanism and diastrophism, are not randomly distributed but occur in linear belts. Most of the internal activity is located in young mountain chains or along the ocean ridge systems.

The composition and dynamic

behavior of our planet appear to be related to its mass. The moon, which has only about one-eightieth the mass of the earth, is a much quieter body geologically. Not only does it lack atmosphere and hydrosphere, but it apparently has no internal cycle like that exhibited by earth. The lunar mountains all are parts of circular structures, and there are no equivalents to the fold mountain system of the earth. Even Mars, with a mass of about one-tenth that of the earth, appears to be a comparatively inactive body.

By contrast, the massive major planets are very different because they have retained the light elements hydrogen and helium. Consequently, their densities are around 1 gram per cubic centimeter, which is one-fourth or less the density of a terrestrial planet.

QUESTIONS

1 What are the three main processes acting on and in the earth to produce change?

2 How are these processes related to the three principal rock types?

3 What is the difference between a gabbro and a basalt?

4 How are sedimentary rocks classified?

5 What is the relation between the foliation of a metamorphic rock and the bedding of the sedimentary rock from which it formed?

6 Where would you expect to find igneous and metamorphic rocks exposed at the earth's surface?

7 Igneous and metamorphic rocks make up about 95 percent of the earth's crust, yet 75 percent of the rock exposed at the surface is sedimentary rock. How do you explain this?

8 Why are meteorite craters not nearly as abundant on earth as they are on the moon or Mars?

9 How do we know that the moon is less active internally than the earth?

10 What determines the escape velocity of a planet? If the velocity of escape on Neptune were the same as the earth's, would you expect it to have a similar atmosphere?

11 A meteorite crater is like the crater formed by a powerful explosive. Why?

12 How does the earth differ from the other planets in the solar system?

13 Is there any surface erosion on the moon?

14 What are the most abundant gases in the atmosphere of Jupiter?

15 The 400-million-year-old Ordovician rocks exposed along the Mississippi River in Minneapolis and St. Paul are essentially flat-lying and undeformed. What does this tell you about the history of earth movement in that area?

16 The hydrologic cycle is driven by energy from the sun. Is this the only energy involved in the rock cycle? Why?

17 We saw in Chap. 4 that minerals are indicators of environment. With this in mind, which of the principal classes of rock would you expect to be most similar in mineral composition?

18 If you wanted to know how fast an area was being lowered by stream erosion, what would you measure?

REFERENCES

Baldwin, Ralph B., "A Fundamental Survey of the Moon," McGraw-Hill Book Company, New York, 1965.

Page, T., and L. W. Page: "Neighbors of the Earth," The Macmillan Company, New York, 1965.

Shelton, John S.: "Geology Illustrated," W. H. Freeman and Company, San Francisco, 1966.

Simpson, B.: "Rocks and Minerals," Pergamon Press, New York, 1966.

Struve, Otto: "Elementary Astronomy," Oxford University Press, New York, 1959.

Whipple, F. L.: "Earth, Moon and Planets," Harvard University Press, Cambridge, Mass., 1968.

7

ENERGY FOR CHANGE

In Chap. 6 we studied some of the major processes that work changes on and in the earth. These processes are no newcomers on the scene. The rock shown in Fig. 7-1 was formed 2 billion years ago. The well-preserved ripple marks on this quartz sandstone are evidence that it formed in a body of water. Weathering, erosion, transportation, and deposition, which interact today to separate resistant quartz from other rock-forming minerals and build layers of sand, must also have been operating 2 billion years ago.

In fact, the geologic record shows that the same types of rocks are found in all eras and that mountain building and vulcanism proceeded in much the same fashion hundreds of millions of years ago as they do today. There is no evidence that these processes are slowing down. The fuel for this great earth machine that continually changes material from one rock into another seems limitless; there appears to be an inexhaustible supply of energy to power the major earth cycles.

Whereas the evidence is strong that the hydrologic cycle and the rock cycle have been operating in about the same way throughout most of the earth's history, other things on earth *have* changed. Life, for example, has evolved from simple one-celled forms to the variety of complex living things in the present biosphere. Recently slight chemical differences have been discovered between rocks of varying ages, which are interpreted as reflecting evolutionary changes in the atmosphere. These one-way, or evolutionary, changes are discussed in Chap. 13 and 18. In this chapter, the focus is on the seemingly eternal earth cycles. Where does the energy to drive them come from? Do the hydrologic and petrologic cycles derive their energy from the same or different sources? These are the main questions to be considered here.

7-1 WHAT IS ENERGY?

For many years inventive men sought to create devices capable of perpetual motion. Of course, we know that none of these machines achieved that goal. Why didn't they succeed? When a force is applied to an object through some distance, *work* has been done on the object. Work is therefore measured in units of force times distance (foot-pounds, dyne-centimeters, newton-meters). When work has been done on an object, that object itself becomes capable of doing work; we say that the object gains *energy*, the ability to do work. Similarly, whatever agent did the work on the object loses energy in the process.

Figure 7-2 shows two situations where work has been done on an object. In Fig. 7-2*A*, where the object has been lifted to a higher level, it is easy to see that

FIGURE 7-1
Ripple marks on an exposure of sandstone in a road cut east of Sault Sainte Marie, Ontario. The sandstone is about 2 billion years old.

there has been no overall loss of energy because the object could perform an equal amount of work by falling back to the original level. In Fig. 7-2B it appears that energy has been lost because we know that the object will not move back to its original position. A careful analysis of this situation, however, shows that the energy expended in moving the object has not disappeared but has been converted into heat.

The nature of heat long puzzled scientists. In the seventeenth and early eighteenth centuries heat was thought to be a fluid that filled the space between the

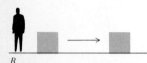

FIGURE 7-2
Two situations where work has been done on an object. *(A)* **Energy has been conserved because the object has acquired potential energy.** *(B)* **The energy appears to have been lost.**

atoms of any substance. According to this theory, each substance contained a specific quantity of heat. Benjamin Thompson (Count Rumford; 1753–1814) finally disproved this theory when he demonstrated that boring a cannon produces enough heat to boil water. Not only did the mechanical movement involved in the drilling generate heat, but the amount of heat generated seemed to depend solely on the amount of drilling or motion. Later the English physicist J. P. Joule (1818–1889) measured the mechanical equivalent of heat using an apparatus similar to that in Fig. 7-3. The descending weight turns a paddle in water, and the energy involved in the downward movement of the mass is converted into heat in the water. By measuring the distance the weight has to fall to raise the temperature of one pound of water one degree Fahrenheit, Joule determined how many units of mechanical energy are equivalent to a unit of heat energy. It takes 778 foot-pounds of work to raise the temperature of 1 pound of water by 1°F, or expressed in other units 4185 joules is equivalent to 1 kilocalorie of heat (where a joule is 1 newton-meter).

In the late 1840s studies of the interrelationships between various types of energy led to the formulation of the law of conservation of energy, which says that energy cannot be destroyed or created. The law is an outcome of careful measurements of conversions from one type of energy into another. In most energy conversions some energy is lost as heat—lost because this heat energy can no longer be transformed into useful work. Once the relationship between heat and work was recognized, it became possible to account completely for the energy in many conversions and thus to establish the law of conservation of energy. The reason for the failure of perpetual motion machines becomes clear. In all such devices some energy is radiated away as heat.

For example, by turning an electric generator, mechanical energy can be converted into electric energy. This electric energy can be stored in a battery as chemical energy. The battery can subsequently be used to turn an electric motor, which can in turn be used to do mechanical work. The amount of work that the electric motor can do, however, will not equal the work put into the generator at the beginning. Energy will have been dissipated as heat in the generator, in the battery, and in the electric motor. The energy input into the generator will equal the energy output from the motor plus the total heat loss.

In the example of the electric generator four kinds of energy—mechanical, electric, heat, and chemical—were mentioned. Other kinds are radiant energy

FIGURE 7-3
Joule's experiment to measure the mechanical equivalent of heat. The potential energy of the weight is first converted into kinetic energy of the paddle wheel, which in turn is changed into heat. Energy is conserved.

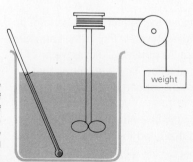

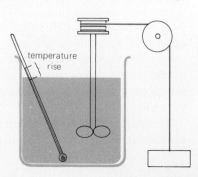

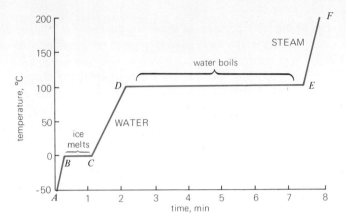

FIGURE 7-4
Graph of temperature versus time for a fixed amount of water, initially ice at −50°C, to which heat is added at a constant rate.

and nuclear energy. The discovery of nuclear energy seemed at first to violate the law of conservation of energy. According to Einstein's famous equation, $E = mc^2$, where E is energy, m is mass, and c is a constant equal to the speed of light, a very small amount of mass can be converted to a very large amount of energy because c is very large. When thought of in another way, however, the discovery of the interrelation of mass and energy does not violate the principle of energy conservation but combines two fundamental laws, the law of conservation of mass and the law of conservation of energy.

The terms *kinetic* and *potential energy* were originally used to describe different kinds of mechanical energy. Kinetic energy (KE) is energy of motion, and the kinetic energy of a moving object is equal to one-half of its mass m times its velocity v squared (KE $= \frac{1}{2}mv^2$). Potential energy is a type of stored energy. It is energy of position. A boulder perched on the edge of a cliff has potential energy. Work will be done if the boulder falls to the bottom. The term is now also used for other types of stored or latent energy. A flashlight battery has potential energy. Moist air has potential energy that will be released when the moisture condenses.

There are many energy conversions in the great earth cycles. When the earth quakes, potential energy is converted into heat and shock waves that ultimately change into heat. Some of the kinetic energy of a turbulent river is changed into heat energy. Heat is clearly radiated to space from a glowing volcanic flow. Like the energy in the unsuccessful perpetual motion machines, most of this heat energy is not available to do further work. The seemingly endless water and rock cycles of the earth are not examples of perpetual motion. Energy must have been continuously available throughout geologic time to drive the systems.

7-2 MATTER AS A STOREHOUSE OF THERMAL ENERGY

Figure 7-4 shows the result of a simple experiment to demonstrate that matter can store energy. From the graph we see how the temperature of a block of ice originally at −50°C varies when it is heated at a uniform rate. Initially the temper-

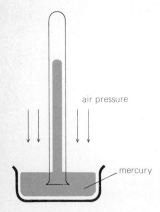

air pressure

mercury

FIGURE 7-5
Torricellian barometer. Mercury rises in this evacuated glass tube because air pressure forces it up. The height of the mercury in the tube depends upon the atmospheric pressure.

FIGURE 7-6
Boyle's law can easily be demonstrated with a J tube. When mercury is added to the column at the left, the air trapped in the tube is compressed. Its volume is found to be directly proportional to the pressure, as indicated by the height of mercury in the left column.

h

air

ature of the ice increases, as shown by the line AB. At point B (0°C) there is a period during which there is no change in temperature even though the rate at which heat energy is put into the system has not changed. What happens to this heat energy? Physically the line BC represents the change from ice to water. Similarly the flat line DE at 100°C corresponds to the change from water to steam. It takes 80 calories to change 1 gram of ice into water and 540 calories to change 1 gram of water into steam. This energy, which produces a change in phase, is stored energy. If we carried out this experiment in reverse, i.e., cooled steam, making it condense into water, we would find that each gram of steam gives up 540 calories in changing from the vapor to the liquid phase and each gram of water gives up 80 calories in changing to solid ice. This, of course, is exactly what one would expect because it conforms to the law of conservation of energy.

The explanation for the behavior of materials like water in response to heating lies in the kinetic-molecular theory of matter. According to this theory, the temperature of a material body is a measure of the kinetic energy of the particles (molecules and atoms) of which it is composed. Consequently when a block of ice is heated, the energy of its constituent atoms is raised. Ice is a crystalline solid, the atoms occupying fixed positions in a space lattice. When ice or any crystalline solid is heated, something inside must change as the temperature rises. We can think of the constituent atoms as vibrating faster about their fixed centers with increasing temperature. It is only when the melting point is reached that they are able to shake away from their sites in the space lattice.

In water the constituent molecules are not in an ordered state but are able to move throughout the space occupied by the liquid. However, the molecules of a liquid are held close together by mutual attractive forces. In the vapor phase the molecules are in a state of rapid motion, colliding occasionally with each other or with the walls of the container.

Because the particles of a gas are freely moving and far apart from each other, there is little attraction between them. An increase in temperature of a gas increases the kinetic energy of the particles. In liquids and solids the constituent atoms are close enough together to be materially affected by electric attractive forces, and although increased temperature in these materials also causes an increase in motion, the relation is not as clear as it is in gases. Energy is required to change from the ordered solid state to the liquid state, and even more energy is needed to free the atoms of a liquid to the gaseous state.

The particles of which matter is made are so small that they are invisible even with the most modern optical instruments. Looking at the denser forms of matter like liquids or solids could not have revealed the existence of fundamental particles to the early investigators. Instead the idea that matter is composed of particles in rapid motion came about as an explanation for the way gases behave. The response of gases to changes in temperature and pressure is much simpler and more predictable than that of liquids and solids; for this reason the behavior of gases became a subject of great interest several centuries ago.

The fact that gases have weight and can exert pressure was illustrated by some experiments in the seventeenth century. In 1643 one of Gallileo's pupils, Evangelista Torricelli, found that mercury in a full closed tube does not completely run out of the tube when it is inverted in a vessel of mercury (Fig. 7-5). Torricelli's explanation was that the air of the atmosphere presses on the exposed mercury of the vessel with a sufficient force to balance the column of mercury in the tube. He noticed that the height of the mercury column in the tube fluctuates slightly from day to day, and he concluded that these fluctuations must be due to changes in the weight (pressure) of the atmosphere. He had thus discovered the barometer, an instrument of immense importance to meteorologists.

During the seventeenth century Robert Boyle, an English scientist, discovered a relation between the volume and pressure of gas using an instrument similar to that shown in Fig. 7-6. By pouring different amounts of mercury into the J tube and thus varying the pressure on the trapped gas, Boyle noted that the volume of the trapped gas is inversely proportional to the pressure provided there is no temperature change. This relation was found to hold (at least approximately) for all gases tested and became known as *Boyle's law*. Expressed symbolically, Boyle's law states that the product of the pressure P and volume V of a gas at fixed temperature equals a constant K, or $PV = K$.

As an explanation for his empirical discovery Boyle adopted the model of Fig. 7-7. He pictured gases as being composed of invisible, motionless but highly compressible particles. One of his reports was called Experiments to Test the Doctrine of the Spring of Air. Boyle's static model for gases was proved wrong because, for example, it cannot account for the speed with which an easily detected gas like ammonia is observed to permeate a room. Moreover, a static model cannot explain why the pressure exerted by a gas is uniform on all sides of a container (Fig. 7-8).

In 1734 a Swiss physicist, Daniel Bernoulli, suggested that gases are composed of myriads of rapidly moving particles. He pictured the particles as being in a state of random motion, which would account for the uniformity of pressure in an irregular-shaped container. This model was not immediately accepted. In fact, the kinetic theory of gases was revised and finally accepted some hundred years after Bernoulli's death. Science often needs a long time to confirm a brilliant guess. Scores of other experiments plus attempts to predict the behavior of gases mathematically on the basis of rapidly moving molecules finally showed the kinetic-molecular explanation to be superior to all others.

Among experiments that led to an acceptance of the kinetic theory were those conducted by the French scientist Jacques Charles. He found that all gases expand by about the same fraction of their original volume when they are heated over the same temperature range at constant pressure. Figure 7-9 is a plot of temperature versus volume for a gas at fixed pressure. If the line on the graph is extended to the left, it shows that the gas should have zero volume at $-273°C$. Of course, this does not happen because the gas is liquefied well before that point. This temperature is important, however, because it is the temperature at which

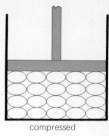
compressed

A

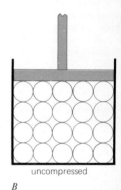
uncompressed

B

FIGURE 7-7
Boyle's interpretation of the structure of gases. To explain the "spring" of the air he visualized it and other gases as being made of compressible particles (*A*) which spring back to their original shape when the pressure is released (*B*).

FIGURE 7-8
The pressure of a contained gas is the same on all walls of the container regardless of its shape.

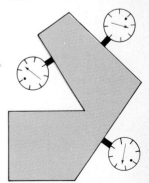

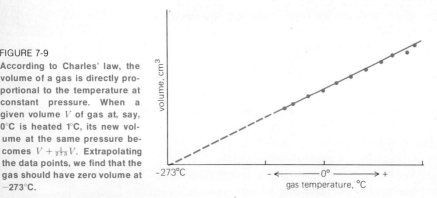

FIGURE 7-9
According to Charles' law, the volume of a gas is directly proportional to the temperature at constant pressure. When a given volume V of gas at, say, 0°C is heated 1°C, its new volume at the same pressure becomes $V + \frac{1}{273}V$. Extrapolating the data points, we find that the gas should have zero volume at −273°C.

molecular motion is believed to cease. It is called absolute zero or 0 K after Lord Kelvin, the English physicist.

This review of some of the early work on the nature of matter should help to clarify several important points. The first of these is the difference between heat and temperature. Temperature is a measure of the mean kinetic energy of the particles of a substance. The higher the temperature the greater the energy of motion of the constituent atoms of a material. Heat, on the other hand, depends not only on the temperature but also on the kind and amount of material involved. The kilocalorie is one unit of heat, and it is defined as the amount of heat needed to raise the temperature of one kilogram of water one degree Celsius. Thus if two containers of water, one of 1 kilogram and the other of 100 kilograms, are heated from 20° to 100°C, the first would require 80 kilocalories and the second 8000 kilocalories of heat energy. If the temperature of something is to be lowered, heat must be taken away. In our example, the 1-kilogram container would have to lose 1 kilocalorie to lower its temperature 1° whereas the 100-kilogram container would have to lose 100 kilocalories to lower its temperature 1°. Clearly the amount of heat in an object is related to the quantity of matter.

The amount of heat needed to raise the temperature of an object by a specific amount is also related to the type of material. Whereas it takes 1 kilocalorie to raise the temperature of 1 kilogram of water 1°C, it takes only 0.19 kilocalorie to cause an equal temperature increase in 1 kilogram of granite. The *specific heat* of a substance is defined as the heat needed to raise the temperature of one kilogram by one degree Celsius. Water has an unusually high specific heat compared to other earth materials.

It should now be clear that matter can store heat energy in many earth processes. When the sun's energy, for example, evaporates water from the ocean, 540 kilocalories of heat energy is required to vaporize each kilogram. This energy is not lost; as we have seen, the same amount of energy is liberated when a kilogram of vapor condenses to rain.

Stored energy also plays a significant role in chemical reactions involving solids. The release of heat energy during burning or oxidation is a familiar phenomenon. When a piece of iron is left exposed to the atmosphere, it rusts, or becomes oxidized. The iron unites with atmospheric oxygen and water vapor to form iron oxide, and heat is liberated:

$$4Fe + 3O_2 + 2H_2O \rightarrow 2Fe_2O_3 \cdot H_2O + heat$$

The iron oxide formed by the oxidation of iron can be changed back into iron by heating:

$$2Fe_2O_3 \cdot H_2O + heat \rightarrow 4Fe + 3O_2 + 2H_2O$$

This is what happens in a blast furnace, but here coke and other constituents must be used to lower the dissociation temperature of the iron oxide.

Metallic iron is a rare constituent of the earth's crust, but the principle involved in this example applies to the more complicated reactions for the formation of common minerals. Most of the iron in the minerals of deep-seated igneous or metamorphic rocks is in the ferrous state. The ferrous ion has two plus charges (Fe^{2+}). When minerals containing Fe^{2+} are exposed at the earth's surface, the ferrous iron becomes oxidized to ferric, Fe^{3+}, iron with the liberation of heat. Many deep-seated minerals require heat energy for their formation. Heat is frequently liberated when these minerals break down into other minerals at the earth's surface.

7-3 THE EARTH'S ENERGY BUDGET

The sun is the major source of energy for the earth. Heat and light from the sun contribute 2 calories of energy per square centimeter per minute at the earth's distance. This value, known as the *solar constant*, is frequently expressed in units called langleys, where 1 langley equals 1 calorie per square centimeter. Because of the spherical shape of the earth, this energy is not uniformly distributed over its surface, as we saw in Fig. 2-26. Tropical regions receive more energy per square centimeter than polar regions.

The sun cannot be the earth's only energy source, however. Measurements of temperature in mines and deep boreholes show that the temperature of the earth increases with depth at an average rate of 1°C per 30 meters. Since heat flows only from warmer to cooler areas, it must be flowing outward toward the surface of the earth, just the opposite of what would happen if the sun were contributing heat to the inside of the earth. The rate of flow of heat from the inside of the earth is only about 1/25,000 that arriving from the sun when it is directly overhead. The *surface* temperatures and processes of the earth are clearly controlled by solar energy.

With this information on the major sources of energy for earth processes let us turn to the question of an energy budget for earth. Here again the rock pictured in

FIGURE 7-10
This rock specimen from the iron-rich sedimentary beds of the Mesabi district of Minnesota is over 1.7 billion years old. The circular structures in the rock are fossilized colonies of algae. *G. Morey, Minnesota Geological Survey.*

Fig. 7-1 becomes significant. This rock and others formed by the action of water some 2 billion years ago tell us that the temperature at the earth's surface then lay between 0° and 100°C, that is, within the range of temperature at which liquid water exists. Figure 7-10 shows another rock of similar age containing fossil algae. The existence of such life forms puts further restrictions on the temperatures that existed during that distant time. The conclusion is that the temperatures at the earth's surface several billion years ago were very close to those of today.

Although heat has been contributed to the surface of the earth by the sun for billions of years and heat has been flowing from the interior for a similar period, the planet has apparently not become significantly warmer or cooler. Therefore the earth must be in a state of balance from an energy standpoint: it must be losing as much energy as it gains, or, in budgetary terms, it must be spending as much as it receives.

The radiant energy which arrives at the outer atmosphere of the earth does not all reach its surface. Some is reflected back by clouds and by particulate matter in the air, and some is absorbed by the atmosphere. Of the radiant energy that does reach the surface some is immediately reflected skyward by the water or land, and only the remainder is available for heating the earth's surface. The earth's warmed surface radiates energy back to space, and obviously the total outgoing radiant energy must equal the incoming solar energy absorbed by the surface materials in order to account for the steady temperature of the earth. It is

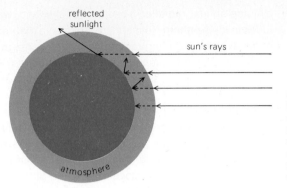

FIGURE 7-11
Not only are the sun's rays spread out over larger areas of the earth's surface where they strike it obliquely, but there is also more reflection of the solar radiation and more atmospheric absorption at high latitudes.

important to realize that the balance between incoming and outgoing energy holds only for the earth as a whole, not for each individual region of the earth.

The sun's radiant energy is not uniformly distributed over the surface of the earth. For a number of reasons, more energy reaches the earth's surface in the tropics than at high latitudes. Not only is the sun more often directly overhead in tropical regions, with the result that there is a higher amount of energy per unit area contributed to this belt,but there is also less reflection of the sun's rays when they shine directly down than when they make an angle with the earth's surface (Fig. 7-11). Moreover, the tropical regions have more water compared to the areas of higher latitude in the Northern Hemisphere, and water absorbs solar energy more efficiently than land. The polar ice caps further act to reflect much of the sun's radiation from these regions.

All these factors have been evaluated, and Fig. 7-12 shows an analysis of the

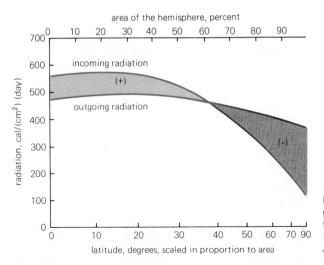

FIGURE 7-12
Mean annual incoming and outgoing radiation at various latitudes of the Northern Hemisphere. *After H. G. Houghton, J. Meteorol., vol. 11, 1954.*

average annual radiation absorbed by the land, water, and air at different latitudes in the Northern Hemisphere. The same diagram gives mean annual values of the average outgoing radiation from the earth. In the belt from the equator to about 39°N latitude the incoming radiation exceeds the outgoing. At about 39° latitude the two values are balanced, whereas at higher latitudes the outgo exceeds the input.

If there were no other process operating on the earth, the equatorial belt would get increasingly hotter and that part of the earth poleward from 39° latitude would get increasingly colder. What keeps this from happening is the transfer of energy from the equatorial regions to the poles by motion of the atmosphere and the oceans. Circulation of the oceans and the global winds in fact results from this unequal heating of the earth.

One of the reasons the atmosphere is able to transport large amounts of heat poleward is the high heat of condensation of water vapor (540 calories per gram). Much of the thermal energy used to evaporate water from sea and land is released to the atmosphere when the vapor condenses, and the global winds tend to shift the point of release toward the polar regions. The oceans also are good carriers of heat energy because of the high specific heat of water. Recall that it takes 1 calorie to raise the temperature of 1 gram of water 1°C. A similar amount of heat energy is released during cooling. Thus north- or south-trending oceans. Circulation of the oceans and the global winds in fact results from this unequal heating of the earth.

It should be clear that the sun is the ultimate source of energy for the gradational processes discussed in Chap. 6. Solar energy drives the hydrologic cycle and the major circulation patterns of the surface of our planet. Each year the sun's incoming radiation evaporates some 440,000 cubic kilometers of water from the surface of our planet, and this amount falls back as rain, dew, or snow. A portion of the precipitation falling on the land goes into rivers, which pick up clay and sand and gouge mighty canyons on their way back to the sea.

7-4 WHAT IS THE SOURCE OF THE SUN'S ENERGY?

The sun is about 93 million miles (1.5×10^8 kilometers) from the earth, a distance which is minute compared to that of the next nearest star, Alpha Centauri. That star is so far away that light from it travels for 4.3 years to reach the earth. Since the speed of light is about 3×10^5 kilometers per second, it only takes about 8 minutes for light to travel the distance between the earth and sun. The sun is the only star whose surface can be seen; all other stars appear merely as points of light in even the most powerful telescope. Yet 93 million miles is by ordinary human standards an almost inconceivable distance, and one may well wonder how scientists have been able to pin down the source of the sun's energy.

The solution of the problem took many centuries and was achieved only through the growing interrelationship of the sciences. In the earliest days of

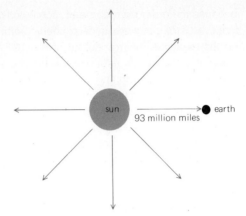

FIGURE 7-13
The sun's radiation measured on the earth amounts to 2 cal/(cm²)(min). Because the sun radiates energy in every direction, its total rate of energy output in calories per minute must be twice the number of square centimeters in a sphere of radius 93 million miles.

science, when men thought of four elements, earth, air, fire, and water, the answer must have seemed obvious. Although they did not know much about combustion or the relationship of heat and energy, men knew that they were warmed by fire and experienced the same warming from the rays of the sun.

As the physical sciences developed in the eighteenth and nineteenth centuries, this naïve explanation had to be discarded. Fire was no longer a mystery but was identified as a rapid chemical reaction between various substances and the oxygen of the air. The concept of heat as a form of energy evolved from experiments. Units of measurement were established for the various forms of energy. The discovery of the spectroscope provided a means of determining chemical composition at a distance. The behavior of materials and, in particular, the relationship between the pressure, volume, and absolute temperature of gases became known. Chemical analyses of earth materials and meteorites provided information on the average composition of the earth. Techniques for measuring the distance from the earth to the sun were developed.

All these advances in physics, chemistry, astronomy, and geology combined to make it clear that the sun is not a burning globe. The sun, we can be sure, radiates equally in all directions; hence every square centimeter of the giant spherical surface of Fig. 7-13 receives the same amount of energy per unit time, namely 2 calories. Since the area of the sphere is

$$4\pi r^2 = 4\pi(1.5 \times 10^{13}\,\text{cm})^2 = 3 \times 10^{27}\,\text{cm}^2$$

the total energy output of the sun is

$$(3 \times 10^{27}\,\text{cm}^2)[2\,\text{cal/(cm}^2)(\text{min})] = 6 \times 10^{27}\,\text{cal/min}$$

What does this large number signify? In a textbook on the sun, written in 1881, C. A. Young, then professor of astronomy at Princeton University, stressed that the sun must have emitted energy at a uniform rate throughout human history because there are no records of momentous climatic change. He then showed that even if the sun were made of solid coal burning in pure oxygen, it could keep up the measured energy output of 6×10^{27} calories per minute for only 6,000 years at most. At this rate, one-third of the sun's mass should have been consumed since the beginning of the Christian era! Clearly mere combustion cannot be the source of the sun's energy.

At the turn of the twentieth century, most investigators attributed the sun's energy output to contraction. When a gas is compressed, its temperature rises. Calculations showed that the sun could generate the observed amount of energy by contracting about 100 yards per year. The sun is a very large body, and a contraction of 100 yards per year would produce no noticeable effects over hundreds or even thousands of years. There should, however, have been marked changes in solar radiation over periods of millions or hundreds of millions of years if the sun's energy were derived from contraction. Today we know that the sun has been shining with about its present strength for about 3 billion years at least because sedimentary rocks of that age tell us that the earth's surface temperature then was about the same as now (see Sec. 7-3). Thus we can make the following calculation:

$$\text{Present rate of energy output} = 6 \times 10^{27} \text{ cal/min}$$

$$\text{Time} = 3 \text{ billion years} = 15 \times 10^{14} \text{ min}$$

$$\text{Total output over 3 billion years} = (6 \times 10^{27})(15 \times 10^{14}) = 7 \times 10^{42} \text{ cal}$$

$$\text{Mass of sun} = 2 \times 10^{33} \text{ g}$$

$$\text{Energy output per gram of sun's mass} = 4.5 \times 10^{9} \text{ cal/g}$$

Each gram of matter in the sun has contributed 4.5 billion calories of energy during the past 3 billion years. The contraction theory must then go out the window, like the combustion theory. Even if the sun had contracted all the way from the orbit of Pluto during the last 3 billion years, this would only account for a mere 1 percent of its calculated energy output. The only process known to produce such large amounts of energy per unit mass are the nuclear processes, involving the conversion of mass into energy. The source of the sun's energy must be nuclear energy.

7-5 THE SURFACE OF THE SUN

We all know from experience that it is uncomfortable even to glance at the sun when it is high in the sky. To look at the sun with an unprotected light-gathering tool such as a telescope or a pair of binoculars is extremely dangerous even during an eclipse. The sun can be examined telescopically, however, by using a dark filter or by projecting its image on a white screen. Its image can also be recorded on photographic plates.

FIGURE 7-14
The sun's corona during an eclipse. *Hale Observatories.*

Telescopic studies show that the main body of the sun is opaque. The visible surface of the sun is called the *photosphere*. During an eclipse it can be seen that the photosphere is surrounded by a solar atmosphere (Fig. 7-14). The inner part of the solar atmosphere, called the *chromosphere*, is only a few thousand kilometers thick. The outer envelope is the *corona*, a very tenuous layer extending for more than a million miles beyond the photosphere.

The sun's surface is very active. Its mottled or grainy appearance (Fig. 7-15) is due to many granules and faculae, huge changing eddies in the photosphere. Superimposed on the granules are dark sunspots, which may last for a few days or weeks. The sunspots can be used to demonstrate the rotation of the sun because they move from day to day. The number of sunspots varies from year to

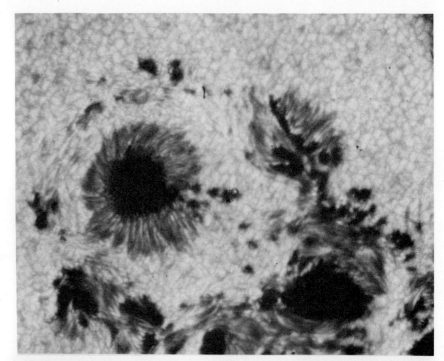

FIGURE 7-15
Sunspots (dark) and the granular nature of the sun are clearly visible in this short-exposure photograph. *Project Stratoscope of Princeton University, sponsored by the Office of Naval Research, the National Science Foundation, and the National Aeronautics and Space Administration.*

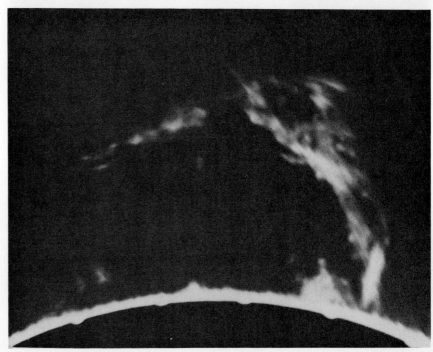

FIGURE 7-16
A solar prominence photographed during a total eclipse. It is about 205,000 miles high, which is 25 times the earth's diameter. *Hale Observatories.*

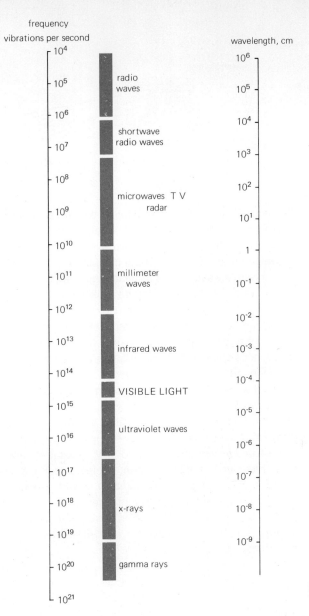

frequency
vibrations per second

wavelength, cm

frequency (vibrations per second)		wavelength, cm
10^4	radio waves	10^6
10^5		10^5
10^6	shortwave radio waves	10^4
10^7		10^3
10^8	microwaves T V radar	10^2
10^9		10^1
10^{10}		1
10^{11}	millimeter waves	10^{-1}
10^{12}		10^{-2}
10^{13}	infrared waves	10^{-3}
10^{14}		10^{-4}
10^{15}	VISIBLE LIGHT	10^{-5}
10^{16}	ultraviolet waves	10^{-6}
10^{17}		10^{-7}
10^{18}	x-rays	10^{-8}
10^{19}		10^{-9}
10^{20}	gamma rays	
10^{21}		

FIGURE 7-17
The electromagnetic spectrum.

year, reaching a maximum every 11 years. Large tongues of hot gas, called *prominences*, (Fig. 7-16) are frequently observed in the chromosphere.

What else can we learn about the sun from our position on earth? Much of our knowledge about the sun comes from spectroscopic studies. Radiation from the sun or from any hot body is electromagnetic energy. We divide the electromagnetic spectrum into classes on the basis of wavelength (Fig. 7-17). At one extreme are high-energy gamma rays and x-rays, which have very short wavelengths, while at the other end are low-energy radio waves with long wave-

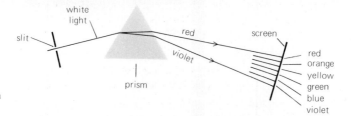

FIGURE 7-18
The refraction of white light by a prism produces a spectrum.

lengths. There is no upper limit to the wavelength, nor are there any natural boundaries between the classes of electromagnetic radiation.

Visible light forms only a narrow band of the electromagnetic spectrum, its wavelength ranging from about 0.00007 to about 0.000035 centimeter. The different visible wavelengths represent different colors of light. White light, which is a mixture of wavelengths, can be broken up into its constituent colors by refraction (Fig. 7-18). A spectroscope uses a prism or a diffraction grating to separate incoming radiation into its constituent wavelengths.

There are three principal types of spectra. When radiation from molten metal, a luminous solid, or an opaque gas is passed through a spectroscope, the spectrum formed is a *continuous spectrum*, like a rainbow. Such sources apparently emit all wavelengths, to form a continuous band of light of various colors. In the other two types only separated wavelengths, or *lines*, occur. When light from a rarefied gas excited by an electric discharge, as in a neon lamp, is passed through a spectroscope, the spectrum is a series of bright lines. Such *emission-line spectra* are produced only by excited gases or vapors, and the lines are characteristic of the element or elements in the gas. When light from an incandescent source which normally would produce a continuous spectrum passes through a cool gas before entering the spectroscope, a *dark-line*, or *absorption, spectrum* is formed. In absorption spectra the dark lines are identical in wavelength to the emission lines that would be produced by the gas through which the light is passed.

When visible light from the sun is passed through a narrow slit system into a spectrograph, the resulting spectrum is a continuous array of color from red to violet interrupted by a series of dark lines. These dark absorption lines in the solar spectrum are called *Fraunhofer lines*, after their discoverer. At the photosphere the hot incandescent sun produces the continuous spectrum. The dark lines are the result of absorption by the cooler gases of the sun's atmosphere. An expert can identify the elements and compounds that produce the dark lines in the solar spectrum.

To date some 60 elements have been detected in the solar spectrum. The element helium, in fact, was discovered in the sun before it was isolated on earth. It is important to emphasize that spectral studies do not tell us what the main body of the sun is made of. The absorption lines indicate merely the composition of the solar atmosphere, which represents only a fraction of 1 per cent of the sun's mass. The continuous spectrum of the photosphere, however, does permit scientists to measure its temperature. We know that a yellow glow in the filament of a light bulb indicates a higher temperature than a reddish glow. Laboratory studies have shown that the wavelength (color) of maximum intensity emitted by a radiating body is related to its absolute temperature. The relation between the absolute temperature T and the wavelength of maximum energy λ_{max} in centimeters is expressed by Wien's law: $T = 0.290/\lambda_{max}$. When the wavelength of maximum intensity received from the sun is substituted in Wien's equation, we find a temperature of about 6000 K for the sun's surface.

Laboratory experiments have also shown that the total energy emitted per unit area of a radiating body in a unit of time is proportional to the fourth power of its absolute temperature, a relation known as the *Stefan-Boltzmann law*. Doubling the temperature of a radiator results in a sixteenfold (2^4) increase in energy output. In equation form the Stefan-Boltzmann law states that $E = 5.67 \times 10^{-5} T^4$, where E is the total energy flow in ergs per square centimeter per second and T is the temperature in kelvins. Since the sun's energy output is known, its surface temperature can be calculated by this law. Again the temperature turns out to be about 6000 K.

7-6   WHAT IS INSIDE THE SUN?

In Chap. 5 we discussed the methods used to construct a conceptual model of the interior of the earth. It is often said that more is known about the interior of the sun than about the earth's interior. This is true because the sun is almost entirely gaseous and gas behavior is much more simple than that of liquids or solids. The sun must be gaseous because of its high temperature. Most materials are volatilized at 6000 K, the temperature of the sun's exterior. Inside the sun temperatures must be even higher, reaching millions of degrees.

Much of the early work on the sun's interior was done by Sir Arthur Eddington, a famous English scientist. The sun is so much larger than the earth that the pressure in its interior must be 100,000 times greater than the pressure at the earth's center. How can any material withstand such tremendous pressure? Why doesn't the sun collapse? The only reasonable answer to these questions is that the interior of the sun is very hot. At any point within the sun the weight of the overlying layers must be balanced by the outward radiation and the pressure of hot gases. Calculations show that the temperature inside the sun must be around 15 million degrees Celsius to prevent collapse.

In Sec. 7-4 we showed that contraction cannot possibly account for the continuous energy output of the sun over several billion years. We are now saying that if a large volume of gas equal in mass to the sun were to contract to the sun's size, its interior temperature would have to be 15 million degrees Celsius. Contraction

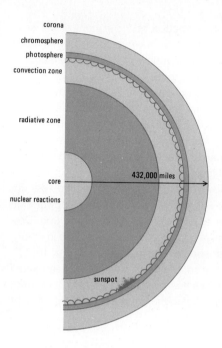

corona
chromosphere
photosphere
convection zone

radiative zone

core

nuclear reactions

432,000 miles

sunspot

FIGURE 7-19
The sun's internal structure. The corona may extend more than a million kilometers from the sun.

during the early stages of the sun's history provided the temperature inside the sun needed to trigger the nuclear reactions.

In his early calculations Eddington assumed that the sun was composed chiefly of iron and other heavy elements. This assumption led to a model sun that radiated many times the energy of the actual sun. Spectral studies had shown the sun's atmosphere to consist chiefly of hydrogen and helium. Perhaps these elements were also the chief constituents of the main body of the sun. About 1930 new calculations based on a model sun with over 90 percent hydrogen and helium gave values for temperature, density, and energy output that agreed well with measurements of these variables in the real sun. Figure 7-19 is a schematic diagram of the sun's interior. The predicted temperatures in the sun's interior are high enough to promote nuclear fusion. This is the sort of reaction that takes place in a hydrogen bomb, where light hydrogen nuclei fuse together to form heavier helium nuclei. In the process a small amount of mass is lost, i.e., converted into energy according to the relation $E = mc^2$. Only about 0.007 gram of mass disappears during the conversion of 1 gram of hydrogen to helium, but the amount of energy created is enormous—quite enough to account for the output of the sun as calculated in Sec. 7-4 (4.5×10^9 calories per gram).

The conversion of hydrogen into helium is thus the most logical explanation for the sun's continuing energy output. This reaction is known to occur in two ways. The first and probably most significant reaction in our sun is between hydrogen nuclei, or protons, in the sun's core:

The proton-proton cycle:

$^1H + {}^1H \rightarrow {}^2H$ + energy

$^2H + {}^1H \rightarrow {}^3He$ + energy

$^3He + {}^3He \rightarrow {}^4He + 2{}^1H$ + energy

In this reaction four protons with a total mass of 4.0304 ultimately unite to form one helium nucleus with a mass of 4.0027. The formation of each helium nucleus thus involves the loss of 0.0277 mass unit. Hydrogen can also be converted to helium by nuclear reactions that involve heavier elements.

The carbon cycle:

$^{12}C + {}^1H \rightarrow {}^{13}N$ + energy

$^{13}N \rightarrow {}^{13}C$ + energy

$^{13}C + {}^1H \rightarrow {}^{14}N$ + energy

$^{14}N + {}^1H \rightarrow {}^{15}O$ + energy

$^{15}O \rightarrow {}^{15}N$ + energy

$^{15}N + {}^1H \rightarrow {}^{12}C + {}^4He$ + energy

The carbon cycle requires higher temperatures for its initiation than the proton-proton reaction and it is not believed to be as important in the sun as in larger and hotter stars. Although there are more steps in the carbon cycle, basically it still involves the conversion of hydrogen into helium with the loss of 0.0277 mass unit for each four protons. Since the reaction begins and ends with ^{12}C, carbon acts as a catalyst in the conversion of hydrogen to helium.

How much hydrogen must be converted to helium in order to account for the sun's energy output? The sun radiates 3.86×10^{33} ergs of energy per second. To find the amount of matter that must be converted to energy each second we can substitute the following known values in Einstein's equation:

$$E = mc^2 \quad \text{or} \quad m = \frac{E}{c^2}$$

$E = 3.86 \times 10^{33}$ ergs

$c = 3 \times 10^{10}$ cm/s

$$m = \frac{3.86 \times 10^{33}}{(3 \times 10^{10})^2} = 4.3 \times 10^{12} \text{ g}$$

This is over 4 million tons of matter converted to energy each second. Since only 0.0071 gram of mass is lost for each gram of hydrogen that is changed to helium, this means that about 600 million tons of hydrogen must be converted to helium each second.

At this rate will the sun soon use up all its hydrogen and lose its energy-producing capacity? The answer to this question is a definite *no*. The sun has a mass of 2×10^{33} grams, most of which is hydrogen. This is a lot of matter. Even if only half the 2×10^{33} grams were hydrogen, this would still be enough to keep the sun going for about 50 billion years. Actually, astrophysicists do not predict a life of 50 billion years for our sun. Only the hydrogen in the very hot core can be converted to helium. This may be sufficiently used up in another 5 to 10 billion years to bring about changes in the sun that will mark its end as a desirable source of warmth for the earth. It is predicted that the sun then will expand to engulf the inner planets.

7-7 ENERGY FROM INSIDE THE EARTH

Next to the 2 calories per square centimeter per minute arriving from the sun, the amount of heat generated within the earth and traveling outward seems very small: it amounts to about 10^{-6} calorie per square centimeter per second. But the fact that heat is traveling outward is most significant. It means that the sun's heat cannot possibly be traveling inward and that the great earth processes of vulcanism and diastrophism must be powered by energy from inside the earth.

When we estimate the total amount of heat energy that has flowed spaceward during the past billion years or so, it becomes clear that ordinary chemical reactions, such as burning, cannot possibly be the source. Once more, nuclear mass-energy conversions must be responsible. The earth's internal energy, however, cannot be due to nuclear *fusion*. Even the most optimistic estimates show the temperature of the earth's interior to be a few thousands of degrees rather than the millions of degrees required to promote the conversion of hydrogen into helium. Besides, hydrogen is only a very minor constituent of the earth.

The rocks of the earth's crust are known to contain minute amounts of radioactive isotopes such as uranium, thorium, and potassium 40. These isotopes are unstable and decay continuously, changing into stable daughter products with a slight loss of mass and a consequent generation of energy. Uranium, for example, decays through a series of steps to lead, or it may split into two lighter

TABLE 7-1
Radioactivity and heat
generation in crustal rocks

Rock	Concentration of radioactive isotopes, grams per gram of rock			Heat production, calories per gram of rock per second			
	Uranium	Thorium	Potassium 40	Uranium	Thorium	Potassium 40	Total
Granitic	400×10^{-8}	13×10^{-6}	3.5×10^{-2}	9.2×10^{-14}	8.2×10^{-14}	3×10^{-14}	20.4×10^{-14}
Basaltic	100×10^{-8}	3×10^{-8}	1.3×10^{-2}	2.3×10^{-14}	1.9×10^{-14}	1.1×10^{-14}	5.3×10^{-14}

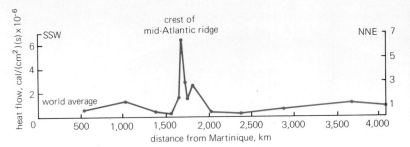

FIGURE 7-20

Heat-flow measurements made across the Atlantic from Martinique to the Canary Islands show that the highest values cluster along the ridge axis. What accounts for this distribution? *Data from R. D. Nason and W. H. K. Lee, Nature, vol. 196, 1962. After A. Holmes, "Principles of Physical Geology," The Ronald Press, New York, 1965.*

nuclei (nuclear fission). Table 7-1 shows the average amounts of radioactive elements in the granitic rocks of the continents and in the basaltic rocks of the ocean basins.

The heat generated by the decay of uranium, thorium, and radioactive potassium is more than enough to account for the earth's heat flow. In fact if we assumed that the material deep inside the earth contains the same concentration of these isotopes as surface materials do (Table 7-1), the total heat generation per square centimeter of surface would far exceed the observed heat flow, so that the material inside the earth would be getting steadily warmer. If such a situation had persisted for a few million or hundreds of million years, the earth would now be molten. We must conclude that the interior contains less radioactive material than the surface.

Each year heat energy flowing from the earth exceeds the estimated total energy involved in earthquakes, vulcanism, and earth movement. There is no question, then, of an adequate energy source for these processes, but we should inquire about the global distribution of the heat flow, for we know from Chap. 5 that earth movements and volcanic activity are largely confined to certain zones.

Many measurements of heat flow have been made in mines and boreholes throughout the world. The data for heat flow from the ocean basins are sketchier but sufficient to demonstrate that, as on the continents, heat flow is not uniform everywhere. Some areas clearly are hot spots, whereas others are cooler than normal. Figure 7-20, for example, summarizes measurements of heat flow made over the mid-Atlantic ridge. As one might expect, this belt of vulcanism and earthquake activity is also a region of exceptionally high heat flow.

There is no evidence that the heat-producing radioactive elements are, on a large scale, unevenly distributed over the earth. The reason for the uneven heat flow must therefore be sought in the flow mechanism itself. Heat energy can be transferred in any of three ways. The sun's energy comes to the earth as *radiation*, which is how energy is transferred through a vacuum or dilute gas. Heat can also be transferred by *conduction* (as anyone knows who has been burned by a spoon half immersed in boiling water). Most materials of the earth are poor heat conductors, and there is no reason to believe that good conductors capable of concentrating heat from the interior are hidden in the mantle or crust.

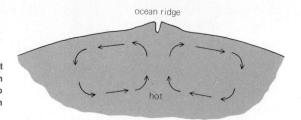

ocean ridge

hot

FIGURE 7-21
The higher than normal heat flow associated with the ocean ridge systems is believed to reflect convection currents in the earth's mantle.

The third method of heat transfer is *convection*, which involves actual physical movement of material from warm to cooler regions. There are strong reasons to believe that convective flow is going on in the mantle of the earth. Although the materials of the mantle are solid, they are hot and compressed and hence deform by flowage rather than fracture. Flow rates of a few centimeters or tens of centimeters per year are possible in such material. The high heat flow of the mid-ocean ridges is believed to be due to convection currents in the mantle (Fig. 7-21). Such currents provide the mechanism for spreading the ocean basins apart at the ridges, dissussed further in Chap. 16.

SUMMARY

Work is measured in units of force times distance. Work is done on an object when it is moved through some distance by a force. Energy is the ability to do work.

Tremendous amounts of work are involved in the great earth cycles. The sun is the major source of energy for the surface processes on earth. It drives the hydrologic cycle, provides the energy for all plant and animal life, and through irregular distribution of its energy, accounts for the global circulation of the atmosphere and the oceans.

The sun delivers 2 calories of radiant energy per square centimeter per minute at the earth's distance. Some of this radiant energy is immediately reflected back to space, and some is temporarily absorbed by the materials of the earth, which in turn radiate heat energy spaceward. On the average, the amount of incoming

solar energy must be balanced by the energy outgo or the earth would be getting warmer or cooler.

An evaluation of the total energy radiated by the sun during the last 3 billion years shows that only nuclear processes are sufficiently powerful to account for this tremendous energy source. Temperatures in the sun's interior are of the order of 15 million degrees Celsius. At such temperatures and at the very high pressures that exist inside the sun, hydrogen is converted into helium by nuclear fusion. During this change from hydrogen into helium small amounts of mass are converted into energy according to Einstein's equation, $E = mc^2$.

The sun is composed mainly of the elements hydrogen and helium. Although some 600 million tons of hydrogen must be converted into helium each second to account for its energy output, there is an ample

supply to keep the sun shining for many more billion years.

Energy for the earth's internal processes of vulcanism and diastrophism comes from inside the earth. The decay of radioactive elements like uranium, thorium, and potassium 40 adds new heat energy to the interior of the earth each year. This thermal energy flows to the surface of the earth and provides the power for the internal earth processes.

QUESTIONS

1 What is the difference between heat and temperature?
2 When a pan of water is heated to boiling, further addition of heat produces no temperature change. What happens to the heat energy transmitted to the boiling water?

3 Why is the sun not considered a possible source of energy for the processes that operate inside the earth?

4 The volume of a gas at 1 atmosphere pressure is 5 liters. What will its volume be if the pressure is reduced to $\frac{1}{2}$ atmosphere with no change in temperature?

5 What is meant by specific heat?

6 Why do we conclude that the energy input and output for the earth must balance?

7 How do we know that the sun's energy cannot be due to burning?

8 How has the sun's surface temperature been determined?

9 How do we know that energy is flowing outward from the earth's interior?

10 How is heat energy transferred from one place to another?

11 How has the composition of the sun been determined?

12 How do we know that the sun has been shining at about its present rate for at least 3 billion years?

13 Where does the heat flowing outward from the interior of the earth come from?

14 Table 7-1 shows the average heat production due to radioactive decay in granite to be 20×10^{-14} calorie per gram of rock per second. The specific heat of granite is 0.19 kilocalorie. How long would it take for a buried 10^{10} kilogram mass of granite to rise in temperature by 100°C if no heat were allowed to escape?

REFERENCES

Abel, George: "Exploration of the Universe," Holt, Rinehart and Winston, Inc., New York, 1969.

Brandt, John C.: "The Physics and Astronomy of the Sun and Stars," McGraw-Hill Book Company, New York, 1966.

Jacobs, J. A., R. D. Russell, and J. T. Wilson: "Physics and Geology," McGraw-Hill Book Company, New York, 1959.

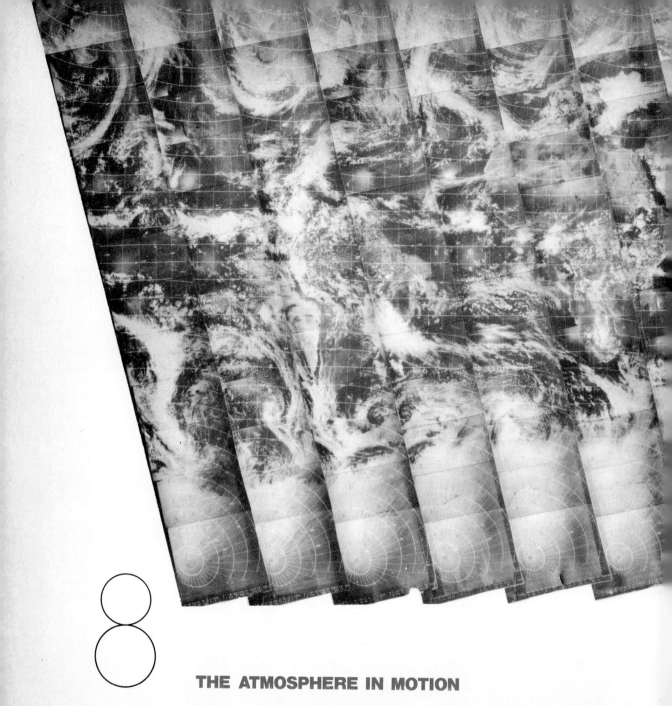

THE ATMOSPHERE IN MOTION

As St. John wrote "the wind bloweth where it listeth." If we had to rely on our own experience at one place, we would not be able to learn much more about the motion of the air. It is only by keeping continuous records of wind direction, velocity, temperature, pressure, and cloud cover at many places that man was led to discover the major patterns of atmospheric movement. Our knowledge expanded greatly when it became possible to observe large sections of the earth from ar-

FIGURE 8-1
World cloud cover as seen by ESSA-3 satellite over a 24-hour period. Note the spiral patterns of many cloud formations. *NASA.*

tificial satellites. Patterns of clouds like those shown in Fig. 8-1 trace large-scale motions in the atmosphere. The photograph clearly shows spirals in the cloud pattern. Such spirals, measuring hundreds of kilometers in diameter, are common in photographs taken from space, just as small eddies, sometimes called dust devils, are often seen in a dusty street or dry field.

In this chapter we investigate some questions of atmospheric motion. What keeps the atmosphere continuously moving? Why are spiral patterns so common? Is there also an up-and-down motion of air? How is atmospheric motion related to the heat balance of the earth?

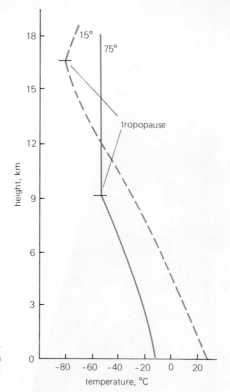

FIGURE 8-2
Average temperature distribution in the atmosphere with height in the Northern Hemisphere at 15° and 75° latitude.

8-1 THE VERTICAL STRUCTURE OF THE ATMOSPHERE

The general composition of the atmosphere was discussed in Chap. 4. Dry air consists chiefly of nitrogen (75.53 percent by weight), oxygen (23.14 percent), and argon (1.28 percent), with very minor amounts of carbon dioxide, neon, helium, methane, and other gases. Air also contains variable amounts of water vapor, usually from 0.1 to 1 percent but occasionally reaching as high as 4 percent. The overall chemical composition of air is remarkably uniform over the globe, as one would expect for an envelope of gas that mixes very rapidly.

The properties of air depend on its altitude. Anyone who has climbed a mountain or driven over a high mountain pass knows that the air becomes thinner with height. In fact at elevations of over 10,000 feet above sea level breathing becomes difficult for most people, and at 15,000 feet supplemental oxygen is needed for survival. Air temperature generally drops with increasing height, which explains why snow remains the year around on some high mountains. During the last century most scientists thought that the temperature of the air would continue to decrease to the outer limits of the atmosphere. Measurements made with high-altitude balloons early in this century proved otherwise. Figure 8-2

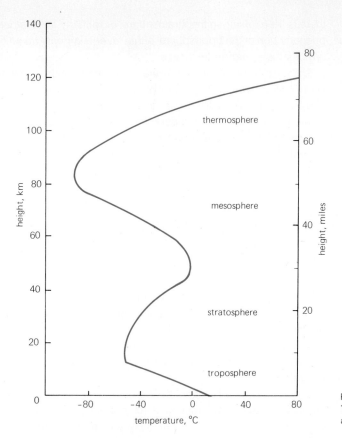

FIGURE 8-3
The four principal layers of the atmosphere.

shows the average atmosphere temperature distribution with height at 15° and 75° N latitude.

More recent measurements at even greater altitudes reveal several inversions of temperature with height. On the basis of such findings the atmosphere is subdivided into four principal vertical zones (Fig. 8-3). In the lowermost zone, the *troposphere*, temperature decreases with height. This temperature gradient promotes mixing, or overturning, and hence the name *tropos* from the Greek meaning "turn." The troposphere is a mixing layer.

The *tropopause*, or point at which the temperature ceases to decrease upward, marks the boundary between the troposphere and the next layer, known as the *stratosphere*. Temperature in the stratosphere is almost constant or increases slightly with height. Air in this layer has much less tendency to mix; instead it tends to stay in layers and hence the term *stratos*, or layered. The air of the stratosphere is also far less dense than that of the lower level. More than three-fourths of the mass of the atmosphere in middle latitudes and more than 90 percent in the tropics lies in the troposphere, i.e., below the stratosphere. Since there is little mixing in the stratosphere, essentially all weather as we know it is a phenomenon of the troposphere, a thin layer of air only about one-thousandth the radius of the earth in thickness.

Upward in the stratosphere the mean temperature rises somewhat until the *stratopause*, which marks the base of the next layer, the *mesosphere*. In the mesophere temperature again falls with increasing height to the *mesopause*, where there is a further temperature reversal. The uppermost thermal zone, the *thermosphere*, gradually fades into outer space. Table 8-1 summarizes how averaged atmospheric properties change with height. From the data it can be calculated that 99 percent of the total mass of the atmosphere lies below an altitude of 33 kilometers.

8-2 HEATING AND COOLING OF THE ATMOSPHERE

We noted in Chap. 7 that the global circulation of air is caused by the differential heating of the atmosphere. As long as 2,000 years ago Aristotle recognized that the winds must somehow be due to the rising of air warmed by the sun. Heated air tends to rise because it is less dense than the surrounding cooler air. The observed circulation of air in the troposphere tells us that this sphere must be heated mainly at the bottom. Heating a column of air at the top would not produce mixing or overturning, nor would uniform heating result in circulation. Before we explore the question of global circulation, therefore, we must first see how the air is heated.

The atmosphere is fairly transparent to shortwave solar radiation. Figure 8-4 traces the average distribution of solar radiation as it passes through the earth's atmosphere. About 9 percent of the radiation returns to space by scattering and diffuse reflection in the upper atmosphere. Most of the scattering involves blue light, and it is this light that is reflected back to our eyes, making the sky seem blue. Only about 10 percent of the sun's radiation is normally absorbed by the atmosphere, but absorption may be much higher where there are clouds. About

TABLE 8-1
Variations in atmospheric
properties with altitude

Altitude, km	Temperature, K	Density, g/cm³
0	288	1.2×10^{-3}
10	225	4.1×10^{-4}
20	217	8.9×10^{-5}
30	231	1.8×10^{-5}
40	261	4.0×10^{-6}
50	283	1.1×10^{-6}
60	245	3.7×10^{-7}
70	173	9.4×10^{-8}
80	168	1.4×10^{-8}
90	176	1.9×10^{-9}
100	208	2.8×10^{-10}
140	662	4.7×10^{-12}
180	1115	1.5×10^{-12}

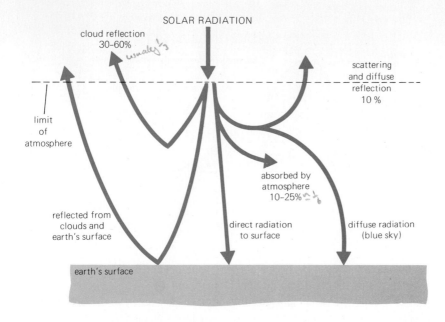

SOLAR RADIATION

cloud reflection
30-60%

scattering
and diffuse
reflection
10 %

limit
of
atmosphere

absorbed by
atmosphere
10-25%

reflected from
clouds and
earth's surface

direct radiation
to surface

diffuse radiation
(blue sky)

earth's surface

FIGURE 8-4
Distribution of the sun's radiant energy as it reaches the earth. The amount of scattering, reflection, and absorption depends also upon the angle the sun's rays make with the atmosphere.

half of the solar radiation on the average passes through the atmosphere to be absorbed by the land or sea surface. On a clear and cloudless day, however, as much as 80 percent of the sun's radiation reaches the surface. Direct absorption cannot be the major cause of atmospheric heating, and it certainly cannot be the cause of the circulation. This absorption, and the accompanying heating, takes place throughout the atmosphere and not at the bottom. Because most of the sun's radiation reaches the earth's surface, it appears that the atmosphere must receive much of its heat by conduction or radiation from the surface of land and sea.

We have seen that about half of the sun's radiant energy normally reaches the earth's surface, there to warm the lands and waters. It is clear that there must also be a way for this energy to escape to space; otherwise the waters would eventually boil and the rocks would melt. We saw in Chap. 7 that the earth does indeed radiate heat energy into space. The amount of outgoing energy over any extended period must equal that coming in from the sun plus the minor contribution from the earth's interior. Were this not so, the surface would either get warmer or cooler.

Whereas the sun radiates most intensely at the wavelength of visible light (0.5 micrometer), the cooler earth radiates at much longer wavelengths (average 10 micrometers). Although the atmosphere is relatively transparent to solar radiation, this is not true of the longer-wavelength earth radiation, as we can see from Fig. 8-5. In fact, only about 20 percent of the heat radiated outward from the earth's surface escapes to space. The remaining 80 percent is absorbed or scat-

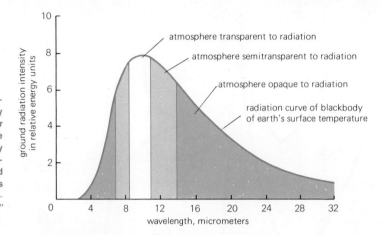

FIGURE 8-5
The spectrum of ground radiation. The earth radiates energy with wavelengths from 4 to over 30 micrometers. Because the atmosphere transmits energy only in the range of 8 to 12 micrometers, much of the ground radiation is absorbed, thus heating the air. *After J. C. Johnson, "Physical Meteorology," M.I.T. Press, 1954.*

tered back to the earth by the atmosphere. Much of this action takes place in the lower atmosphere, providing an effective method for heating the air.

It is chiefly the small but variable amounts of water vapor and the trace amounts of carbon dioxide in the atmosphere that make it opaque to ground radiation. These constituents are said to exert a *greenhouse effect* on the earth's temperature because, like the glass in a greenhouse, they allow the sun's rays to pass but prevent the long waves radiated within from passing outward. Estimates suggest that the earth's temperature would be some 50° F colder than it is now if it were not for the greenhouse effect.

Still another method of adding heat to the air is the condensation of water vapor. It takes 540 calories of heat energy to change 1 gram of water to steam. When the steam condenses to water droplets, an equal amount of heat energy is liberated. Water evaporated from the seas and lands condenses in the atmosphere to fall back as rain or snow. More than half the heat energy of the atmosphere is believed to be contributed by condensation of water vapor.

TABLE 8-2
Annual means of incoming solar radiation and outgoing earth radiation for the Northern Hemisphere*

Latitude	Incoming radiation absorbed, g cal/(cm³)(min)	Outgoing radiation lost, g cal/(cm³)(min)	Difference
0°	0.339	0.271	+0.068
10°	0.334	0.282	+0.052
20°	0.320	0.284	+0.036
30°	0.297	0.284	+0.013
40°	0.267	0.282	−0.015
50°	0.232	0.277	−0.045
60°	0.193	0.272	−0.079
70°	0.160	0.260	−0.100
80°	0.144	0.252	−0.108
90°	0.140	0.252	−0.112

*From G. T. Trewartha "An Introduction to Climate," 4th ed. Copyright © 1968 by McGraw-Hill, Inc. Used with permission of McGraw-Hill Book Company.

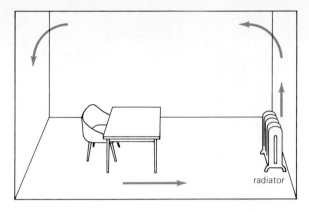

FIGURE 8-6
A hot radiator in a room sets up a convective circulation of air.

We can see from this discussion that the atmosphere is heated by the sun, but mostly indirectly. The sun's radiant energy warms the earth's surface, which in turn—through evaporation and condensation, longwave radiation, or direct conduction—adds heat to the lower atmosphere. In earlier chapters we have already touched on the main factors which produce an uneven distribution of solar energy over the earth's surface. Table 8-2 shows measurements of this unequal global heating. Between the equator and about 40° latitude the incoming solar radiation is greater than the outgoing earth radiation, whereas at higher latitudes the reverse is true. Clearly, there must be some process for transferring heat energy from the equatorial regions to the poles. This transfer is effected by motion and mixing in the atmosphere and hydrosphere.

8-3 THERMAL CONVECTION AND GLOBAL CIRCULATION

The retention in the tropics of more solar heat than in polar regions causes the large-scale atmospheric motions. Warm air is less dense than cold air. Like the air in a room with a radiator at one end (Fig. 8-6), the surface air in the overheated tropical belt rises, to be replaced laterally by cooler polar air. This type of circulation, convection, is an effective means of mixing air masses of different temperatures.

FIGURE 8-7
If the analogy with a room radiator held precisely, the atmospheric circulation pattern would look like this.

If the analogy with room heating were exact, we could expect a global circulation pattern like that in Fig. 8-7. The prevailing winds in the Northern Hemisphere should be southward (northerly winds). This, as we know, is not the actual observed wind direction. Although locally the winds vary in direction from hour to hour, years of records show that in the belt from the equator to about 30°N latitude the prevailing winds are from the east. From about 30° to 60°N latitude winds characteristically blow from the west. Clearly, something is very wrong with the simplified circulation model of Fig. 8-6.

An important fact not considered in our analogy with simple convection in a room is that the earth is turning. During the mid-eighteenth century an English-

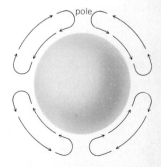

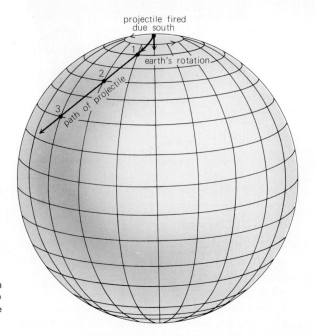

FIGURE 8-8
A projectile fired due south from the North Pole will appear to veer to the right because of the motion of the earth beneath it.

man, George Hadley, took this into account and reasoned that the westward direction of the tropical trade winds must be the result of the eastward turn of the earth. The effect of the earth's spin on winds, ocean currents, projectiles, or any moving object was given a refined description by the French mathematician G. G. Coriolis during the nineteenth century. This effect is now known as the *Coriolis force*, although it is not a force at all but simply a matter of a rotating reference system.

Consider a projectile shot southward along a meridian from the North Pole (Fig. 8-8). We recall that a point on the equator is moving east at about 1,000 miles per hour whereas a point at the pole has no such eastward motion. As the imaginary projectile moves southward, it will not stay on the meridian but because of the motion of the earth beneath, the projectile will progressively appear over points 2, 3, and so forth. To an observer on earth, the projectile will be turning to the right; it will seem as though some force is pushing the projectile westward. We can recognize that no such force operates but that the curving path traced by the projectile in Fig. 8-8 is due to the rotation of the earth.

The same sort of deflection to the right is observed in a parcel of air or other object moving north from the equator. At the equator all objects have an eastward speed of about 1,000 miles per hour. As an air mass starts northward along a meridian, it retains the eastward speed of its point of origin whereas points on the ground beneath have progressively slower eastward speeds. The moving parcel of air thus outruns points on the ground with a slower eastward turn, and the effect again is a turn to the right, as observed on earth.

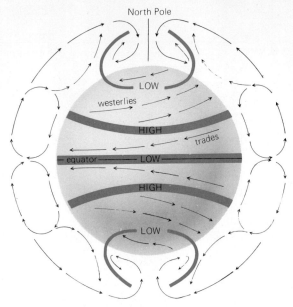

FIGURE 8-9
The general circulation cells of the atmosphere and the horizontal flow of air resulting from the Coriolis effect.

In the Northern Hemisphere, the Coriolis force always results in a deflection to the right. Turns to the left are the rule in the Southern Hemisphere. Let us now see how this effect ties in with the observed winds. In the tropical belts north and south of the equator, trade winds blowing mainly from the east prevail. This is consistent with a general flow of air toward the equator (Fig. 8-7) because the Coriolis deflection would be toward the west. The prevailing winds between about 30° and 60° latitude are from the west. Since the Coriolis effect is to turn the wind to the right in the Northern Hemisphere, this suggests an original northward movement. Obviously, some major change is required in the simplified circulation pattern of Fig. 8-7 in order to account for the actual prevailing winds. Figure 8-9 illustrates a system of circulation cells which, together with the Coriolis effect, would produce the measured winds.

An additional reason for adopting the circulation cells of Fig. 8-9 is that they also offer a reasonable explanation for the general precipitation patterns of the world. At and near the equator, air is converging horizontally and rising. The rising of moist air promotes condensation, cloud formation, and rain. Rain in all seasons is the rule in the belt within about 5° north and south of the equator. This, moreover, is the belt that has been known as the doldrums since the days of sailing ships, and we can see in Fig. 8-9 why it is a region of light horizontal surface wind.

In the belt from about 20° to 30° latitude, the reverse situation occurs. This is a region of horizontal divergence. Opposing wind directions and the downward flow provide conditions that are just the opposite of those needed for cloud formation. As expected, this is an area of little rain. Great deserts like the Sahara lie along this belt.

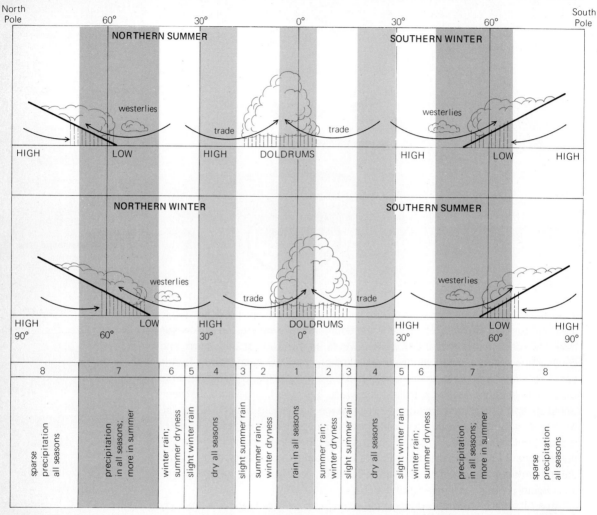

FIGURE 8-10

Main zones of atmospheric convergence and divergence and their relation to seasonal precipitation. *After G. T. Trewartha, "An Introduction to Climate," 4th ed. Copyright © 1968 by McGraw-Hill, Inc. Used with permission of McGraw-Hill Book Company.*

In the temperate belt, another convergence occurs. Warm air moving northward is forced up against cold polar air. The exact position of the boundary between these masses varies with the seasons, and sometimes masses of dense polar air detach themselves to move southward under the less dense warmer air. The result again is a situation where warm air is uplifted to produce clouds and precipitation.

Figure 8-10 diagrammatically shows the relationship between the general convective circulation and the major belts of precipitation. We must recognize, however, that this is a simplification of the real world. In the belt of eastward winds, the winds do not always flow from the west. Winds from every compass direction are recorded at any station over a period of time. Weather-satellite pho-

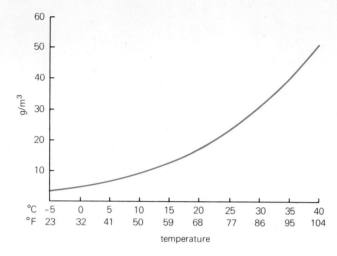

FIGURE 8-11
Variation in the water-vapor capacity of air at different temperatures.

tographs like Fig. 8-1 show a feature that we have not explained in our model thus far. Great eddies, or spiral whorls, seem to be the rule in the cloud pictures taken from space, and these cloud patterns are known to reflect wind directions—indeed, to mark storm centers. Before we explore the question of these spiral cloud patterns, let us see how clouds are formed.

8-4   HOW DO CLOUDS FORM?

Clouds are composed of tiny droplets of water or crystals of ice, usually ranging from 0.02 to 0.06 millimeters in diameter. These droplets are formed by the condensation of invisible water vapor, normally around a tiny nucleus, which may be a dust particle or a microscopic bit of salt that worked its way into the air from the ocean surface. To see when such condensation can take place we must first examine the air's capacity to hold water vapor.

Everyone has heard the term *relative humidity* in daily weather forecasts. Relative humidity is one measure of the vapor content of air. It is not expressed in absolute units. A relative humidity of 80 means that the air contains 80 percent of the water vapor that it could potentially hold at the given temperature. When the relative humidity is 100 percent, the air is said to be *saturated*.

If instead of remaining constant, the temperature varies while the amount of stored water vapor stays fixed, we obtain another important measurement called the *dew point*. This is the temperature at which the given content of water vapor produces saturation. The dew point can be found by using a condensing hygrometer, a glass plate cooled by evaporating ether from it. When moisture first begins to appear on the plate, the dew point has been reached. Knowing the dew point, we can determine the actual amount of water vapor present and the relative humidity of the air at the original temperature from a graph like Fig. 8-11.

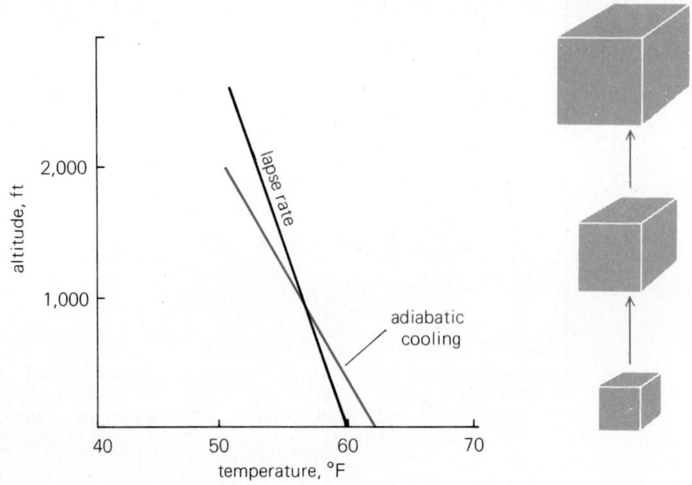

FIGURE 8-12
The average lapse rate is 3.5°F per 1,000 feet, whereas the average adiabatic cooling rate is 5.5°F per 1,000 feet. A parcel of air heated 2°F above its surroundings thus will expand and cool adiabatically to the temperature of the surrounding air at a height of about 1,000 feet.

The graph of Fig. 8-11 helps to explain the condensation of vapor into clouds and rain. Air at a temperature of 30°C and a relative humidity of 50 contains about 15 grams of vapor per cubic meter. If it is cooled to a temperature of 20°C with no change in moisture, the relative humidity will have risen to about 85. At about 17°C the same air will have reached its dew point, and any further cooling should result in condensation. Actually condensation into clouds may take place before the dew point is reached due to the effect of nuclei of dust and salt in the air.

How is air cooled to form clouds? One way of cooling air, of course, is to expose it to cool ground or water. Fog over cool water or night fog over cold land areas is evidence for this sort of cooling. But clouds occur above the surface, and so the question is how moist air from the surface is cooled as it is moved upward.

We have already noted that the temperature decreases upward in the lower atmosphere. The rate of decrease with height is known as the *lapse rate*, the average being about 3.5°F per 1,000 feet (1°C per 100 meters). Since air is a very poor conductor of heat, it would take a rising column of warm air a long time to lose its heat to its surroundings and therefore the cooling of rising air columns cannot be attributed to the lapse rate. When a gas expands, it becomes cooler; when it contracts, it becomes warmer. Such changes in temperature are called *adiabatic* changes because heat is neither lost to the surroundings nor gained from them. Most cooling of rising air parcels is adiabatic cooling.

Consider a volume of air near the ground, say over a plowed field, that has been heated 2°F warmer than the surrounding air. This air becomes less dense (increases in volume) and hence buoyant. As it rises, it encounters progressively lower pressures, resulting in still further expansion. The expansion produces an adiabatic fall of temperature, which on the average amounts to 5.5°F per 1,000 feet. We can see from Fig. 8-12 that the faster adiabatic cooling will cause the rising air to reach the temperature of the surrounding air at a height of 1,000 feet.

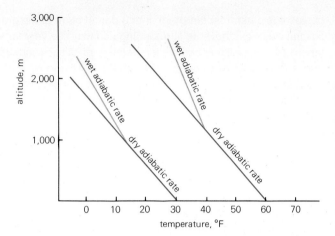

FIGURE 8-13
The dry adiabatic cooling rate is the same for air at any temperature. When moisture in the air condenses as it is cooled during its upward rise, clouds form and heat is released. The result is a retarded wet adiabatic cooling rate. Both the height where clouds begin to form and the wet adiabatic rate depend upon the original air temperature, which determines how much moisture air can hold.

Actually the rising parcel of air would move upward past this level because it takes some distance for it to decelerate, but it should eventually settle there.

A parcel of moist air that is rising, expanding, and cooling will eventually reach its dew point, with the resulting condensation of moisture and the formation of clouds. Once condensation begins, cooling proceeds more slowly because of the heat energy liberated in the transition of water vapor to liquid form. This liberated heat of condensation in fact causes further expansion and rising. Figure 8-13 shows how the adiabatic cooling for moist air compares with that for dry air. Heating due to condensation is much more pronounced in tropical than in polar regions because the air of the tropics is warmer and more humid than polar air.

So far in referring to the lapse rate or the measured decrease of air temperature with height, we have been using the average rate of 3.5°C per 1,000 feet. However, the lapse rate varies from place to place and from day to day. Figure 8-14 illustrates a situation where the lapse rate is lower than average (steeper

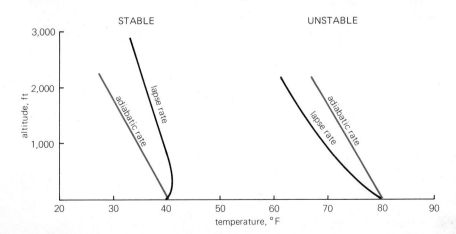

FIGURE 8-14
Where the adiabatic rate is greater than the lapse rate, a parcel of air forced upward will remain cooler and hence denser than the environment. As a result it will sink. Such a situation is said to be *stable*. On the other hand, where the lapse rate is greater than the adiabatic rate, rising parcels of air will continue upward because they are warmer and hence less dense than the surrounding air. This *unstable* situation promotes thermals and mixing.

A

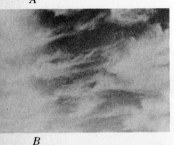

B

C

FIGURE 8-15
Some of the principal cloud types: *(A)* **cumulus;** *(B)* **cirrus;** *(C)* **cumulus and towering cumulus (cumulonimbus).** *Used with permission of Ward's Natural Science Establishment, Inc., Rochester, N.Y.*

curve). It is clear from the graph that a parcel of air at the ground that is heated several degrees above its surroundings cannot rise very far with the prevailing lapse rate before it reaches the temperature of its surroundings. Where the lapse rate is lower than average the atmosphere is said to be *stable* because an unusual amount of heating is required to effect any significant adiabatic rise. On the other hand, atmospheric *instability* exists where the lapse rate is such that a few degrees of differential heating may result in thousands of feet of adiabatic rise.

The buoyant ascent of parcels of air in an unstable environment produces heaping *cumulus clouds.* They are the marks of strong updrafts. Clouds should not form under stable atmospheric conditions because there is no reason for the air to rise. However, where another air mass pushes such stable air upward or where passage over a mountain range causes it to move upward, large cloud sheets with a great horizontal extent are formed. Such clouds are known as *stratus clouds.*

There are many different cloud types, but all can be grouped into the two main classes described above. Most cumulus clouds float in the lower atmosphere below about 10,000 feet. Some, however, extend upward to over 30,000 feet; they are called *cumulonimbus* clouds. At very high elevations (over 25,000 feet) clouds consist mainly of tiny ice crystals; they are called *cirrus clouds.* Table 8-3 shows the relation between the principal cloud types, and Fig. 8-15 pictures some of the classes.

8-5 CYCLONES, ANTICYCLONES, AND WEATHER FRONTS

One of the measurements reported daily by weather forecasters is atmospheric pressure. In weather broadcasts barometric pressure is usually reported in inches of mercury, but another system of recording pressure is in millibars. One standard, or normal, atmosphere of pressure is called a *bar,* and a millibar is $\frac{1}{1000}$ bar. Weather maps frequently show lines, called *isobars,* which connect points of equal barometric pressure.

Air tends to flow from areas of high to low pressure, wind speed depending upon the magnitude of the pressure difference. In the diagram of Fig. 8-16 the

TABLE 8-3
Principal cloud types*

Class	*Low*	*Middle*	*High*
Stratus	Stratus	Altostratus	Cirrostratus
	Cumulus	Altocumulus	Cirrocumulus
Cumulus	Towering cumulus		
	Cumulonimbus		

*After H. Riehl, "Introduction to the Atmosphere," 2d ed. Copyright © 1972 by McGraw-Hill, Inc. Used by permission of McGraw-Hill Book Company.

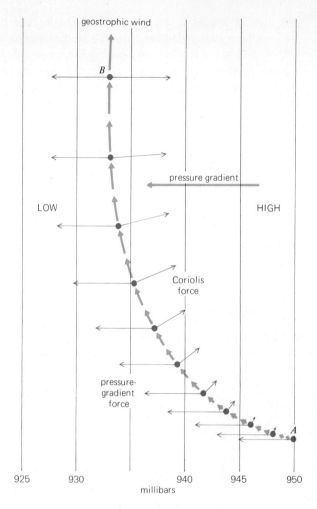

FIGURE 8-16
A parcel of air starting from a position of rest at A **is deflected until it is moving parallel with the isobars at** B. *After S. Petterssen, "Introduction to Meteorology." Copyright © 1958 by McGraw-Hill, Inc. Used with permission of McGraw-Hill Book Company.*

wind would move parallel to the pressure gradient (the direction of fastest pressure change is perpendicular to the isobars) if the earth were not rotating. The earth is rotating, however, and so we must take into account the Coriolis effect. Although, as we have seen, the Coriolis effect is not a force, we can think of it as one for this analysis. The Coriolis effect acts horizontally in a direction at right angles to the path of the object being turned, and its magnitude increases with speed and with latitude. With this in mind, let us return to Fig. 8-16 and consider the motion of a parcel of air at position A. Starting from rest, the parcel begins to move directly down the pressure gradient. Since our map is located in the Northern Hemisphere, the Coriolis force turns the parcel slightly to the right. As the speed of the air increases, so too does the Coriolis force. Eventually the air parcel is turned to flow parallel to the isobars, where the Coriolis effect (which acts at right angles to the direction of motion) just balances the pressure-gradient force. With the forces thus balanced, further turning ceases. Winds that flow parallel to the isobars are *geostrophic*, or earth-turning, winds.

Figure 8-16 would show the turning in the opposite direction if the map were in the Southern Hemisphere. We can see, therefore, that in the Northern Hemisphere anyone standing with his back to the geostrophic wind will find the region of low pressure to the left; in the Southern Hemisphere it will be to his right. This relation of pressure to wind was first stated in the nineteenth century by the Dutch meteorologist Christoph Buys Ballot, and the rule bears his name.

A *cyclone* is defined as a center of low barometric pressure; an *anticyclone* is a center of high pressure. In the Northern Hemisphere cyclones are marked by a counterclockwise (as viewed from above) flow of winds; the flow is clockwise in the Southern Hemisphere. Air should flow directly toward the low-pressure centers, but, as we have seen, the earth's spin makes the winds turn so that they tend to parallel the isobars. The result is a spiraling movement of air. This explains how the spiral patterns we encountered in Sec. 8-3 are formed.

Although it is easy to see how spiral wind motions (and hence cloud patterns) develop around centers of low or high pressure, the question remains of how such centers themselves arise. Because cyclonic storms (those associated with a center of low pressure) are particularly prevalent in the middle and high latitudes, we focus specifically upon them in attempting to explain the formation of pressure centers.

Before considering how the mid-latitude cyclones form, we must be familiar with the concept of air masses. An *air mass* is a large body of air (extending usually for thousands of kilometers) with unique and uniform values of temperature and humidity. Different air masses arise because air is exposed to different conditions. In the continental polar regions, for example, the air is cold and dry. In maritime polar regions it tends to be cold and moist. Dry, hot air prevails over the arid regions of the southwestern part of the United States. Hot, humid air is characteristic of maritime tropical regions. We know that the earth's envelope of air is in continual motion; therefore an air mass that achieved its characteristics of temperature and humidity in the continental polar regions, for example, will eventually find itself over a maritime environment, where it acquires new characteristics. Distinct air masses generally resist mixing, but mixing does take place at their boundaries. These boundaries are called *fronts*, and it is along fronts, where air masses are in conflict, that most violent weather forms.

The cyclonic storms we are considering develop along the polar front, which, according to our earlier circulation model, is where cold polar air meets the warmer air from the subtropics (Fig. 8-17). The upward rise of air along the polar front marks a trough of low pressure. To explain the spiraling cyclonic storms we need to know how distinct centers of low pressure form along such a low-pressure trough.

Early in the twentieth century a group of Norwegian meteorologists formulated

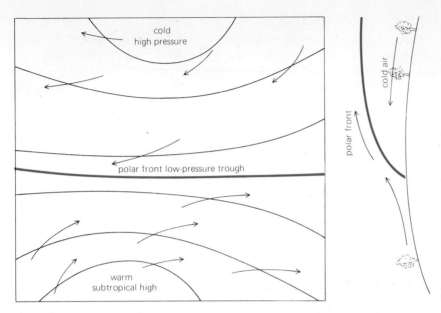

FIGURE 8-17
Where cold polar air with easterly winds pushes against warm subtropical air, a trough of low pressure develops. It is along this polar front that the cyclonic storms of the mid-latitudes evolve.

a theory to account for the generation of low-pressure centers and hence cyclonic storms along the polar front. According to their polar-front theory of cyclones, a cyclonic storm begins with the formation of a wave or indentation in the front. Such a wave may be due to topographic effects, to differential heating, to turbulence in the winds aloft, or to all three. Whatever the cause, once such a kink develops, it tends to intensify itself. As we can see by Fig. 8-18, because of the opposing wind directions along the polar front, an initial small indentation becomes a sharp wave whose crest is a center of low pressure. As the winds circle this center, the pressure is reduced still further, with a corresponding increase in wind speed. Finally the low-pressure center is pinched off the front entirely, eventually to dissolve.

Figure 8-19 is a surface weather map showing the conditions of pressure, wind, and temperature associated with an actual cyclonic storm on two consecutive days. In map *A* a distinct wave (and its center of low pressure) is already well developed. On the west limb of the wave, dense cold air is moving against warm, moist air. This situation is called a *cold front*. As the denser cold air along the cold front pushes under warm, humid air, the latter is forced to rise, resulting in cloud formation and rain. A typical cold front has a relatively steep slope of about 1 mile vertically to 50 miles along the ground.

On the eastern limb of the wave in Fig. 8-19*A*, warm air is flowing over cold air. This represents a *warm front*, which characteristically has a lower slope (1 mile vertical in 200 miles along the ground) than a cold front. If the rising warm air is stable, decks of stratus clouds result from the adiabatic cooling accompanying the ascending warm air. Steady light rains frequently accompany such rising sta-

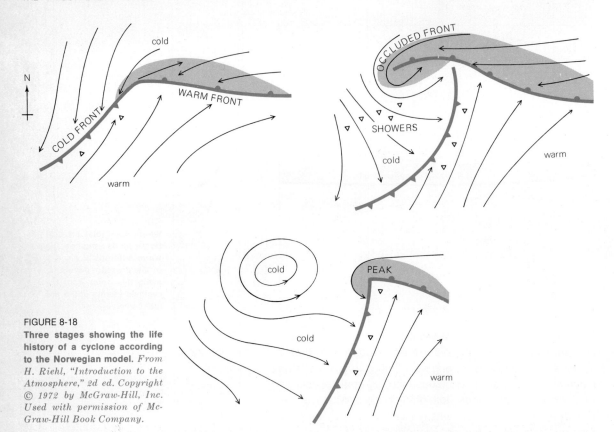

ble air. Where the rising warm air is unstable, cumulus clouds and thundershowers are more common.

Cold fronts usually advance faster than warm fronts. When a cold front overtakes a warm front, the warm air is completely uplifted from the surface and replaced by denser cooler air. Such a front is known as an *occluded front* (Fig. 8-19*B*). Again, in an occluded front clouds and accompanying rain or snow are associated with the uplifted warm air.

Several interesting features of cyclonic storms are shown in Fig. 8-19. First, such storm regions tend to grow in size. An embryonic cyclone typically covers an area of several states. By the time it becomes occluded, it may bring clouds and rain to a region as large as one-fourth of North America. Second, cyclonic storms move with the prevailing winds. In the Northern Hemisphere they typically travel eastward to northeastward. A cyclonic storm normally lasts 3 to 5 days, during which time it moves several thousand kilometers. Figure 8-20 shows some cyclones in various stages of development. A cyclone eventually disappears when the air involved becomes thoroughly mixed.

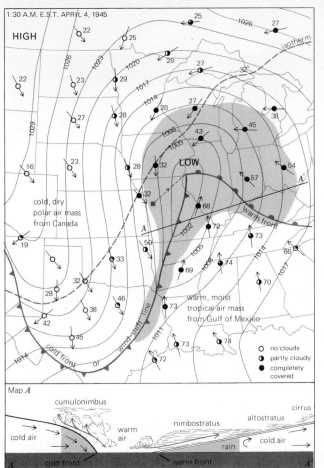

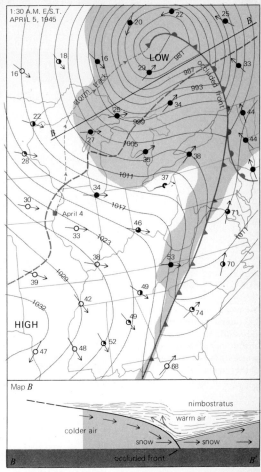

Map A

Map B

FIGURE 8-19
Surface map showing two stages in the development of a cyclonic storm. Note that during the occluded stage the region of overcast and precipitation extends over many states. Arrows show wind directions. *From A. K. Lobeck, "Climates of the World," C. S. Hammond Company.*

FIGURE 8-20
Schematic map covering an area thousands of miles across in the Northern Hemisphere and showing two families of wave cyclones. *After S. Petterssen, "Introduction to Meteorology." Copyright © 1958 by McGraw-Hill, Inc. Used with permission of McGraw-Hill Book Company.*

CYCLONE FAMILY

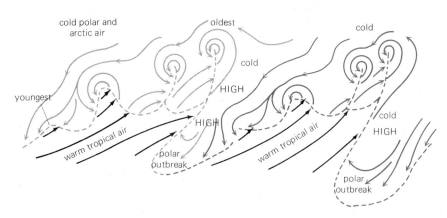

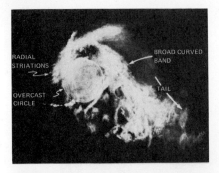
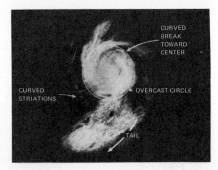
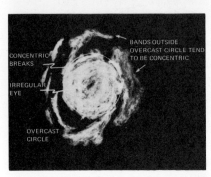
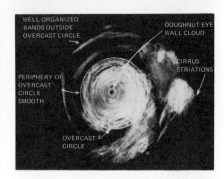

FIGURE 8-21
A typical hurricane has a well-developed center of low pressure. Winds spiraling toward this center rise to heights of tens of thousands of feet. These photographs show four categories of hurricanes. *NOAA.*

Cyclonic storms of the type just described are uncommon in the tropics because the air masses there are more uniform in composition. Much of the precipitation in the tropics is due to the upward convective flow of air rather than to horizontal mixing of different air masses. Very strong cyclonic storms, called *hurricanes* or *typhoons*, do develop in the tropics, however.

It is always over warm tropical waters that hurricanes form initially. Most of their energy comes from heat released to the atmosphere by the condensation of water vapor picked up from the warm seas. Tropical hurricanes are much more circular in outline than mid-latitude cyclones because the center of low pressure is more intense and clearly defined (Fig. 8-21). At the lower levels of a hurricane there is a spiraling inflow of air which is compensated for by a spiraling outflow aloft. Because of the heat liberated by condensation, such storms may extend to heights of 40,000 feet or more. The core of the disturbance becomes a center of very low pressure, called the *eye* of the storm.

The hurricanes that reach North America (those which each year are given names alphabetically as Alice, Betsy, etc.) typically begin in the tropical Atlantic and move slowly westward with the trade winds, usually reaching full hurricane strength in the Caribbean. As they approach the continent, they turn right, or poleward, until they reach the belt of westerly circulation, where they gradually turn to the east. Figure 8-22 shows the actual tracks of some North American hurricanes.

Hurricanes lose their energy source quickly when they leave the warm tropical waters of their birth. Rarely does the entire Northern Hemisphere receive as many as 50 in any one year. By contrast there may be as many as 30 mid-latitude cyclonic storms per day. We have noted that over land or over cooler ocean waters the chief energy supply for hurricanes, the heat of condensation of water, is cut off. A possibility for hurricane control would be to spread some material over the tropical waters which would retard evaporation.

8-6 THE EFFECTS OF LAND AND WATER ON WINDS AND WEATHER

In discussing the general circulation pattern of the atmosphere, the formation of clouds, and precipitation we have not mentioned the influence of the different materials the air is in contact with or the effect of the topography on winds and weather. One would expect the material at the earth's surface to influence the convective circulation because water and rock behave very differently during heating. It takes about five times as much heat to raise the temperature of 1 kilogram of water by 1° as to raise the temperature of an equal quantity of rock by the same amount. During cooling, then, five times as much heat must be liberated by a unit mass of water as by a unit mass of rock to produce the same temperature drop. Because of this marked difference in specific heats, land areas tend to

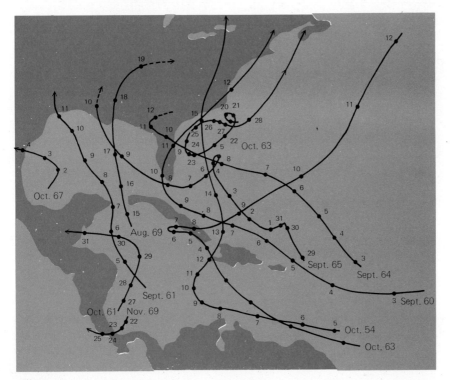

FIGURE 8-22
Tracks of 11 major hurricanes in the Atlantic between 1954 and 1969. Positions shown at 24-hour intervals. *After H. Riehl, "Introduction to the Atmosphere," 2d ed. Copyright © 1972 by McGraw-Hill, Inc. Used with permission of McGraw-Hill Book Company.*

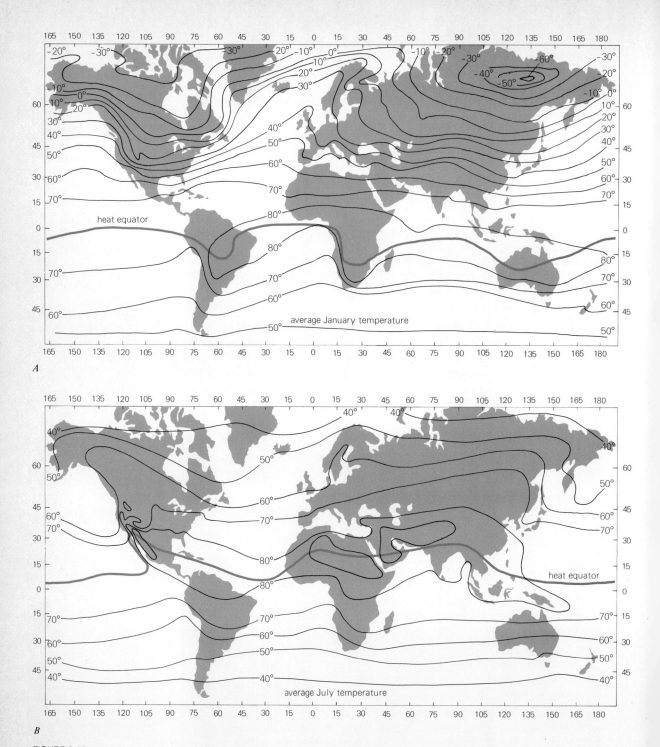

FIGURE 8-23

Average sea-level temperatures in (A) January and (B) July. The heat equator marks the belt of highest temperature. *U.S. Weather Bureau Service.*

become heated more quickly by day and to cool more rapidly at night than adjacent bodies of water.

Not only can a given quantity of water hold more heat than a comparable mass of rock, but a body of water also absorbs more solar energy because the sun's rays penetrate beneath its surface. Since the atmosphere is heated in part by conduction, the air temperatures over water and land reflect the differences in heating and cooling of these materials. Another important difference between the continents and oceans lies in the fluid nature of water. Ocean currents involve the physical transport of water and its contained heat energy, resulting in a tendency toward global temperature equalization.

Figure 8-23 shows the mean sea-level temperatures for January and July. As expected, the lines of equal temperature (isotherms) are materially distorted by the continents. In January the isotherms are bent southward over North America and Asia, whereas in July they are bent the opposite way, attesting to the more rapid heating and cooling of the continents compared to the seas. Only in the southern quarter of the globe, where there is little land, do the isotherms nearly parallel the lines of latitude.

The different rates of heating and cooling of land and sea sometimes produce seasonal reversals of winds. Consider a hypothetical land mass in the Northern Hemisphere (Fig. 8-24). In summer the land becomes warmer than the sea, with the result that ascending warm air creates a weak region of low pressure. Winds therefore blow toward the land from the sea. These moisture-laden winds bring rain. In winter the land cools more quickly than the sea, and a high-pressure center of dense cold air accumulates on the land mass. Anticyclonic circulation develops, with winter winds that blow away from the high-pressure center toward the sea. The cool, dry air flowing seaward does not produce rain.

Such reversing wind systems are called *monsoons*. Areas like India, China, and parts of Australia experience monsoon winds. Characteristically these regions are marked by wet summers, when moist winds blow landward from the sea, and dry winters, when the prevailing winds blow off the land masses. The monsoon winds of actual land areas like India are not as simple as those in our hypothetical land mass of Fig. 8-24; other factors besides the difference in radiative heating and cooling of the continental mass compared to the oceans come into play. This difference works to modify and complicate the general circulation of the earth.

On an even more restricted scale many shoreline regions experience breezes from the water during the day and land breezes at night. The reason for this type of reversal becomes clear when we recall that the materials of the land have much lower specific heats than water. The land and its air thus become warmer during the day, causing convective rise. At night the situation is reversed, the land areas cooling more rapidly; this results in a movement of the denser cool air of the land toward the warmer air over the water.

Wind direction at low levels is influenced by the amount of friction at the inter-

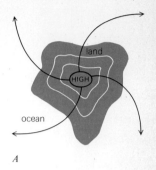

A

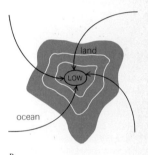

B

FIGURE 8-24
(*A*) Monsoon winds develop because in winter the land is colder than the ocean. As a result winds blow away from the cold high-pressure region. (*B*) In summer the land warms more quickly, causing air to rise and a low-pressure center to form. Winds then blow landward.

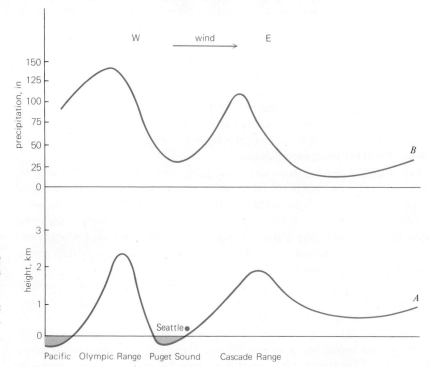

FIGURE 8-25
East-west profile of *(A)* **mountain ranges and** *(B)* **annual precipitation across the state of Washington. Profile passes through Seattle.** *After H. Riehl, "Introduction to the Atmosphere," 2d ed. Copyright © 1972 by McGraw-Hill, Inc. Used with permission of McGraw-Hill Book Company.*

face between air and underlying materials. Friction is usually more marked over land than over water. In our simplified description of geostrophic winds we said that flow parallel to the lines of equal pressure would result from a balance between pressure forces and the Coriolis effect. A more exact analysis would have to include other minor forces in the balance, of which friction is one.

We have seen how warm air can be made to ascend by a moving mass of denser cool air at a cold front, with the resulting formation of clouds. Air parcels can also be forced upward by mountain ranges. Major mountain systems that lie in the path of prevailing winds, e.g., the Rocky Mountains and the Andes, often influence climate for thousands of kilometers beyond their boundaries. Figure 8-25 is an east-west profile across the state of Washington showing the mean annual precipitation. Note how sharply the precipitation is controlled by the topography. Moist air from the Pacific Ocean moving eastward is forced upward by the mountains of the Cascade Range. The cooling accompanying the ascent results in the condensation of the moisture, most precipitation occurring on the windward side of the mountains. By the time the air reaches the lee side of the Range it is very dry, and almost desert conditions prevail in that part of the state.

Whereas parcels of air are cooled adiabatically as they expand in moving upward to regions of lower pressures, descending air masses become com-

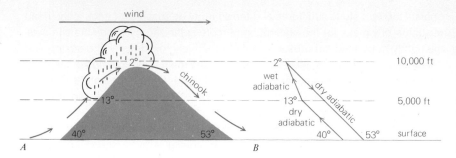

FIGURE 8-26
Diagrammatic representation of (*A*) **a chinook and** (*B*) **adiabatic rates associated with it.** *After G. T. Trewartha, "An Introduction to Climate," 4th ed. Copyright © 1968 by McGraw-Hill, Inc. Used with permission of McGraw-Hill Book Company.*

pressed and heated. The occasional warm winter winds on the lee side of mountains originate by such compressive heating. Figure 8-26 illustrates the conditions necessary for the generation of these warm chinook, or foehn, winds.

In many mountain valleys a twice-daily (diurnal) alteration of wind is experienced because of differential heating and cooling. During the day the air over mountain slopes is heated faster than that in the valley bottoms, causing winds to flow up the valley walls. At night cooling is more pronounced on the mountain slopes, and the dense cooler air flows toward the valley bottom. Marked temperature inversions sometimes develop in valleys in the evening as dense cooled air collects at the valley bottom to displace air that has been warmed during the day.

Large cities have a measurable effect on the local weather. Figure 8-27 is a temperature map of Washington, D.C., at 10 P.M. on a summer day. The expanse

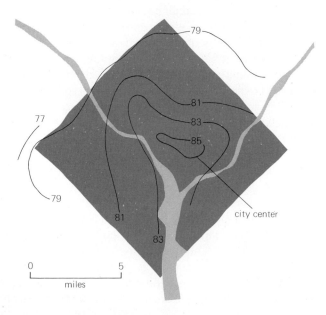

FIGURE 8-27
Temperature distribution (Fahrenheit) in Washington, D.C., and suburbs at 10 P.M., August 11, 1949, showing the city heat island. *After H. Riehl, "Introduction to the Atmosphere," 2d ed. Copyright © 1972 by McGraw-Hill, Inc. Used with permission of McGraw-Hill Book Company.*

of blacktop and stone structures and the scarcity or absence of trees in the heart of such a city make for the absorption of more solar energy. When the sun sets, the lightly populated suburbs, with a comparatively low density of blacktop and concrete, cool rapidly. At the same time the pavement and buildings of the inner city radiate heat to the atmosphere, delaying the daily low temperature. Convective rise of warm air over large cities sometimes results in localized evening showers.

The differences in heat capacity of water and rock, the effect of topography, and the transport of heat energy by ocean currents all work to modify the general atmospheric circulation pattern that is due to the differential distribution of radiant solar energy over the globe. With so many factors operating to influence the daily variation of wind, cloud cover, and precipitation, it is small wonder that weather forecasters cannot predict far into the future.

8-7 THE IONOSPHERE

So far we have been focusing chiefly upon the activities of the troposphere, the lowermost region of the atmosphere. Before leaving the subject of the atmosphere we should look at least briefly at some of the activity and characteristics of its upper reaches. Whereas we can feel the winds and measure their directions and speeds, our knowledge of the upper atmosphere must come chiefly from indirect measurements.

In 1901 Marconi transmitted the first radio signal from England to North America. Seen as a great feat by the general public, it was a puzzling accomplishment to physicists because radio waves, like light waves, were believed to travel in straight paths. How did the radio signal manage to curve around one-fourth of the earth's circumference?

The answer to this question came quickly from the scientific community. In 1902, Oliver Heaviside, of England, and Arthur Kennelly, of the United States, suggested simultaneously that the only reasonable explanation for the apparent bending of radio waves lay in the existence of some sort of conducting layer high in the atmosphere. The radio transmission across the Atlantic could then have been achieved by reflection between this atmospheric conductor and the ocean waters. In 1924 the Kennelly-Heaviside layer was finally located experimentally by sending very short radio pulses straight up into the atmosphere and measuring the time it took for them to be reflected back. These experiments showed that actually there are several conducting layers.

How do these conducting layers form? Early experimenters soon learned what we have all experienced; radio reception is much better at night than during the day. It appeared, therefore, that the conducting layers are somehow affected by the sun's radiation. Laboratory experiments following this clue revealed that gases can be made to lose electrons and become ionized when exposed to ultraviolet or x-radiation. Since the sun emits this type of radiation, it seemed clear that the conducting layers are formed by photo-ionization of the gases in the

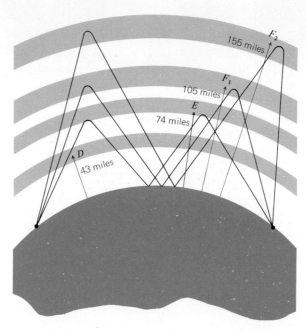

FIGURE 8-28
The principal layers of the ion-osphere.

upper atmosphere. This hypothesis accounts well for the boundaries of the ionized zone. The upper limit of the conducting layer at about 400 miles is explained by the fact that the particle density above that level is so small that there cannot be a significant electron density even if most atoms or molecules are ionized by the sunlight. On the other hand, at the lower limit, about 50 miles above the earth's surface, the sun's ionizing rays have spent their energy. With the interpretation that the conducting layers of the atmosphere are due to free electrons resulting from the ionization of gas molecules, the Kennelly-Heaviside layers became known as the *ionosphere*.

The layers of the ionosphere are designated by letters, D, E, F_1, F_2 (Fig. 8-28). If the electrons stay close to where they are released, the number of electrons present in any layer must represent a balance between the number generated by the ionizing radiation and the number that reattach themselves to the atoms or molecules of the air. Since the amount of ionizing radiation depends upon the angle at which the sun's rays hit the atmosphere, we would expect to find the greatest degree of ionization near the equator, where the sun's rays are most intense. The E and F_1 layers do indeed exhibit the expected change of electron density with latitude. But the F_2 layer does not behave according to theory. Instead of having the highest electron density at midday this layer sometimes actually shows a decrease in electron density at noon. Moreover, its electron density has been found to be higher in winter than in summer, when the sun's input is most intense. This anomalous behavior suggests that there must be some movement of electrons to account for these unusual electron densities.

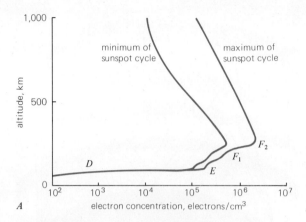

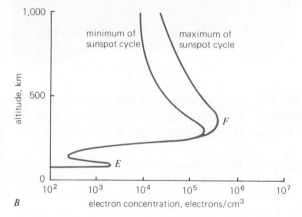

FIGURE 8-29
Normal electron distributions in the atmosphere at the extremes of the sunspot cycle: (A) daytime; (B) nighttime. *From F. S. Johnson (ed.), "Satellite Environment Handbook," Stanford University Press, 1965.*

Figure 8-29 shows some measured average values for electron densities at various altitudes during day and night. Among other things, the figure indicates that the lowermost (D) layer vanishes at night. This layer has the property of absorbing rather than reflecting radio waves. Now we can see why radio reception is so much better at night.

For the most part, the sun radiates energy at a uniform rate, but there is an 11-year sunspot cycle during which the rate of energy radiation varies slightly. During quiet sun periods the electron density in the ionosphere is generally lower than during periods of sunspot maxima. Unusual solar activity, e.g., a flare, can result in a marked increase in the density of the D layer, with the resulting fading of radio signals. By keeping track of ionospheric activity, scientists can monitor the condition of the sun even when the sky is completely overcast.

SUMMARY

The envelope of air surrounding the earth is composed chiefly of the elements nitrogen and oxygen. There is no clear upper boundary to the atmosphere, but 99 percent of its mass lies below an altitude of 33 kilometers (20 miles).

Although the atmosphere absorbs some of the sun's radiant energy directly, most atmospheric heating occurs at the earth's surface. This surface heating is reflected by a decrease in temperature upward to a height of about 10 kilometers. At higher levels several temperature reversals form the basis for the classification of the atmosphere into the troposphere, stratosphere, mesosphere, and thermosphere.

The earth is heated more strongly in the equatorial belt than in the polar regions; this differential heating causes the major atmospheric circulation. Warm air in the equatorial belt rises, to be replaced by cooler air from the higher latitudes. Were it not for this poleward transport of heat by the winds and by ocean currents, the mid–and upper-latitude regions of the earth would become progressively colder.

The general circulation pattern of the atmosphere is complicated by a number of other factors. Most important is the Coriolis effect, which tends to produce geostrophic winds. The differing specific heats of rock and water further complicate the circulation, as does the effect of friction over rough, mountainous land regions.

Ascending parcels of warm air encounter increasingly lower pressures, resulting in expansion and adiabatic cooling. A buoyant mass of air rises until it reaches air of similar temperature and density. Adiabatic cooling results in the condensation of water vapor and the formation of clouds and possibly rain.

The contact between air masses of different properties is called a weather front, the three main types being cold fronts, warm fronts, and occluded fronts. In the mid-latitude regions, where cold polar air is in contact with moist and warm tropical air, centers of low pressure called cyclones develop where waves form in this polar front. Much of the weather in these regions is related to these moving cyclonic storms. In the tropics cyclonic storms called hurricanes owe their power to convective rise aided by heat added to the air by the condensation of water vapor.

At heights of from 40 to 400 miles above the surface, the atmosphere is a conductor because of the free electrons found there. This ionosphere owes its existence to the ionizing power of the sun's radiant energy. Thanks to the ionosphere long-distance radio communication is possible.

QUESTIONS

1 What properties of the atmosphere have been used as a basis for subdividing it into layers such as troposphere, stratosphere, mesosphere, and thermosphere?

2 Where would you expect to find more abrupt temperature changes between day and night —in a desert region or in a humid area? Why?

3 How do water vapor and carbon dioxide in the air help keep the earth warm?

4 The earth's average temperature is slightly higher during the Northern Hemisphere summer, when the earth is farthest from the sun, than during the Northern Hemisphere winter. Can you account for this?

5 How is the D layer of the ionosphere related to long-distance radio communication?

6 It is often said that a rainstorm clears the air. In the northern United States is the cool, clear air that frequently follows a period of rain the result of such clearing?

7 The speed of radio waves is about 186,000 miles per second. How long would it take such a wave to move up to the F_2 layer and be reflected back to the ground?

8 Air at 80°F is found to have a dew point of 30°F. Using the diagram of Fig. 8-11, determine the relative humidity of the air.

9 What is the polar-front theory of cyclones?

10 When you stand with your back to the wind in the Northern Hemisphere, is the center of low pressure to your right or left? Would this be the same in the Southern Hemisphere? Why?

REFERENCES

Flohn, Hermann: "Climate and Weather," McGraw-Hill Book Company, New York, 1969.

Petterssen, S.: "Introduction to Meteorology," McGraw-Hill Book Company, New York, 1958.

Riehl, Herbert: "Introduction to the Atmosphere," 2d ed., McGraw-Hill Book Company, New York, 1972.

Rumney, George R.: "The Geosystem: Dynamic Integration of Land, Sea and Air," Wm. C. Brown Company Publishers, Dubuque, Iowa, 1970.

THE OCEANS

Oceanography is one of the most exciting branches of earth science today and one of the most popular. Its appeal stems from the pioneering nature of the work done by oceanographers. Although the job of exploring the hidden depths of the seas was begun in the nineteenth century, most of what is currently known about the configuration and composition of the sea floor and about life and water movements in the ocean deeps has been discovered since World War II. On this "last frontier" new findings and new interpretations are constantly appearing.

That the oceans are a last unexplored frontier is small wonder when we consider that they blanket almost three-fourths of the earth's surface. Although man has watched the ceaseless pounding of the shores by ocean waves since his beginnings and sailed the rolling seas for centuries, it is only within the past two or three decades that he has learned how to explore the alien world beneath the seas. With the aid of instruments that can sense the ocean floors, with the help of new sampling and drilling techniques, and with the development of navigational systems that make up for the absence of landmarks in the open sea, the undersea world is rapidly becoming less foreign.

Exploration of the vast oceans is very expensive. Large vessels big enough to withstand the open sea and equipped with costly instruments and tools are needed to gather data from the ocean surface (Fig. 9-1). Submersible research vessels that permit scientists to explore the undersea world directly must be specially constructed to withstand the enormous pressures of the depths and provide life-support systems for extended periods. Because of the large investment in vessels and equipment, scientists from many disciplines work together on oceanic exploration to gather the maximum information during any voyage. This close cooperation has been largely responsible for the great increase in our knowledge of the dark undersea world within the past few decades.

9-1 WHAT ARE THE OCEAN BASINS LIKE?

The various oceans of the world—Atlantic, Pacific, Mediterranean Sea, etc.—form a single, connected sheet of water covering 71 percent of the earth's surface. This vast sheet is in constant motion. Waves and swells break on the beaches, forever changing the exact position of the edge of the sea. In spite of this continuous motion, mean sea level is widely used as a reference for eleva-

FIGURE 9-1
Ocean scientists preparing to launch a current meter.
Woods Hole Oceanographic Institution.

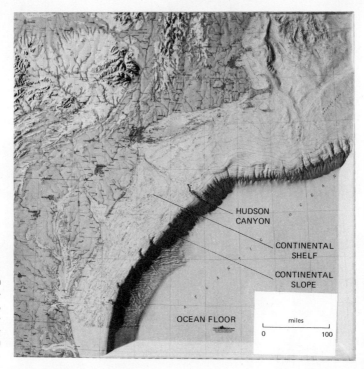

HUDSON
CANYON

CONTINENTAL
SHELF

CONTINENTAL
SLOPE

OCEAN FLOOR

miles

0   100

FIGURE 9-2
Relief map of the northeastern
United States showing the continental shelf, continental slope,
and the beginning of the continental rise. The shelf here extends for over 100 miles from
the shore. *A. J. Nystrom & Co.*

tions on land. In a lifetime the mean level of the sea does not change appreciably, but a look at the rocks of the continents shows that the position of the edge of
the sea has fluctuated greatly over longer periods of times. There are rock layers
bearing the remains of marine organisms almost everywhere on the continents,
proof that the present shorelines have not been permanent throughout geologic
time.

If the shorelines have moved so much in the past, is there any natural boundary between the ocean basins and the continents? The relief map in Fig. 9-2 shows
the configuration of the sea floor off the New York coast. From this map we can
see that there is a distinct boundary between the continent and the Atlantic
Ocean basin, but the boundary is as much as 100 kilometers seaward from the
present coastline. The relatively featureless flat region adjoining the continent is
called the *continental shelf*. Its width varies markedly from place to place, but
its topography and geology are everywhere a continuation of the features of the
adjacent continents. The continental shelves of the world are parts of the land
masses covered by a maximum of about 500 meters of water.

The continental shelf is separated from the abyssal, or deeper, parts of the
ocean floor by the continental slope (Fig. 9-3). Whereas the typical slope of the
continental shelf is of the order of 1 in 1,000, the gradient of the continental slope
is more nearly 1 in 40. In most places the continental slope is bordered by a fea-

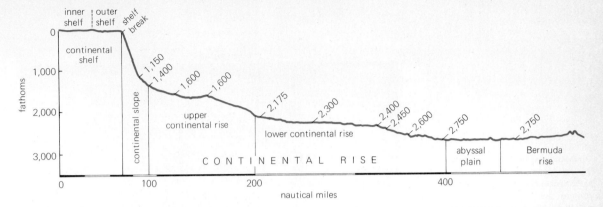

inner | outer | shelf
shelf | shelf | break

continental shelf

continental slope

1,150
1,400
1,600
1,600

upper continental rise

2,175
2,300

lower continental rise

CONTINENTAL RISE

2,400
2,450
2,600

2,750

abyssal plain

2,750

Bermuda rise

fathoms: 0, 1,000, 2,000, 3,000

nautical miles: 0, 100, 200, 400

FIGURE 9-3
A typical cross section of the continental margin off the eastern United States. A fathom is 6 feet, or 1.82 meters. *After B. C. Heezen, M. Tharp, and M. Ewing, The Floors of the Oceans, Geol. Soc. Am. Spec. Pap. 65, 1959.*

ture called the *continental rise*. As can be seen in Fig. 9-3, this is not a true rise but an apron with a much lower gradient (about 1 in 700) than the steep continental slope.

We referred to the existence of ridge systems in the ocean basins in Chap. 6 (see Fig. 6-18). In the Atlantic basin the ridge system bisects the ocean floor and is known as the *mid-Atlantic ridge*. This and the other ocean ridge systems are major structural features of the earth. Although they outclass in size even the major mountain chains like the Andes and the Rockies, they were fully discovered only by soundings made in the 1950s. The ridges are the sites of most geological activity in the ocean basins. It is along the ridges that most faulting and related earthquake motion recorded in the oceans occurs. They are also the site of most volcanic activity in the seas and in fact owe their origin to the outpouring of lava along major zones of weakness in the earth's crust.

The expeditions that made the soundings (Fig. 9-4) of the ocean ridge systems also discovered vast, featureless plains in the very deep (abyssal) parts of the ocean basins. In the Atlantic basin these abyssal plains are found between

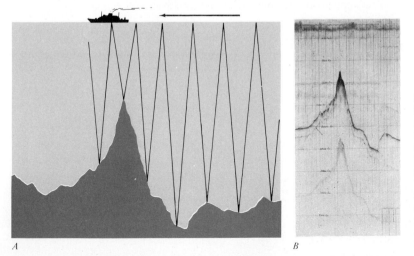

A

B

FIGURE 9-4
Sounding the ocean floor. (*A*) **As oceanographic vessels move back and forth across the surface, echo sounders "ping" the ocean floor with high-frequency sound waves.** (*B*) **The returning echos are enscribed on a graph to draw an accurate profile of the land beneath the water.** *U.S. Naval Hydrographic Office, "The Water Planet," 1969.*

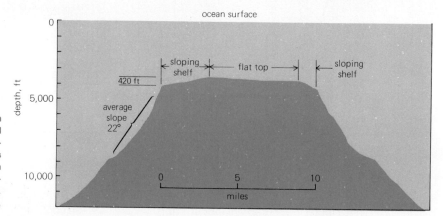

FIGURE 9-5
Soundings in the Pacific Ocean during World War II disclosed the presence of many flat-topped submarine mountains called guyots. The guyot shown is one of the first to be discovered. *Redrawn from H. H. Hess, Am. J. Sci., vol. 244, 1946.*

the ridge and the continental rises. The plains of the Pacific are more frequently disrupted by what appear to be volcanic cones, called *seamounts*, or flattened cones, called *guyots* (Fig. 9-5), which are frequently buried under several kilometers of water. Sometimes volcanic cones like the Hawaiian islands rise above the level of the sea.

Undersea valleys are a prominent feature of many continental margins; the one located off the mouth of the Hudson River is shown in Fig. 9-2. The origin of these *submarine canyons*, as they are called, was a subject of heated debate a decade or two ago, and the problem is not yet entirely settled because different canyons probably have different histories. Of particular interest to researchers on submarine canyons was the discovery that underwater muddy currents (turbidity currents) like the laboratory current of Fig. 9-6 are a significant undersea process. Such underwater rivers arise because turbid waters are denser than clear waters. Turbidity currents are known to play a major role in keeping the submarine canyons open, and many canyons were probably formed by turbidity-current scouring.

In the first third of this century little was known of turbidity currents because they are hidden from view. Consequently the early investigators of submarine

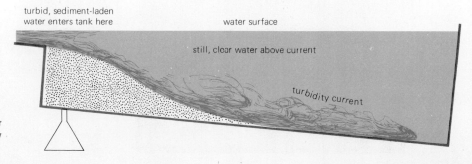

FIGURE 9-6
An experimental underwater turbidity current in a laboratory tank.

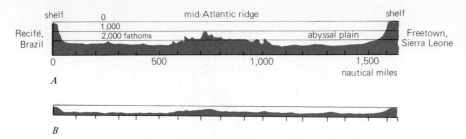

FIGURE 9-7
Two profiles across the Atlantic basin: (A) vertical exaggeration of 40:1; (B) vertical exaggeration of only 10:1. If the vertical and horizontal scales were made equal, the ocean would appear as a line. *Data from B. C. Heezen, M. Tharp, and M. Ewing, The Floors of the Oceans, Geol. Soc. Am. Spec. Pap. 65, 1969.*

canyons naturally attributed their formation to a familiar process, namely stream erosion during a time of lowered sea level. Certainly the sea must have been several hundred feet lower during the geologically recent Ice Age, when a large portion of the earth's water supply was tied up in glacial ice. However, as the ocean depths became more completely plumbed, it became evident that many submarine canyons extended to depths that far exceed even the most liberal estimates of former lowered sea levels. Thus, the interpretation that the canyons were cut by streams was no longer tenable, and it became evident that many must have been carved by subocean turbidity currents.

Before leaving the configuration of the sea floor, with its abyssal plains, continental shelves and slopes, and steep canyons, we must look at the question of scale. In true cross section the major oceans resemble the edge of this page. Even with their apparent staggering depths, the oceans are but thin films of water over our globe. To study and illustrate the configuration of the ocean basins investigators must plot cross sections with a significant vertical exaggeration. Figure 9-7 shows two cross sections of the Atlantic, one with a vertical scale that is 40 times as large as the horizontal scale and the other 10 times. It is only when the vertical scale is significantly exaggerated that we can begin to see some of the details of the Atlantic basin. All other cross sections of the oceans, and for that matter the lands, used in this book are drawn with an appreciable vertical exaggeration.

9-2 THE CHARACTERISTICS OF SEAWATER

Just as winds in the atmosphere are caused primarily by density differences in the air, deep currents in the oceans arise primarily from density differences in seawater. The density of seawater is controlled by three factors, temperature, salinity, and pressure. In its response to temperature changes seawater differs from fresh water. Whereas the density of fresh water increases with decreasing temperature down to 4°C and then decreases between 4° and 0°C, where it freezes into ice, seawater increases in density all the way down to its freezing point at −2°C.

Salinity is a measure of the total amount of dissolved materials in water. It is

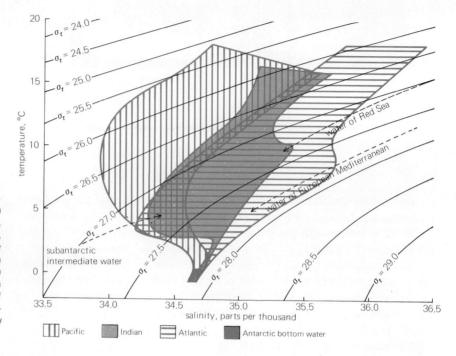

FIGURE 9-8
**The relation between tempera-
ture and salinity below 200
meters for the major oceans.
Density is expressed as** σ_t**,
which is the measured density
at 1 atmosphere pressure (in
grams per cubic centimeter)
times 1,000. Seawater with a
density of 1.0285 has a** σ_t **of
28.5.** *After G. Dietrich, "General Oceanography," John Wiley
& Sons, Inc., 1963.*

frequently expressed in terms of parts per thousand by weight of dissolved salts.
The average salinity of seawater is 34.73 parts per thousand, the salinity of surface waters ranging from 30.5 to 35.7 parts per thousand. The more saline the
water the higher its density. Figure 9-8 illustrates variation in water density with
changes in temperature and salinity and the ranges of temperature and salinity
of the major oceans. Note that the characteristics of Atlantic and Pacific waters
converge toward the value for the dense Antarctic water.

In general, cold or saline waters sink because of their higher densities, while
warm and less salty waters tend to rise. The vertical circulation caused by these
density differences has some important effects. Recall that it takes 1 kilocalorie
of heat energy to raise the temperature of 1 kilogram of water 1°C. By contrast, the
specific heat of, say, lead is only 0.03 kilocalorie. Because water heats and cools
so much more slowly than other materials, the oceans have a tremendous influence on world climates. Dense polar waters sink and move slowly toward the
equatorial regions. At the same time warm tropical surface waters move
poleward to maintain balance. This oceanic circulation shifts vast quantities of
excess heat absorbed from the sun in the tropical regions to the higher latitudes.
Together the oceanic and atmospheric circulation work toward a uniform distribution of heat over the earth.

We have looked at the relationship between temperature, salinity, and water
density. What of pressure? We do not normally think of water as being compressible, but under the tremendous pressures that exist in the deep sea it does

indeed become compressed. In fact, it has been calculated that mean sea level would be some 100 feet higher today if there were no compression of water. To get an idea of the pressures that exist in the deeper parts of the oceans study Fig. 9-9. Normal atmospheric pressure is 14.7 pounds per square inch, or about 2,000 pounds per square foot. At the ocean surface water is under a pressure of 2,000 pounds per square foot. Now consider a cube of water 1 foot on a side located 10,000 feet beneath the surface of the sea. In addition to the 2,000 pounds of air above the top of the cube there is also a column of water 10,000 feet high and 1 foot square. Since 1 cubic foot of uncompressed water weighs 62.4 pounds, the column weighs at least $10,000 \times 1 \times 62.4 = 624,000$ pounds. The total weight or pressure on a square foot of water at a 10,000-foot depth is thus $624,000 + 2,000 = 626,000$ pounds. Small wonder that even a relatively incompressible material like water is compressed somewhat.

One of the significant contributions of the famous *Challenger* expedition of 1873–1876 was the discovery that although the total salinity of seawater varies slightly from place to place, the relative abundances of the major dissolved components are constant. Many thousands of analyses of seawater made since the *Challenger* voyage have added support to this conclusion, and the idea of a uniform (constant) relative abundance of dissolved species has become a law of oceanography. Table 9-1 shows the relative proportions in weight percent for the major ions.

The relative constancy of dissolved ions in seawater makes the job of determining the salinity much easier for the ocean scientist. Thanks to this characteristic, the total salinity of seawater can be determined by analyzing for only one constituent. For example, if a sample of seawater is found to contain 18.0 parts per thousand of dissloved chloride, then, according to Table 9-1, the total salinity must be $\frac{100}{55} \times 18.0 = 32.7$ parts per thousand. With a device like that illustrated in Fig. 9-10 water samples can be collected at any desired depth. Chlorinity, the amount of dissolved chloride ion, is easily determined by titration with a soluble silver salt because silver forms an insoluble precipitate with the chloride ion. Salinity can also be deduced from measurements of the electric conductivity of seawater, which depends upon the amount and kinds of dissolved materials. Since the kinds and proportions of dissolved ions are fixed, conductivity must also be a measure of total salinity.

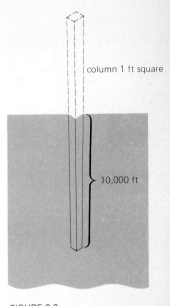

FIGURE 9-9
The pressure on 1 square foot 10,000 feet beneath the ocean surface is equal to the weight of a column of air 1 square foot in cross section extending to the edge of the atmosphere plus the weight of a column of water 1 foot square and 10,000 feet deep.

column 1 ft square

10,000 ft

Ion	Percent of total dissolved material	
Na^+	30.6	TABLE 9-1
K^+	1.1	**The major constituents of sea-**
Mg^{2+}	3.7	**water**
Cl^-	55.0	
SO_4^{2-}	7.7	
Other (HCO_3^-, Br^-, Sr^{2+}, Ca^{2+})	1.9	
	100.00	

FIGURE 9-10

Putting a Nansen bottle on a hydrographic wire. The bottle is used to collect water samples from various parts of the sea. It has valves at both ends and is lowered with them open. At the depth where a sample is desired a cylindrical weight is dropped down the cable; it releases a catch at the upper end of the bottle, causing it to reverse, which in turn closes the valves, thus trapping a water sample. Attached to the bottle are two thermometers. One, protected from the water pressure by a glass case, measures the temperature of the sea where the sample is taken. The second is unprotected and gives a slightly different reading due to the water pressure on the thermometer wall. This difference in temperature can be translated into pressure and hence depth. *Woods Hole Oceanographic Institution.*

Looking at Fig. 9-11, we see that the surface waters on either side of the equator have higher than average salinities and the polar surface waters exhibit the lowest salinities. What causes these differences? To answer this question we must first analyze the factors that control salinity. One is obviously the amount of precipitation; surface waters should be least saline where there is the greatest influx of fresh rainwater. Another thing that influences salinity is evaporation. The waters of the Mediterranean Sea, for example, are more saline than those of the Atlantic because there is more evaporation, particularly in the dry eastern part of the Mediterranean basin. Our reasoning is borne out by the second graph of Fig. 9-11, which is a plot of the average of evaporation minus precipitation against latitude for the world oceans. Where the precipitation is greater than evaporation (negative values for evaporation minus precipitation), the salinity is low because of dilution. Where evaporation is greater than precipitation, the salinity is high because of the loss of fresh water.

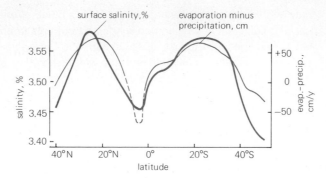

FIGURE 9-11
The changes of surface salinity and evaporation minus precipitation at different latitudes; average for all oceans. *After Wust, from H. U. Sverdrup, M. W. Johnson, and R. H. Fleming, "The Oceans," Prentice-Hall, Inc., 1942.*

Freezing must also affect the salinity because ice contains little or no salt; where it crystallizes, the remaining water is left with the salts to become more saline. However, since measurements reveal that the surface waters near the poles exhibit low salinities, we must conclude that the effect of reduced evaporation near the poles more than offsets the influence of freezing.

We have noted that currents in the deeper parts of the oceans result chiefly from the response of waters of slightly different densities to gravitational forces. Just as denser cold-air masses flow beneath warmer less dense air, waters of greater than normal density tend to move beneath less dense waters. The movement of water masses in the oceans, like that of air masses, is influenced by the Coriolis effect.

Oceanographers use the term *water type* to refer to bodies of water that plot as points on temperature-salinity diagrams such as Fig. 9-8. The Antarctic bottom water shown on that diagram is an example of a water type. It attains its distinctive temperature and salinity at the surface in the Antarctic, where it forms continuously. A *water mass*, on the other hand, is a very large volume of water that can be represented by a line or broad band on a temperature-salinity graph. Water masses result from the slow but continuous mixing of water types (see, for example, in Fig. 9-16).

9-3 SURFACE CIRCULATION IN THE OCEANS

The existence of the Gulf Stream as a major current of the Atlantic Ocean has been known for a long time. Benjamin Franklin published the first map of this current when he was Deputy Postmaster in the late 1700s. His interest in the Gulf Stream was aroused when he noticed that some mail packets took up to 2 weeks longer to make the crossing from Europe than others. A sea captain familiar with the waters of the Atlantic provided Franklin with an explanation for the difference in travel times: the slow ships were bucking an ocean current. Continued observation finally led to the map of the Gulf Stream.

The first comprehensive chart of ocean surface currents was published in 1855 by an American naval officer, Matthew Fontaine Maury. Crippled by an accident at the age of thirty-three, Maury had to give up active service for shore

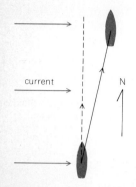

FIGURE 9-12
A ship steering due north will be moved 1 nautical mile off course in an hour by an easterly current of 1 knot.

duty and was placed in charge of the Navy's office of charts and instruments. Lacking sufficient information on winds and currents to prepare correct charts, Maury had special logbooks issued to captains. By analyzing their observations and comparing the actual path of a ship with its heading, or compass direction, he was able to identify and map the major surface currents (Fig. 9-12).

The average global circulation of the oceans is now reasonably well known as a result of years of current measurements using drift bottles and (more recently) current meters. Figure 9-13 is a map of the surface circulation. The wide availability of such maps does not mean that surface currents are completely understood or that there is no need for further work. Detailed studies of the Gulf Stream, for example, show it to shift in position by as much as 300 kilometers within a few days. Moreover, it is now recognized as a series of filaments that shift and bend like the weather systems (Fig. 9-14).

The continuing task of monitoring the details of ocean circulation is complicated. Recognizing short-term fluctuations in ocean currents requires simultaneous measurements at many stations. At present there is no network of observation posts on the seas comparable to the many weather stations on land that record temporal atmospheric changes. Moreover, until fairly recently the problem of studying ocean currents was compounded by the difficulty of locating ships at sea accurately. With the development of radio navigation devices and, more recently, earth satellites for navigation it has become possible to fix locations at sea more exactly and thus to measure some of the finer details of oceanic circulation. New instruments that determine motions of seawater by measuring electric potentials induced as the water moves through the earth's magnetic field have simplified the problem.

Surface currents are driven chiefly by the winds. As we can see in Fig. 9-13 these currents move in great loops, or gyres, which turn clockwise north of the equator and counterclockwise in the Southern Hemisphere. This is just the situation one would expect if the surface circulation were indeed the result of the prevailing winds, as pictured in Fig. 9-15. Our idealized model, however, fails to explain how the actual circulation gyres become shifted westward to form strong currents like the Gulf Stream, the Kuroshio, or the Brazil Current (Fig. 9-13). To account for this westward intensification of the circulation gyres we must introduce another variable into our simplified model, namely the Coriolis effect. This effect is minimal at the equator and increases with latitude. In the Northern Hemisphere the Coriolis effect works to turn the surface currents to the right of the driving winds, whereas in the Southern Hemisphere the turning is to the left. Together these characteristics of the Coriolis effect act to shift the circulation cells westward and thus intensify the western currents.

9-4 DEEP CIRCULATION IN THE OCEANS

Wind-generated surface currents are not the only currents in the oceans. We have already noted that the deep-seated circulation of the oceans is due chiefly to differences in density of water masses. Since water density is determined

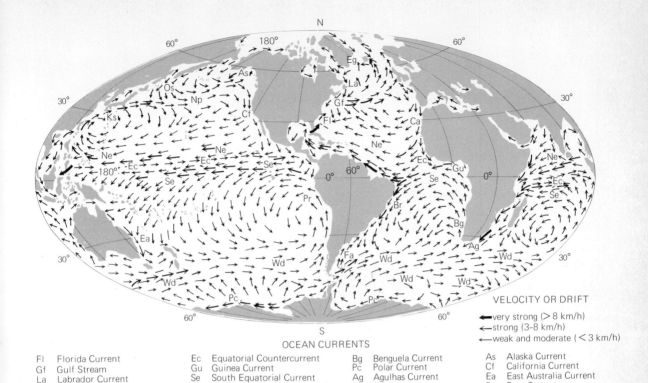

VELOCITY OR DRIFT

⬅ very strong (> 8 km/h)
⬅ strong (3–8 km/h)
⬅ weak and moderate (< 3 km/h)

OCEAN CURRENTS

Fl	Florida Current	Ec	Equatorial Countercurrent	Bg	Benguela Current	
Gf	Gulf Stream	Gu	Guinea Current	Pc	Polar Current	
La	Labrador Current	Se	South Equatorial Current	Ag	Agulhas Current	
Eg	East Greenland Current	Br	Brazil Current	Ks	Kuroshio	
Ca	Canary Current	Fa	Falkland Current	Os	Oyashio	
Ne	North Equatorial Current	Wd	Westwind Drift	Np	North Pacific Current	

As	Alaska Current
Cf	California Current
Ea	East Australia Current
Pr	Peru Current

FIGURE 9-13
Currents at the surface of the world oceans during northern winters. *After G. Dietrich, "General Oceanography," John Wiley & Sons, Inc., 1963.*

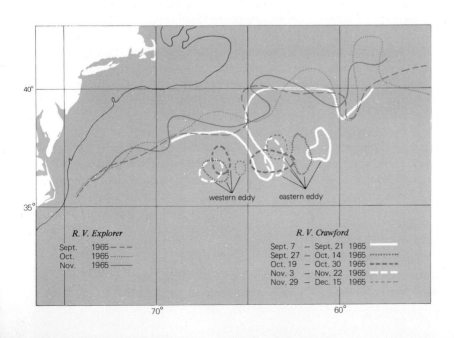

western eddy   eastern eddy

R. V. Explorer

Sept. 1965 ----
Oct.   1965 ········
Nov.   1965 ———

R. V. Crawford

Sept. 7 — Sept. 21 1965 ━━━
Sept. 27 — Oct. 14 1965 ----
Oct. 19 — Oct. 30 1965 ········
Nov. 3 — Nov. 22 1965 ━ ━ ━
Nov. 29 — Dec. 15 1965 ----

FIGURE 9-14
Trend of the Gulf Stream during September to December 1965 as determined by the *R.V. Explorer* **and** *R.V. Crawford.* **Note that the axis of the stream as represented by the various lines moves over significant distances and that eddies are occasionally broken off the main stream.** *Woods Hole Oceanographic Institution.*

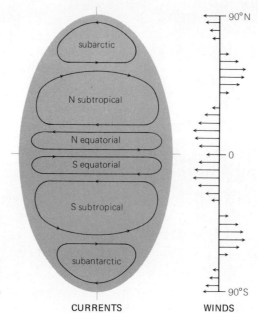

CURRENTS   WINDS

FIGURE 9-15
Surface currents for a hypothet-ical ocean. *P. K. Weyl, "Ocean-ography: An Introduction to the Marine Environment," John Wiley & Sons, Inc., 1970.*

mainly by its temperature and salinity, the deep movements of seawater are called *thermohaline circulation.* We recall that the atmosphere is heated mainly at its base. Differential heating of air causes local expansion, and buoyant forces lift the lighter warm air to start circulation. Ocean water, like the air, is heated by the sun, but the heating is at the top. The sun's rays penetrate at most only a few hundred meters of ocean, and consequently the convective circulation in the oceans differs from that in the atmosphere.

The deep oceanic currents are due mainly to cooling. In the arctic and antarctic regions surface waters become cool enough, and hence dense enough, to flow under the neighboring surface water. Density may be further increased by freezing, which leaves the unfrozen water more saline. Figure 9-16 illustrates how these denser polar water masses are believed to sink and flow toward the equator. For every current, of course, there must be a countercurrent. As the cold polar waters sink, surface waters warmed by the sun in the equatorial belts flow poleward to replace them. Within the ocean, waters of varying origin are stratified as a result of density differences. There is slow but continuous mixing between water masses.

Deep ocean currents are even more difficult to trace than surface ones. Much of the deep circulation is very slow and hard to detect by current meters. Submerged buoys weighted to float at fixed levels are sometimes used to follow deep currents, but the number of measurements made in this way is small because of the time involved in following a single buoy. Therefore, most studies of deep currents are made by indirect methods.

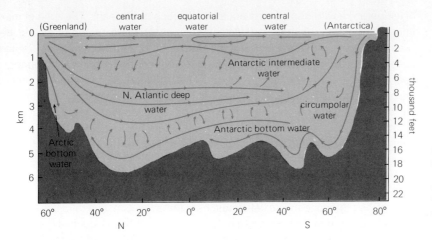

FIGURE 9-16
Diagrammatic cross section of the Atlantic Ocean showing the major water masses and their movements. *After J. Williams, "Oceanography," Copyright © 1962, Little, Brown and Company.*

It is much simpler and faster for the ocean scientist to measure temperature and salinity at various depths than it is to measure currents. As we have seen, the density of seawater can be found from its temperature and salinity. The deep currents can then be computed from the density data by applying the theory of fluid flow. In the simplest case, that of a nonrotating earth, dense water would sink and flow beneath less dense water to form a bottom layer. Just as with atmospheric circulation, however, the actual current paths are complicated by the Coriolis effect. Instead of flowing down the pressure gradient, actual deep currents (like winds) tend to be geostrophic; they are turned from the direction of the pressure gradient by the effect of the earth's spin.

We can see from Fig. 9-17 how the existence of deep currents can be deduced from temperature measurements alone. The graph shows the variation

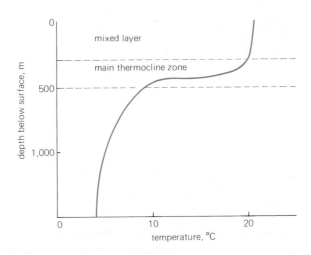

FIGURE 9-17
Variation of temperature with depth in the open ocean at low latitudes.

of temperature with depth in the equatorial parts of the oceans. The zone of maximum temperature change, called the *thermocline*, is a region of mixing between the warm surface water and the denser cold deep water. In the tropical oceans the position of the thermocline does not change significantly during a year or from year to year. We already know that the input of solar energy exceeds the output of radiant energy in the tropics. Therefore, if there were no currents, the thermocline should be continually lowered as more thermal energy is absorbed by the surface waters. Since this is not happening, we conclude that there is a continuous influx of cold water and an outflow of warm surface water which maintains the fixed position of the thermocline.

Although the deep ocean currents are slow, there is a way of following the cold dense bottom water from its source in the polar regions to the deep central parts of the major oceans. In the atmosphere there is a constant ratio between the amounts of carbon 14 and carbon 12 even though ^{14}C is continually formed through the bombardment of nitrogen by cosmic rays. ^{14}C is radioactive and continuously decays back to nitrogen, thus accounting for the unvarying $^{14}C/^{12}C$ ratio in the atmosphere. Because the sea constantly exchanges carbon dioxide with the atmosphere, its surface waters exhibit the same ratio of radiocarbon (^{14}C) to normal carbon (^{12}C) found in the air. Once the surface waters sink, however, they lose contact with the atmosphere, where new ^{14}C is generated. Consequently the amount of ^{14}C decreases as this isotope undergoes radioactive decay.

Measurements of the $^{14}C/^{12}C$ ratios in Antarctic surface water and in the cold bottom waters of the Pacific, which originated in the Antarctic, reveal a steady decrease in the ratio toward the north. The decay rate of ^{14}C, which is known, can be used to calculate the elapsed time since the deep-water samples were last in contact with the surface. Such measurements show that it takes Antarctic water over 500 years to travel from 60°S latitude to 20°N latitude in the Pacific. At first glance this seems almost too slow a movement to accomplish much transfer of heat from the equatorial to the polar regions. When we consider, however, that this is an estimate of the average rate which applies to the total cross-sectional area of deep water in the Pacific, we can see that the total water moved per unit of time is indeed significant.

One of the main goals of geology is to decipher the conditions of the earth's past from evidence preserved in its rocks. Until recently geologists, believing that all deep currents were slow, interpreted current-ripple marks in rocks as evidence of shallow-water deposition. Photographs of the ocean bottom, such as those of Fig. 9-18, taken at depths of about 3 kilometers are evidence of rapid currents in the deeps. Consequently, although the mixing of deep water masses is indeed slow, there are locally relatively fast and erratic currents in the deep parts of the oceans.

We have discussed the surface ocean currents and the deep thermohaline currents separately. They differ in that the surface circulation is driven chiefly by the wind, whereas the deep circulation involves convective vertical motion caused by density differences. Because of the nature of fluids, however, the two

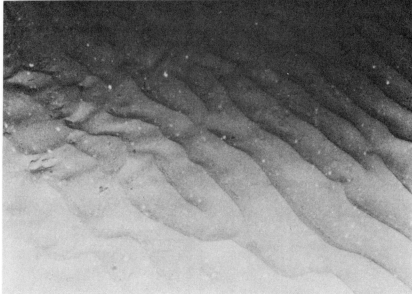

FIGURE 9-18
These ripple marks in the bottom sediments at a depth of about 1,800 fathoms in the South Pacific are evidence of rapid currents in the deep parts of the sea. *Woods Hole Oceanographic Institution.*

types of current are interrelated. A surface current moving away from a coast, for example, must be balanced by a countercurrent because of water's tendency to form a level surface. For this reason, cold deep waters upwell along some coastlines where the surface flow is away from the coast, bringing with them nutrients to support large populations of fish and other forms of marine life. The thermohaline circulation thus is modified by the surface circulation and vice versa.

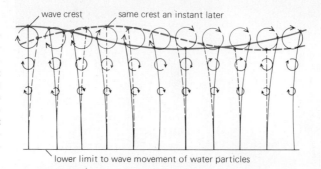

FIGURE 9-19
Water particles in a deep water wave move through circular orbits. The full lines indicate the positions of water particles at one instant, and the dashed lines show the same particles one-quarter period later. Almost no motion occurs at depths of over one-half wavelength. *After U.S. Navy Hydrographic Office Publ. 11.*

9-5 WAVES AND SHORELINES

Anyone who has spent much time on the water has noticed the discrepancy between the movement of floating objects and the movement of the waves. Floating objects do not share in the apparent horizontal motion of the waves but bob up and down instead. Studies made in tanks show the motion of particles in water waves to be as illustrated in Fig. 9-19. Instead of moving laterally, the individual particles of water involved in wave motion oscillate in nearly circular orbits. At a depth of about one-half wavelength the motion of the water particles has decreased almost to zero.

Although water waves are deceptive in appearing to transport water on a large scale, they do transport energy. Figure 9-20 illustrates circular wavefronts being generated in a wave tank. These waves transfer energy from the vibrators to the tank walls, just as the waves from a pebble tossed into a pond transfer the stone's kinetic energy to the shoreline.

To understand waves on water we must be familiar with the terminology and behavior of ideal waves. Figure 9-21 is a drawing of a wave with the parts labeled. The distance between adjacent wave crests is called the *wavelength*. The vertical distances between trough and crest is the *wave height*. The time required for a crest to reappear at any one location is the *wave period*. A wave with a period of 10 seconds would repeat 6 times per minute. This rate is called its *frequency*. We can thus see that the speed of a water wave is equal to its frequency times its wavelength.

Experiments in wave tanks and the theory of wave motion show that the wavelength of an ideal water wave is related to its period according to the relation $L = (g/2\pi)\ T^2$, where L is the wavelength, g is the acceleration of gravity, and T is the period. Notice that only wavelength (not height) is related to period. Wave height depends upon the energy put into the wave. For a given wavelength, however, there is an upper limit to wave height. Experiments show the maximum height of a wave to be about one-seventh its length. Waves steeper than this tend to break at their crests.

So far we have been discussing ideal waves. The waves of the sea seem to

FIGURE 9-20
The interference of water waves. As they spread out from the two vibrating sources, the ripples reinforce each other along the line AB **but interfere and cancel each other along the line** CD. *From "PSSC Physics," D. C. Heath and Company, 1965.*

bear little relation to these simple waves, but we must realize that waves at the sea surface almost always represent a combination of waves from many sources. When waves from separate sources come together, interference results. Two waves of about equal wavelength and height which meet so that crest matches crest produce resultant waves with amplitudes double that of the original waves. This is *constructive interference*. On the other hand, when waves of similar height and length meet so that the trough of one coincides with the crest of the other, the wave motion cancels out. This is *destructive interference*. In Fig. 9-20 the line AB illustrates constructive interference: the crests are high and well marked. Along the line CD the crests of the resultant waves are small or absent,

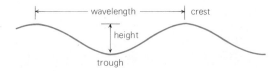

FIGURE 9-21
The parts of a wave.

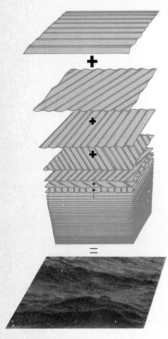

due to destructive interference. Ocean waves from many sources combine with both constructive and destructive interference to form the choppy surface known as the *sea* (Fig. 9-22).

If a wave is moving over deep water, no motion is transmitted to the bottom water; but what if the waves are moving in shallow water? Where the depth of water is less than one-half the wavelength we would predict from Fig. 9-19 that there should be some interaction between the wave and the bottom material. Experiments support this prediction. Shallow-water waves are more complicated than waves in deep water and behave according to somewhat different rules.

The influence of water depth on waves produces some interesting phenomena. Figure 9-23 shows how waves are refracted, or bent, in moving from deep to shallow water. Since water depth usually decreases shoreward, refraction accounts for the curious fact that waves usually move toward the shore regardless of the irregularity of the shoreline (Fig. 9-24). Refraction also explains why prominences of land or headlands like that diagrammed in Fig. 9-25 are eroded more rapidly than embayed areas. As they reach shallow water and begin to "feel" the bottom, waves are refracted, with the result that more of their energy is focused

FIGURE 9-22
The rough surface of the ocean, called the sea, results from the superposition of many regular wave patterns of varying direction, wavelength, and amplitude. *U.S. Navy Hydrographic Office Publ. 603.*

FIGURE 9-23
The refraction of water waves in a shallow tank. Waves move more slowly in the shallower water on the left side of the tank and hence are refracted. *From "PSSC Physics," D. C. Heath and Company, 1965.*

FIGURE 9-24
**Wave refraction along a coast-
line.** *U.S. Navy photograph.*

on the headlands. This concentration of most of their erosive force on prominences tends to straighten out irregular shorelines, a process further aided by
the deposition of sediment in bays.

As a wave moves into increasingly shallow water along a coast, the kinetic
energy of its orbital motions must become concentrated in less and less water.
Shoaling of water makes the wavelength decrease and wave height increase,
with the result that the wave becomes too steep for stability. Motion at depth is
prohibited by the shallow water, and thus movement must be concentrated in the
crest, which is already too steep. As a result the waveform collapses and
becomes a breaker, in which the oscillitory motion has been changed into an actual forward transport of water onto the shore.

Water thus set into lateral motion by the breakers washes forward and back

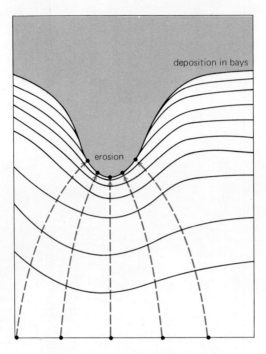

FIGURE 9-25
Because waves are bent toward the shore as they approach shallow water, a high proportion of wave energy becomes focused on prominences. This works to wear them back and smooth the coastline.

across the beach, keeping the particles of sand in motion. How the sand moves depends upon the character of the waves and the resulting surf. Figure 9-26 shows the profile of the beach at Carmel, California, on different dates. The amount of sand exposed in September is about 300 feet wider than that exposed in April. An analysis of the waves in the region reveals that in winter large storm waves are common, whereas the waves of summer, while persistent, are small. The small waves seem able to pick sand up from the buried part of the beach and deposit it on the shore, while the large storm waves wash the sand from the exposed beach back into the sea.

FIGURE 9-26
Beaches change constantly. The cross section shows the beach at Carmel, California, during the spring and summer. Sand builds up over the summer to be removed by the waves of winter. Vertical exaggeration is 10:1. *From Willard Bascom, "Beaches." Copyright © 1960 by Scientific American, Inc. All rights reserved.*

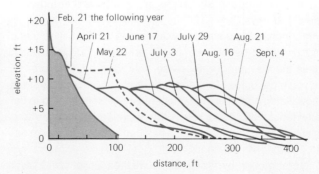

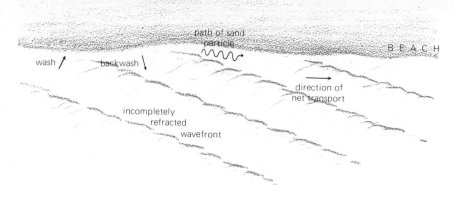

FIGURE 9-27
Waves approaching a shoreline at an angle are often not completely refracted. When such waves break their wash hits the shore at a slight angle. The result, as shown above, is that sand grains in the beach zone are moved back and forth with a net transport along the beach in the direction of the waves. Currents thus generated are called longshore or littoral currents.

Sand in the beach zone does not move only toward or away from the shore. In fact, most of the coastal transport of sand is actually in a longshore direction. Although refraction tends to bend waves toward the shorelines, the bending is often not complete, so that waves frequently arrive obliquely at the shore. Where the waves strike the shore at an angle, longshore, or littoral, currents develop. Time-lapse photographs of marked sand particles or observations of dye dropped into the water reveal a motion like that illustrated in Fig. 9-27.

That such longshore movement of sand occurs is evident where manmade structures interfere with the transport. For example, beach sand typically piles up behind groins, which are retaining walls built perpendicular to the shore. Similarly, beaches tend to widen where offshore breakwaters shield the shoreline and cut off the energy for longshore drift. Such structures retard the longshore motion only temporarily because the moving sand eventually fills in the structures and continues along the shore. Natural sandbars, called *spits* and *baymouth bars*, are further evidence of massive longshore transport of sand (Fig. 9-28).

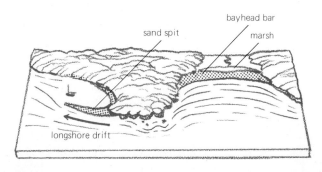

FIGURE 9-28
Sand spits, bayhead bars, and related features are further evidence for the continual longshore transport of sand. *Adapted from "Principles of Geology," 3d ed., by James Gilluly, Aaron C. Waters, and A. O. Woodford. W.H. Freeman and Company. Copyright ©1968.*

Energy from the wind is transformed into wave motion in various parts of the seas. Some of the energy input is transformed into heat by the wave motion, but a significant remainder is eventually transferred to the shorelines. Breakers crashing against a coast grind up rock. Currents resulting from wave action move sediment in the beach zone. Slowly but steadily this expenditure of energy along the earth's coastlines works to straighten the coastal configuration.

9-6 SEDIMENTS ON THE DEEP OCEAN FLOORS

Most of the great bulk of material eroded from the land each year by rivers, wind, or glaciers finds its way to the sea. Of the erosional agents streams are by far the most productive transporters of sediment. A river is able to keep sediment in suspension and move it downstream because of its energy of motion. When the ribbon of moving water reaches the sea, both its motion and its sediment-carrying capacity slow to a stop. As a result sediment is steadily dumped at the ocean margin. The coarsest particles settle quickly, followed by successively finer grains. Even the finest particles tend to cluster together (flocculate) and settle out when they come in contact with the ions of seawater.

We have seen how longshore currents move the sediment in the beach zone. Waves, tidal currents, and other subsurface ocean currents also work to redistribute the sediment delivered to the edges of the continents. Most of the sedimentary rocks exposed on the continents today are of the type formed at the continental margins. The structure and texture of these land-derived sediments will be discussed in greater detail in Chap. 14.

In this section our interest is chiefly in the sediments of the deep portions of the seas. Borings and indirect measurements both reveal that sediment thicknesses are much less in the ocean deeps than at the continental shelves. This we would expect from our observation that most of the land-derived sediment is first dumped at the edge of the sea. How does any sediment work its way to the central parts of the oceans?

To answer this question we must know something of the types of sedimentary materials found on the ocean floors. The first detailed study of such material was made on samples collected by the *Challenger* expedition of the 1870s. Scientists studying the *Challenger* samples recognized two main types of deep-water sediments, which they called *pelagic* and *terrigenous*. The term pelagic refers to the open sea. In samples taken from the floors of the central parts of the oceans they found red clays, calcareous oozes, and siliceous oozes. Terrigenous means from the land. Near islands the samples taken by the *Challenger* contained material such as volcanic muds or coral sand that was clearly land-derived.

From the composition of the pelagic sediments we get clues to their origin. Many samples from the deep-sea bottoms contain the remains of organisms known to inhabit the open oceans. Indeed, the remains of coccoliths, foraminiferans, and pteropods are major constituents of the calcareous oozes (Fig. 9-29).

FIGURE 9-29
**Fossil remains of coccolitho-
phorids from the tropical Indian
Ocean taken from depth of
5,140 meters. These tiny organisms (magnification 5,400) live
in the upper reaches of warm
seas. Their skeletons are made
of calcium carbonate.** *Photographed through a Zeiss EM
9A electron microscope; elec-
tron-microscope preparation
by W.R. Riedel and Annika San
Fillipo, Scripps Institution of
Oceanography.*

These organisms, which have *tests* (external skeletons) composed of calcium
carbonate, $CaCO_3$, swim or float in the upper sunlit layers of the open sea. When
they die, their skeletons fall slowly to the bottom. Radiolarians and diatoms have
hard parts composed of silica, SiO_2; their remains are abundant in the siliceous
oozes. Other less abundant life forms contain shells made of phosphatic material
or sulfates. Because the tests of organisms are composed of material removed
from the sea, the ultimate source for the $CaCO_3$ or the SiO_2 in the pelagic oozes is
the land, which, by weathering, replenishes the sea's storehouse of dissolved
materials.

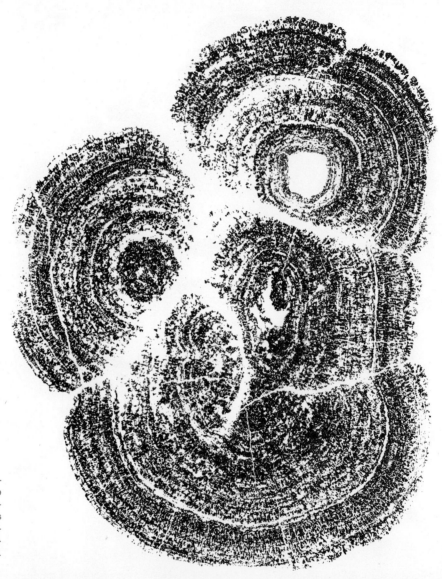

FIGURE 9-30
Cross-sectional view of a manganese nodule from the deep sea floor. The onion-skin layering shows that such nodules grow within the ocean from material precipitated from seawater. *Courtesy of Raymond C. Gutschick.*

New minerals also form in the sea by inorganic precipitation of the dissolved ions in seawater. Figure 9-30 is a cross section of a manganese nodule from the floor of the Indian Ocean. The circular growth rings and the shape of the nodule are convincing evidence that the manganese and iron oxide composing the nodule were precipitated from seawater. In certain parts of the deep ocean basins photographs show that such nodules locally cover the sea floor completely (Fig.

FIGURE 9-31
Manganese nodules on the floor of the Pacific Ocean at a depth of 5,000 meters. *Photograph taken from USNS El-tanin. Courtesy of National Science Foundation.*

9-31). In fact, there is considerable activity today toward developing commerical techniques for "mining" these nodules. In addition to manganese, many nodules are rich in elements like copper and cobalt.

The clays of the deep sea consist largely of solid weathered material from the land. The term *clay* is used in two ways by geologists. Clay minerals are aluminum silicates with potassium, magnesium, or calcium. Formed by surface weathering of silicate rocks, these minerals are extremely fine-grained. Clay also refers to any sediment with an average size of less than $\frac{1}{256}$ millimeter. In this sense clay usually contains clay minerals, because they are so fine-grained, but it may also contain fine particles of quartz, feldspar, and other silicates. Fine clay-sized particles are brought to the central parts of the oceans by the wind. Much of the haze observed over the ocean is wind-blown dust, which settles very slowly to the sea bottom. In the polar regions glaciers bring finely ground rock to the seas. Even some of the fine-grained material brought to the sea by rivers may settle so slowly that it is carried to the open sea by waves and currents.

Earlier we noted that the particles carried by a river begin to settle when the motion of the river stops. As one would expect, the rate of settling of a given particle depends upon its size. For spherical particles with radii of less than $\frac{1}{10}$ millimeter the velocity of settling is predicted by a relation known as *Stokes' law*:

$$v = \frac{2r^2(e_1 - e_2)g}{9\eta}$$

FIGURE 9-32

(*A*) **Sedimentary layers that settle from turbidity currents exhibit graded bedding, i.e., a gradation in grain size from bottom to top. (*B*) We can see how graded beds form by imagining a mixture of sediment stirred up in a glass cylinder. When the stirring stops, the coarsest particles fall fastest, but since some fine particles are already near the bottom, the resulting sediment, despite the fines concentrated at the top, has some clay sizes throughout. Graded beds are also usually clayey sands.**

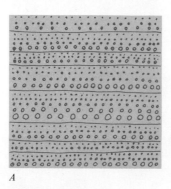

A

B

where v = settling velocity

r = radius of particle

e_1 = density of particle

e_2 = density of fluid

g = acceleration of gravity

η = viscosity of fluid

We can see that for any two particles of equal density the settling velocity in water is proportional to the square of the radius because the other terms in the equation do not change. Thus if a particle with a radius of $\frac{1}{100}$ millimeter settles at the rate of 0.025 centimeter per second, the settling velocity of a particle one-tenth as large would be $(\frac{1}{10})^2 = \frac{1}{100}(0.025) = 0.00025$ centimeter per second. A grain of clay settling at 0.00025 centimeter per second will require over 1 year to fall through 100 meters of water. During that time the particle may well be moved many kilometers by even the weakest of ocean currents. Thus some of the clay-sized material brought to the sea by rivers may be carried beyond the limits of the continental shelves to fall eventually to the ocean deeps.

In Sec. 9-1 we discussed flows of dense turbid water beneath clear water and their role in carving submarine canyons. Such turbidity currents, coursing down a submarine canyon or starting as mud slides at the margin of the continental shelf, provide a mechanism for moving coarser particles to the ocean deeps. Deposits from turbidity currents have a distinguishing texture. Picture a mixture of grain sizes in suspension in a moving turbid undercurrent. When the flow completes its downhill run and uses up its kinetic energy, the particles settle, to form a blanket deposit. The coarser grains, settling the fastest, will be concentrated near the bottom of the bed, and the finer ones will be more abundant near the top. This gradation of grain size from coarse to fine within a layer is known as *graded bedding* (Fig. 9-32).

Recent studies suggest that turbidity currents may indeed be the chief mechanism for transporting land-derived sediment to the more central parts of the ocean basins. Turbidity-current deposits are common in the continental rise, and some cores taken from the deep parts of the Atlantic exhibit graded bedding. Now we can see how some of the abyssal plains referred to in Sec. 9-1 might have formed. Turbidity currents offer an effective means not only of bringing particles of sediment to the deep sea but also of smoothing the sediment already there.

Recapitulating, we have found that the materials of deep-sea sediments fall into two groups according to origin: (*1*) minerals precipitated from seawater (*chemical fraction*), either directly or through the action of organisms, and (*2*) fine particles of minerals or rocks brought as discrete grains (*clastic fraction*) from the lands. Before leaving this subject, let us briefly examine the distribution of these classes of material in the sediments.

We must recognize that sedimentation in the deep sea is a very slow process. The bulk of the chemical fraction in the deep-sea sediments is in the form of shells of tiny animals that lived in the surface waters. The clastic fraction is chiefly clay-sized particles which, like the shells, settled slowly to the deep-sea floor from the surface. We might suspect that these two *genetic* classes of material would be uniformly mixed in typical deep-sea sediments. This, however, is not the case.

To illustrate the variation in the ratio of the chemical to the clastic fraction in actual sediments, we shall consider the distribution of calcium carbonate, $CaCO_3$, in deep-sea deposits because it is the most abundant of the chemical fraction. Figure 9-33 shows the concentration of $CaCO_3$ in the sediments of the Atlantic floor. The highest concentrations are found in the shallow regions near the continents and along the mid-Atlantic ridge. There is good reason for this. The solubility of $CaCO_3$ increases with depth, becoming marked at depths of over 4,000 meters. At depths of less than 4,000 meters, e.g., along the mid-Atlantic ridge, $CaCO_3$ accumulates along with clay and other materials. At greater depths the calcareous remains of animals that slowly rain down become redissolved by the seawater, with the result that clastic particles predominate in the bottom materials.

9-7 CYCLES OF THE SEA

We know that the rivers of the world continually pour water into the sea, and there is ample evidence that they have been doing this for several billion years. An estimate based on flow measurements shows that the rivers now carry some 37×10^3 cubic kilometers of water to the sea each year. Since the oceans have a volume of about $1,370 \times 10^6$ cubic kilometers, we can see that at the present rate the rivers would completely fill the ocean basins in $(1,370 \times 10^6)/(37 \times 10^3) = 37,000$ years. Man has kept records of sea level for several hundred years—long enough to recognize that the level of the sea is not

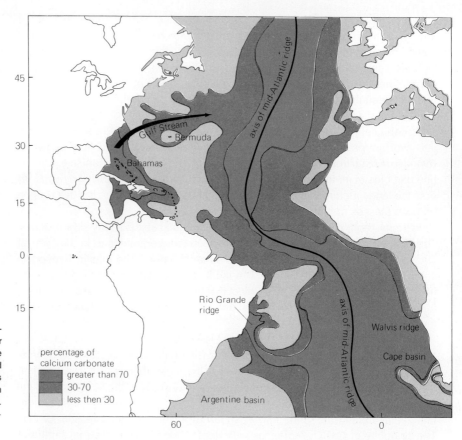

FIGURE 9-33
The distribution of calcium carbonate on the deep ocean floor of the Atlantic Ocean. The highest values are associated with the ridges and with areas of high biological activity such as the Gulf Stream. *After K. K. Turekian, "Oceans," Prentice-Hall, Inc., 1968.*

being raised by this steady influx from the rivers. The amount of water added to the oceans each year by the rivers is balanced by water lost by evaporation. The water of the seas is simply recycled. The value of 37,000 years thus represents the time it takes for rivers to completely recycle a volume of water equal to that in the oceans. It represents the mean residence time of river water in the oceans. What about the other materials that are added annually to the seas? Do they continually build up in the sea, or are they, like water, in a state of balance?

One of the early attempts to arrive at a numerical value for the age of the earth was based on the premise that the sodium added to the seas annually by the world's rivers accumulated in seawater, gradually increasing its salinity. That most of the sodium in the seawater came originally from weathering solutions from the lands is a reasonable assumption because no other significant source of sodium ions has been discovered If the sodium ions brought to the seas by rivers stay in the sea and are not recycled, the number obtained by dividing the total amount of sodium in the sea by the annual input should represent the age of the oceans. Such an estimate was first made in 1898 by John Joly, an Irish geologist, who reported that the oceans were between 80 and 90 million years old.

Since Joly made his initial calculation many more analyses of river water have been made, and the estimate of the annual supply rate of sodium to the seas is known more exactly. More important, studies have shown that much more sodium finds it way back to the land via the atmosphere than Joly suspected. Any calculation of the age of the sea based upon the rate of sodium influx must therefore be corrected for sodium that is recycled through the atmosphere. Even taking into account the recycled sodium and using modern estimates of river salinities and flows the value of (total sodium in ocean water)/(annual input of sodium by rivers) still comes out to only about 200 million years. We know that the earth is about 4.5 billion years old and that the oceans cannot be much younger. Obviously the value obtained by dividing the total sodium in the oceans by the annual sodium input does not give the age of the oceans. We must think of this number instead as the average time a sodium ion spends in the oceans. Just as rivers bring enough water to the oceans to completely fill them in about 37,000 years, so they carry sufficient sodium to completely replace the sea's storehouse of sodium ions in about 200 million years.

Table 9-2 gives average values of the relative abundance of the major dissolved materials in river water and in seawater. Seawater, of course, has a much higher total percentage of dissolved solids than river water does, but here we are concerned with the proportions of the dissolved ions. We can see from Table 9-2 that river water contains on the average $20.4/5.8 = 3.5$ times as much calcium as sodium in solution. By contrast seawater contains $30.6/1.2 = 25.5$ times as much sodium as calcium in solution. How can this be?

The dissolved materials in river water are weathering solutions from the land. There is ample geologic evidence that weathering has proceeded for hundreds of millions of years in much the same fashion as it does today. The gross difference in the relative abundances of sodium and calcium in seawater and river water must therefore be due to oceanic processes which give calcium a much lower mean residence time than sodium.

We can compute the mean residence time for calcium as we did earlier for sodium by dividing the total amount of calcium dissolved in seawater by the annual influx of calcium. The result turns out to be only about 1 million years, which is

TABLE 9-2
Average abundances of the major ions dissolved in river and seawater expressed in percent of total dissolved material

Constituent	River water	Seawater
HCO_3	35.2	0.4
SO_4^{2-}	12.1	7.7
Cl^-	5.7	55.0
Ca^{2+}	20.4	1.2
Mg^{2+}	3.4	3.7
Na^+	5.8	30.6
K^+	2.1	1.1
SiO_2	11.7	Trace

indeed very much smaller than the 200 million years for sodium. We have only to look at the sediments of the ocean floors and the marine sediments of the continents to find where the large quantities of calcium brought to the sea each year end up. The calcareous oozes and the great quantities of marine limestone on the continents are deposits of calcium carbonate that formed from the dissolved materials brought to the sea.

Silica is a significant dissolved constituent of river water but only a trace constituent of seawater. In Sec. 9-6 we noted that radiolarians and diatoms abstract silica from seawater and that when these organisms die, their siliceous skeletons fall to the sea bottom to build up siliceous sediments. Silica also remains in the sea for only a short time.

The seas not only are vast storehouses of dissolved materials; they also are the main receptacle for the solid materials eroded from the lands. Yet neither have they become filled with sediment over the eons of geologic time nor has the composition of seawater changed significantly over the past few hundred million years. Recent evidence shows that the ocean basins are not static troughs existing as such since early in the earth's history. As we shall see in Chap. 15, there is strong evidence that the sea floors are spreading apart at the ocean ridge systems. This spreading is related to the generation of new oceanic crust along the ridge systems and the assimilation of older oceanic rock at some continental boundaries. So far no rocks older than about 200 million years have been found in ocean-bottom materials or in oceanic islands. The ocean basins are truly a dynamic part of the earth.

SUMMARY

The rocks and structures of the continents continue under the waters of the sea to the edge of the continental shelf, where the continental slope, which joins the shelf and the abyssal parts of the sea bottom, marks the true boundary of the ocean basins. Fans of sediment from the shelf line the lower limit of the continental slope. This sediment is largely material deposited from underwater turbid flows, which also are thought to be chiefly responsible for submarine canyons dissecting parts of both the continental shelf and continental slope.

Seawater contains an average of 3.5 percent dissolved solids, of which about 85 percent is NaCl. Although waters from different parts of

the oceans vary slightly in total salinity, the relative abundance of the dissolved materials is constant. The density of seawater depends mainly upon its total salinity and its temperature.

Surface circulation in the oceans is chiefly the result of interaction between winds and the sea surface. Deep circulation is effected by the action of gravity on waters of different density. Cold dense polar waters flow beneath the warmer surface waters. Like the winds, oceanic circulation is modified by the Coriolis effect. The overall movement of ocean water works to distribute solar energy more uniformly over the globe. It is the uneven heating of the globe that creates the winds and the density differences in water masses.

Wave motion is a means of transferring energy from one place to another. Winds generate waves in various parts of the sea, and much of this energy is ultimately transferred to the shorelines. Breakers crashing against the shore erode the land. Waves and littoral currents continually sift, sort, and redistribute the sediment along a coastline.

Most of the sediment brought to the oceans by the rivers is deposited along the margins of the continents. The deep-sea bottoms contain mainly material that has been chemically or biochemically precipitated from seawater or fine clay-sized particles. Submarine turbidity currents are the only significant means of moving coarser particles from the shelf areas to the deep-sea regions.

The oceans are the ultimate dumping ground for the solid debris and weathering solutions from the lands. The steady influx of dissolved material into the sea has not significantly changed the composition of seawater over the past 600 million years. Some elements, like calcium, remain in the sea for comparatively short periods. The rivers bring to the oceans an amount of calcium that would replace all the calcium now in seawater in about 1 million years, but calcium is continually removed from the sea in the form of lime deposits on the sea floor. Other elements, like sodium, build up in seawater and have relatively long mean residence times. Even the solid debris brought to the ocean basins must have been continually removed because sediments older than 200 million years have not been found on the sea floor and most sediments are considerably younger.

QUESTIONS

1 What is the speed of a wave having a period of 10 seconds and a wavelength of 50 meters?

2 If a particle with a radius of $\frac{1}{10}$ millimeter settles at 0.1 centimeter per second, how fast would a particle 1/1,000 millimeter in radius settle in the same fluid?

3 What type of sediment would you expect to be abundant along the flanks of the continental slope?

4 Calcium is the principal positive ion in river water whereas sodium is the most abundant ion in seawater. How can this be when the dissolved materials in the seas came from the rivers?

5 How can measurements of temperature and salinity be used to evaluate deep currents?

6 The Pacific basin is separated from the surrounding continental masses by deep trenches. How would such trenches influence turbidity-current action in the central parts of the Pacific? Would you expect the Pacific to have as many turbidity-current deposits as the Atlantic?

7 What classes of materials are found in deep-sea sediments?

8 The continental slope marks the true boundary between continental and oceanic crust. How do the two types of crust differ?

9 Why are prominences and headlands eroded more rapidly by waves than bays?

10 Why do waves behave differently in shallow and deep water?

11 The circulation of both the atmosphere and the hydrosphere arises because of the unequal heating of the globe by the sun. How do the two differ?

12 What causes variations in the salinity of seawater from place to place?

13 What makes sand travel laterally along the beach zone?

14 At the Straits of Gibraltar there is a surface flow of Atlantic water into the Mediterranean and a counterbalancing bottom current out of the Mediterranean. How do you account for this?

15 A ship traveling due north at 6 knots (nautical miles per hour) finds itself 1 nautical mile east of its course at the end of 1 hour. Can you tell what currents it encountered from the information given?

16 Using the relation $L = (g/2\pi)T^2$, what is the length of a water wave with a period of 1 second? What is the length of a wave with a period of 3 seconds? ($g = 32$ feet per second per second; $\pi = 3.14$.)

REFERENCES

Bascom, Willard: "Waves and Beaches," Doubleday & Company, Garden City, N.Y., 1964.

Bates, D. R.: "The Planet Earth," Pergamon Press, New York, 1964.

Carson, Rachel L.: "The Sea around Us," (rev. ed.), Oxford University Press, New York, 1961.

Gross, Grant M.: "Oceanography," Charles E. Merrill Books, Inc., Columbus, Ohio, 1971.

———: "Oceanography: A View of the Earth," Prentice-Hall, Inc., Englewood Cliffs, N.J., 1972.

King, C. A. M.: "An Introduction to Oceanography," McGraw-Hill Book Company, New York, 1963.

"The Ocean," A Scientific American Book, W. H. Freeman and Company, San Francisco, 1969.

"Oceanography," A Scientific American Book, W. H. Freeman and Company, San Francisco, 1971.

Pickard, G. L.: "Descriptive Physical Oceanography," Pergamon Press, New York, 1963.

Turekian, Karl K.: "Oceans," Prentice-Hall, Inc., Englewood Cliffs, N.J., 1968.

Weyl, Peter K.: "Oceanography: An Introduction to the Marine Environment," John Wiley & Sons, Inc., New York, 1970.

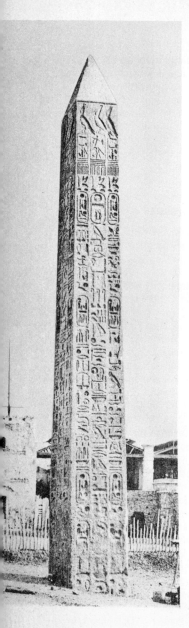

A

FIGURE 10-1
Cleopatra's Needle (*A*) after standing for over 3,000 years in Egypt and (*B*) after less than a century's exposure in Central Park, New York where artificial preservatives were finally applied to protect the remaining markings. *Courtesy of the Metropolitan Museum of Art.*

B

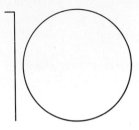

WEATHERING AND CLIMATE

In earlier chapters we referred to the products of weathering and their transportation to the oceans by rivers and other erosional agents. But what of the process of weathering itself? Precisely what makes rocks exposed at the earth's surface crumble and decompose? Do all rocks weather alike? How, in detail, is weathering related to climate?

If anyone doubts that weathering depends on the weather, the classic case of Cleopatra's Needle should prove convincing. As Fig. 10-1 shows, the markings on this granite obelisk remained perfectly clear during 20 centuries of exposure to the Egyptian climate, yet they were almost erased in a few *short* decades of exposure in New York's Central Park. The photographs of Fig. 10-2 showing gravestones of roughly the same age in the same cemetery tell another story. Since these stones were exposed to the same climatic elements, we must conclude that rock types differ significantly in their resistance to weathering.

To know that climate plays a role in weathering and that rocks differ in their weathering resistance is not enough. To understand the relation between weathering and climate we must first investigate the characteristics of the major climate types; to explain why one mineral weathers faster than another we must study the chemical reactions involved in mineral decomposition. To appreciate the interrelationships between soil, climate, and rock type we must learn what products of weathering accumulate to form soils.

FIGURE 10-2
Gravestones of about the same age in the West Willington, Connecticut, cemetery have been exposed to the same climatic conditions. Not only do stones made of different rocks weather at varying rates, but they also weather differently. (*A*) Sandstone (right) breaks down fastest by scaling; marble (left) also weathers relatively fast, but it does so without significant scaling. (*B*) Granite is most stable. *Courtesy of Perry H. Rahn.*

A

B

TABLE 10-1
Mean monthly temperature (°F) at St. Louis, Mo., and Quito, Ecuador, throughout the year

	St. Louis	Quito
Jan.	32	59
Feb.	34.5	59
Mar.	45	58.5
Apr.	56	58.5
May	66	58.5
June	75	58
July	79.5	58
Aug.	78	59
Sept.	71	59
Oct.	59	59
Nov.	48	58.5
Dec.	35.5	59
Year	56.5	59

TABLE 10-2
Mean monthly rainfall (inches) at St. Johns, Newfoundland, and Bathurst, Gambia

	St. Johns	Bathurst
Jan.	5.3	0.1
Feb.	4.9	0.1
Mar.	4.6	0.0
Apr.	4.2	0.0
May	3.6	0.4
June	3.5	2.3
July	3.5	11.1
Aug.	3.7	19.7
Sept.	3.8	12.2
Oct.	5.3	4.3
Nov.	5.9	0.7
Dec.	5.5	0.1
Total (year)	53.8	51.0

10-1 CLIMATES

In Chap. 8 we discussed the motions of the atmosphere and the elements of weather. Weather is the combination of temperature, air pressure, wind, rain or snow, cloud cover, etc., at a particular time and place. Climate has been defined as the weather over an extended period of time or the statistical average of weather at any place. A single thunderstorm or even a momentary gust of wind is part of the weather. The total precipitation of many rainstorms and the distribution of thunderstorms in time are characteristics of the climate of a region.

The principal climatic determinants are temperature and precipitation, but it is difficult to define a climate in terms of these two elements alone. Average yearly temperature by itself, for instance, is not a good measure of climate. The mean annual temperature at St. Louis, Missouri, and at Quito, Ecuador, are about the same: yet these places have markedly different thermal climates. From Table 10-1 we can see that the mean monthly temperature at St. Louis fluctuates by 47.5°F during the year whereas at Quito there is only a 1°F spread in the monthly averages. An even greater difference exists in the ranges of mean daily temperatures at the two places.

Similarly, two regions may experience the same total annual precipitation and yet be very different. Table 10-2 shows the monthly rainfall at St. Johns, Newfoundland, and Bathurst, Gambia. Whereas the total precipitation is about the same at both places, the distribution of rainfall throughout the year is very different. At Bathurst over 90 percent of the yearly rain falls during the period from July to October, and the months from December through March are almost completely dry. On the other hand, the rain at St. Johns is more or less uniformly distributed throughout the year. Climate thus cannot be considered merely as the average yearly weather. The annual variation in temperature or the yearly distribution of precipitation are as significant as the mean temperature or total precipitation in determining the climate of a region.

Even the yearly variation of climatic elements gives only part of the overall picture. Diurnal changes in temperature are a further characteristic of climate. The diagrams of Fig. 10-3 illustrate a method of presenting both the annual and diurnal variation in the temperature of a locality. The lines on the diagram are *thermoisopleths*, lines of equal temperature. The ordinate represents the hour of the day and the abcissa the month of the year. The thermoisopleth diagram for Belém, Brazil, shows the noon temperature (12 hours) to vary by only 1° throughout the year. A vertical line drawn through any date gives the daily variation in temperature. For example, on an average April day the temperature at Belém reaches a high of 29°C and a low of 24°C.

The thermoisopleths of Fig. 10-3 illustrate some ranges in annual and diurnal temperature variations and show how temperature and precipitation are sometimes related. At Belém, the climate provides a greater daily than annual temperature range. As we noted, the noon temperature there varies by less than 2°C during the year, whereas the daily temperature range is consistently about 6°C. At the other extreme, the thermoisopleth map for Sagastyr, U.S.S.R., exhibits almost

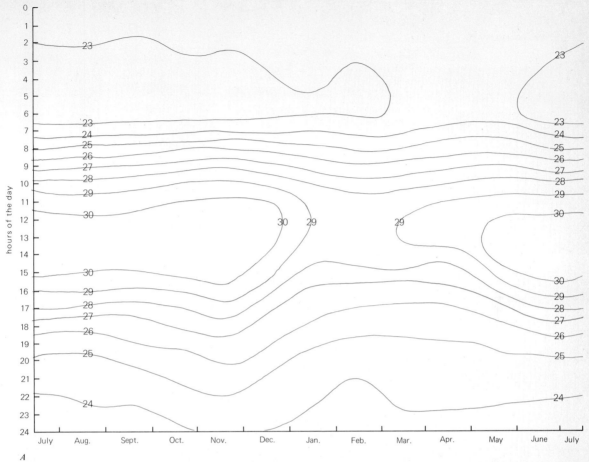

A

FIGURE 10-3
Thermoisopleth diagram showing temperature in degrees Celsius for (*A*) Belém, Brazil, humid tropical climate. On pages 230 and 231, (*B*) Sagastyr, U.S.S.R., continental tundra region; and (*C*) Nagpur, India, tropical wet and dry climate. *After Troll, from G. T. Trewartha, "An Introduction to Climate," 4th ed. Copyright © 1968 by McGraw-Hill, Inc. Used with permission of McGraw-Hill Book Company.*

no diurnal variation but a significant seasonal change. The diagram for Nagpur, India, illustrates a relationship between precipitation and temperature. Two temperature peaks, one in May (41°C) and the other in October (31°C), are evident. The highest temperature occurs well before the sun reaches its highest point in June. The low June and July temperatures here are related to the seasonal monsoon rains and to the heavy cloud cover accompanying that season. Following the rainy season the noon temperatures again rise to form an October peak.

It should be evident from this brief survey of the variability inherent in the elements of a climate that the problem of classifying or grouping climates is not easy. The years of records of temperature and precipitation at thousands of places on earth could be processed to show an infinite number of climates. No two places have identical climatic characteristics, nor are the climates exactly the same for any two years.

10-2 THE CLASSIFICATION OF CLIMATES

Every science begins with classification, and climatology is no exception. The aim of classification is to group and simplify a large number of data so that pat-

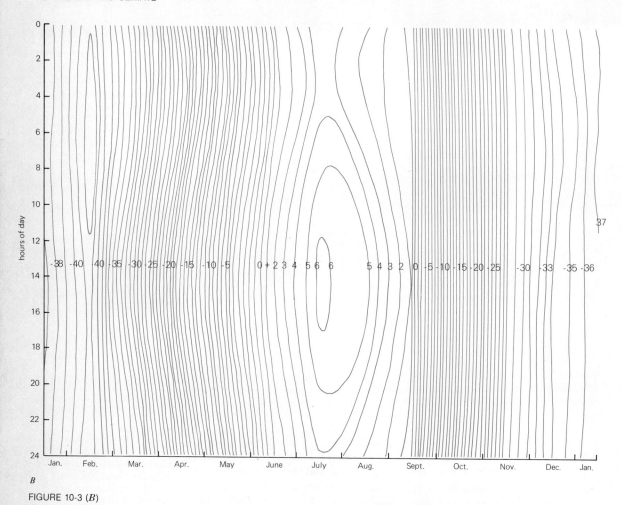

B

FIGURE 10-3 (*B*)

terns or relationships can be recognized. From such relationships explanations for climatic differences ultimately evolve.

The earliest attempts to classify climates were based only on temperature. The relationship between temperature and the altitude of the sun has been known since the time of the ancient Greeks, and the subdivision of the earth into a tropical zone, north and south temperate zones, and two polar zones is almost as old. The following excerpt from the 1794 edition of the "American Universal Geography" by Jedidiah Morse illustrates a refinement in classification based on solar radiation alone.

The word climate has two significations, the one common and the other geographical. In common language, the word is used to denote the difference in seasons and the temperature of the air. When two places differ in these respects, they are said to be in different climates.

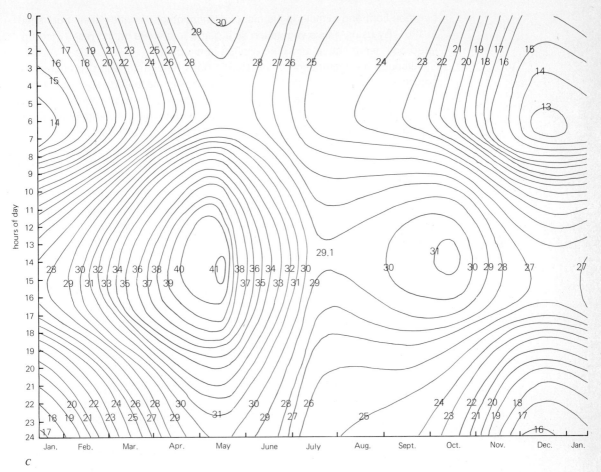

C

FIGURE 10-3 (*C*)

In a geographical sense, a climate is a tract of the earth's surface, included between the equator and a parallel of latitude or between two parallels of such breadth, as that the length of day in the one, be half an hour longer than in the other.

The latitudinal approach to the classification of climates can at best give a rough approximation of the world's climates. If the earth were covered completely by water and there were no continents to modify oceanic and atmospheric circulation, the temperature and precipitation of an area would be related to latitude.

Wladimir Köppen, born in Russia in 1846, is considered the father of modern climatology. A botanist by training, Köppen was impressed by the relationship between climate and plant life. As a botanist, he was aware of the sensitivity of vegetation to the climatic elements. Land plants are particularly adapted to specific conditions of both temperature and moisture. Köppen used the relationship between flora and climate in his first classification of climatic zones, published in 1901. By using native vegetation as a guide to climate he indirectly incorporated both temperature and precipitation in his plan.

Although the distribution of vegetation does reflect climatic conditions, the adjustment time of plant life to gradual changes in these conditions is not well known. Thus, vegetation cannot serve as a *dynamic* guide to climate. Köppen recognized this difficulty. He worked for many years as a meteorologist at the German Naval Observatory, where he had access to voluminous climatic data, upon which he based a revised system of classification in 1918. The boundaries of his new climatic zones still reflected differences in native vegetation but were based on measurements of temperature and precipitation.

Köppen's system of classification is still widely used. His major climatic groups and their boundaries are listed in Table 10-3. Each climatic group and type is defined in terms of quantitative climatic data. For example, tropical climates, designated by the letter A, are areas where the temperature of the coolest month is above 64.4°F (18°C). This temperature is significant because certain tropical plants cannot survive exposure to lower temperatures. The climatic groups are further subdivided into types coded with lowercase letters. An Af climate is a tropical wet climate with at least 6 centimeters (2.4 inches) of rainfall during the driest month. Aw stands for a tropical wet and dry climate with the dry season occurring during the low-sun period, when at least one month receives less than 6 centimeters of rainfall. Other symbols allow for further refinement of the climatic boundaries.

Köppen's system has been criticized for being too empirical and thus neglecting some of the causes of climatic differences. This, however, is as much a strength as a weakness. As a science, climatology is still very much in the descriptive stage. Although the major climatic belts can be explained in terms of the atmospheric circulation pattern discussed in Chap. 8, that pattern is not static. Climates change, and the climatic boundaries as measured by an empirical system also shift. Explanations for such climatic changes are still very tentative. It is thus important to continue to accumulate empirical data on climates with the expectation that patterns revealed by such information will eventually lead us to the exact causes of climatic changes.

The climatic groups and types of Table 10-4 represent a simplified and

TABLE 10-3
The major climatic groups according to Köppen

Climatic group	Symbol	Characteristics
Tropical rainy climates	A	Coolest month above 64.4°F
Dry climates	B	Evaporation greater than precipitation
Mild temperate rainy climates	C	Coolest month less than 64.4°F but over 26.6°F
Cold snow-forest climates	D	Coldest month below 26.6°F and warmest month above 50°F
Polar climates	E	Warmest month below 50°F

TABLE 10-4
Scheme of climatic groups and climatic types*

| Groups of climate | Types of climate | Pressure system and wind belt | | Precipitation |
		Summer	Winter	
A. Tropical humid	Ar, tropical wet	Doldrums, equatorial westerlies	Doldrums, equatorial westerlies	Not over two dry months
	Aw, tropical wet-and-dry	Doldrums, equatorial westerlies	Drier trades	High-sun wet (zenithal rains), low-sun dry
C. Subtropical	Cs, subtropical dry-summer	Subtropical high (stable east side)	Westerlies	Summer drought, winter rain
	Cf, subtropical humid	Subtropical high (unstable west side)	Westerlies	Rain in all seasons
D. Temperate	Do, oceanic	Westerlies	Westerlies	Rain in all seasons
	Dc, continental	Westerlies	Westerlies and winter anticyclone	Rain in all seasons, accent on summer; winter snow cover
E. Boreal	E, boreal	Westerlies	Winter anticyclone and polar winds	Meager precipitation throughout year
F. Polar	Ft, tundra	Polar winds	Polar winds	Meager precipitation throughout year
	Fi, icecap	Polar winds	Polar winds	Meager precipitation throughout year
B. Dry	BS, semiarid (steppe):			
	BSh (hot), tropical-subtropical	Subtropical high and dry trades	Subtropical high and dry trades	Short moist season
	BSk (cold), temperate-boreal		Continental winter anticyclone	Meager rainfall, most in summer
	BW, arid (desert):			
	BWh (hot), tropical-subtropical	Subtropical high and dry trades	Subtropical high and dry trades	Constantly dry
	BWk (cold), temperate-boreal		Continental winter anticyclone	Constantly dry

*From G. T. Trewartha, "An Introduction to Climate," 4th ed. Copyright © 1968 by McGraw-Hill, Inc. Used with permission of McGraw-Hill Book Company.

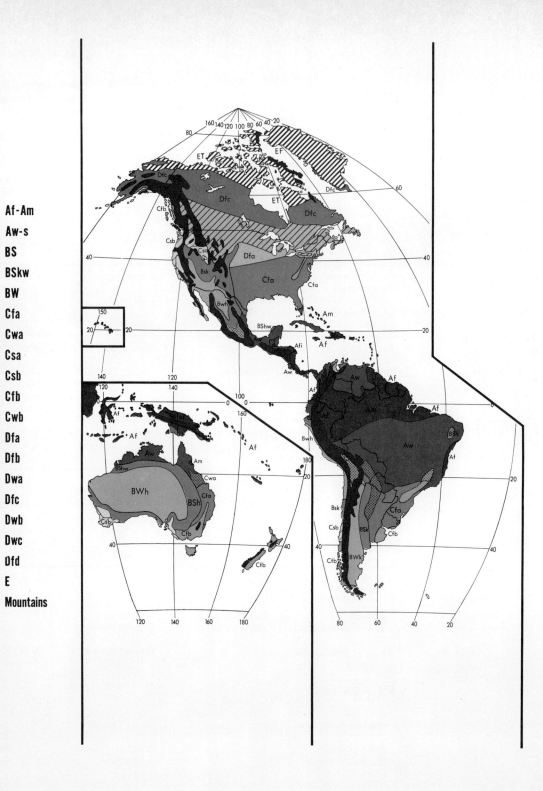

Af-Am
Aw-s
BS
BSkw
BW
Cfa
Cwa
Csa
Csb
Cfb
Cwb
Dfa
Dfb
Dwa
Dfc
Dwb
Dwc
Dfd
E
Mountains

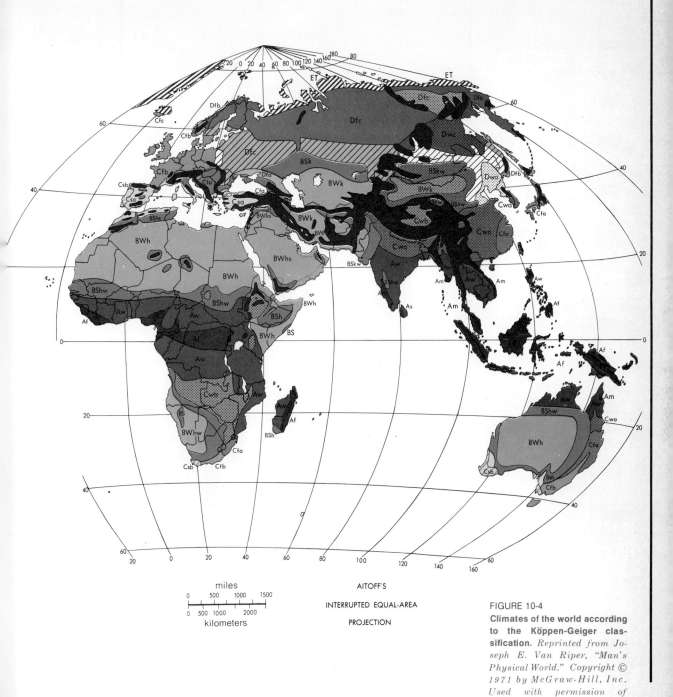

miles

0   500   1000   1500

0   500 1000   2000

kilometers

AITOFF'S

INTERRUPTED EQUAL-AREA

PROJECTION

FIGURE 10-4

Climates of the world according to the Köppen-Geiger classification. *Reprinted from Joseph E. Van Riper, "Man's Physical World." Copyright © 1971 by McGraw-Hill, Inc. Used with permission of McGraw-Hill Book Company.*

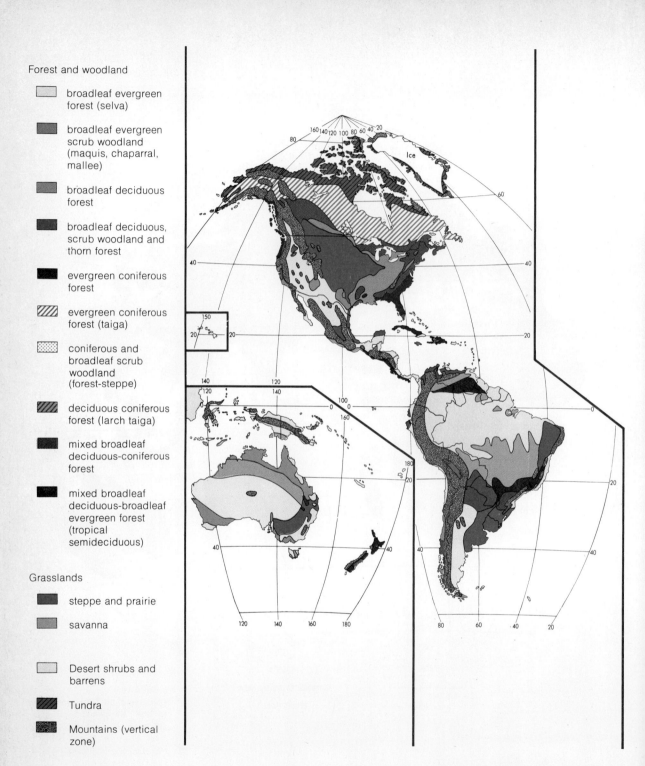

Forest and woodland

- broadleaf evergreen forest (selva)
- broadleaf evergreen scrub woodland (maquis, chaparral, mallee)
- broadleaf deciduous forest
- broadleaf deciduous, scrub woodland and thorn forest
- evergreen coniferous forest
- evergreen coniferous forest (taiga)
- coniferous and broadleaf scrub woodland (forest-steppe)
- deciduous coniferous forest (larch taiga)
- mixed broadleaf deciduous-coniferous forest
- mixed broadleaf deciduous-broadleaf evergreen forest (tropical semideciduous)

Grasslands

- steppe and prairie
- savanna

- Desert shrubs and barrens
- Tundra
- Mountains (vertical zone)

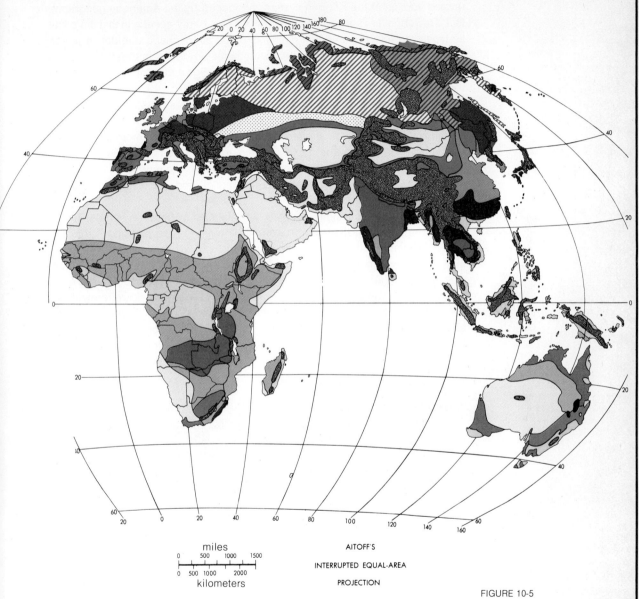

miles

AITOFF'S

INTERRUPTED EQUAL-AREA

PROJECTION

kilometers

FIGURE 10-5
**World distribution of principal
vegetative types.** *Reprinted
from Joseph E. Van Riper,
"Man's Physical World." Copy-
right © 1971 by McGraw-Hill,
Inc. Used with permission of
McGraw-Hill Book Company.*

revised version of the Köppen system, introduced by the American geographer G. T. Trewartha. In Table 10-4 the classification is partly genetic in that the climatic types are linked with those elements of the atmospheric circulation pattern which produce them. For instance, Aw climates are found in those parts of the world which are alternately in the belt of the doldrums and in the zone of the trade winds because of the moving sun.

Figure 10-4 is a map of the world climates. The climatic classification used in the map is called the Köppen-Geiger system because it represents a late revision of Köppen's original plan in collaboration with the German climatologist Rudolph Geiger. As we would expect, the map shows the major thermal climatic groups (A, C, D, E) to be strongly related to latitude. The modifying influence of the oceanic circulation, of differential heating of land and sea, and of mountainous belts, are also very evident.

In our earlier discussion we noted the relationship between vegetation and climate. Figure 10-5 displays the world distribution of the principal vegetative types. Comparing this map with the climate map of Fig. 10-4, we note a remarkable correspondence. The invisible difference between the two maps is that the boundaries of the climatic map shift slightly from year to year because the annual temperatures and precipitation records of succeeding years are rarely if ever identical. The boundaries of the vegetative types also move, but much more slowly. The boundaries between soil types, which also correlate with climatic boundaries, are even slower-moving because it takes so long to form a soil.

10-3 HOW DO ROCKS WEATHER?

We now turn our attention to rock weathering. We have already examined some of the erosional processes active at the earth's surface, and we first ask why weathering should be considered apart from erosion. The erosional processes are dynamic, involving mass transport over great distances. Weathering, on the other hand, is the essentially static physical and chemical breakdown of rock at and near the earth's surface.

The surface of the earth is the interface between three great spheres: the atmosphere, the hydrosphere, and the lithosphere. Although the boundaries between these spheres may look sharp, this is not actually the case. Air penetrates the cracks and pores of rock and soil; water fills some of the same spaces; and there is a continual interchange of gases between the three spheres.

Weathering is the adjustment of rocks and their constituent minerals to the water and air, and to the temperature and pressure conditions that characterize the surface environment. Picture an igneous or metamorphic rock formed many miles beneath the surface that is subsequently exposed as the overlying materials are eroded away. Pressure within the earth is determined by the weight of the overlying rocks. Removal of the overlying materials thus gradually exposes the rock in question to lower and lower pressures. This release of pressure causes

expansion which results in cracking and spalling (Fig. 10-6). When the rock is finally exposed at the surface, its constituent minerals, grown in a high-temperature environment essentially devoid of free oxygen and water, come in contact
with both of these substances. Chemical reactions involving water and air slowly
change the original minerals into new ones that are adjusted to the surface environment. The sum of such changes taking place at the earth's surface is weathering. Deep-seated rocks are not the only ones affected by weathering; even sediments formed beneath the seas encounter new conditions at the surface.

Junkheaps of rusted cars demonstrate a form of weathering—indeed, a cycle
of weathering. Most of the iron ore deposits of the world are the products of
former surface oxidation. As illustrated in Fig. 10-7, the iron in such deposits is in
the ferric, Fe^{3+}, state in the minerals hematite, Fe_2O_3, or goethite, $Fe_2O_3 \cdot H_2O$.
When this type of iron ore is heated with coke in a blast furnace, the oxygen is
driven off and metallic iron is formed. Automobiles and other objects which are
manufactured from the iron slowly rust (weather) back to iron oxide, which
marked the start of the cycle.

FIGURE 10-7

Most iron ore is formed by weathering, which oxidizes the iron in deep-seated minerals to insoluble ferric oxide and leaches out the other constituents. When ferric oxide is heated in a blast furnace, particularly in the presence of carbon, it is reduced to metallic iron and the oxygen is driven off. When objects like junked cars are exposed at the earth's surface, they ultimately rust to ferric oxide, completing the cycle.

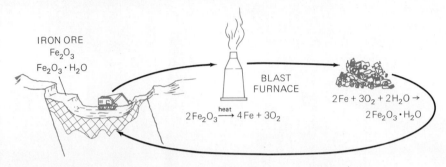

IRON ORE
Fe_2O_3
$Fe_2O_3 \cdot H_2O$

BLAST FURNACE

$2Fe_2O_3 \xrightarrow{heat} 4Fe + 3O_2$

$2Fe + 3O_2 + 2H_2O \rightarrow$
$2Fe_2O_3 \cdot H_2O$

A similar cycle occurs in crustal rocks. The iron in deep-seated rocks is mainly in the ferrous, Fe^{2+}, form, in minerals such as iron silicates or magnetite. When ferrous minerals are exposed at the earth's surface, they rust, or oxidize, to form the ferric minerals hematite or goethite. When these iron oxides become deeply buried and exposed to the elevated temperatures associated with the depths, they are again reduced to the ferrous state. We know this must be so because there is no sign that younger igneous and metamorphic rocks contain less ferrous iron than older ones. Moreover, if there were no internal earth process to drive the oxygen trapped by iron during surface oxidation back into the atmosphere, we would no longer have any atmospheric oxygen. The oxidation of iron at the surface would have used it all up!

Weathering is usually classified into two types: (*1*) *mechanical* weathering (disintegration) and (*2*) *chemical* weathering (decomposition). These two forms of weathering work together in nature, but for convenience let us look at each separately. Mechanical weathering includes the physical breakdown of rocks at the earth's surface. We know that water expands on freezing. In areas where the temperature hovers around 0°C for extended periods the alternate freezing and thawing of water in cracks in the rocks works to break them into angular fragments (Fig. 10-8). Similarly the prying action of roots, the alternate heating by day and cooling by night, the action of grass fires and forest fires, and the release of pressure by erosive uncovering promote the mechanical breakdown of rock at the earth's surface.

Chemical weathering involves the chemical breakdown of minerals under surface conditions. The solvent action of water and particularly water charged with carbon dioxide or humic acid works to decompose minerals chemically. Oxidation of iron at the earth's surface illustrates another type of chemical weathering. Some minerals react with water at the surface to form new minerals, a process known as *hydrolysis*. Still other minerals change chemically upon absorbing water in a process known as *hydration*.

Mechanical and chemical weathering go on hand in hand. In general, however, mechanical weathering is more pronounced at high latitudes and at high elevations, where there is often much alternate freezing and thawing. Chemical

weathering dominates in humid tropical regions, partly because chemical reaction rates increase with temperature. Since the chemical reactions of weathering are between natural solutions and solids, their speed depends in large part upon the available surface. Breaking a rock down physically greatly increases the surface area available for chemical decay. A cube of rock 1 centimeter square has a surface of 6 square centimeters. When such a cube is broken into pieces $\frac{1}{100}$ centimeter on edge, the new surface area becomes 600 square centimeters. On the other hand, new minerals formed by chemical decay usually have lower densities and thus higher specific volumes than the deep-seated minerals from which they form. The formation of new minerals of higher volume causes expansion, which promotes the physical breakdown of rock (Fig. 10-9).

10-4 HOW DO THE INDIVIDUAL MINERALS REACT TO WEATHERING?

The crust of the earth is composed chiefly of igneous rocks, with granite predominating in the continental crust and basalt in the oceanic crust. In Chap. 6 we learned that igneous rocks are composed chiefly of feldspar and possibly quartz together with one or more of the ferromagnesian silicates biotite, hornblende, augite, or olivine. A typical granite consists of orthoclase feldspar, quartz, and biotite. Basalt is composed of plagioclase feldspar, augite, or some other pyroxene and/or olivine. Any one igneous rock usually has only three or four major minerals.

The igneous rock-forming minerals crystallize from magma in a regular order known as the Bowen reaction series after its discoverer, N. L. Bowen (Fig. 10-10). Olivine and calcium-rich plagioclase are the first minerals to crystallize. As the temperature drops, olivine reacts with the remaining silica-rich liquid to form

FIGURE 10-9

Chemical weathering is fastest at the corners of jointed blocks, because here there is the greatest amount of surface area per unit volume. New minerals formed by weathering have greater specific volumes than the original minerals, causing expansion and spalling at the corners. In this way weathering produces rounded blocks from angular fragments.

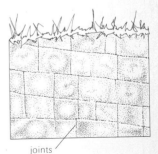

joints

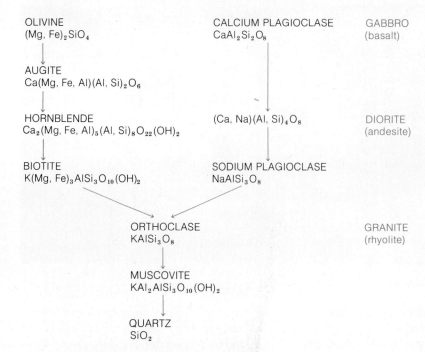

HIGH TEMPERATURE

OLIVINE
$(Mg, Fe)_2 SiO_4$

CALCIUM PLAGIOCLASE
$CaAl_2 Si_2 O_8$

GABBRO
(basalt)

AUGITE
$Ca(Mg, Fe, Al)(Al, Si)_2 O_6$

HORNBLENDE
$Ca_2 (Mg, Fe, Al)_5 (Al, Si)_8 O_{22} (OH)_2$

$(Ca, Na)(Al, Si)_4 O_8$

DIORITE
(andesite)

BIOTITE
$K(Mg, Fe)_3 AlSi_3 O_{10} (OH)_2$

SODIUM PLAGIOCLASE
$NaAlSi_3 O_8$

ORTHOCLASE
$KAlSi_3 O_8$

GRANITE
(rhyolite)

MUSCOVITE
$KAl_2 AlSi_3 O_{10} (OH)_2$

LOW TEMPERATURE

QUARTZ
SiO_2

FIGURE 10-10
The Bowen reaction series, which shows the normal order of crystallization of silicate minerals from a rock melt (magma.) Some of the principal types of igneous rocks are shown on the right. A gabbro and its fine-grained equivalent basalt, for example, are composed of plagioclase, augite, and/or olivine, which all crystallize early in the sequence.

augite, and at a still lower temperature augite reacts to form the amphibole hornblende, and so forth. Hence the name reaction series.

This does not mean that every time a rock melt crystallizes all minerals from olivine to quartz will form. The ratios of magnesium and iron to silica are higher in olivine than in augite, where in turn the ratios are higher than in hornblende. If the original magma is rich in magnesium and iron, crystallization may be complete once olivine and feldspar have solidified. On the other hand, if the magma is rich in silica, the olivine reacts with the siliceous melt to form augite; this in turn reacts to form hornblende, which finally changes to biotite. The resulting rock then would be composed of feldspar, biotite, and free quartz. The free quartz in a rock like a granite represents silica left over after the magnesium and iron have

TABLE 10-5
Stability of the common rock-forming minerals in the weathering sphere

Stability	No. of oxygen atoms shared by silicon-oxygen tetrahedrons	Mineral
Greatest	4	Quartz
	3	Muscovite
	3	Orthoclase
	3	Biotite, sodium plagioclase
	2,3	Hornblende, calcium sodium plagioclase
	2	Augite
Least	0	Olivine, calcium plagioclase

taken their share to form ferromagnesian silicates and after the calcium, sodium, and potassium have joined with sufficient silica to form the feldspars.

For this discussion the chief significance of the reaction series is its classification of minerals in terms of their temperature of formation and the fact that it permits us to predict the principal minerals in common types of igneous rocks. As illustrated in Fig. 10-10, a gabbro and its fine-grained equivalent, a basalt, are composed chiefly of calcium-rich feldspar, pyroxene, and olivine. Granites and rhyolites, on the other hand, consist chiefly of orthoclase feldspar, sodium plagioclase, quartz, and biotite or muscovite.

What is the behavior of the common rock-forming silicates during weathering? If we agree that weathering represents an adjustment to a new environment, we intuitively expect olivine to be the most susceptible to decomposition at the earth's surface and quartz the least. Since olivine forms at the highest temperature during crystallization, it seems logical for it to be the least stable under surface conditions because those conditions put it farthest from its temperature of formation. This tentative conclusion is supported by observation. In 1938, S. S. Goldich studied a number of soil profiles to determine the relative stabilities of the rock-forming silicate minerals during weathering. In rocks containing both olivine and augite or another pyroxene, for example, he found that the olivine weathers first. From other observations of rocks containing different mineral suites he was able to establish the normal order of decomposition of the common rock-forming silicates. The arrangement of minerals in Goldich's weathering-stability series (Table 10-5) is identical to that of the reaction series (Fig. 10-10). The Goldich series differs from the Bowen series in that there is no suggestion that one mineral reacts to form the next; instead each mineral forms the characteristic decomposition products listed in Table 10-6.

The internal atomic structure of the silicate minerals provides an explanation

TABLE 10-6
Decomposition products of the common igneous rock-forming minerals

Mineral	Composition	Weathering products	
		Secondary minerals	*Material removed in solution*
Orthoclase	$KAlSi_3O_8$	Clay minerals Kaolinite $= Al_2Si_2O_5(OH)_4$	K^+, colloidal silica
Plagioclase	$(Na,Ca)(Al,Si)_4O_8$	Clay minerals	Ca^{2+}, Na^+, collodial silica
Quartz	SiO_2	Not appreciably affected	
Olivine, pyroxene, amphibole, biotite	Mg,Fe silicates or aluminosilicates	Clay minerals, iron oxides	Mg^{2+}, collodial silica
Muscovite	$KAl_2(Al,Si_3)O_{10}(OH)_2$	Clay minerals (muscovite resists decomposition)	K^+

of their weathering characteristics. In Sec. 4-4 we found that the silicon ion is surrounded by four oxygen ions in all silicate minerals. The silicon ion has a charge of $+4$, which means that one unit of charge is linked to each oxygen ion. This is a very strong bond, difficult to break by physical or chemical means. By contrast the potassium ion in silicates is usually surrounded by 12 oxygen ions so that its one plus charge has to pull 12 ways. The result is a much weaker bond.

In olivine the silicon-oxygen tetrahedrons occur as islands in the structure. They do not share oxygens but are held together by other ions, such as magnesium and iron. To decompose olivine it is not necessary that silicon-oxygen bonds be broken. In quartz, on the other hand, each oxygen is shared by two tetrahedrons so that the entire structure consists of strong silicon-oxygen bonds. As Table 10-5 shows, the degree of sharing of oxygen ions between silicon-oxygen tetrahedrons increases regularly from olivine to quartz. Since the silicon-oxygen bond is so strong, we would expect an increasing resistance to decomposition as the number of such bonds in the structure increases; and this is just what Goldich's studies revealed.

We have seen how the common rock-forming minerals differ in their weathering resistance. Before leaving the subject of the behavior of minerals during weathering let us look in detail at the fate of the most abundant minerals, the feldspars, during weathering. We can illustrate the decomposition of the feldspars by the equation

$$2KAlSi_3O_8 + H_2CO_3 + H_2O \rightarrow Al_2Si_2O_5(OH)_4 + K_2CO_3 + 2SiO_2$$

| Orthoclase feldspar | Carbonic acid | Water | Kaolinite | (Soluble products) |

A similar equation for the decomposition of plagioclase feldspars, $(Ca,Na)(Al,Si)_4O_8$, differs only in that $CaCO_3$ and Na_2CO_3 replace the K_2CO_3. Both K_2CO_3 and Na_2CO_3 are soluble. $CaCO_3$ is relatively insoluble in pure water, but it too dissolves in carbonated natural water:

$$CaCO_3 + 2H_2O + 2CO_2 \rightarrow Ca(HCO_3)_2$$

| Calcium carbonate | Water | Carbon dioxide | Calcium bicarbonate (soluble) |

Decomposition of the feldspars thus results in the formation of soluble compounds of potassium, sodium, and calcium, which enter the groundwater and move slowly toward the sea. In addition some silica, SiO_2, is released to natural waters, either in true solution or as extremely finely divided charged particles which do not mechanically settle out of water, known as *colloids*. The remaining silica and the alumina combine to form insoluble clay minerals that accumulate in the weathering residuum.

Other rock-forming silicate minerals decompose in a similar fashion. If they contain K, Na, Mg, or Ca, these elements are dissolved by groundwater just as they are in feldspars. Silicates containing ferrous iron become oxidized in contact with air to form iron oxides. Of the common silicates only quartz resists

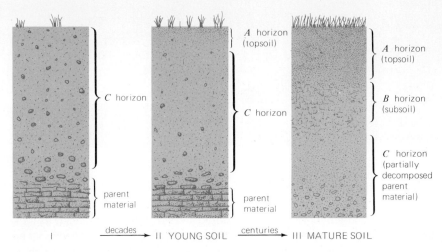

FIGURE 10-11
How soil is formed. (I) Disintegration and decomposition breaks up the parent rock. (II) Decades later a young soil forms at the top as plant growth increases. (III) Topsoil deepens, and a mature soil develops after many more decades. In the mature soil the *A* horizon, known as the *zone of outwash*, consists chiefly of resistant minerals like quartz mixed with humus. The fine weathering products from this horizon have been washed into the *B* horizon, which contains such weathering products as the clays and iron oxides. The *C* horizon is partially decomposed parent material.

decomposition almost completely. This is why beach sands and sandstones are composed chiefly of quartz.

10-5 SOILS, THE WEATHERING RESIDUUM

Most of the land areas of the world are covered by a layer of unconsolidated material. Hard bedrock is exposed chiefly in mountainous regions or along valley walls, where rivers have cut through the loose clay, silt, sand, or gravel of the surface. In central North America most of the bedrock is covered by tens and sometimes hundreds of feet of uncemented debris left by the continental glaciers of the Pleistocene. In other regions the loose material at the surface has been deposited by streams or wind. The unconsolidated surface layer that covers most of the land surface clearly represents material deposited by the erosional agents. We call this layer the *regolith* to distinguish it from soil. Engineers frequently use the term *soil* for all the materials of the regolith, but according to our definition, soil is the *weathered* surface layer, and it may form on glacial till or river silt as well as on solid rock. In either case, in a temperate climate it will have a definite structure, as illustrated in Fig. 10-11

The *A* horizon, or topsoil, is a zone of outwash. Rain entering the ground must pass through this horizon, and in so doing it washes down both the soluble and the fine-grained solid products of weathering. The *A* horizon thus slowly becomes enriched in quartz and other minerals that resist weathering. These minerals, together with the organic debris that accumulates at the surface as plant humus, constitute the topsoil. The *B* horizon, or subsoil, is a zone of inwash. The very fine-grained particles of clay or iron oxides washed out of the topsoil gradually accumulate in the *B* horizon. Beneath the *B* horizon lies a zone of partially decomposed parent material (*C* horizon), which grades downward into parent rock.

Weathering is a slow process by human time standards, a well-developed soil

FIGURE 10-12
The soil represents a balance between weathering and erosion. Weathering works to increase the thickness of soil; erosion works to remove the weathered debris. Where erosion is more rapid than weathering, soil cannot form.

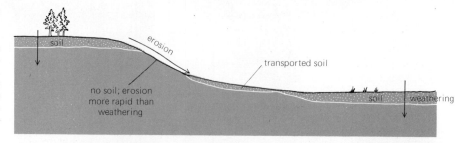

profile like that described above being the result of centuries of weathering. The soil layer represents a balance between weathering and erosion (Fig. 10-12). If particles weathered from the rock are carried away by erosion as quickly as they are released, soil cannot form. This is why bare rock is exposed on very steep slopes. Mineral grains slide downhill as quickly as they are released by weathering. It is only where decomposition and erosion are in balance that a regular soil can develop. A soil with distinct horizons representing separation of the weathering products is said to be *mature*. Figure 10-11 diagrammatically portrays the steps involved in the formation of a mature soil.

Man makes extensive use of soils in agriculture, and for this reason, as well as for scientific reasons, soils have been intensively mapped and studied. Soil science is known as *pedology*. Studies of the soils of the world have revealed that the type and maturity of soil at any place are determined chiefly by these factors: (*1*) climate, (*2*) parent rock, (*3*) plants and animals, (*4*) relief, and (*5*) time.

It is now recognized that climate is the most important soil-forming factor. Early investigators of soils plausibly assumed that the nature of the parent material was most significant. As mapping of the soils on various continents proceeded, it became clear that characteristic soil types develop in specific climatic zones regardless of the character of the underlying rock. For example, in humid tropical and subtropical areas a type of soil known as *laterite* covers much of the surface. Laterites are unique in that they contain significant amounts of aluminum and iron oxides in place of clay minerals. In the tropics, the intensity of chemical weathering is such that even silica is leached from minerals like the feldspars. The decomposition of feldspar under lateritic weathering conditions proceeds as follows:

$$KAlSi_3O_8 + H_2CO_3 + H_2O \rightarrow KHCO_3 + 3SiO_2 + Al(OH)_3$$

| Orthoclase feldspar | Carbonic acid | Water | (Soluble) | (Soluble) | (Insoluble) |

Where intensive lateritic weathering of rocks deficient in iron occurs, the enrichment of aluminum oxide in the soil layer may be sufficient to make it valuable as an ore of aluminum. The reason that the source rocks must be low in iron is, of course, that iron also turns into insoluble iron oxide during weathering. The more iron there is in such a weathering residuum, the less aluminum. *Bauxites* are laterites that are sufficiently rich in aluminum oxide to be used as ores of aluminum. Bauxite forms on many kinds of source rocks. Some of the best bauxite deposits occur on nepheline syenite, an igneous rock with no free quartz and with only a minor amount of ferromagnesian minerals. In Jamaica, bauxites are known to have formed by the weathering of limestone. Pure limestone is composed of calcite, $CaCO_3$, from which it would be impossible to form aluminum oxides. Most limestones, however, contain minor impurities of clay minerals, and it is these which have decomposed to aluminum oxides in the Jamaican bauxite deposits.

All modern bauxites and other laterites are found only in tropical climates, clearly demonstrating the dominant role of climate in soil formation. At the other extreme are the soils of the arctic tundra. The long, cold winters inhibit chemical decomposition, and tundra soils clearly reflect the absence of chemical weathering, being chiefly a stony rubble. The alternate freezing and thawing during the short, mild summers work to churn up and mix the surface layer.

Though second in importance to climate, the nature of the parent rock being weathered obviously must influence the resulting soil. We have just said that many bauxite deposits are found over syenite. The absence of quartz and the low abundance of iron in syenite results in the formation of a highly aluminous laterite under tropical conditions. Moreover, because of the absence of quartz the laterite will be low in silica, which is a quality demanded by aluminum-reduction plants. Where laterization occurs on an iron-rich parent rock, the resulting soil is red due to the iron oxides. Some lateritic soils are sufficiently rich in iron to be marketable as iron ores.

The physical character of the source material also plays a significant role in soil formation. In the central plains region of North America most of the surface is covered by glacial deposits. The minerals in this glacially ground-up rock are relatively undecomposed. Weathering proceeds much faster on this pulverized rock than on solid rock, and a mature soil profile forms much more rapidly on glacial till than on solid rock.

So far our discussion of soil formation and weathering has been restricted to the inorganic components. Plants and animals also contribute significantly to soil formation. Humus, the decaying remains of plants, is an important constituent in the A horizon of many soils. This decaying organic debris produces humic acids and carbon dioxide, which, added to groundwater, make it more effective as a weathering agent. Roots of grasses and trees penetrate the weathered mantle and in taking nutrients from the minerals further the process of decomposition. Burrowing animals, earthworms, and digging insects promote thorough mixing and disaggregation of soil. Such mixing and grinding help promote decomposition. Most important of all of the animals is man. By tilling the soil, adding organic and chemical fertilizers, and forcing plant growth by irrigation he has doubtless speeded soil formation more than anything else. At the same time, however, he has also been responsible for the loss of much soil by leaving plowed fields open to the action of wind and water.

Since where erosion is more rapid than weathering soil cannot form, in general, thicker and more mature soils are expected in regions of low relief rather than in steep areas. In fact, soils could not persist at all on hillsides were it not for the binding action of roots and the protective cover that vegetation provides against the direct onslaught of rain. The intensive gullying found in fresh road cuts or on bulldozed hillsides is proof of the importance of vegetation in preventing rapid erosion.

We list time as a soil-forming factor because it takes much time for weathering to produce a mature soil. Because of the many variables involved in soil formation, we cannot determine in absolute units the time required to form a soil from unweathered material. It takes tens of thousands of years to form a well-developed soil on bedrock in a temperate climate. By contrast, soils form in a few centuries on glacial till under otherwise similar conditions.

Although we have discussed climate, parent material, plants and animals, topographic relief, and time separately, it should be evident that all these factors are interrelated. For example, climate not only influences the path of weathering directly, it also plays a significant role in governing the varieties and numbers of plants and soil organisms of a region, which in turn influence the resulting soil. As we shall see in Chap. 11, the topography of an area is in part determined by the type or types of underlying rock. To a lesser degree, the vegetation is also influenced by the underlying geology, and so forth.

The soil-forming factors interact to form many different soil varieties. Pedologists classify soils into 10 major orders, which in turn are subdivided into many suborders, groups, families, and series. Their classification considers not only the composition of soils but also the manner in which soils behave under cultivation, the plant nutrients in the soil, the texture, and many other qualities. Since our concern here is chiefly with the general composition of the weathering residuum, we can simplify their classification by focusing on the three major soil-forming processes, laterization, podzolization, and calcification.

We have already seen that laterization is a soil-forming process of the humid tropics. Laterites seem to develop particularly well in tropical regions with a marked seasonal rainfall. Such conditions promote the complete chemical breakdown of silicate minerals, with the dissolution and ultimate removal of silica. Lateritic soils are unique in that they are thoroughly leached of soluble ions, including silica, and thus enriched in aluminum and iron oxides. Where they are exposed to air by the removal of the vegetative cover, they become hard as brick, whence the name laterite, from the Latin *later*, meaning "brick."

In normal temperate regions the process known as podzolization dominates. The podzols belong to a group of soils known as pedalfers, a name derived from *ped*, meaning "soil," plus the chemical symbols Al for aluminum and Fe for iron. In pedalfers, aluminum is enriched in the B horizon as clay minerals, and iron is present there as iron oxides. The upper A horizon of such soils is thoroughly leached, being composed principally of quartz and humus. The more soluble products of weathering like sodium, calcium, magnesium, and potassium are at least partially removed from the lower soil horizons.

Calcification is a soil process characteristic of warm, arid regions. Soils formed under such conditions are known as *pedocals* because they are marked by a concentration of calcite (cal) or mixed calcium and magnesium carbonate in their *B* or *A* horizons. Table 10-6 showed calcium and magnesium ions as two of the soluble products of weathering normally leached from the weathering residuum. Arid regions do not provide conditions conducive to leaching. Evaporation in such regions is rapid, and much of the sparse water that falls as rain soon returns to the atmosphere via evaporation. Even water that has already entered the soil rises by capillary action to replace that evaporated at the surface. This process inhibits the removal of calcium and magnesium, and they become concentrated in a hard crust at the surface. The terms *hardpan* and *caliche* are used for soils thus cemented by carbonates of calcium or magnesium.

10-6 MAJOR CLIMATIC CHANGES

We have seen how the principal floral zones and major soil types are adjusted to climate. Before leaving the topic of weathering and climate let us examine the question of climatic change. The earth's climatic belts have shifted dramatically in the recent geologic past. Consequently many of today's soils have been exposed to climates different from the modern ones. Some present soils, in fact, still contain blurred markings of exposure to other climates.

How do we know that the climates have indeed changed? Large boulders like that in Fig. 10-13 are evidence for a recent dramatic change in climate. Boulders of this sort are found in many parts of northern North America and Europe. Frequently they differ in composition from the bedrock of the region where they rest. There is only one known erosional agent that could have moved these big blocks of rock—glacial ice. Figure 10-14 shows a smoothed and striated rock surface that also is evidence of past glacial erosion. Geologists have recon-

FIGURE 10-13
A glacial erratic east of Mansfield, Washington. This large boulder resting on unconsolidated glacial till could have been moved to its present position only by a glacier. *D.A. Rahm, "Slides for Geology," 1971. Used with permission of McGraw-Hill Book Company.*

FIGURE 10-14
The smoothed surface and the scratches (striations) on this rock exposure in the Northwest Territories of Canada are evidence for the Ice Age. *Geological Survey of Canada.*

FIGURE 10-15
The maximum extent of glacial ice during the Pleistocene Epoch as reconstructed from the mapping of glacial deposits, striated rock surfaces, and glacial erratics.

structed the maximum extent of the continental glaciers during the Pleistocene Epoch by mapping the distribution of glacially transported boulders (glacial erratics), polished and striated rock surfaces, and other glacial deposits. The results of such mapping for North America are shown in Fig. 10-15. Certainly the climates of this continent must have been very different when about half of it was covered by a thick ice sheet.

This is not the entire story of the Recent Ice Age. The North American glacier was not stationary. Four major advances occurred during the 2 to 3 million years of the Pleistocene Epoch. Some of the interglacial periods were sufficiently long to allow soil profiles to develop on material deposited by a previous advance (Fig. 10-16).

Radiocarbon dating (discussed on page 208) of plant remains in the most recent glacial deposits tells us that the continental glacier last retreated from middle North America some 10,000 to 11,000 years ago. To find out how the climate has changed since then let us imagine an area in the Great Lakes region newly exposed by the retreating ice sheet. At first the region would be barren of plant life and spotted with meltwater lakes. Soon lichens and grasses, followed by shrubs and trees that can withstand the existing climate, would take hold, as they do where glaciers retreat today. As the ice moved farther away and finally

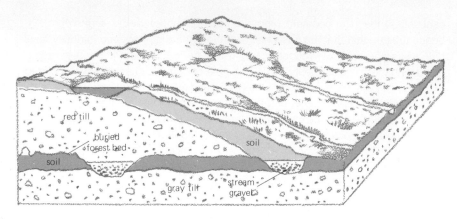

FIGURE 10-16
In a number of places in the
north central United States successive deposits of glacial till
are found. The glacier that deposited the gray till must have
retreated far from the region in
order for the forest and buried
soil to have formed.

melted altogether, the accompanying climatic changes of the region would be
reflected in the vegetation. A natural record of this former plant life exists. Pollen
from trees is blown far and wide, and some falls into lakes, there to become incorporated in the bottom sediment. Cores of lake sediments contain a pollen
record of changes in vegetation with time.

Analysis of the pollen content of glacial-lake sediments in both North America
and Europe, coupled with carbon-14 dating of the sediments, discloses a
postglacial temperature maximum about 5,000 years before the present. The
climate of formerly glaciated regions was first cold as the ice retreated, then
became warmer until about 5,000 years ago, and since then has become generally colder. The warm period is variously referred to as the *climatic optimum* or
the *hypsithermal* period.

What can have caused the drastic shifts in the earth's climatic belts associated with the recent glacial period? In searching for an explanation we look
to the sun and to the atmospheric and oceanic circulation patterns which work to
distribute solar energy more evenly over the earth. Some possibilities for the
changes in energy flow or distribution are:

1 Fluctuations in the total amount of solar energy reaching the earth due to
  a Actual variations in the sun's energy output
  b Changes in the earth's atmosphere that would influence the amount of solar
     energy arriving at the earth's surface
2 Changes in the distribution of solar energy over the earth resulting from
  a Variations in the inclination of the earth's axis or other changes in its orbital
     path
  b Shifts in the major circulation patterns of the atmosphere and hydrosphere
     which work to distribute solar energy more evenly over the earth

Let us look first at the possibility of actual fluctuations in the energy output of
the sun (*1a*). Within the period of instrumental record there has been no signifi-

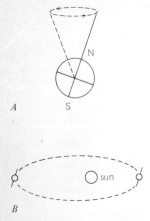

FIGURE 10-17
The earth's axis precesses with a period of about 26,000 years (A). Consequently its orientation does not stay the same as the planet revolves about the sun (B) but varies by about 50 seconds per year. When combined with the precession of aphelion and perihelion, the earth's axial precession results in a precession of equinoxes with a cycle of 21,000 years. In other words, every 10,500 years the earth will be alternately closest and farthest from the sun during northern winters. At present we are closest to the sun in winter. When we are at aphelion during northern winters, temperatures are slightly lower.

cant shift in the solar constant. Moreover, as we found in Sec. 7-4, geologic evidence tells us that the sun has been radiating at about the same intensity for 3 billion years. A cycle of sunspot activity with a period of about 11 years is recognized, and there is a suggestion that some minor climatic change may be related to this cycle, but the overall evidence indicates a relatively steady sun.

Even with a constant solar output, the amount of radiant energy available for heating the earth's surface may be influenced by certain atmospheric conditions. Dust in the atmosphere produced by major volcanic explosions acts to scatter sunlight and reduce the amount arriving at the earth's surface (1b). The explosion of the small volcanic island of Krakatoa (near Java) in 1883 blew so much dust into the air that the skies of the region were darkened for 48 hours. Some of the finest dust particles from this explosion stayed in the atmosphere for years, traveling many times around the globe. Instruments in Europe sensed a sudden drop in solar radiation several months after the eruption, and lower than normal values persisted for several years as the Krakatoa dust circled the earth.

We have seen earlier that carbon dioxide in the atmosphere acts in the opposite way by tending to increase temperatures through the greenhouse effect. Although man has recently become a prodigious consumer of fossil fuels and thus a producer of CO_2, there is no evidence that the CO_2 content of the atmosphere has fluctuated significantly in the recent geologic past. Nor is there any evidence that volcanic explosions were more prevalent during periods of glacial advance than during nonglacial times. Although these factors can indeed produce minor climatic changes, the cause of the recent glacial period must be elsewhere.

In Chap. 2 we saw that the seasonal variation in the amount of solar radiation received at various localities is related to the motion of the earth (2a). In particular, the cycle of seasons depends upon the fixed inclination of the earth's axis during the year. The tilt of the axis relative to the plane of orbit is not constant. Over a long time it varies by a few degrees in a 40,000-year cycle. Moreover, the earth's axis precesses with a period of about 26,000 years, so that over an extended period the earth is sometimes farthest from the sun during northern winters (Fig. 10-17). The ellipticity of the earth's orbit also changes according to a 92,000-year cycle. None of these cyclical motions of the earth influences the total amount of energy received from the sun, but they do affect the distribution of solar energy. In addition to the annual seasons we should therefore expect very weak longer-term cycles in heat distribution on the earth.

In 1920, M. Milankovitch, a Yugoslavian meteorologist, first calculated the combined effect of these three cyclical changes in the earth's motions. He refined his calculations in 1938, and they were subsequently recalculated by other scientists. The results, shown in Fig. 10-18, are expressed in terms of equivalent latitude for 65°N latitude. This means, for example, that 230,000 years ago the 65°N reference area was receiving solar radiation presently experienced at

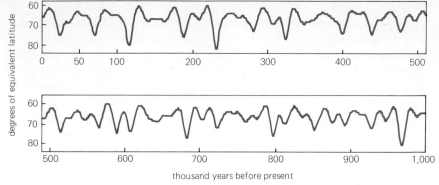

degrees of equivalent latitude

thousand years before present

FIGURE 10-18
The calculated mean solar heat received at 65°N latitude expressed in degrees of equivalent latitude. *From C. Emiliani, J. Geol., vol. 63, 1955.*

about 80°N latitude. It must then have been considerably colder, in fact about 5°C colder than now.

The Milankovitch curve of changes in the distribution of solar energy is particularly attractive as a possible explanation for the Pleistocene glaciation because it predicts cyclical temperature changes which might account for the several ice advances and retreats. However, we must recognize that the earth motions upon which the calculations were based have been going on since the solar system was formed. Geologic investigations show that glacial periods have been rare in the history of the earth. If anything, the available evidence points to generally warmer climates in the geologic past. Consequently, although the changes in distribution of solar heat related to cyclical motions of the earth's axis and orbit may have played a role in the climatic change of the Ice Age, they cannot have been the only cause.

We have found that ocean currents transport vast quantities of heat from the equatorial regions toward the poles. There is convincing evidence that the positions of the earth's poles have shifted relative to the continents (Chap. 16). Because of the drifting of continents, it is only recently that the North Pole has become nearly surrounded by land. Previously it was located in the North Pacific.

Two American earth scientists, Maurice Ewing and W. L. Donn, proposed a theory of the ice ages based upon circulation in the Arctic Ocean (2b). When the North Pole was located in the open ocean, the polar climate could not have been as severe as at present because of the free circulation. As the pole shifted to the closed basin of the Arctic Ocean, a new situation developed. Circulation in the semirestricted Arctic Ocean at first produced abundant precipitation in the northern reaches of Canada, in Greenland, and in northern Europe. Some of the snow remained the year round, and gradually great ice masses began to grow and spread over the continents.

Since the amount of water in the hydrosphere is fixed, the growth of continental glaciers would be accompanied by a lowering of sea level. As sea level fell, interchange between the major oceans and the nearly landlocked Arctic Ocean would gradually be cut off. With no new heat being pumped into the Arctic Ocean it would freeze over. Precipitation in the polar regions would necessarily decrease, resulting in a retreat of the glaciers and a corresponding rise in sea level. Gradually interchange between the oceans would be reestablished, and the cycle would repeat.

Although the Ewing-Donn hypothesis seems to account for the pulsating ice advances, it has some drawbacks. For one thing the centers of the continental ice sheets in North America were located on the east and west sides of Hudson's Bay, a long way from the poles. Meteorologists doubt that these glaciers were fed by precipitation that had its source in the Arctic Ocean. In fact, there is some evidence that the Arctic Ocean was frozen over during most of the Ice Age. Further work is needed to establish the exact cause of the climatic change associated with the Pleistocene. No doubt several of the potential causes that we have considered were involved.

SUMMARY

Climate is weather over an extended period. The climates of the world are classified on the basis of weather statistics into five or six broad groups, which in turn are divided into many climatic types. The major climatic groups are closely related to latitude, thus exhibiting the strong influence of solar radiation on climate. Deviations from latitudinal pattern are due to the influence of the atmospheric and oceanic circulation systems and to the distribution of land areas. Still smaller-scale irregularities in climatic boundaries relate to the effects of mountain systems and continental shape.

Rocks exposed at the earth's surface are broken up by alternate freezing and thawing, root action, and other agencies. Some of their constituent minerals decompose in the presence of air and water to form new minerals that are stable under surface conditions. These combined processes are called weathering. The weathering residuum that accumulates at the surface is soil.

Minerals differ in their resistance to weathering. In the common rock-forming silicates weathering resistance is related to internal atomic structure. Olivine, which contains single silicon-oxygen tetrahedrons, is the least resistant to decomposition, whereas quartz, in which each tetrahedron shares all four oxygens, is most resistant. Clay and iron oxide minerals are the most common secondary products of weathering.

The type and intensity of weathering depends upon a number of variables, the most significant being climate. In wet tropical regions laterization produces soils enriched in aluminum and iron oxides. Podzolization, which predominates in humid temperate belts, leads to soils with distinct clay and iron oxide enrichment. Decomposition is less complete in arid regions, where the soils have higher contents of calcium and magnesium, normally leached out during weathering.

The earth's climatic belts have shifted significantly during the past 2 million years. The exact cause of the recent glacial climates is still a question for research.

QUESTIONS

1. Why are yearly averages of temperature and precipitation inadequate as guides to the climate of a region?
2. What is the average range in temperature on March 1 at Belém, Brazil (see Fig. 10-3)?
3. Why are some of the great arid and desert regions of the earth found along about 30° latitude?
4. Why is latitude not an exact guide to climate?
5. How is weathering related to climate?
6. The feldspars are the most abundant mineral in the earth's crust. What do they decompose to?
7. Name which of the following rock-forming minerals is least resistant to decomposition by weathering and which is the most resistant: biotite, feldspar, olivine, muscovite, quartz, hornblende.

8 What conditions are necessary for the formation of bauxite?

9 How do such ions as Ca^{2+} and Mg^{2+} become trapped in pedocal soils?

10 What are the principal soil-forming factors?

11 What are some possible causes of the drastic climatic changes associated with the Recent Ice Age?

12 How do we know how much of North America was covered by glacial ice during the recent geologic past?

13 How would the earth's climates change if its axis were inclined at only 10° from the perpendicular to the plane of its orbit?

14 Which of the following minerals would you least expect in the A horizon of a mature soil: quartz, muscovite, olivine, orthoclase?

REFERENCES

Bloom, Arthur, L.: "The Surface of the Earth," Prentice-Hall, Inc., Englewood Cliffs, N.J., 1969.

Keller, W. D.: "Principles of Chemical Weathering," Lucas Bros. Publishing Co., Columbia, Mo., 1957.

Millar, C. E., L. M. Turk, and H. D. Foth: "Fundamentals of Soil Science," John Wiley & Sons, Inc., New York, 1965.

Strahler, A. N.: "Introduction to Physical Geography," John Wiley & Sons, Inc., New York, 1965.

Trewartha, G. T.: "An Introduction to Climate," 4th ed., McGraw-Hill Book Company, New York, 1968.

11 HYDROGEOLOGY

We use tremendous quantities of water in the United States. Some 10 million gallons of water are required to satisfy the home, industrial, and agricultural needs of *each individual* during his lifetime. Moreover, the use of water is growing at a faster rate than the population.

The churning action of boulders in the riverbed carved out these potholes in the channel of the James River, Henrico County, Virginia. *C. K. Wentworth, U.S. Geol. Survey.*

Can we continue to use increasing quantities indefinitely, or is there a limit to our water supply? If we think carefully about this question, we soon realize that the word *use* is inexact. In our industrial society most of the water utilized is only borrowed, or temporarily sidetracked on its way to the sea. The rivers of our country carry about 13.5 million gallons of water to the sea each second. This is many times the total water borrowed by the population and its supporting industries. Moreover the water of any river can ideally be utilized many times by cities along its banks. It would appear that there should be no shortage of water in the foreseeable future. But we have water shortages already!

An increasing quantity of the water used by man is consumed only to the extent that it is taken out of surface circulation. Water used for irrigation, for instance, is largely transpired into the atmosphere and thus removed from river flow. Much of the water diverted from its natural flow into large urban systems returns to its channels filled with pollutants, so that it and the water it mixes with are no longer suitable for many uses. Moreover, the flow in most rivers fluctuates widely throughout the year. An oversupply during one season is frequently balanced by a shortage in another. All these factors, together with others, have worked to create some serious water shortages.

Human activities tend to modify the hydrologic cycle, e.g., building dams, cutting timber, plowing fields, covering vast areas with concrete or asphalt, mining groundwater, and irrigating. The long-term effects of man's intervention are not completely predictable because of the complexities of the cycle. If a number of individual water molecules could be tagged for identification, we would find that some make rapid trips from the sea, into the atmosphere, into a river, and back to sea. Others might spend millennia tied up in glacial ice or moving ever so slowly through tiny pore spaces in the rocks on their way back to the sea. Many would move between the soil and the atmosphere over and over before returning to the hydrosphere. As we study the great water cycle in this chapter, we must realize that we are dealing with a sensitive mechanism that adjusts to compensate for changes in any of its parts.

11-1   WHERE DOES THE WATER COME FROM?

All the rivers run into the sea; yet the sea is not full; unto the place from which the rivers come, thither they return again.   ECCLESIASTES

The source of water in rivers was a major puzzle to early man. The ancient Greeks were impressed by the large and persistent flow of rivers which seemed to dwarf the runoff of even a major rainstorm. They realized that much of the water flowing in rivers comes from springs. Many springs appeared to flow eternally, and the most common explanation for their source (despite logical difficulties) was the oceans.

Even during the seventeenth century the idea of a direct connection between the ocean and underground water received support from such a distinguished scientist as Kepler. The chief stumbling block in any such answer is that seawater is salty but the springs are fresh. Kepler proposed that the earth, like a living thing, had a metabolism involving the ingestion of salt water from the sea and the eventual expulsion of fresh water after digestion.

The source of river water was eventually found. Pierre Perrault (1608–1680) measured the rainfall in the basin of the Seine River from 1668 to 1670. During the same period he estimated the total volume of flow of the river and found it to be only about one-sixth of the volume of the rainfall in the basin. Whereas intuition had previously suggested that more water flowed in rivers than could be accounted for by rainfall, measurement revealed the reverse to be true. At about the same time another French scientist, Edme Mariotte (1620–1684), explained the source of spring water. He measured the rate of infiltration of water into a cellar in Paris. His observations showed that the infiltration, like the rate of flow of springs in the region, depended upon the rainfall. He concluded that the springs that keep the rivers flowing must be fed by rainwater soaking into the ground.

Further work by the famous astronomer Edmund Halley (1656–1742) on the evaporation rate from the Mediterranean Sea rounded off the picture of the earth's great water cycle. Halley's measurements revealed that the water evaporating from this sea is more than adequate to account for all the water flowing into it. No longer was there any mystery about the source of fresh water for the world's rivers. The sun's radiant energy drives the giant engine. Pure water distilled from the oceans falls onto the land to feed the rivers both directly and indirectly by replenishing the water in the ground from which springs arise.

Refinements in measurements of precipitation and stream flow helped solve other puzzles. A *drainage basin* is the area drained by a river and its tributaries, and the boundary between adjacent basins is a *drainage divide* (Fig. 11-1). The total water flowing out of any basin via the stream system is called the *runoff*. Measurements of runoff and total precipitation in many basins invariably show the precipitation to be greater than the runoff. We know that over any extended period of time the input to a drainage basin must equal the output. If this balance were not maintained, the land would either be flooded or turn into a desert. We also know that stream runoff includes both groundwater from springs and surface flow. In order for the input and output to balance there must be other methods of outgo.

The only other way water can move out of a basin is upward. Heat energy from the sun acts to evaporate significant quantities of water from lakes, ponds, and soil. Even more important is *transpiration*, whereby plants release water vapor to the air. Plant rootlets frequently extend many feet into the ground, well below the point to which solar heating penetrates. Thus they are capable of bringing water to the surface which otherwise could not be evaporated directly. *Evapotranspiration* refers to combined effects of evaporation and transpiration.

The actual evapotranspiration (AE) of a region can be measured by applying our earlier formula that input equals output. We can now say that total precipitation equals AE plus runoff. Precipitation can be measured by using rain gauges, and runoff can be determined from the velocities and cross-sectional areas of streams. The difference between these two measurements is the AE for a region that is in balance, i.e., neither being flooded nor becoming arid.

Another variable of interest in assessing the water balance is potential evapotranspiration (PE). It should be clear that the AE of a region depends upon the amount of water in the soil available for evaporation and transpiration. Anyone

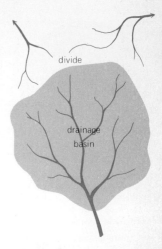

FIGURE 11-1
A drainage basin is the region drained by a river and its tributaries. Boundaries between drainage basins are called divides.

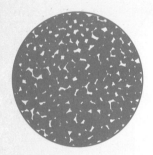

FIGURE 11-2
Magnified view of a well-sorted sandstone. Such a rock has a high percentage of pore space. Porosity in percent is

$$\frac{\text{pore-space vol}}{\text{total vol}} \times 100$$

who has experienced temperatures of 100° and over in the dry regions of the southwestern United States knows that ample solar energy is available for evaporation. Lakes and other open water bodies near Phoenix, Arizona, lose an average of 70 inches of water per year by evaporation. The AE of such a region is low, however, because there is little or no soil moisture or plant life. When water is made available through irrigation in such an area, the evapotranspiration increases greatly. The amount of water that could be evaporated from a region if water and the accompanying plant life were available is the PE. If we recall that it takes 540 calories to evaporate 1 gram of water, it becomes clear that the chief factor determining the PE of a region must be the availability of thermal energy. PE is generally high at low latitudes, where the sun is directly overhead, and low toward the poles, where the oblique sun's rays spread over larger areas.

11-2 GROUNDWATER

Water that falls on the land as rain flows off the surface directly into streams, sinks into the ground, or is evaporated. We noted earlier that much of the earth's surface is covered by a regolith of unconsolidated material and that even the solid rock within a few miles of the surface is fractured and sometimes porous. The volume percent of pore space in a rock is called its *porosity*. A sandstone like that in Fig. 11-2 may have a porosity of 35 percent. A bucketful of such a sandstone could hold 0.35 bucket of water in its pore space.

The porosity of the surface materials influences the degree to which precipitation soaks into the ground. More important than porosity, however, is *permeability*, a measure of the ease with which fluids can pass through a substance. In many instances permeability and porosity of rocks are directly related. The porous sandstone of Fig. 11-2, for example, would also be a highly permeable rock. It is possible, however, for a rock or soil to be porous yet relatively imperme-

FIGURE 11-3
Water in the ground. Pore spaces in the zone of saturation are filled with water. Air plus moisture percolating downward fill the pore spaces in the zone of aeration.

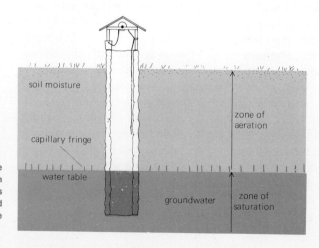

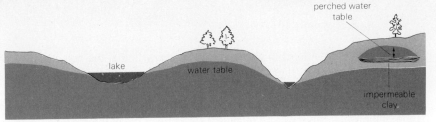

FIGURE 11-4
The water table is not flat but gradually rises and falls with the topography. A perched water table may form above the normal groundwater level, where an impermeable layer traps water and impedes its downward migration.

able. This is particularly true of very fine-grained clays, in which the pore spaces, although numerous, are so tiny that water cannot move freely. A clay or shale may have a 25 to 40 percent porosity and yet be highly impermeable.

Knowing that the porosity and permeability of the soil or rock controls the amount of water these materials can hold and the rate at which water can pass through them, let us look beneath the surface at the water in the ground. If we dig a deep hole, we reach a point where it begins to fill with water. The inflow of water occurs at the level where the pore spaces of the soil or rock are filled with water. Water will gradually fill the hole to the top of this level of saturation, known as the *water table*. The water filling the pore spaces in the zone of saturation is known as groundwater (Fig. 11-3).

The term water table is perhaps somewhat misleading because the top of the zone of saturation is not flat. It rises and falls gently with the topography, and these differences in level cause groundwater to flow. Locally the presence of an impervious layer may result in the formation of a *perched water table* (Fig. 11-4). Where the water table intersects the surface, flowing springs may form.

Water that fills the pore spaces of rock in the zone of saturation comes from the surface and thus must pass through the layers of material between the water table and the surface. During a rainy period water sinks from the surface under the influence of gravity until it reaches the saturated layer. The term *vadose zone* is used to describe this region of downward-percolating water. Careful examination of the well in Fig. 11-3 would reveal a moist layer immediately above the water table known as the *capillary fringe*. Some moisture is also trapped in the soil by fine clay particles and organic debris, to form the zone of *soil moisture*.

Like surface waters, groundwater moves slowly downhill in response to the force of gravity. A French hydrologist, Henri Darcy, first discovered the law governing the flow of groundwater while studying the water supply of the city of Dijon in 1850.

$$Q = K\frac{(h_2 - h_1)A}{L}$$

where Q = volume of water moving through a given cross-sectional area in unit time

A = cross-sectional area

K = a constant proportional to permeability; measured in volume per unit area per unit time for a given hydraulic gradient

$\dfrac{h_2 - h_1}{L}$ = hydraulic gradient, feet drop per mile or meters per kilometer

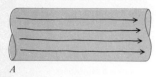

A

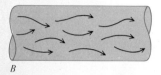

B

FIGURE 11-5
(*A*) **Laminar flow;** (*B*) **turbulent flow.**

FIGURE 11-6
Measuring the velocity of groundwater percolation. Water is a poor conductor of electricity, but addition of an electolyte such as NH,CL turns it into a conductor. When an electrolyte is poured into well *A*, **it migrates toward well** *B*, **causing a current to flow between the metal well casing and the electrode when it reaches** *B*. **This current shows up as a deflection on the ammeter.**

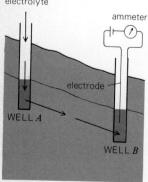

The important relationship shown by Darcy's law is that the volume of flow through a given area is directly proportional to the hydraulic gradient and the permeability. In regions with permeable rocks the flow will be sufficiently fast to keep the gradient low. On the other hand, in relatively impervious materials the slope of the water table will be relatively steep because of the slow flow rate.

Because it moves so slowly through the tiny pore spaces in rock and soil, groundwater migrates chiefly by *laminar flow* (Fig. 11-5). Flow of water in rivers by contrast is *turbulent* and hence is governed by different laws. Rates of flow of groundwater can be measured directly between two wells by placing an electrolyte in the upper well and noting how long it takes to move to the second well (Fig. 11-6). Velocities can also be determined from Darcy's law, $V = K(h_2 - h_1)/L$. Most groundwater moves from 5 feet per day to 5 feet per year although measurements made in highly permeable materials have disclosed velocities of several hundred feet per day. Figure 11-7 illustrates the probable path of groundwater motion in uniformly permeable material.

11-3 WATER BUDGETS

The level of water in wells fluctuates with the seasons or year, but the fact that the same general level has often been observed in a region for hundreds of years suggests that a natural balance exists in the water budgets of most regions. Water stored in the ground or in lakes and other natural reservoirs is like money in an ideal checking account; it is continually spent, but there is a perpetual if sporadic inflow to balance the outgo.

Water that falls as rain in a drainage basin runs off the surface, is evapotranspired, or sinks into the ground. What determines how much follows each of these routes? We have already noted that the amount entering the ground is influenced by its permeability. The amount and kind of plant cover also regulates the proportion between rainwater running off and sinking into the soil. The potential evapotranspiration of an area determines the degree to which rainwater is evaporated.

To make the analogy between groundwater and a checking account complete we would have to stipulate that the checking account hold only a fixed amount of cash and can accept deposits only slowly. Let us look at the water budget of a region to see why these conditions must be set.

Figure 11-8 is a graph of the average monthly values for the three principal variables (PE, AE, and precipitation) in the water budget for Houston, Texas. In January the average precipitation at Houston is 3.6 inches. During the same month the PE is 0.8 inch, and because there is ample water available from the rains, the AE is also 0.8 inch. We can see by Fig. 11-8 that the precipitation is greater than the PE until early April. During this period there is a surplus of water.

From early April to late September the PE is greater than the precipitation. Until about July the AE and PE remain the same in spite of the fact that the AE is

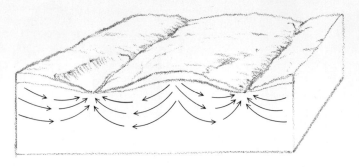

FIGURE 11-7
Paths of groundwater movement in a uniformly permeable medium. *After M. K. Hubbert.*

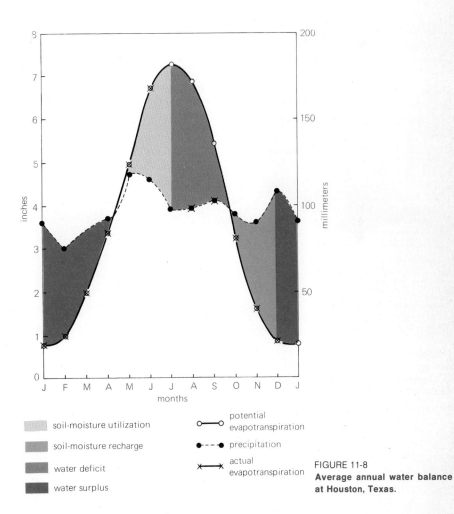

soil-moisture utilization

soil-moisture recharge

water deficit

water surplus

potential evapotranspiration

precipitation

actual evapotranspiration

FIGURE 11-8
Average annual water balance at Houston, Texas.

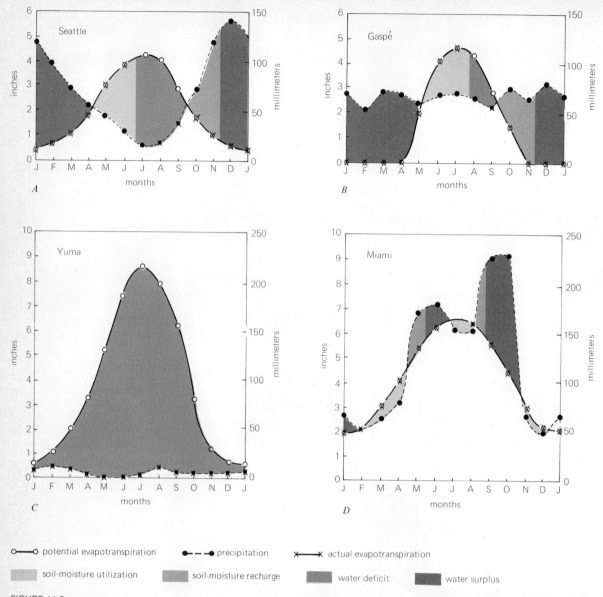

○———○ potential evapotranspiration　　●– – –● precipitation　　✕———✕ actual evapotranspiration

soil-moisture utilization　　soil-moisture recharge　　water deficit　　water surplus

FIGURE 11-9
Average annual water balances at (A) Seattle, (B) Gaspé; (C) Yuma, and (D) Miami.

greater than the precipitation. This is possible because of the reservoir of soil moisture. By July the available soil moisture has been used up, and the AE equals the precipitation. The period from July through October is one of water deficit. From October through January the precipitation again is greater than the PE. At first the excess goes to replace the soil moisture. By December there is a water surplus.

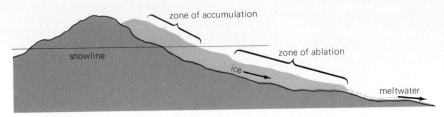

zone of accumulation

snowline

zone of ablation

ice →

meltwater →

FIGURE 11-10
The regimen of a glacier. In the region above the snowline the snow of one season does not melt completely before the next snow season (zone of accumulation). The excess flows out as glacial ice to the extent that the influx as snow in the zone of accumulation is just balanced by melting in the region below the snow line (zone of ablation).

The relative amounts of precipitation going into direct runoff, soil moisture, evapotranspiration, or the groundwater reservoir clearly depend upon fluctuations in precipitation and solar energy during the year. Figure 11-9 shows average annual water-balance statistics for four other places in North America. The graph of mean monthly precipitation and PE for Yuma, Arizona, portrays the situation in an arid region, where almost all the precipitation is evapotranspired. Seattle, Washington, is an example of a region with little summer precipitation with a resulting water deficit between July and October. Miami, Florida, receives almost twice the total precipitation of Seattle, yet it experiences a much smaller yearly water surplus. Why?

The water-balance diagram for Gaspé, Quebec, is the only one where some precipitation occurs as snow. From November to April the evapotranspiration is about zero, and the precipitation accumulates as snow. Certainly during the snow season our rule that income equals outgo seems to be violated. There is no runoff and relatively little evaporation, but there is input as snow. The snow, however, melts during the summer to balance the water budget.

What of a region where the snow does not melt in the summer? The area in the center of the Greenland ice cap is an example of such a region. Although there is no runoff and only minor evaporation, this region too is in a state of balance. The glacial ice flows seaward from the center of the ice cap at about the rate of snow accumulation. Water that falls as snow may take thousands of years to return to the sea, but return it does, to balance the water budget. Figure 11-10 illustrates the regimen of a glacier schematically. The position of the terminus at any time depends upon the balance between accumulation and ablation.

Looking at the earth's overall water budget, we find that the continental areas receive an average of 99×10^3 cubic kilometers of water from the atmosphere each year (Fig. 11-11). Evapotranspiration moves 62×10^3 cubic kilometers back to the atmosphere each year, and 37×10^3 cubic kilometers runs to the sea. For land areas this certainly represents a balance, but the atmosphere seems to be overspending if it loses 99×10^3 cubic kilometers per year and gains only 62×10^3 cubic kilometers per year. The amount needed to balance the atmosphere's water budget comes from the oceans. The diagram of Fig. 11-11 shows 37×10^3 cubic kilometers of ocean-derived atmospheric moisture moving over

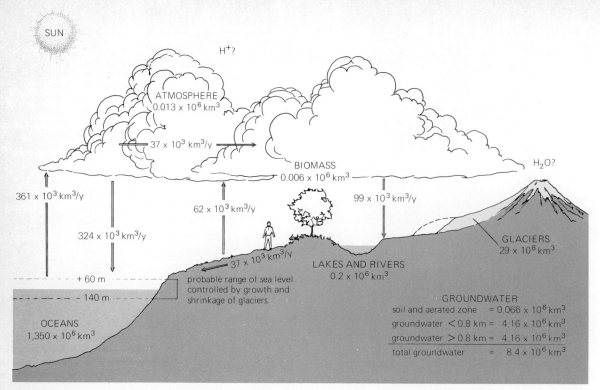

SUN

H$^+$?

ATMOSPHERE
0.013 x 10^6 km^3

37 x 10^3 km^3/y

BIOMASS
0.006 x 10^6 km^3

H$_2$O?

361 x 10^3 km^3/y

62 x 10^3 km^3/y

99 x 10^3 km^3/y

324 x 10^3 km^3/y

GLACIERS
29 x 10^6 km^3

+ 60 m

37 x 10^3 km^3/y

LAKES AND RIVERS
0.2 x 10^6 km^3

– 140 m

probable range of sea level
controlled by growth and
shrinkage of glaciers

GROUNDWATER

OCEANS
1,350 x 10^6 km^3

soil and aerated zone	= 0.066 x 10^6 km^3
groundwater <0.8 km	= 4.16 x 10^6 km^3
groundwater >0.8 km	= 4.16 x 10^6 km^3
total groundwater	= 8.4 x 10^6 km^3

FIGURE 11-11

The hydrosphere, or the water on or near the surface of the earth. For comparison the amounts of water in the principal reservoirs are given in millions of cubic kilometers (10^6 km^3); the annual exchange of water among the reservoirs (the hydrologic cycle) is given in thousands of cubic kilometers per year (10^3 km^3/y). *From A. L. Bloom, "The Surface of the Earth," Prentice-Hall, Inc., 1969.*

the lands each year. This is a net value. The total amount of ocean-derived moisture moving over the lands each year is 10 to 20 times greater. Much of the atmospheric moisture over the continents, however, eventually ends up as precipitation in the seas.

The clouds of smoke that belch from active volcanoes consist largely of steam. Some of the steam is simply groundwater vaporized by the hot lava, but some was an integral part of the magma where it originated in the earth's mantle. This fraction of water coming from the depths is important in that it has never been in the hydrosphere before. Called *magmatic* water to distinguish it from the meteoric water of the hydrosphere, it represents a small imbalance in the budget. We shall see in Chap. 18 that there is strong evidence that the primitive earth lacked a hydrosphere and that the existing hydrosphere represents the accumulation of magmatic water from the rocks of the interior since the earth's beginning.

11-4 STREAM HYDRAULICS

Before we study the actual flow of water in streams, let us see what happens to the water of a typical rainstorm. We know that some of the water will eventually end up in streamflow to become a part of the total runoff and that some will be evapotranspired to the atmosphere. The streamflow, or total runoff, is made up of

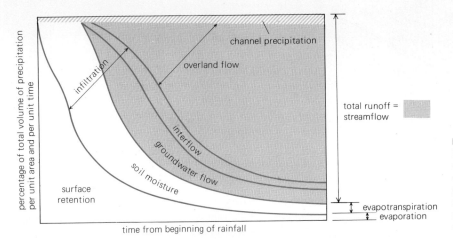

FIGURE 11-12
Distribution of a rainstorm of uniform intensity. At first most of the rain is retained on leaves, grasses, or in the soil. As these reservoirs fill, more and more rainfall flows overland to stream channels.

a number of components, the most significant being direct channel precipitation, overland flow, interflow, and groundwater flow. A small fraction of the total rain falls directly into stream channels. Most of the increased flow of streams following rainstorm is surface or overland flow. The amount of overland flow depends, of course, upon the composition and condition of the soil. Overland flow does not become significant until the soil is saturated. Interflow refers to the lateral movement of water in the zone above the water table. The continuing streamflow is maintained by the flow of groundwater.

Figure 11-12 diagrammatically portrays the partition of water from a typical uniform rainstorm. The portion labeled *surface retention* refers to water droplets held by leaves and grasses. The relative amounts of water in the various categories vary from place to place and from season to season. Figure 11-13 illustrates the great differences between drainage basins in terms of annual streamflow and evapotranspiration.

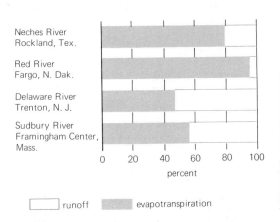

FIGURE 11-13
Percentages of runoff and rainfall lost by evapotranspiration for selected river basins. Evapotranspiration is calculated by subtracting measured runoff from measured rainfall. *Data from Williams et al., after M. Morisawa, "Streams." Copyright © 1968 by McGraw-Hill, Inc. Used with permission of McGraw-Hill Book Company.*

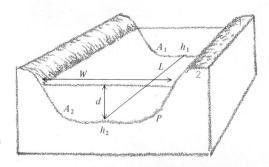

FIGURE 11-14
Characteristics of a stream channel.

FIGURE 11-15

Apparatus for gauging a large river. At the bottom is a 50-pound sounding weight with rudder and on top a Price current meter. *J. Q. Stacy, U.S. Geological Survey.*

Let us examine streamflow by taking an imaginary trip down a river system from its headwaters to its mouth. In the highland, or mountain, regions, where our stream begins, the water is clear and appears to be moving rapidly. There are many rapids over large boulders; these, together with eddies, demonstrate the turbulent nature of the flow. The stream is generally shallow and runs over bedrock or coarse rock debris.

As we move downstream, the character of the river gradually changes. Most obvious is an increase in water that results from the influx of many tributaries. The stream becomes wider and deeper to accommodate this additional flow. The channel material also changes. Although the river has become so deep that the bottom is no longer visible, the sand and gravel of the banks and sand bars in the center of the channel show that it now flows over its own sediment. The bedrock and large boulders that lined the channel earlier have disappeared.

Still farther downstream the base of the river valley becomes very wide, and the entire bottom is lined with *alluvium*, or river deposits. The large and seemingly quiet river flows in curving meanders across the alluvium. Many eddies and backwaters attest to the fact that flow is still turbulent. The water is gray with finely divided silt.

Our impression from such a trip is that rivers become wider, deeper, and slower in a downstream direction. The amount of water flowing increases as successive tributary systems dump their loads into the main stream. Sediment becomes finer-grained in a downstream direction, and alluvium makes up most of the valley bottoms.

We must recognize that these impressions are purely qualitative. Let us now see how measured stream parameters vary with position. Figure 11-14 illustrates some of the variables of a stream channel. The width W, depth d, wetted perimeter P, and the elevations h_1 and h_2 of points in the channel can be determined from soundings and survey measurements. From values thus obtained the stream gradient $(h_1 - h_2)/L$, which is the drop in elevation per unit of length, can be calculated, as can the cross-sectional area A of the channel. The hydraulic radius of a stream is defined as its cross-sectional area A divided by its wetted perimeter P.

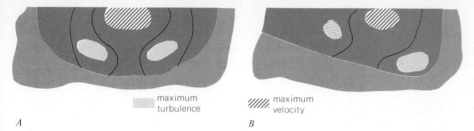

A   *B*

maximum
turbulence

maximum
velocity

FIGURE 11-16
Zones of maximum velocity and turbulence in (A) symmetrical and (B) asymmetrical stream channels. *After J. B. Leighley, Geograph. Rev., vol. 24, 1934.*

Besides these channel characteristics the velocity of the water at any place can be measured using flowmeters (Fig. 11-15). As anyone who has been canoeing on a river knows, the velocity of flow is not uniform. Within the river there are filaments of fast-moving water. Figure 11-16 illustrates the distribution of velocity in several channels. A flowing fluid can be thought of as a myriad of thin layers, each shearing over the next like a deck of playing cards. The friction between the water layers is small, but it is very high at the base, where flow is over solids. As one would expect, therefore, velocity measurements disclose the lowest values at the base. This idea of thin fluid layers moving over each other holds only for very slow laminar flow. In streams the flow is turbulent, but the relationship between velocity and depth still applies (Fig. 11-17). When we speak of velocity at any gauging station, we are referring to the average of many velocity measurements. The product of this average velocity V and the cross-sectional area A must equal the volume of water passing that section in a unit of time, called the discharge Q. We can see from Fig. 11-14 that if between sections 1 and 2 no new water enters the stream and no water is drained off, then $A_1 V_1 = Q$ and $A_2 V_2 = Q$, or $A_1 V_1 = A_2 V_2$. Any decrease in cross-sectional area must be compensated for by an increase in velocity, and vice versa.

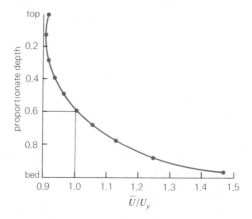

proportionate depth

top
0.2
0.4
0.6
0.8
bed

0.9   1.0   1.1   1.2   1.3   1.4   1.5

$\overline{U}/U_y$

FIGURE 11-17
Vertical velocity profile of the Mississippi River near Vicksburg, Mississippi. $\overline{U}/U_y$ **is the ratio of average velocity to the velocity at depth** y**. At six-tenths the total depth the velocity is average** ($\overline{U} = U_y$**; so** $\overline{U}/U_y$ **= 1). At greater depths the velocity is less than average.** *After Toffaleti, from M. Morisawa, "Streams." Copyright © 1968 by McGraw-Hill, Inc. Used with permission of McGraw-Hill Book Company.*

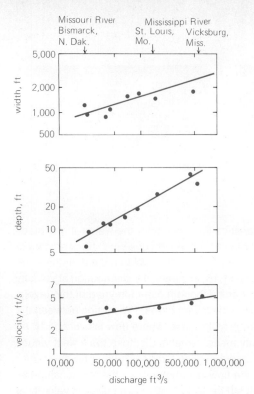

Figure 11-18 presents in graph form the results of some width, depth, velocity, and discharge measurements. As we predicted from our imaginary river journey, the width consistently increases as the discharge increases in the downstream direction. Depth similarly exhibits a downstream increase, and since width times depth equals cross-sectional area, that too increases. Most surprising is the increase of velocity in a downstream direction in each of the streams investigated. Our view of rushing headwaters turning into sluggish rivers downstream was illusory. There is a distinct if slight increase in velocity accompanying the downstream rise in discharge in all the streams monitored.

The graphs of Fig. 11-18 can be expressed by the equations

$$W = aQ^b \qquad D = cQ^f \qquad V = kQ^m$$

where W, D, V, and Q are width, depth, velocity, and discharge; a, c, and k are constants; and b, f, and m are numerical exponents that vary slightly from stream to stream or from gauging station to gauging station on one stream. We know that width W times depth D equals cross-sectional area and that area times velocity V equals discharge Q. Putting these together we find

$$Q = W \times D \times V$$
$$= aQ^b \times cQ^f \times kQ^m$$
$$= a \times c \times kQ^{b+f+m}$$

and so

$$a \times c \times k = 1 \quad \text{and} \quad b + f + m = 1$$

These relations between the parameters of streams are useful for a number of reasons. First, they help hydrologists predict how a stream will change if one of the variables is changed. Second, because of the interrelations of width, depth, velocity, and discharge, it is possible to monitor all these variables by measuring only one or two of them. For downstream changes in a permanent river system the average exponent values are

$$b = 0.5 \quad f = 0.4 \quad m = 0.1$$

We can see from these average exponent values that width increases most rapidly downstream, depth almost as rapidly, and velocity only slightly.

The slope or gradient of almost every stream decreases in a downstream direction. We know that slope is an important factor in governing the velocity, but it cannot be the only factor or velocity would regularly decrease downstream. If there were no friction, the velocity of the water at any height below the source would be the same as if the water had fallen vertically through that height. Friction within the water and between the water and the channel walls acts to slow this otherwise mad rush to the sea. Quantitative hydraulic studies of the relationship between velocity and channel characteristics have provided us with a number of empirical formulas. One, known as the Manning formula, is

$$V = \frac{1.49}{n} R^{2/3} S^{1/2}$$

where V = velocity

n = a constant related to channel roughness

R = hydraulic radius (the cross-sectional area divided by the wetted perimeter; Fig. 11-14)

S = stream gradient

From the equation we can see that the hydraulic radius R, which depends upon the wetted perimeter and thus must help control channel friction, exerts more of an influence on velocity than the gradient does. The actual downstream increase in velocity in spite of lower gradients must therefore be due to a decrease in friction resulting from the greater depths and finer-grained bottom materials.

11-5 TRANSPORTATION, DEPOSITION, AND THE GRADED-STREAM PROFILE

We have often referred to rivers as the chief gradational agents. They move tremendous quantities of sediment to the sea each year. In moving matter from one place to another the rivers do work, because it takes force to move a boulder or a sand grain, and work is defined as force times distance. The ability to do

FIGURE 11-19
**The churning action of boulders
in the riverbed carved out these
potholes in the channel of the
James River, Henrico County,
Virginia.** *C. K. Wentworth, U.S.
Geol. Survey.*

work is called energy. We recall that one of the most fundamental laws of nature
is that energy cannot be created or destroyed; it can only be converted from one
form into another.

With these ideas in mind, let us look at the energy conversions that take place
in a river system. Water in a river possesses energy of position, or potential
energy, because of its height above the outlet. This potential energy is continually changed into energy of motion, or kinetic energy. The kinetic energy of
any particle is equal to $\frac{1}{2}mv^2$, where m is its mass and v its velocity. At first
glance it may seem that the kinetic energy is not converted into other forms of
energy because the water keeps moving downstream; but this is definitely not
the case. As we pointed out earlier, water in a river at; say, 1,000 feet vertically
below its source would have the velocity gained in this much free fall if there
were no friction (about 170 miles/per hour). Rivers, of course, do not flow anywhere near that fast. The kinetic energy is constantly changed into heat energy
through internal turbulence and channel friction, and this stabilizes the velocity.

Some of the change into heat occurs in the erosion of the channel. Certainly
heat must be generated where potholes are bored in solid rock by churning
boulders caught in whirlpools (Fig. 11-19). Since new energy cannot be created
in a river system, the sum of the energy converted into heat by internal and channel friction and that used in erosive work is constant for a fixed flow.

Figure 11-20 shows that only a small fraction of the material removed in a typical valley is directly eroded by its stream. Most of the material is moved to the
stream by slumping, soil creep, or sheetwash. Streams transport weathered
debris in three principal ways:

1 By rolling, bouncing, or sliding materials along their bed. This *bed load* is the
   coarsest fraction being moved by the stream.
2 By holding fine particles in suspension. The fine silt and clay particles and
   occasionally sand-sized particles so held make up the *suspended load*. This
   is an effect of the turbulence of flow.

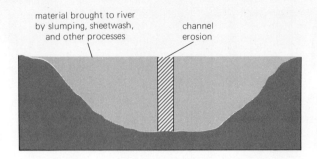

material brought to river
by slumping, sheetwash,
and other processes

channel
erosion

FIGURE 11-20
**Only a small part of the total
volume of material eroded to
form a valley actually represents direct channel erosion.**

3 By carrying some of the weathered constituents in chemical solution (the *dissolved load*).

Two terms are commonly used in describing the sediment-carrying ability of
streams. *Competence* refers to the size of the largest particle a given stream can
move. Experiments show that the competence varies as some power of the velocity: doubling velocity results in a threefold or greater increase in the maximum
size of particle that can be moved. The *solid load* of a stream is defined as the
rate at which sediment is transported through a given cross section. There are
two types of solid load, suspended load and bed load. As one might expect, load
is related to our now familiar Q. Figure 11-21 is a graph of the relation between
discharge Q and suspended-sediment load at a gauging station. We can see
that the load increases many times faster than the discharge. According to the

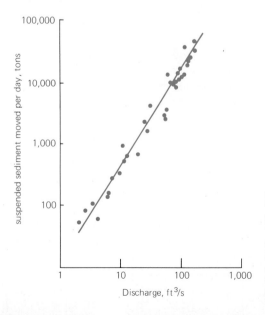

FIGURE 11-21
**The suspended load of streams
increases rapidly during floods.
This graph is based upon mea-
surements in the Rio Puerco,
New Mexico.** *From Luna B.
Leopold and John P. Miller,
U.S. Geol. Surv. Prof. Pap.
282A, 1956.*

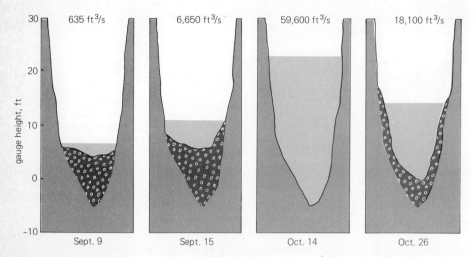

FIGURE 11-22

Cross sections of the San Juan River channel near Bluff, Utah, showing changes during a flood in 1941. On September 9 and 15 the river flowed on a bed of river gravel (alluvium) within the bedrock channel. On October 14 floodwaters swept the gravel downstream, exposing the bedrock channel. By October 26 new gravel deposits, brought from upstream, again lined the channel as the flood subsided. *Adapted from L. B. Leopold and T. Maddock, Jr., U.S. Geol. Surv., Prof. Paper 252, 1953.*

diagram for this river, a tenfold increase in discharge results in about a twenty-fold increase in sediment load. Studies on other river systems give similar results.

From the above discussion, and particularly the data of Fig. 11-21, it should be clear that the eroding and transporting ability of most streams varies significantly with the seasons. As the quantity of water increases during a spring flood, for example, the resulting velocity increase must cause an exponential rise in both competency and capacity. In fact most of the erosive and transporting work of rivers is done during times of unusual flood. Figure 11-22 portrays this vividly. It shows a series of cross sections of the San Juan River before and after a major flood. The sections reveal that from September 15 to October 14 the water level rose about 12 feet. The maximum water depth, however, increased by about 22 feet because of channel scour. Similar studies on other rivers show that many sweep alluvium out of their channels during spring floods and deposit new materials as the floods subside.

Only rivers flowing on alluvium can quickly lower or raise the levels of their beds with changing discharge. This ability of rivers flowing on alluvium to adjust their channels up or down and thus to modify their gradients is important. It accounts for the fact that many rivers have been able to adjust all or parts of their longitudinal profiles to a balanced condition known as *grade*. J. Hoover Mackin[*] describes a graded stream as one in which:

. . . over a period of years, slope is delicately adjusted to provide, with available discharge and with the prevailing channel characteristics, just the velocity required for the transportation of the load supplied from the drainage basin. The graded stream is a system in equilibrium; its diagnostic characteristic is that any change in

[*]J. Hoover Mackin, *Geol. Soc. Am. Bull.*, vol. 59, p. 471 (1948).

any of the controlling factors will cause a displacement of the equilibrium in a direction that will tend to absorb the effect of the change.

How do streams achieve the condition of grade? To answer this question we must learn which of the important variables the stream can itself act to change. We already know that discharge is a significant factor. A stream, however, has no control over its discharge, which is determined by the climate and the materials and vegetation of the drainage basin. In the same way a stream has little control over the total new sediment load because most of it is washed in from the valley walls.

The width, depth, and sediment size at any place along a river are adjustable variables, as is the velocity. However, as we saw earlier, these variables are interrelated, and all depend upon discharge. It is not possible for the stream to change one of these variables without making a counterchange in at least one of the others.

The only variable a river can adjust independently is its slope or gradient. Of course, it has no control over the ultimate base level to which it flows, but by channel cutting or channel filling it can adjust its slope and thus achieve a steady, or graded, state.

A stream that is lowering its level by downcutting is said to be *degrading*, whereas one that is building up its channel is *aggrading*. It is easy to understand the degradational action of streams because every steep valley attests to this process. Aggradation is more difficult to visualize. Let us assume that a river by virtue of its velocity and channel characteristics is moving a full sediment load and that it reaches a stretch where these conditions no longer permit transport of the total sediment load. Some of the sediment must be deposited in the channel. By depositing this sediment the river has moved toward adjustment in two ways. On the downstream side of the deposit the gradient has been increased, providing additional energy for the transport of sediment. At the same time the buildup of channel sediment lowers the upstream gradient, resulting in a headward wave of sediment deposition. Together these adjustments work to maintain a smooth profile.

To see how the combined action of erosion or degradation and aggradation ultimately results in a balanced profile let us examine the evolution of a stream and its valley. On a newly uplifted landmass the first stream to form follows low areas in the topography (Fig. 11-23). We would expect such a stream to have a very irregular profile; in some places it would drop steeply in rapids or waterfalls, and in others it might expand into a quiet lake. Erosion would be most rapid at the steepest slopes. With the passage of time steep gorges develop at these sites. Ultimately the headward retreat of falls and rapids drains any lakes along the stream's path.

As the stream's valley deepens, it provides the relief necessary for tributary valleys to develop. They bring increasing quantities of sediment to a river which has already decreased its slope by valley cutting. Ultimately the main stream de-

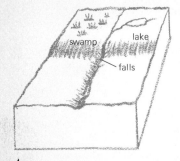

A

FIGURE 11-23

The evolution of a stream valley. (*A*) Initially the stream has an irregular longitudinal profile with rapids and perhaps lakes along its channel. (*B*) Erosion and deposition work to smooth out the long profile, eliminating lakes and rapids. (*C*) Ultimately the stream achieves the graded state, and a floodplain is formed. Continued erosion by lateral planation widens the valley to form a broad floodplain.

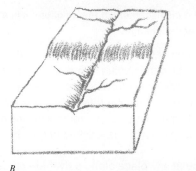

B

C

FIGURE 11-24

Destruction of the knickpoint on Cabin Creek, Montana. An earthquake in this region created a steep falls in this creek. (*A*) The stream profile immediately after formation of the falls. (*B*) Profile a few months later. (*C*) The regraded profile 3 years later. *After M. Morisawa, "Streams." Copyright © 1968 by McGraw-Hill, Inc. Used with permission of McGraw-Hill Book Company.*

velops a profile and slope that is just able to carry the incoming sediment load. There is no excess energy for erosion. The stream has developed an equilibrium profile, with the amount of sediment coming into any section balanced by the amount moving out of it. In short, the stream has become graded.

Where a stream must carve its valley in solid rock, the establishment of an equilibrium profile requires thousands of years. An earthquake in Montana caused a sharp displacement in the channel of a stream flowing on unconsolidated alluvium, thus providing an accelerated view of stream adjustment. Figure 11-24 shows cross sections of the channel measured on successive dates after the faulting; they clearly illustrate how grade was reestablished by the stream.

Grade is usually established first in the downstream parts of rivers. Once graded, the river flows on alluvium, and there no longer is any short-term tendency to lower the valley. The condition of grade gradually extends upstream, but the small tributaries of even a well-graded river system may still be carving their valleys into solid rock. The presence of loose alluvium in the channel is an important requirement for grade. A river flowing on hard bedrock cannot adjust its base to sudden surges, but one flowing in alluvium can. In fact the presence of alluvium in the channel acts as a buffer to help absorb the energy accompanying sudden floods.

Once a stream is graded, it ceases rapid downcutting and begins to widen its valley by *lateral planation.* This sideways cutting takes place on the outside of

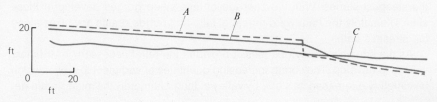

FIGURE 11-25
Meanders and floodplain of the Mudjalik River, northern Saskatchewan. *Canada Department of Energy, Mines and Resources.*

bends, where the channel runs against the valley walls. On the inside of bends deposition occurs because of lower velocities. Gradually a wide floodplain covered with alluvium develops.

Many graded rivers meander, sometimes tortuously (Fig. 11-25), over their floodplains. The complex meander patterns sweep slowly downstream, leaving arcuate scars or crescent-shaped lakes (oxbow lakes) where they have passed. The effect of meandering is to increase the length and thus to decrease the gradient of the river. Studies of many rivers show that the amplitude and wavelength of the meanders are related particularly to discharge and to the type of sediment load.

Not all rivers adopt the meandering pattern. Some, like the rivers of Fig. 11-26, take on a braided appearance. The braided pattern is marked by many islands of sediment and by intricate branching. Braided patterns usually develop because of aggradation by the stream. As sediment is deposited, forks in the flow develop. Although aggradation is a characteristic of most braided streams, this does not mean that sediment is not moved. Particularly during flood stage many of the channel bars may disappear or move downstream.

A meandering river lowers its gradient by increasing the length of its path. A braided river tends to increase its gradient slightly by deposition. One might suspect, therefore, that meandering streams should show lower slopes for a given discharge than braided streams. Two American hydrologists, L. B. Leopold and M. G. Wolman, found from a survey of many rivers that meandering stretches can

FIGURE 11-26
Braided pattern of the Snake River, Jackson Hole, Wyoming. The vegetational pattern on the gravel bars in this stream shows that they are not stationary. The oldest bars have large trees; intermediate bars support small shrubs; and the youngest bars are raw gravel. *D. A. Rahm, "Slides for Geology," 1971. Used with permission of McGraw-Hill Book Company.*

be distinguished from braided reaches on the basis of channel slope (Fig. 11-27) and that for a given discharge braided rivers always exhibit a higher slope. Other investigations have suggested that braided patterns develop where the sediment load is coarser. This or some other cause could be the reason for the greater channel slope of braided rivers.

FIGURE 11-27
Bank-full discharge plotted against channel gradients for meandering, and braided stretches of streams. The data suggest that for a given discharge meanders tend to occur at lower slopes than braiding. *After L. B. Leopold and M. G. Wolman, U.S. Geol. Survey Prof. Paper 282B, 1957.*

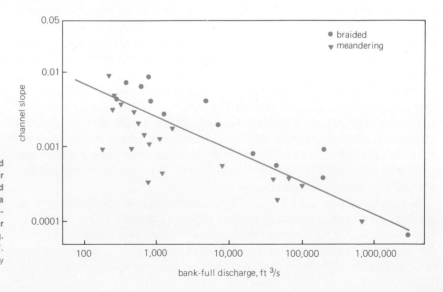

SUMMARY

Water is transferred to the atmosphere by evaporation and transpiration. It falls to the ground as rain or snow, of which some is again evapotranspired, some runs off the surface to streams, and some sinks into the ground to reappear as springs.

The top of the zone saturated with groundwater is called the water table. Beneath the water table water moves slowly downslope, according to Darcy's law. The flow of groundwater is laminar, and the velocity is related to permeability of the medium and the gradient. Groundwater provides rivers with a continual source.

On an average the input of moisture into a drainage area must be balanced by outgo. The yearly water budget of a region is tied closely to its potential evapotranspiration, which is a measure of the amount of moisture that could evaporate if it were present. The PE depends largely upon the availability of thermal energy. When the PE is greater than the precipitation, soil moisture is lost and there is a water deficit. When the precipitation is greater than the PE, the excess moisture is stored in the soil and in the groundwater reservoir.

The channel morphology (width, depth, and hydraulic radius) of a permanent stream is related to discharge and type of sediment load. As discharge increases, width, depth, and (to a lesser extent) velocity also increase. Rivers adjust their channel slopes by erosion and deposition. A graded stream is one whose profile is so adjusted that it is just able to carry the sediment load delivered to it with no significant long-term erosion.

Once graded, streams flow in straight, meandering, or braided paths on their floodplains. The flow pattern is related to discharge and type of sediment load. Meandering streams have lower channel slopes than braided streams for any particular discharge.

QUESTIONS

1 The total yearly precipitation of a region equals its AE plus runoff. How can this be? Doesn't some of the precipitation sink into the ground?

2 In some wells the water flows freely without pumping (artesian wells). Sketch the subsurface conditions that would produce such free flow.

3 Name a porous yet impermeable rock.

4 Why is it much more serious to pollute groundwater than river water?

5 A desert has been defined as a region where precipitation equals evaporation. Why is this a better definition than one in terms of average annual precipitation?

6 The hydraulic gradient $(h_2 - h_1)/L$ of the groundwater in a region is 100 meters per kilometer, and the flow of groundwater is 3 meters per day. What flow rate would you expect in an area with the same rocks where the gradient is 50 meters per kilometer?

7 If the velocity of a stream is 2 meters per second at a point where its cross-sectional area is 10 square meters, what is its velocity at a second point where the cross-sectional area is 15 square meters? What do you have to as-sume in order to solve this problem?

8 How do streams transport material?

9 What do you predict would happen in a graded reach of a river if new sediment from a mining plant continues to be fed to the stream?

10 How can a river adjust its gradient?

11 Where would you expect the groundwater table to slope most steeply, in a region underlain by sand or one underlain by fine clay? Why?

12 The treeless region of northern Canada is dotted with innumerable lakes. How do you account for this in view of the fact that much of the region, like the arid southwest United States, receives less than 10 inches of precipitation per year?

REFERENCES

Davis, S. N., and R. J. M. DeWiest: "Hydrogeology," John Wiley & Sons, Inc., New York, 1966.

DeWiest, R. J. M.: "Geohydrology," John Wiley & Sons, Inc., New York, 1965.

Leopold, L. B., and W. D. Langbein: "A Primer on Water," U.S. Government Printing Office, Washington, D.C., 1960.

————, M. C. Wolman, and J. P. Miller, "Fluvial Processes in Geomorphology," W. H. Freeman and Company, San Francisco, 1964.

Morisawa, Marie: "Streams: Their Dynamics and Morphology," McGraw-Hill Book Company, New York, 1968.

A

B

E

12

GRADATION AND LANDSCAPES

The face of the earth exhibits an incredible richness of features, which photographs like those of Fig. 12-1 can only hint at. The shapes of the land are the work of streams, glaciers, winds, and ocean waves—and man. Today, with power shovels, bulldozers, giant trucks, and scrapers, man moves more material from place to place than any natural force.

This chapter will concentrate on natural grading processes, which, although slower than man's activities, have been in operation much longer. As a result,

C

D

F

FIGURE 12-1
Variety in landscapes. (*A*) **Mountain region in the Antarctic. The folded rocks here are being weathered by mechanical processes.** (*Courtesy of C. Craddock.*) (*B*) **Monument Valley, Arizona. Erosion has left only remnants of a once continuous layer of sandstone.** (*I. J. Witkind, U. S. Geological Survey.*) (*C*) **Mt. Shasta, an extinct volcanic cone dominates this California landscape.** (*Southern Pacific Railway.*) (*D*) **Death Valley, California. Even in this arid region gradation by running water predominates.** (*Courtesy of Mary Hill.*) (*E*) **Wind deposition shaped this terrain in Saudi Arabia. The circular structure is a meteorite crater.** (*Arabian American Oil Company.*) (*F*) **Glacial deposition produced this hummocky terrain in Wisconsin.** (*W. C. Alden, U.S. Geological Survey.*)

most landscape is still the product of these processes. Moreover, the natural grading processes are simpler than man's operations; since they are all driven by gravity, they can move material in only one direction—downward. By wearing down high areas and filling in low ones they tend toward an overall leveling of the land.

How much gradational processes have leveled the land depends upon how long they have been working and their rate of erosion. Erosion rates are a function of energy. In high country, where the potential energy is great, erosion is rapid. Where the terrain is low, erosional processes work slowly or not at all.

Landforms are the surface expression of continued degradation and aggrada-

FIGURE 12-2
Gemini IV photograph of the Gulf of Aden region, Aden Protectorate. Streams here, as in most places on earth, are the dominant sculptors of the landscape. *NASA.*

tion by the leveling processes. In this chapter we shall investigate how the various natural agents cooperate in the work of landscaping. We shall also examine the eroded materials, which ultimately form sedimentary rocks, the subject of Chap. 14.

12-1 A SURVEY OF THE LEVELING PROCESSES

The hills are shadows, and they flow
From form to form, and nothing stands;
They melt like mist, the solid lands,
Like clouds they shape themselves and go.   TENNYSON

Streams are the dominant gradational process. A satellite view of the Gulf of Aden (Fig. 12-2) vividly illustrates the effectiveness of rivers in dissecting the land. Except for about 10 percent of the land area now covered by glaciers

FIGURE 12-3
A glacier in Antarctica. *U. S. Geological Survey.*

(chiefly in Antarctica and Greenland), all continents are crisscrossed by river systems. In assigning rivers the first place as levelers we must recall that they are greatly aided by the sliding and slumping of materials along the valley walls (Fig. 11-20). It is the rivers, however, that move the eroded debris to the sea.

Glaciers (Fig. 12-3) are the most powerful erosional agents, but, as we have noted, they now operate on only about 10 percent of the land areas. Because glacial ice covered almost half of North America during the Pleistocene Epoch, it might seem that we should accord glacial ice preeminence as a leveler. However, geologic evidence shows that the 2.5 million years of the Pleistocene Epoch were the exception rather than the rule. Throughout most of the 3,000 million years and more of earth history recorded in the rocks of the crust, continental glaciation is a rare phenomenon.

Wind is significant as an erosional agent only in places where fine, unconsolidated sediment is exposed at the surface. Even in arid regions which meet this requirement and which lack binding by plant roots, temporary streams

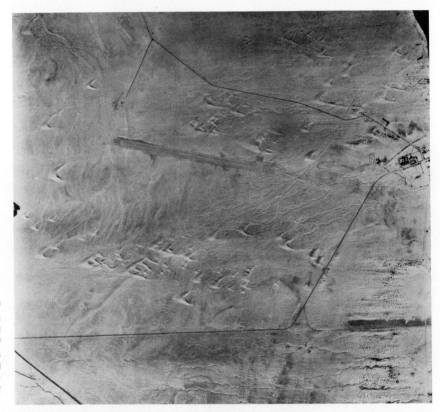

FIGURE 12-4
Aerial view of the terrain west of Salton Sea, California. Although the moon-shaped barchan sand dunes are positive evidence of wind action, the many gulleys are proof that even in this arid region running water is a significant leveler. *U. S. Geological Survey.*

FIGURE 12-5
Sea cliffs in Alaska. Note the former shorelines and the terraces cut by waves over inclined layered rocks. *S. R. Capps, U.S. Geological Survey.*

are usually the chief erosional agents. Figure 12-4 shows an area west of the Salton Sea, California, where crescentshaped sand dunes (barchans) are evidence of wind action. The dunes here, which are from 150 to 800 feet high, are being blown slowly eastward. Although there are no permanent streams, the many gullies in the photograph clearly show that temporary streams flowing during sporadic rainstorms are effective levelers.

Waves crashing against a coast and the flow of longshore currents erode in somewhat the same way as rivers. Waves create sea cliffs like those in Fig. 12-5. Because only a very minor part of the total area of the continents is in direct contact with the sea, wave action cannot compare with stream erosion as a land leveler.

To what depth can the various processes degrade the land? Rivers all ultimately flow to the sea, and their maximum depth of erosion (except for undersea turbidity currents) is sea level. We recall from Chap. 11 that the kinetic energy of a river is spent in overcoming internal friction, in erosion or channel friction, and in transportation. Since a minimum slope is required to keep the water flowing without any erosion, we can conclude that the ultimate base to which a river system can erode is a surface sloping gently seaward.

Wind erosion does not stop at sea level. As long as fine, loose sediment is available, wind continues to degrade (Fig. 12-6). When wind is eroding sediment of mixed size, its downward scour is halted where heavy cobbles and boulders become concentrated at the surface as the fines are blown away. Such coarse deposits, called *lag gravels*, line many of the world's great deserts. Wind erosion is also stopped by the water table because wind is not effective against wet sand.

Glaciers too are able to degrade below sea level. Although these thick masses of moving ice flow downhill like rivers, they are much more powerful scourers. The very thick continental glaciers of the last Ice Age were locally able to carve out depressions below sea level. Some parts of the basins occupied by the Great Lakes, which were scoured during the last Ice Age, extend several hundred feet below sea level.

Since the various erosional agents transport sediments differently, materials deposited by, say, glaciers are not the same as those laid down by rivers. This will be of particular interest to us when we look at the rock record in Chap. 14, where we shall attempt to deduce the nature of the transporting agent from the properties of a given sedimentary rock.

We have already seen that rivers are selective transporting agents. Much of the solid load of a stream is brought to it by valley-side processes. *Mass wasting* is a general term for the downslope movement of rock debris in response to gravity, of which soil creep, slumping, mudflows, and rockslides are examples (Fig. 12-7). These processes are not selective transporters, but when they feed into a stream, the moving water soon separates the various sizes. Superimposed on the selective transport is a general diminution in size of larger particles as they bump and grind against each other during downstream transport. Where the

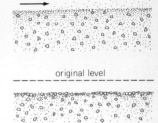

original level

FIGURE 12-6
The formation of lag gravels by continued wind erosion.

FIGURE 12-7
Some forms of mass wasting. Earth materials move downhill in response to gravity either slowly by soil creep (*A*) or rapidly by landsliding, slumping (*B*), or rockfalls. (*C*) The apron of angular boulders typically found at the base of steep slopes as a result of continued rockfall is called talus.

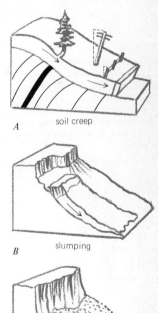

A   soil creep

B   slumping

C

FIGURE 12-8
Glacial till. This unsorted sediment composed of sizes ranging from the finest clay to coarse boulders could only have been deposited by a glacier. *W.J. Hail, Jr., U.S. Geological Survey.*

FIGURE 12-9
Imagine a tributary beginning on a steep valley wall. At first the tributary is only a small gulley (position 1). As it erodes and deepens its channel it reaches points 2, 3, 4 and so on. In effect its valley grows headward.

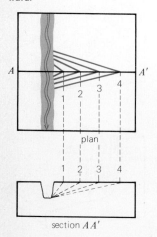

forward motion of the river is slowed and finally stopped, the coarsest materials are dropped first, followed by progressively finer sizes.

Rivers also carry matter in chemical solution. Most of the dissolved load of a river comes from groundwater that has been in intimate contact with subsurface rocks for many decades before emerging as a spring to feed a river. The material in solution in river water is not affected by the motion of the water. A river's dissolved load is precipitated when a change in chemical conditions is encountered.

Wind too is a very selective transporter of sediment. Because of its much lower density, air transports much finer particles than water moving with the same velocity. Only the finest dust is lifted into suspension by wind, finally to fall as a blanket deposit known as *loess*. Sand-sized particles are rolled or bounced along the ground. Windblown dune sands are normally much better sorted than water-transported sands. Also individual sand grains that have been moved by wind are generally better rounded than those moved only by water. During the 1950s, P. H. Kuenen, a Dutch geologist, made some interesting experiments simulating the transport of sand. He found that medium-sized sand particles lose only 0.01 percent of their mass during the equivalent of 100 miles of stream travel. At this rate a cube of sand would have to travel a distance equal to 20 times the earth's circumference to be rounded to a sphere. On the other hand, wind-tunnel experiments reveal that quartz sand loses mass 100 to 1,000 times as fast in air as it does in an equal distance of water transport. Because windblown sand grains suffer many sharp collisions during transport, they usually are frosted in appearance. The cushioning effect of water prevents the sharp impacts, and so stream-transported sand grains tend to be more polished.

Figure 12-8 shows a poorly sorted sediment. The mixture of sizes from boulders to the finest clay could not have been deposited together by either wind or water. The deposit in the photograph is glacial till. Glaciers are nonselective transporters, simultaneously moving and depositing particles ranging from boulders many feet in diameter to the finest rock flour. Moreover, whereas wind and water generally erode the weathered mantle, glaciers are sufficiently abrasive to scrape and grind up significant amounts of bedrock. As a result much of the ground-up rock in glacial deposits is unweathered.

12-2 DISSECTING THE LAND

Let us now see how the rivers incise the land with networks of interconnecting valleys. Imagine a block of land without any streams that has suddenly become uplifted with respect to the sea by diastrophism. This imaginary block of land may have been a part of a former sea bottom or a flat piece of the continent previously eroded to base level. For the present, let us further assume that the uplift was rapid and uniform, so that a steep slope developed at the edge of the sea. This need not be so in the real world, and in fact uplift is normally slow and continuous over long periods and may involve tilting. Our model, however, will serve to illustrate how a newly exposed surface becomes dissected.

We have all seen gullies develop along steep road cuts or other man-made embankments. Similar gullies will develop along the steep face of our imaginary block of land. As rain falls upon the land, it tends to collect into rivulets, and whichever gully happens to lie where most water accumulates will be cut deepest. This initial stream will lengthen its valley by *headward erosion*. As illustrated in Fig. 12-9, the valley carved by a river grows in the direction opposite to the direction of flow. An original stream on a newly uplifted land surface is called a *consequent stream*. Part I of Fig. 12-10 shows a newly developed consequent stream.

As the consequent valley extends headward into the land, it provides the slope for new gullies and finally new streams to form along its valley side. In the first part of Fig. 12-10, for example, there is no slope along section AA'. When the consequent stream valley reaches this section, it provides the slope for streams from the side to develop. These too extend their valleys headward to provide the relief for still other streams, until the entire landscape is dissected by valleys (Fig. 12-10, part III). The secondary, or tributary, streams thus formed are called *subsequent streams.*

In 1802 the Scottish geologist John Playfair wrote what has since become known as *Playfair's law*:

Every river appears to consist of a main trunk, fed by a variety of branches, each running in a valley proportioned to its size, and all of them together forming a system

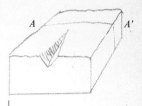

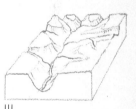

FIGURE 12-10
A region being dissected by stream erosion. Initially there is no slope along AA'. Headward erosion by the primary stream, however, eventually generates slopes for secondary streams whose valleys provide starting places for still other tributaries.

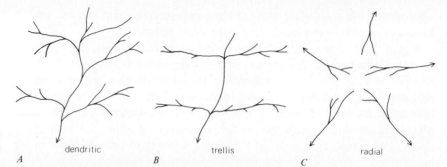

FIGURE 12-11
The principal drainage patterns: (*A*) **dendritic;** (*B*) **trellis;** (*C*) **radial.**

of valleys, communicating with one another, and having such a nice adjustment in declivities, that none of them join the principal valley, either on too high or too low a level; a circumstance which would be infinitely improbable, if each of these valleys were not the work of the stream that flows in it.

It is clear from our imaginary landscape of Fig. 12-10 why subsequent valleys always enter main valleys at just the level of the main stream. The tributaries start at that level. As they lengthen their valleys headward, they provide relief for still other tributaries, which again begin at the level of the streams from which they in turn originate.

In a region where the materials being eroded are relatively homogeneous we would expect the subsequent streams to develop at random low spots. The resulting drainage network should thus display a random pattern resembling the branches of a tree. This *dendritic pattern* (Fig. 12-11*A*) is indeed found where streams evolve on materials of uniform hardness. When the underlying rocks are folded sedimentary rocks of varying hardness, the tributary valleys tend to grow along the bands of softer rock, to form a *trellised* drainage pattern (Fig. 12-11*B*). *Radial* drainage patterns evolve on volcanic mountains or in regions of local upwarping (Fig. 12-11*C*).

As the rivers of a region cut downward, the areas between streams stand out as topographic highs. This produces some unusual effects where trellised patterns are involved. In Fig. 12-12 the Susquehanna River flows right through several parallel mountain ridges. The mountains could not have been there when the river started or it would have flowed around them. This river must have started when the terrain was flat. Its tributaries developed along the softer sedimentary layers and as the entire drainage system eroded downward, the harder rock layers gradually stood out as ridges.

In the 1930s an American hydrologist, R. E. Horton, discovered some interesting relationships between the various streams of a drainage network. To appreciate his laws of stream numbers we must first study Fig. 12-13, which illustrates the hierarchical ordering of streams in a drainage basin. Streams without tributaries are called *first-order* streams. Where two first-order streams join, a second-order stream begins. Two second-order streams unite to form a third-

FIGURE 12-12
The Susquehanna River must
have developed its course before the mountains were
created by erosion. *A. J. Nystrom and Company.*

order stream, and so forth. It is only where streams of equal order meet that a
higher-order stream is formed. Where streams of unequal order come together,
the resulting stream has the same order as the greater of the two.

Table 12-1 lists the number of stream segments of various order in the

TABLE 12-1
The Allegheny River drainage
basin*

Stream order	Number of segments	Average segment length, miles
1	5,966	0.09
2	1,529	0.3
3	378	0.8
4	68	2.5
5	13	7
6	3	20
7	1	†

*From M. Morisawa, *Geol. Soc. Am. Bull.* 73, 1962.
†Not measurable in study area.

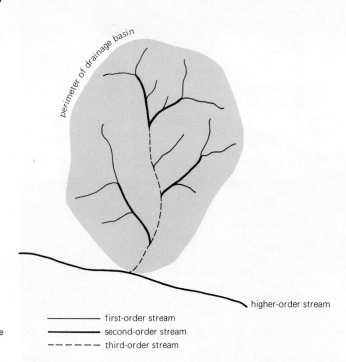

FIGURE 12-13
Orders of streams in a drainage basin.

——————— first-order stream
———————— second-order stream
– – – – – third-order stream

Allegheny drainage basin in Pennsylvania. It is clear from the table that the number of stream segments decreases in a geometric fashion as the order increases arithmetically. Figure 12-14 graphs this relationship for several other drainage basins. Horton found that this relationship holds for most drainage basins. He also discovered that the lengths of streams of successive orders increases according to a geometric progression and that stream gradients decrease geometrically with increasing order.

Figure 12-15 shows two drainage networks. Both seem to conform to Horton's rule of stream numbers because there are many more first-order streams than second-order, and so forth. The two networks, however, are very different in terms of the actual numbers of streams per unit area (drainage density). In the region of high drainage density (Fig. 12-15A) many small tributaries are obviously required to maintain the major channels. Generally where a watershed is composed of relatively impermeable substances, like silt or clay, a dense drainage pattern develops. On the other hand, watersheds in permeable sands characteristically require a larger drainage area to maintain streams and hence the more open pattern (Fig. 12-15B). Climate also is a contributing factor in determining drainage density, both directly in influencing runoff and indirectly in controlling vegetation. Other things being equal, regions of high relief have a higher drainage density than low areas.

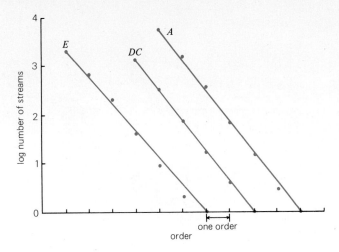

FIGURE 12-14
Plot of logarithm of number of streams against stream order. A = Allegheny River; DC = Daddy's Creek, Tennessee; E = Emory River, Tennessee. *After M. Morisawa, "Streams." Copyright © 1968 by McGraw-Hill, Inc. Used with permission of McGraw-Hill Book Company.*

12-3 IS THERE A REGULAR EROSION CYCLE?

In Chap. 11 we traced the evolution of a typical valley from its narrow V-shaped beginning, to the development of a flood plain, to the formation of a wide, open valley brought about by lateral planation of a meandering stream. Let us now survey an entire region to see how it can be expected to change with continued erosion.

We begin with a newly uplifted region and a developing drainage network (Fig. 12-16). The area is relatively flat, poorly drained, as evidenced by lakes and swamps, and has few streams. This is the stage of youth. As tributaries develop, and as they in turn are fed by still other tributaries, the region becomes criss-

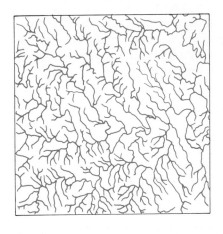

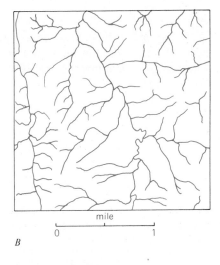

FIGURE 12-15
Each drainage network covers an area of 1 square mile. Although drainage in both regions [(A) in South Dakota, (B) in Missouri] conforms to the law of stream numbers, the density of valleys is very different.

A

B

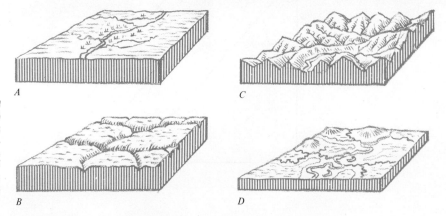

FIGURE 12-16
Ideal stages in the evolution of a region by stream erosion: (*A*) **initial stage;** (*B*) **early youth;** (*C*) **maturity;** (*D*) **old age.** *Redrawn from A. N. Strahler, 1969, "Physical Geography," 3d ed., John Wiley & Sons, Inc., based on drawings by Erwin Raisz.*

crossed by valleys. Lakes and swamps become drained, and the flatness disappears as the many valleys make slopes everywhere. This is the stage of maturity. With continued erosion the major streams (and finally also the tributary streams) become graded. They meander within the confines of their banks to cut at the valley sides and produce wider and wider valleys. The tendency is toward a flat terrain like that marking the beginning of our cycle but at a lower elevation. When the leveling processes have almost reduced the region to a plain again, the region is said to have reached old age. This final stage is called a *peneplain* (from *pene*, meaning "almost"). Any change in base level due to uplift would reenergize the streams and initiate a new erosion cycle.

Table 12-2 summarizes the stages in the ideal cycle of erosion as envisioned in humid temperate regions. This concept of an erosional cycle, proposed by the American geographer W. M. Davis, is based on the assumption that a region undergoes a quite rapid uplift followed by a lengthy period of erosion. Indeed, many thousands of lifetimes of observation would be required to view a complete cycle. Various stages, however, are on view in different parts of the continents, which suggests that there is indeed such a cyclical development.

TABLE 12-2
Characteristics of the stages in the ideal cycle of erosion in humid climates

Youth	Terrain relatively flat; poorly drained Lakes and bogs Few tributaries Valleys youthful; rapids and falls common
Maturity	Terrain all in slope because of network of valleys Valleys chiefly youthful with some higher-order streams in mature stage Well drained because of many tributaries
Old age	Terrain again near flat: peneplain Marked by meandering rivers with broad flood plains Occasional low hills (monadnocks) are erosional remnants that escaped river peneplanation

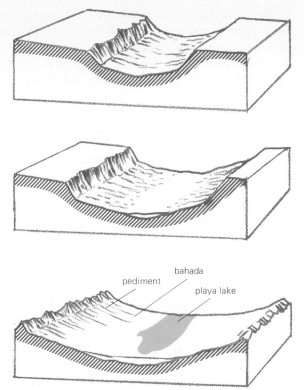

FIGURE 12-17
In arid regions the topography is much more angular than in humid areas because there is less decomposition and soil formation. The diagrams illustrate how retreat of slopes in arid climates produces sloping rock surfaces called pediments. Playa lakes are ephemeral features. Water from sporadic rainstorms evaporates quickly, leaving great salt flats called playas.

Davis's scheme has been widely criticized because it fails to account for some of the observed characteristics of landscapes. Most damaging to the theory is the fact that extensive peneplains have not been identified as part of the present landscape. Most of the many extensive flat areas on earth are depositional rather than erosional surfaces. Partially dissected flat erosional surfaces are known, but they occur in distinct steps, or benches. According to the Davis's scheme, one would not expect to find such benches because the higher levels should have been dissected before uplift exposed the lower levels.

Other models of landscape evolution have been proposed to overcome some of these weaknesses. One explains the existence of steplike flat regions by the parallel retreat of the escarpments between levels. This kind of topographic development has been observed in arid to semiarid regions, where there is little chemical decomposition or soil formation. In such regions erosion proceeds as is illustrated in Fig. 12-17. Occasional flash floods feed temporary streams to produce gently sloping rocky erosion surfaces called *pediments*, which grow by the parallel retreat of mountain slopes. The debris washed off the pediment accumulates at the foot in broad alluvial blankets called *bahadas*.

There are also places, however, where steep slopes appear to be fixed rather than retreating. In Fig. 12-18, for example, we can see that although weathered

FIGURE 12-18
Although weathered debris is moving over this escarpment, the slope itself remains in one position.

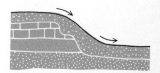

debris is continually moving over the slope, its actual position as determined by the bedrock is not changing. We must conclude, therefore, that neither the peneplain concept nor the idea of parallel retreat of escarpments accounts for all the observed characteristics of actual landforms. Much work remains to be done before it is possible to make accurate predictions of the path of erosion in any region.

12-4 SCULPTURING BY GLACIERS

Today glaciers occupy about 10 percent of the land area of the earth. Continental ice sheets are found only in Greenland and Antarctica. Except for the spectacular scenery carved by ice in some high mountainous regions (Fig. 12-19), glaciation might seem to occupy a minor role in the evolution of landforms, particularly since the rock record shows the earth to have been essentially free from ice throughout most of geologic time.

But glaciers account for much more of the existing scenery than is suggested by their present distribution. Within the past 2 to 2.5 million years (during the Pleistocene Epoch) the extent of glacial ice fluctuated considerably, several times covering up to about 30 percent of the world's land areas. The last retreat of ice from Canada, the northern United States, and northern Europe occurred only about 10,000 years ago. Consequently, the topography of these vast stretches is in large part of glacial origin because streams and other erosional agents have not yet had time to erase the effects of glaciation. Moreover, when continental glaciers extended south to Kansas and Nebraska, they pushed all the climatic belts southward. Many of the deserts now found along the belt between 15° and 25°N latitude experienced much cooler and wetter climates then. The effects of these wetter climates are still visible in the desert landscape.

How do glaciers originate? We considered this problem in Chap. 11 in connection with our discussion of water balances. In winter, when precipitation falls as snow, the input of moisture to a region exceeds the outgo, and snow accumulates. In most places the annual water balance is maintained when the snow melts during the spring. Where the winter snow does not completely melt or evaporate during the summer, old snow is still left when a new snow season begins. If such an imbalance persists year after year, snow eventually builds up to form a glacier, which flows away from the center of accumulation to restore the balance.

Newly fallen snow is usually light and powdery, consisting of tiny hexagonal crystals of ice. During a melting season this light material soon changes into sugary granular snow, called *firn* or *névé*. As firn is compacted under the weight of years of accumulation, it loses its porosity and changes to compacted ice, which flows if the thickness (pressure) is great enough. The elevation above which melting of winter snow is incomplete, called the *snow line*, varies from sea level in the polar regions to about 20,000 feet in the equatorial regions of the Andes.

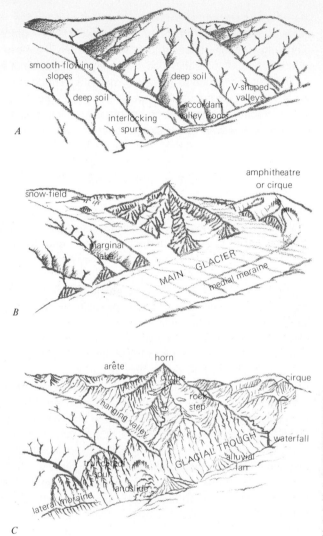

FIGURE 12-19
Evolution of a mountainous region by glacial erosion (A) before, (B) during, and (C) after glaciation. *Adapted from A. K. Lobeck, "Introduction to the Study of Landscapes," Copyright © 1939 by McGraw-Hill, Inc. Used with permission of McGraw-Hill Book Company.*

As we saw in Fig. 11-10, a glacier consists of two principal zones. Above the snow line lies the *zone of accumulation*, where there is a net input of new snow. Below the snow line is the *zone of ablation*, where ice is lost by melting and evaporation. The position of the glacial terminus depends upon the balance between input in the accumulation zone and outgo in the zone of ablation. An increase in precipitation with no temperature change should cause a glacial advance. A decrease in ablation due to a drop in temperature should promote advance.

If we apply pressure to an ice cube, it fails by cracking, or rupturing. This is

A

B

FIGURE 12-20
(A) **A glacial horn in the Himalaya** (*Clyde Rice*). (B) **Glaciated terrain in the Sierra Nevada, California** (*C. K. Gilbert, U.S. Geological Survey*).

the normal behavior of a brittle solid. Some of the ice in a glacier, however, behaves in quite a different manner; it flows. Markers placed on the surface of a glacier have been observed to move from a few inches to about 3 feet per day. How can glacial ice behave so differently from the ice of everyday experience?

The behavior of ice in the upper glacial layers does indeed conform to what we observe in ice cubes. Here we see large cracks (crevasses), corresponding to the fractures that develop in pieces of ice pounded or squeezed. The crevasses, however, rarely extend deeper than 100 feet; below that level ice deforms by flowage and begins to behave like a viscous fluid rather than an elastic solid.

The exact mechanism of flow of glacial ice is imperfectly understood. Ice crystals possess a cleavage plane and can be made to slip along this plane and become elongated; but the ice crystals in glaciers are not unduly elongated, and so there must be other flow mechanisms. Glacial flow is believed to be due to a combination of causes, including the deformation of ice crystals, the recrystallization of ice grains by freezing and thawing, and the slippage of glacial ice over the underlying rock.

A moving glacier is a powerful erosional agent. Glacial ice contains many trapped rock fragments that act like the teeth of a file, scraping and abrading the surface over which the glacier moves. Rock trapped in glacial ice has been plucked from the bed by the moving ice or has fallen onto the glacial surface from valley walls, where it was loosened by frost wedging.

Sediment deposited by glaciers is called *drift*. The term dates back to the early nineteenth century, before a detailed history of the Pleistocene Epoch had been worked out. It was thought then that the layers of unsized material ranging from clay to boulders had been drifted to their present positions by the flood of Noah. There are two kinds of glacial drift: unstratified and unsorted drift, called *till*, and stratified and sorted drift, called *stratified drift*. Till is a true glacial deposit composed of finely ground-up rock together with boulder-sized fragments. The rock flour in till differs from the clayey material formed by weathering in being mainly ground up rock rather than chemically decomposed material. The boulders in till are frequently flattened and scratched from scraping against the underlying bedrock. Stratified drift is glacial material that has been moved and deposited by meltwaters. It has been sorted by size and formed into layers.

12-5 RECONSTRUCTING PAST GLACIAL POSITIONS

Figure 12-19 diagrammatically traces the evolution of a mountain region that has undergone glaciation. Mountain glaciers begin in amphitheater-shaped depressions called *cirques*. At first these are local sites of snow accumulation, where the surrounding rock is broken by alternate freezing and thawing. As ice gradually accumulates to greater and greater thickness, it begins to flow down the mountain valleys. The mass of moving ice in such a valley glacier has a

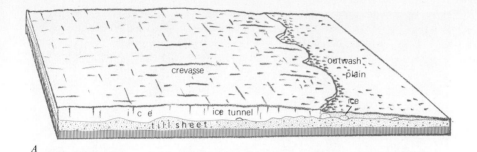

A

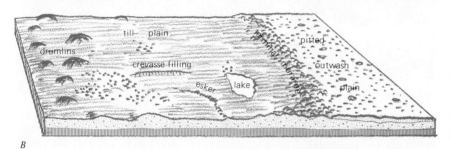

B

FIGURE 12-21
**The terminal region of a conti-
nental glacier (*A*) during and (*B*)
after glaciation.** *From V. C.
Finch, G. T. Trewartha, A. H.
Robinson, and E. H. Ham-
mond, "Physical Geography."
Copyright © 1957 by McGraw-
Hill, Inc. Used with permission
of McGraw-Hill Book Com-
pany.*

marked effect upon the valley shape. V-shaped stream valleys are changed into
deeper U-shaped valleys by glacial scouring. Where a main valley is deepened
by glacial scouring, the tributary valleys are left as *hanging valleys*. Spurs between adjacent tributaries become truncated by the abrading ice mass. The
headward extension of cirques promoted by frost activity on the high, bare rock
surfaces produces the sharp topography distinctive of glacially carved mountains (Fig. 12-20).

It should be clear from Fig. 12-19 and the preceding discussion that the effects of glaciation in mountainous areas are sufficiently distinctive to be easily
recognizable even after the glaciers have vanished. A glaciated valley can be
identified by such features as (*1*) its U shape, (*2*) the presence of hanging
valleys, (*3*) truncated spurs, (*4*) glacial striations and grooves on the exposed
rocks, and (*5*) glacial deposits.

In Chap. 10 we saw how the maximum extent of the continental ice sheets during the Pleistocene Epoch were reconstructed by mapping the positions of
glacial deposits and glacial erratics. Geological detective work has done more
than reveal the total area covered by ice: it has shown in detail the points
reached by lobes of ice during the four major and the several minor periods of
ice advance.

To see how this history was reconstructed we must be familiar with some of
the features associated with continental glaciers. Whereas the most striking effects of glaciers in mountainous regions are erosional, the principal remains of
large continental glaciers are depositional. Figure 12-21 is a block diagram of

A

B

FIGURE 12-22
(*A*) **Air photograph of a glacial esker in the Northwest Territories, Canada. Eskers mark the sites of former subglacial rivers that flowed through tunnels near the glacial terminus.** *(Department of Mines, Energy and Resources, Canada.)* (*B*) **Ground view of another esker in the same region. Eskers are composed of water-deposited gravels and sands.** *(B. G. Craig, Geological Survey of Canada.)*

FIGURE 12-23
Looking southeastward along the margin of the moraine left by a lobe of the continental glacier between Chelan and Grand Coulee, Washington. *From John S. Shelton, "Geology Illustrated," W. H. Freeman and Company. Copyright © 1966.*

the terminus of a large continental ice sheet. Meltwaters rush from the glacial terminus to form a broad outwash plain of sorted sediment. Mixed with the outwash may be large stagnant blocks of ice that become buried. When these melt, they leave closed depressions, which commonly fill with water and are called *kettles*. When the terminus of a glacier remains in one position for an extended period, material trapped in the ice gradually accumulates there to form an *end moraine*. The end moraine marking the farthest advance is called a *terminal moraine*.

When such an ice mass recedes, several unique depositional landforms are exposed. One landform consists of narrow, winding hills of sand and gravel marking the sites of meltwater tunnels near the glacial terminus. These sinuous ridges are called *eskers* (Fig. 12-22). *Drumlins* are elongate, smooth oval hills composed of till usually occurring in fields or clusters. In a drumlin field the individual drumlins exhibit a parallel orientation, suggesting that they are deposits of an advancing or moving ice sheet. A sheetlike blanket of till laid down when a glacier melts is called *ground moraine*.

By carefully mapping the locations of end moraines, outwash plains, eskers, and drumlins geologists have been able to resolve the glacial puzzle. Figure 12-23 shows a glacial limit in the state of Washington. The hummocky nature of

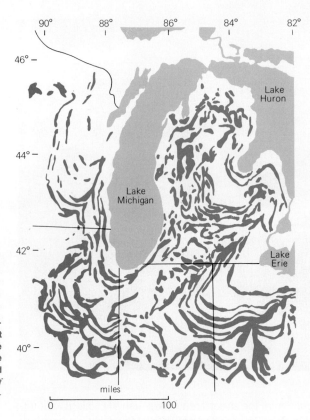

FIGURE 12-24
Map of terminal and recessional moraines of the Great Lakes region. Each moraine marks the place where an ice lobe remained for an extended period. *After Glacial Map of North America, Geological Society of America.*

the terminal moraine clearly distinguishes it from the more featureless outwash plain. The map of Fig. 12-24 shows the many end moraines that have been mapped in the Great Lakes region. Each of the end ridges marks a place where the glacial terminus stood for an extended time.

When glaciers move over bedrock, the glacial grooves and scratches are clues to the direction of movement. Sometimes the general direction of movement can also be determined by tracing material found in till back to its source. For example, in the Keweenaw Peninsula, Michigan, there are deposits of native copper in basalts and conglomerates that are not found anywhere else in the United States. Pieces of native copper have been found in the glacial drift of southern Illinois and Nebraska. Such indicator materials in the drift provide information about glacial flow directions.

The opposite problem is illustrated in Fig. 12-25, which shows the locations of quality diamonds found in the glacial drift of the Great Lakes region. Although the source of these diamonds is unknown, the direction of glacial motion has been established from other evidence. It appears that the diamonds must have

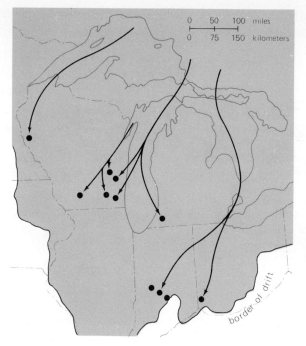

FIGURE 12-25
Sketch map of east central North America showing occurrences of diamonds (dots) in glacial drift and conjectural paths of travel (arrows) of the glaciers deduced from striations, drumlins, and other directional features. *Modified after W. H. Hobbs, from R. F. Flint, "Glacial and Pleistocene Geology," John Wiley & Sons, Inc., 1957.*

come from somewhere in Ontario. So far several extensive exploration ventures have failed to pinpoint the diamond deposit or possible sources.

12-6 SOME SPECIAL LANDSCAPES

Landscapes formed by wind

Wind is effective as an erosional agent only where there is a supply of fine, dry, loose sediment. The chief form of wind erosion is by deflation, the lifting and blowing away of such loose material. Figure 12-26 is an aerial view of a portion of the northern coast of Brazil near Fortaleza. The prevailing winds blow toward the land, picking up beach sand and making it travel as dunes. The sand in the beach is continually replaced from the ocean. A stretch of barren desert, an aggrading stream, a glacial outwash plain, a beach—all are potential sources of sediment for the wind.

We have seen that wind is a very selective agent of transportation. Figure 12-27 graphs the settling velocities of various particle sizes in air. A turbulence or updraft equal to or greater than the settling velocity will keep a particle in suspension. Normal wind speeds are such that sand-sized particles are usually carried within a meter or so of the ground surface by *saltation* (bouncing). At the

FIGURE 12-26
A stretch of the northeast coast of Brazil near Fortaleza. The narrow beach near the top of the picture is the source of sand for all the dunes migrating landward.

same speed, finer silt particles are winnowed out from the sand and carried at higher levels in true suspension.

When windblown sand near ground level encounters an obstruction, it may accumulate into a sand dune. If the supply of sand is relatively sparse, dunes often occur as individual crescent-shaped varieties called barchans. The horns of a barchan point downwind. In places where sand is abundant, transverse

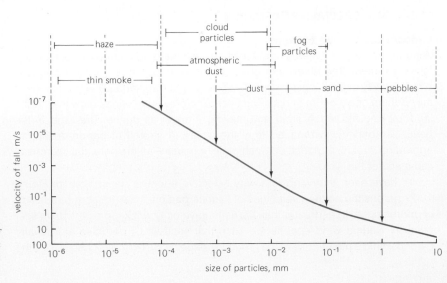

FIGURE 12-27
Relationship of settling velocity to particle size in air. *After R. A. Bagnold, "The Physics of Blown Sand and Desert Dunes," William Morrow & Company, Inc., 1942.*

FIGURE 12-28
Desert dune sands. Most of the dunes here are transverse dunes. *Arabian American Oil Company.*

dunes and parabolic dunes are formed. Parabolic dunes are also horned, but their horns point upwind, opposite those of barchans. In regions of strong, shifting winds, dunes are sometimes strung out in long chains. Some dunes of this type in Iran rise as high as 700 feet and can be traced for tens of kilometers (Fig. 12-28).

The fine-grained material carried in suspension by wind is deposited in blanket form. Fine windblown silt is called loess. Because of its excellent sorting and fine size loess is able to stand in almost vertical cliffs with only the cohesive forces between the small angular grains holding the material together.

Extensive deposits of loess blanket parts of the central United States, covering large areas of southeast Nebraska, Iowa, Illinois, Missouri, western Tennessee, and Mississippi and sometimes reaching a thickness of 100 feet. In places the loess exhibits characteristics suggestive of water transport. Its distribution, however, speaks for an eolian origin for most of the blanket. The loess deposits in the central United States are intimately related to the major glacier-fed valleys. When the continental ice sheet melted, great areas of bare outwash must have been exposed along these valleys, providing an adequate source of unconsolidated debris for the wind to blow away. The association of loess deposits with glaciated regions in other parts of the world lends support to this interpretation.

Landscapes formed by groundwater

Most of the dissolved load of a river comes from groundwater. Soils and rock are composed of relatively insoluble materials, and precipitation that immediately goes to runoff does not remain in contact with the solid materials of the surface long enough to acquire a significant dissolved load. Water fed to a stream via springs, on the other hand, has been in intimate contact with rocks for years during its slow travel through the ground.

Moving groundwater thus slowly but irreversibly removes material from the rock through which it flows. For the most part, this type of erosion has no recognizable effect on the topography. In areas that are largely underlain by carbonate rocks, however, a special type of landscape sometimes develops as a result of this solvent action of groundwater.

Carbonate rocks (limestones and dolomites) are composed of the minerals calcite, $CaCO_3$, and dolomite, $CaMg(CO_3)_2$. Compared to the more common silicate minerals, carbonate minerals are relatively soluble, particularly in slightly acid waters. In the presence of weak carbonic acid, the carbonates form bicarbonates, which dissolve readily. Calcite dissolves according to the reaction

$$CaCO_3 + H_2O + CO_2 \rightleftharpoons Ca(HCO_3)_2$$

(Solid)   Water   Carbon   (Soluble)
                         dioxide

The reaction proceeds to the right (solution of $CaCO_3$) in slightly acid waters, and it proceeds to the left (precipitation of $CaCO_3$) under neutral to alkaline conditions. Because carbon dioxide and water together form weak carbonic acid, the reaction is highly sensitive to the availability of carbon dioxide.

When it moves through fractures in carbonate rocks, groundwater sometimes dissolves enough material from the walls to form large underground caverns. The caverns represent the solution of $CaCO_3$, whereas the stalactites and stalagmites found in the caverns illustrate the precipitation of calcite from water.

Sometimes underground caves form so close to the surface and become so large that the roof collapses. The resulting depression is called a *sinkhole*. Where there are many sinkholes and a system of connecting underground passageways there can be no normal surface drainage. As illustrated in Fig. 12-29, streams enter the sinks and flow underground. The name *Karst topography* has been given to regions with many sinkholes and without organized surface streams, after an area in the Karst district of the Adriatic coast where such terrain is well developed.

12-7 WHAT ACCOUNTS FOR THE GREAT VARIABILITY OF LANDSCAPES?

In the preceding survey we have developed a model of the gradational processes in which running water is the chief sculptor of landscapes. Uplift

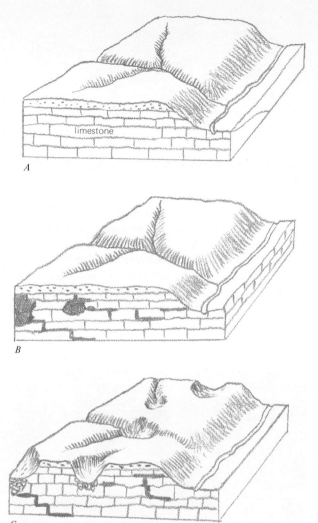

FIGURE 12-29
The formation of sink holes and karst topography by ground-water: (*A*) initial stage; (*B*) formation of underground caverns; (*C*) collapse of caverns to form sinks.

through diastrophism exposes land to the carving action of streams, which slowly incises the surface in a series of interconnecting valleys to form the topography. Thus the shape of the land should depend largely on the rates of uplift and erosion and the time erosion has had to do its work.

If the evolution of landscapes were indeed as simple as suggested by this model, a traveler crossing the country by car should see many examples of the same scene where similar balances between uplift and erosion have occurred. In

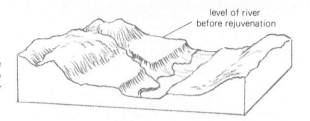

level of river
before rejuvenation

FIGURE 12-30
Uplift in a region where the rivers have reached grade causes them to seek lower levels.

a very general way he does observe a repeated pattern, but he is more likely to be struck by the great *diversity* of the scenery.

We already know that some of the diversity is due to the effects of the other erosional agents—mass wasting, wind, groundwater, and glaciation. Climate also leaves its mark upon the landscape in several ways. The amount of water flowing in streams—and thus the amount available to carry out erosive work—depends upon the total precipitation. Furthermore, the type and intensity of chemical weathering and soil formation are related to climate. Lack of chemical weathering and the accompanying paucity of vegetation tend to make the topography in arid regions more rugged and angular than in their soil-covered humid counterparts.

FIGURE 12-31
Air view of the McDonald Fault at the east end of Great Slave Lake, Northwest Territories, Canada. *Geological Survey of Canada.*

A

folds
B

C

D

FIGURE 12-32
Relation between underlying rock and topography: (*A*) horizontal strata; (*B*) folded strata; (*C*) homogeneous crystalline masses; (*D*) volcanoes. *Redrawn from A. N. Strahler, 1969, "Physical Geography," 3d ed., John Wiley & Sons, Inc.*

Earth movements too are more variable than we have so far recognized. They are generally divided into orogenic movements, which involve folding and faulting of rocks typically observed in mountainous regions, and epeirogenic, or slow, movements, which involve no significant rock deformation. Although rate of uplift was included in our model, we must recognize other complications associated with diastrophism. Blocks of the earth's crust may move up or down, and the movements may be continuous or steplike. If after a long period of erosion a region is suddenly reuplifted, its graded streams will be given new life: they will become rejuvenated (Fig. 12-30). Compound landscapes that exhibit characteristics of several stages of the ideal erosion cycle are the result of such rejuvenation. Faulting between blocks of the crust introduces linear patterns into the terrain (Fig. 12-31).

Two regions with similar histories of erosion and uplift and with the same climate may exhibit different landscapes because of the nature of the rocks being eroded. The effect of alternating bands of hard and soft rocks (folded sediments) on the topography was noted in Sec. 12-3. Areas underlain by flat-lying sediments are eroded to form features such as buttes and mesas, which are absent in regions underlain by rocks of uniform hardness. Figure 12-32 summarizes the relation between topography and rock type.

These various factors still are not the only causes of landscape diversity. Landscapes undergoing normal evolution are sometimes involved in accidents that markedly change their appearance. Landscape accidents are of two main types: volcanic and climatic. Figure 12-33 shows the volcano Paricutin in Michoacán, Mexico, as it appeared in 1945. Two years earlier the area occupied by the volcanic cone was a cornfield. By 1945 the rim of the cone was 1,000 feet

FIGURE 12-33
The volcano Paricutín in Michoacán, Mexico, as it appeared in 1945. Two years earlier this was a cornfield. *Courtesy of the American Museum of Natural History.*

above the field on which it grew. Its height in 1972 was almost 7,500 feet. Terrain is modified in other ways by surface vulcanism. Lava flows sometimes dam river valleys and occasionally bury the existing topography completely. Basalt flows of the Miocene Epoch blanket an area of about 150,000 square miles in Washington and Oregon.

Climatic accidents result from the shifting of climatic zones. Glaciation is a climatic accident which modifies the terrain not only in the ice-covered region but in adjacent areas as well. A long drought in an otherwise temperate region produces a marked change in vegetation and a corresponding increase in erosion. Thus areas that have experienced climatic accidents contain within the landscape evidence of exposure to several climates.

The reason for the great diversity of scenery should now be apparent. Streams are the dominant levelers, but when we superimpose the effects of climate, of climatic accidents, of earth movement and its variations, of rock type, of vulcanism, and the age of the topography, it is easy to see why we get endless variety. Geomorphology is the part of earth science concerned with the nature and origin of landforms. The geomorphologist attempts to read from a terrain the many landscape-shaping influences to which it has been subjected and thus to reconstruct its history.

SUMMARY

Running water, glaciers, wind, mass wasting, and ocean waves are the chief agents of erosion. They work to wear down high regions and to build up low areas. Of these levelers, running water is the most important.

Stream valleys grow headward, and tributary streams begin their valleys at the main stream. A newly uplifted flat region thus gradually changes to one that is everywhere sloping as more and more stream valleys are born. The character of the drainage pattern depends upon the type of bedrock and the climate.

According to W. M. Davis, the landforms of temperate regions evolve from a flat stage of youth, to sloping maturity, where the terrain is dissected by valleys, to a flat peneplained stage of old age. Although this classical scheme of landform evolution explains some of the observed diversity, it fails to account for

many characteristics. The existence of level surfaces at different altitudes suggests an evolution of landforms via the parallel retreat of slopes. Actual landforms are too complicated to be explained by either of these models.

Glaciers, wind, and groundwater each produce distinctive types of topography. In addition, climate, diastrophism, vulcanism, and the nature of the bedrock influence the landscape formed at any place.

QUESTIONS

1 Why can water transport larger particles than wind?

2 How can you distinguish between stream-deposited and glacially deposited materials? Between a river sand and a dune sand?

3 The Colorado River and its tributaries drain an area of about 230,000 square miles. About 1×10^7 tons of material is carried by the river each year. At this rate how long would it take the river to lower its drainage area by 100 feet? (Assume that 10 cubic feet of soil or rock equals 1 ton.)

4 How would you distinguish topography due to erosion from that due to deposition?

5 What is the fate of any lake?

6 How can you distinguish a valley that has been glaciated from one that has not?

7 In the Sierra Nevada of California the valleys on the west side of the range show the effects of former glaciation to a much lower elevation than the valleys on the east. Suggest an explanation.

8 Rivers form valleys which are open depressions in that water flows in them. How can closed depressions occupied by lakes or bogs be formed by erosion?

9 Explain how it is possible for a river to flow through a mountain ridge.

10 Why are underground caverns found chiefly in limestone?

REFERENCES

Bloom, A. L.: "The Surface of the Earth," Prentice-Hall, Inc., Englewood Cliffs, N.J., 1969.

Davis, W. M.: "Geographical Essays," Dover Publications, Inc., New York, 1954.

Dyson, J. L.: "The World of Ice," Alfred A. Knopf, Inc., New York, 1962.

Flint, R. F.: "Glacial and Pleistocene Geology," John Wiley & Sons, Inc., New York, 1957.

Leopold, L. B., M. G. Wolman, and J. P. Miller: "Fluvial Processes in Geomorphology," W. H. Freeman and Company, San Francisco, 1964.

Shelton, John S.: "Geology Illustrated," W. H. Freeman and Company, San Francisco, 1966.

13

LONG PERIODS OF TIME

Time is an important variable in all the earth sciences. In studying the structure of the earth's crust, the geophysicist is concerned with very short periods of time because intervals of $\frac{1}{1,000}$ second and smaller are significant in working with seismic waves. At the other extreme, the geologist is concerned with long periods of time because 1 million years is a relatively short period geologically speaking. Sidereal time, solar time, the time zones, and the year were discussed in Chap. 2, where our interest was chiefly in the use of the earth's rotation and revolution as reference systems for measuring time. In this chapter, we devote our attention to the longer periods of geologic time.

One of the main objectives of geology is to unravel the history of our planet from its birth to the present. This history is written in the rocks of the earth, but since they are not easy to read, indirect as well as direct methods and the knowledge and techniques of all the sciences are needed to study the earth. Time is an integral part of history, and long time periods are the backbone of much geologic thought. The establishment of an earth history is not the sole end of geology. As we have seen, the science strives to answer certain questions about the earth, and without a knowledge of time, these questions cannot even be asked intelligently let alone answered.

To illustrate, let us look at the question of how mountains are formed. There are several chains of lofty mountains in North America today. In addition, there are areas on the continent where the rocks are folded and crumpled, where they are fractured and faulted, and where they generally exhibit the same features observed in the rocks of existing mountain chains. These areas are no longer mountainous, but it seems clear that they are old eroded mountains. If we wish to pursue the question of how mountains form further, we must know (*1*) whether there was any periodicity in mountain formation, (*2*) how long it takes a mountain chain to develop, and (*3*) whether there has been an increase or decrease in mountain building with time. Without answers to these questions geologists would not know where to look for the sources of the tremendous energy involved in the formation of mountain chains. The same is true for most geologic problems: time is of the essence.

13-1 RELATIVE TIME

Until the early part of this century, geologists had no precise way of measuring the age of rocks. This does not mean that they were not concerned with time or that they were unable to work at deciphering the past. Before discovering techniques for measuring long periods of geologic time, geologists had to make do

These layered sedimentary rocks in Newfoundland must have been subjected to strong compressional stresses after they were laid down flat. *Geological Survey of Canada*.

with relative time, with establishing a sequence of events that could eventually be tied into a measured time scale when such a scheme was developed.

How are geologic events ordered? The establishment of a relative time scale is based on the application of a few simple truths. These laws or principles or rules (as they are varyingly referred to in the literature) seem obvious today, but their discovery was a momentous scientific achievement.

1 *The principle of uniformitarianism*. This principal states that the natural laws governing the transfer of energy and materials on and in the earth were the same in the geologic past as they are today. Accordingly, the geologic

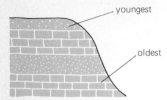

FIGURE 13-1
Because of the way in which sedimentary rocks form, the oldest layers are always at the bottom in undeformed rocks.

FIGURE 13-2
These layered sedimentary rocks in Newfoundland must have been subjected to strong compressional stresses after they were laid down flat. *Geological Survey of Canada.*

processes operating on the earth today to produce rocks, mountains, or plains, have been operative throughout time. Without this broad concept, there would be no geology because ancient rocks can be interpreted only in the light of existing processes.

2 The principle of superposition. In any sequence of sedimentary rocks (rocks like limestone or sandstone that form as beds, or layers, in the ocean) the oldest beds are at the bottom. This is the only way in which sediments can form in present-day depositional environments (oceans, lakes, etc.), and hence this is an application of uniformitarianism (Fig. 13-1).

3 The principle of original horizontality. Sedimentary rocks are deposited in essentially flat layers, or beds. This is so of modern sediments and is the result of the low angle of repose of particles in a moving water system. This idea again is an application of uniformitarianism. If layered sedimentary rocks are found in a highly contorted and folded condition, one must conclude that at some time since they were laid down they have been subjected to external forces (Fig. 13-2).

4 The principle of intrusive relations. An igneous rock is always younger than the rocks that it intrudes.

With these ideas in mind, let us see whether we can work out the relative ages of the rocks and the sequence of events indicated by the rock units shown in Fig. 13-3, a view in cross section of a small part of the earth's crust. Obviously, the geologist cannot pluck out a section of the crust like that shown in Fig. 13-3, and we might first ask how he would arrive at this type of interpretation. Most of the surface of the earth is covered by soil and vegetation, bedrock being exposed only occasionally. By carefully mapping exposures of bedrock over a wide area, by noting relationships between rocks shown in road cuts, along cliffs, and in records of rock encountered in deep drilling the geologist is able to reconstruct a picture of the subsurface. In his mapping, he pays particular attention to contacts; i.e., to interfaces where two rock units come together. By studying contacts, he is able to tell whether an igneous body, for example, is intrusive into other rocks or was laid down on older rocks as a lava flow and subsequently covered over by younger materials.

Assuming that this work of field mapping, of piecing together the parts of the puzzle, has been properly done in Fig. 13-3, let us proceed to work out the history and relative ages of the rocks and events shown by the diagram. Events are commonly ordered from oldest to youngest, and in our present case, the order is:

1 Deposition of the layered or bedded rocks a, b, and c. These rocks were originally deposited in a flat-lying position in a marine (ocean) environment.

2 A period of folding and mountain building. This must have followed the deposition of a, b, and c because rock units d and younger have not been affected by this folding.

3 Intrusion of molten rock to form the granite body labeled d. This must have preceded rocks labeled e, f, and g because they have not been intruded by this granite mass.

FIGURE 13-3
If all the layered sedimentary rocks in the diagram are marine sediments, what is the sequence of geologic events in the region? See text.

4 A period of erosion to form the surface labeled XX' on the diagram.

5 A readvance of the ocean and the deposition of rocks e, f, and g.

6 Intrusion of the igneous rocks labeled h.

7 The present erosion.

We have thus established a relative time scale for the rocks and the events in this area, but we have no idea of the time in years encompassed by any of the events or of how this area might be compared with any other region.

In this section we are interested primarily in the time relationship between various rock units. Our goal in the example above was to establish a sequence of events and a relative order for the various rock units. We recall from Chap. 3 that rocks are made up of minerals and that minerals are important environment indicators. Thus in studying a rock critically an earth scientist may be able to tell whether it formed in a marine or a nonmarine environment, whether it was deposited in alkaline or acid waters, or whether it formed at a high or low temperature. Sedimentary rocks contain structures useful in deciphering earth history. For example, rain or hail impressions or the fossilized remnants of dinosaur tracks in a sedimentary rock tell us that it was exposed during deposition. Other structures, such as cross-bedding, ripple marks, and graded bedding, and their significance in regard to past conditions, are discussed in the next chapter. Here we continue with the problem of establishing a time sequence, remembering that we are interested not only in developing a chronology for the individual rock layers but also in assigning a time dimension to the environmental information which the layers may contain.

13-2 FOSSILS AND CORRELATION

The principles of superposition and intrusive relations work well in establishing a time sequence in a region like the Grand Canyon area, where the contacts between the various rocks involved are somewhere exposed. These principles, how-

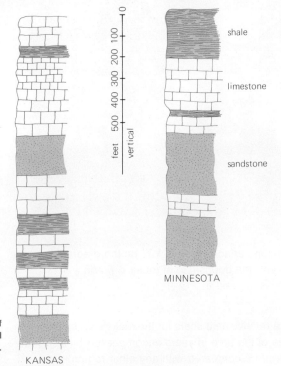

FIGURE 13-4
**Geologic sections of parts of
the sedimentary columns found
in Kansas and Minnesota.
Which beds correlate?**

ever, are of no help in comparing the ages of the rocks from one continent to
another. On the continents, where extensive regions having no rocks are exposed, some principle is needed to correlate from area to area in order to develop a continental and ultimately a worldwide relative time scale.

Lithology, or the character of rock units, is not a good criterion for regional correlation. Figure 13-4 shows two geologic sections, one in Minnesota and the
other in Kansas. Both sections have several beds of sandstone. Which of the
sand layers in the Minnesota section matches with the sandstone bed in the
Kansas section? Without further information, this question cannot be answered.
Moreover, there is no reason for a sandstone in one area necessarily to be the
time equivalent of a sandstone in another region. A look at present-day sediments
shows that beach sands, lime muds, mudstones, or shales are all forming somewhere on earth. Thus a sandstone bed in Minnesota might correlate with a shale
or limestone layer in Kansas. Obviously, something other than lithology is
needed to correlate between broad areas. It turns out to be the fossilized remains
of organisms that lived at different times in the past.

William Smith, born in Oxfordshire, England, in 1769, was the first to use fossils for correlation between widely separated rock exposures. He had very little
formal education, but he learned the rudiments of surveying as an apprentice,

and his work as a surveyor took him over much of England. Smith's interest in rock layers, or strata, was a practical interest. Much of his work related to building canals to service the coal-bearing regions of his country. He soon recognized the utility and desirability of being able to predict what types of rock would be encountered under soil-covered terrain, because the job of canal building was intimately related to the type of rock to be trenched. Also, knowing whether or not there was coal in a region depended upon knowing the position of coal beds in the sequence of rock layers.

Since childhood, Smith had been intrigued by the fossils preserved in the rocks of his home area. As his travels took him farther and farther afield, he noticed that a given rock layer could frequently be recognized by the types of fossils it contained. Although a given composition, or lithology, like limestone might be repeated many times in a sequence of horizontal strata, fossil assemblages seemed not to repeat. Here then was a possible means of correlating layers from exposure to exposure and from region to region.

While William Smith was working in England, two learned Frenchmen, Georges Cuvier and Alexandre Brongniart, were studying the rocks and fossils of the Paris basin. They also recognized that the fossil assemblages in different layers of rock were not the same, and furthermore, being trained zoologists, they realized that the older the rock layer, the more it contained fossils different from living assemblages.

Such studies were the percursors of the theory of evolution. However, Cuvier did not propose evolution to explain the changing character of the animal assemblages with age. He thought instead that the world had gone through a series of catastrophes during which most life was annihilated. These earth revolutions in turn were believed to be followed by new periods of creation. Many natural scientists of that time identified the most recent fossil-bearing materials as deposits from Noah's flood. As a result of the observations of Smith, Cuvier, and Brongniart, fossils contained in layered sedimentary rocks could be interpreted as unique features of certain layers. Accordingly they were recognized as a means by which certain beds could be traced or correlated from outcrop to outcrop. Used in this way, fossils were like an unusual physical property of a given rock layer.

With the presentation of the theory of evolution by Darwin in 1858, fossils gradually acquired a new status. If evolutionary trends could be established, it should be possible to place a rock unit in its position in a sequence on the basis of its fossils rather than vice versa. This sounds like a relatively straightforward task, but for a number of reasons the job of working out an evolutionary sequence is difficult, and it is remarkable how successful paleontologists have been.

The Darwinian principle of evolution proposes that all organisms evolved from common ancestors over the long expanse of geologic time. If representatives of every species that ever lived were somewhere preserved and exposed in a neatly layered pile of sedimentary rocks, it would be a simple matter to trace evolutionary history. Such, however, is not the case. Sedimentary rocks exposed

FIGURE 13-5
Erosion destroys the sedimentary record at one place while a new record is built by deposition at another locality.

erosion
deposition

FIGURE 13-6
The progressive coiling of the clam *Gryphaea* **is one of the best-documented series of evolutionary change. The photograph shows how populations of these invertebrates changed during the 20 million years of the Middle Jurassic in England.** *Photograph by G. R. Adlington from an exhibit at the American Museum of Natural History.*

at the surface of the earth are eroded to form new sediments; therefore, vast segments of the rock record are missing at any one place. Fortunately the same events do not occur everywhere at once, and consequently on a worldwide scale there was the possibility of filling many gaps, because in the past, as in the present, degradation and deposition occur simultaneously. As is shown in Fig. 13-5, a part of the record missing at one locality might well be present somewhere else.

The problem of using fossils for correlation and the task of constructing an evolutionary pattern are further complicated by the isolation of animal groups. Today, for example, there is a marked difference between the mammals of Australia (and to a lesser extent of South America) and those of the rest of the world. In Australia many mammals are marsupials; i.e., they raise their young in pouches in the mother's abdomen. The kangaroo, the koala bear, the wallaby, and many other Australian animals have this characteristic. In the rest of the world most mammals are of the placental type: their young, fed through the placenta, grow inside the body of the mother. It seems clear that sometime in the recent geologic past the Australian mammals became isolated from other mammals and evolved along different paths. Other cases of isolation certainly must have occurred in the geologic past, and thus it is probable that dissimilar sequences may represent the same time span in different parts of the world. In spite of such problems, paleontologists have successfully reconstructed many parts of the evolutionary ladder. Figure 13-6 illustrates how one group of marine invertebrates evolved during a 20-million-year period of the Jurassic.

A problem also exists in correlating between different environments. For example, there is a great difference between the animals of the sea and of the land. How could a future geologist establish a contemporaneity between a modern horse and a modern shark when the two never occur together? If he were lucky enough to find the remains of a horse that had drowned in the ocean, there would be no problem, but otherwise he would have to reconstruct the past by careful mapping in order to establish a correlation between marine and nonmarine rocks.

Today enough is known about the evolution of animals and plant groups to make it possible, in most cases, to assign rocks to a position in the time scale on the basis of their fossils. The precision of such sequential dating depends upon the life span of the species used and upon the level of the work. Correlations between continents or between evolutionary provinces will always be approximate. Correlations based on fossils in small areas, on the other hand, may be quite precise if the rocks contain abundant remains of species with relatively short histories.

13-3 THE GEOLOGIC TIME SCALE

In order to build up an order, or sequence, of the events of earth history by the procedures just discussed geologists needed names to define various segments of geologic time. This system of naming rock units or time intervals evolved slowly. Some names were proposed and forgotten, whereas others were adopted by geologists throughout the world, eventually becoming incorporated in the geologic time scale shown in Table 13-1. Let us see how the names of the relative time units shown in Table 13-1 evolved.

We recall that Cuvier, of France, one of the early students of paleontology, supported the idea of catastrophism. He interpreted the extinction of certain faunas in the fossil record as being due to great cataclysms or revolutions that differed from any events experienced by modern man. In one form or another this concept pervaded geologic thinking until a few decades ago, and it certainly influenced the positioning of the boundaries of the geologic periods.

Most of the geologic systems shown in the relative time chart of Table 13-1 are named for areas in which rocks of a particular part of the rock record are especially well preserved. Cambrian comes from the medieval Latin name for Wales. Ordovician and Silurian, derived from the names of ancient Welsh tribes, were used to describe the sequence of rocks in and near Wales. The name Devonian was first used to describe the fossil-bearing strata of Devonshire. Per-

TABLE 13-1
The geologic time scale

Era	Period	Epoch	Millions of years ago (approximate)	History
Cenozoic	Quaternary	Recent		
		Pleistocene	2.5	Man
	Tertiary	Pliocene	7	
		Miocene	26	
		Oligocene	38	
		Eocene	54	
		Paleocene	65	Mammals
Mesozoic	Cretaceous		136	
	Jurassic		190	First bird
	Triassic		225	Beginning of dinosaurs
Paleozoic	Permian		280	
	Pennsylvanian		325	First insects
	Mississippian		345	First reptiles
	Devonian		395	First amphibians
	Silurian		430	
	Ordovician		500	First vertebrates (fish)
	Cambrian		570	
Precambrian*			3,500	Oldest rock
			4,500	Birth of earth

*No universally accepted subdivision.

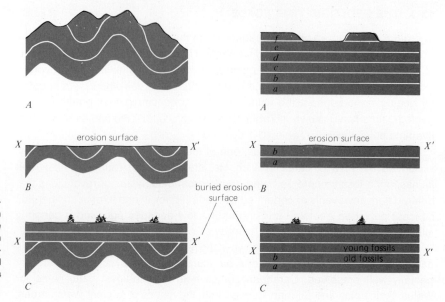

FIGURE 13-7
The types of buried erosion surfaces (unconformities). In both cases there is a break in the sedimentary record at *XX'*. On the left there is angular discordance between the old and young beds, whereas the beds are concordant on the right.

FIGURE 13-8
An extensive layer of sandstone formed at the edge of an advancing sea is not formed at one time. The original part of the layer is older than the landward extension. Although shale (mudstone) ends up on top of the sandstone, both are building up simultaneously.

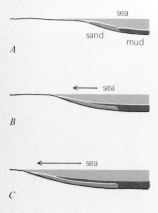

mian came from the province of Perm in Russia. The Pennsylvanian and Mississippian Systems were named for type localities in the United States.

Most of the boundaries between systems were placed at breaks in the geologic record in the area where the system was named. Figure 13-7 shows some of the types of breaks, or unconformities, used to establish boundaries between geologic systems. From the diagram we can see that unconformities are buried erosion surfaces. They represent periods of uplift and erosion followed by redeposition. Certainly such breaks tie in nicely with the idea of catastrophe because the required uplift can be considered a revolutionary event.

The boundaries of the Cambrian System of the Paleozoic Era, for example, were originally defined in Wales. Geologists on other continents were able to correlate rocks with those of the type area on the basis of their fossils. Consequently names like Cambrian, Ordovician, and Devonian spread throughout the parts of the world containing such fossil-bearing rocks. Whereas the boundary between the Cambrian and the Ordovician Systems in the original area may have been an easily recognizable unconformity, in other parts of the world the same situation did not always pertain. In fact, breaks or gaps in the sedimentary layers in one area are frequently represented by a rock record in another region. We can see why, because erosion at one place must always be accompanied by deposition elsewhere. While there is still some argument among earth scientists on this subject, most workers currently support the conclusion that the boundaries between geologic systems are indeed arbitrary. This is not to say that the names of the geologic periods are not useful; they are essential for worldwide dialogue.

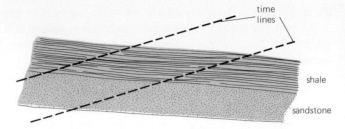

time
lines

shale

sandstone

FIGURE 13-9
**Because of marine trans-
gressions and regressions,
lines of equal time (time lines)
should cross the sedimentary
layers. Compare with Fig. 13-8,
which shows how sandstone
and shale may form at the same
time.**

As geologists analyzed the rock and fossil record and the processes that produce rocks, it became obvious that even continuous rock layers are not time-equivalent. Figure 13-8 shows how an extensive layer of marine sand might be formed. The sand shown is forming at the margins of an advancing (transgressing) sea, and it is clear that one end of the eventual bed will be younger than the other. Moreover, although at any one place the shale or mudstone is younger than the sandstone because it overlies it, parts of the shale layer may actually be older than parts of the underlying sand layer. Figure 13-9 shows how equal time lines should cut across rock layers. The degree of crosscutting would not be as sharp as in the illustration, which is highly diagrammatic, but such relations have been observed between time zones based on fossils and actual rock layers.

Because most beds do not represent time contemporaneity, geologists make a clear distinction between theoretical, or idealized, time periods and time rock units. The terms Cambrian System, Ordovician System, or Cretaceous System, refer to the rock deposited during these periods of time. On the other hand, the term Devonian Period refers to a specific time interval of the geologic past. Table 13-2 gives the nomenclature for time units and for time-rock units.

As originally developed, geologic time is a scale of relative time. In the past three or four decades considerable effort has been devoted to the task of establishing radioactive dates for specific events in the time scale. The dates in years shown in Table 13-1 are the result of such work.

13-4   THE DURATION OF TIME

We have discussed the principles used in the development of a relative time scale without concern for the real measure of time involved in the scale. Now we turn to the question of the duration of geologic time: How old is the earth? How many years since the extinction of the dinosaurs? When did the oceans form? These questions are all concerned with the problem of measuring time.

The first attempts to estimate the extent of geologic time were not very successful from today's vantage point. In the seventeenth century Archbishop Ussher of Ireland dated the time of creation by adding the life spans of individuals recorded in ancient Hebrew scriptures. He concluded from this evidence that

TABLE 13-2
Stratigraphic units

Time-rock units	Time units
—	Era
System	Period
Series	Epoch
Stage	Age

the earth was born on the night preceding the twenty-third day of October in the Julian year 710 (4004 B.C.). This date, recorded in several authorized editions of the English Bible in the eighteenth century, impeded study and further work because of its official religious sanction.

Several natural scientists of the eighteenth century objected to the short 6,000-year lifespan for the earth. They saw a relation between the layers of sedimentary rock and the processes acting upon the earth's surface. If layers of sandstone were indeed formed from material eroded from the land by rivers and waves, one should be able to develop some appreciation of the length of geologic time by observing those processes. To the careful observer it soon became obvious that many more than 6,000 years were needed to carve a great valley. Moreover, the thick layers of sediment exposed along cliffs were evidence for what seemed an infinite amount of time.

We noted back in Chap. 1 that James Hutton, an eighteenth-century Scottish geologist, was the first to formalize the idea that the rock record shows no trace of a beginning and no evidence of an end. He proposed that the layers of sedimentary rock exposed in many parts of the world had accumulated in the same way in which sands and other sediments form in and along the existing seas. His idea that the record of the past as recorded in the rocks must be interpreted in terms of present processes became known as the doctrine of uniformitarianism. While Hutton and his immediate followers made no significant contributions toward establishing the length of geologic time, they nonetheless introduced the idea that the earth must have experienced a very long history. The need for vast stretches of time became even more evident with Darwin's theory of evolution. His concept of the evolution of living things through natural selection required sufficient time for millions of generations. Darwin, in fact, speculated that some 300 million years must have elapsed since the end of the Mesozoic Era.

The first widely accepted value for the age of the earth was made by Lord Kelvin, the famous British physicist for whom the units of Kelvins are named. Kelvin was an authority on heat and heat transfer. Assuming that the earth was molten in the beginning, he computed the time required to cool such a body to its present temperature. In his calculations he applied the theory of the behavior of radiating bodies, and he used measurements of the earth's heat flow. There were many assumptions in his method of arriving at the earth's age, but they all seemed reasonable at the time. His figure of 20 to 40 million years for the age of the earth did not please many earth scientists, but it was widely accepted.

The error in Kelvin's work was due to an undiscovered phenomenon, *radioactivity*, which later became the basis for the accurate measurement of long time periods. Since Kelvin's calculations did not consider the heat generated by radioactive decay, they were in error by several orders of magnitude.

In Chap. 9 we saw how John Joly, an Irish geologist, attempted to compute the age of the oceans from their salt content at the turn of this century. Average river water contains much less sodium in solution than seawater, but the rivers of the earth continually flow into the oceans, carrying with them in a year's time significant amounts of sodium. The return of water from the oceans to the land is by evaporation. Joly reasoned that there was no way for sodium leached from the rocks of the continents and carried to the seas by the rivers to get back to the land. By dividing the total amount of sodium in the seas as determined from volume and salinity measurements by the amount of sodium delivered to the seas each year by rivers he found the oceans to be about 100 million years old.

Although Joly's estimate was more palatable to geologists than Kelvin's short 40 million years, it still seemed low. We know from the evidence presented in Chap. 9 that the value obtained by dividing the total sodium in the sea by the annual influx is more reasonably interpreted as the mean residence time of sodium in the sea than as the age of the sea. Joly and his contemporaries did not know that significant amounts of salt water are blown from the sea surface by winds and find their way back to the lands via the hydrologic cycle. It now is clear that the salt in the sea has been recycled many times since the earth and the oceans began.

Another method of estimating the length of geologic time popular around 1900 involved the measurement and estimation of the total thickness of sedimentary rocks and the rates at which sediments accumulate. This method was limited because the total thickness of sediments is nowhere exposed, and great thicknesses of sedimentary rocks have been eroded to form new rocks. Even more serious was the fact that deposition rates are not precisely known. Most estimates made by this method ranged under 100 million years and possibly were influenced by Lord Kelvin's fame and the desire to support his estimate.

The discovery of radioactivity by Henri Becquerel in 1896 provided a means of measuring long time periods accurately. It was not until many years later, however, that the interpretation of radioactive decay and the refinement in analytical techniques made it possible to date minerals by radiometric methods.

13-5 RADIOACTIVE DATING

Since Becquerel's original discovery of radioactivity, many atoms have been found to have unstable nuclei. Atoms in which the nuclei decay spontaneously are said to be *radioactive*. Recall from Chap. 3 that the number of protons in the nucleus of an atom determines its atomic number whereas the total number of protons and neutrons in the nucleus represents its mass number. Atoms of the same element (same atomic number) that differ in mass (mass number) are called *isotopes*.

Radioactive decay of an atomic nucleus may occur in several ways. The nucleus, for example, may lose an *alpha* particle, which is the equivalent of a helium nucleus consisting of two protons and two neutrons. In this type of decay the parent nucleus changes to a daughter product with a mass number that is lower by four units and an atomic number that is lower by two units. Any change in atomic number, of course, means that a different element has been formed.

When an alpha particle is given off by the nucleus of a radioactive element, there is also an emission of gamma rays, a type of shortwave electromagnetic radiation like x-rays. Careful analysis of the masses involved in alpha decay shows that the mass of an alpha particle plus the mass of the daughter isotope does not quite equal the mass of the parent isotope. As we saw in Chap. 7, the lost mass is converted into energy, according to Einstein's famous equation, $E = mc^2$, where E is the energy, m is the mass lost or converted to energy, and c is the speed of light. Since the speed of light is a very large number, a minute loss of mass results in an appreciable generation of energy. This is the energy that Kelvin did not take into account in his computation of heat balance.

Some radioactive isotopes decay by expelling a beta particle from the nucleus. A beta particle is a fast-moving electron derived from a neutron. Expulsion of an electron with a single negative charge changes the neutron into a proton with a single positive charge. The daughter product thus formed has the same mass number as the parent, but it contains one additional proton. This type of decay is called *beta decay*. Beta particles are much more penetrating than alpha particles because electrons are so much smaller than the helium nuclei of the alpha radiation.

A final method of radioactive decay involves the capture of an electron by an atomic nucleus. Again this type of decay produces no change in mass number, but the atomic number decreases by 1 because the captured electron changes a proton into a neutron to form a new element.

Uranium 238 is one of the uranium isotopes. Through the following steps involving both alpha and beta decay this isotope changes to the stable daughter product, lead 206:

$$^{238}_{92}\text{U} \rightarrow ^{234}_{90}\text{Th} \rightarrow ^{234}_{91}\text{Pa} \rightarrow ^{234}_{92}\text{U} \rightarrow ^{230}_{90}\text{Th} \rightarrow ^{226}_{88}\text{Ra} \rightarrow ^{222}_{86}\text{Rn} \rightarrow ^{218}_{84}\text{Po} \rightarrow$$

$$^{214}_{82}\text{Pb} \rightarrow ^{214}_{83}\text{Bi} \rightarrow ^{214}_{84}\text{Po} \rightarrow ^{210}_{82}\text{Pb} \rightarrow ^{210}_{83}\text{Bi} \rightarrow ^{210}_{84}\text{Po} \rightarrow ^{206}_{82}\text{Pb}$$
$$\text{(Stable)}$$

The half-lives of the many intermediate steps from $^{234}_{90}\text{Th}$ to the stable daughter product ^{206}Pb range from microseconds to a few hundred thousand years. For radiometric dating, therefore, the half-life of the series can be considered to be 4.5 billion years, which is the half-life of the parent ^{238}U. Notice that the difference in mass number between parent and daughter is 32 and the difference in atomic number is 10.

Uranium 235, another uranium isotope, also decays by alpha and beta emission to stable lead but ends up as lead 207. Whereas the uranium isotopes decay through a series of steps to stable lead, other radioactive elements change directly into stable products. Potassium 40, for example, changes to argon 40 by electron capture and to calcium 40 by beta decay. Rubidium 87 decays directly to strontium 87 by beta decay.

Because radioactive decay involves only the nuclei of atoms, it is insensitive to external physical and chemical conditions. The rate of decay of a given radioactive substance is constant regardless of whether the substance is in solution or

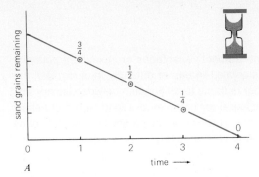

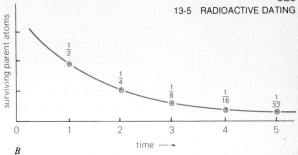

FIGURE 13-10
Straight-line depletion (A) and the radioactive-decay curve (B). In radioactive decay during each half-life one-half of the remaining radioactive atoms are lost. The curve thus approaches zero but never reaches it.

part of a solid. Moreover temperature and pressure appear to have no effect on decay rates. Here, then, are potentially valuable and rugged clocks that may well be used to measure geologic time.

It has long been known that the number of atoms of any radioactive substance that decay in a given interval of time is proportional to the total number of radioactive atoms present. There are several ways of indicating the rate of decay. Since the process of decay is statistically random, the probability of decay can be indicated by a decay constant λ, which is a measure of the proportion of radioactive atoms that will decay within a fixed time. The number of atoms decaying in a unit of time will thus be λN, where N is the total number of atoms present. As decay proceeds, N continually decreases, and therefore λN, the number of atoms decaying per unit of time, also decreases. The total lifetime of a radioactive substance is thus theoretically infinite because the number of atoms decaying per unit time keeps decreasing as time progresses.

The rate of decay of a radiometric substance is frequently given in terms of the *half-life* of the decay, or the time required for one-half of the parent atoms to decay to the daughter product. Half-lives vary greatly, some being only a fraction of a second and others billions of years. The half-life of potassium 40, for example, is 1.3 billion years. Starting with a given amount of potassium 40, one-half of the original atoms would be left in 1.3 billion years. In the second 1.3 billion years one-half of the remaining one-half, or one-fourth, of the atoms would decay and so forth. Radioactive decay is not a straight-line type of depletion, as so many common phenomena are. Figure 13-10 shows the difference between radioactive decay and the straight-line type of depletion exhibited by an hourglass or a burning candle. Table 13-3 lists the half-lives of the isotopes commonly used in radiometric dating.

TABLE 13-3
Isotopes most frequently used for radioactive dating

Parent	Half-life, millions of years	Stable daughter product	Minerals used for dating
Uranium 238	4,510	Lead 206	Zircon, uraninite
Uranium 235	713	Lead 207	Zircon, uraninite
Potassium 40	1,300	Argon 40	Micas, feldspars, hornblende
Rubidium 87	47,000	Strontium 87	Micas, feldspar

It must be obvious by now that radioactive isotopes are excellent potential clocks for measuring long time intervals. An earlier difficulty in using, say, the uranium minerals as clocks was our inability to distinguish between isotopes. A chemical analysis of a uranium mineral for uranium and lead would not show how much of the uranium was ^{238}U or ^{235}U or would distinguish between the many isotopes of lead. Without a knowledge of isotopic abundances radioactive ages are not reliable because there is no way of recognizing small quantities of original lead in a mineral or of distinguishing between lead formed from ^{238}U and that formed from ^{235}U, each of which has a different half-life.

With the development of the mass spectrometer reliable radioactive dating became possible because this instrument can measure isotopic abundances. Modern mass spectrometers not only determine the quantities of individual isotopes in a sample but do so with accuracy on extremely small (less than $\frac{1}{1,000}$-gram) samples. Consequently, minerals such as zircon, which contains only minor amounts of uranium, are now regularly used in dating.

By measuring the quantity of ^{238}U and ^{206}Pb in a mineral, the age t of the mineral can be calculated from the decay constant of the series ^{238}U-^{206}Pb according to the relation $t = 1/\lambda \ln (D/P + 1)$, where D/P is the ratio of the daughter product (^{206}Pb) to the parent isotope (^{238}U). The age thus obtained may still be incorrect, even though the measurements are accurate, if uranium, lead, or any of the intermediate products was leached from the mineral being dated at some time since it was formed. Uranium-bearing minerals, however, contain both ^{238}U and ^{235}U, and many also contain radioactive thorium 232. Therefore a single mineral may possess three different clocks, since all these radioactive isotopes have different half-lives and produce different lead isotopes. If the ages determined independently from ^{238}U, ^{235}U, and ^{232}Th agree, one may be reasonably sure that there has been no loss by leaching and that the age determined is correct.

Actually the age of a mineral containing uranium can be determined without analyzing for uranium simply by determining the relative abundances of the lead isotopes. Since various isotopes of lead are produced at different rates (Table 13-3), their proportion in any sample will be a measure of the age of the sample.

We have already noted how the development of sensitive mass spectrometers made it possible to determine uranium-lead ages on minerals like zircon that contain only trace amounts of uranium. This, of course, permitted dating of many more rocks than was possible when only rare uranium minerals were used. A further development that opened up even more new ground was the use of isotopes that are more widespread in crustal materials than uranium. The decay constants for potassium 40, a very common isotope in crustal rocks, was developed during the 1950s, and many rocks have since been dated by the ^{40}Ar-^{40}K method. Similarly the rubidium-strontium decay scheme has added to the flexibility of radioactive dating.

Much research is still being conducted in the field of geochronology, and new methods are being sought. Information on some of the experimental techniques

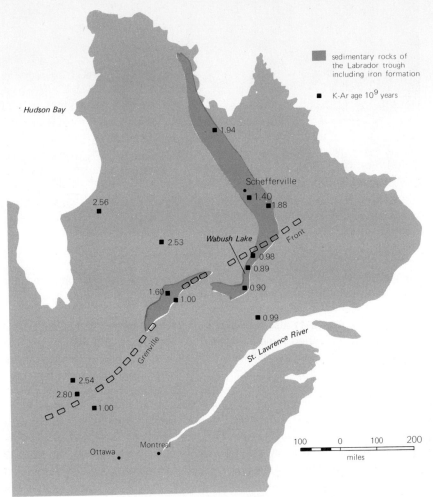

Hudson Bay

sedimentary rocks of
the Labrador trough
including iron formation

■ K-Ar age 10^9 years

1.94

Schefferville
■ 1.40
■ 1.88

2.56

2.53

Wabush Lake   Front
□ □ □ □ □
□ ■ 0.98
■ 0.89

1.60 ■ □ □ □
■ 1.00   ■ 0.90

□
□   ■ 0.99
□
□
□ Grenville
□   St. Lawrence River
□
■ 2.54 □
2.80 ■ □
□ □ ■ 1.00 □

Montreal
Ottawa

100   0   100   200

miles

FIGURE 13-11
**Sedimentary rocks of the La-
brador trough and $^{40}Ar/^{40}K$
ages. Although the iron-bearing
units within the sediment
sequence can be traced more
or less along the entire length
of the sediment belt, indicating
that all were formed at about
the same time, radiometric
ages within the belt differ by
about 500 million years.**

currently being investigated will be found in the references at the end of this
chapter.

13-6 INTERPRETING RADIOMETRIC AGES

The problems of radiometric dating are not all of an analytical or technological
nature. To illustrate some of the geologic problems associated with radiometric
dating let us look at Fig. 13-11. The sparsely inhabited area of Quebec around
Schefferville and Wabush Lake became the subject of intensive geological study
during the 1950s, when the iron ores of the region were first exploited. The iron
ores here, as in most parts of the world, occur within layered sedimentary rocks.
The iron-rich sediments, called *iron formations*, are composed chiefly of chert,
SiO_2, and iron minerals such as magnetite, Fe_3O_4, or hematite, Fe_2O_3. Because
of their magnetic character they are easily traced by airborne magnetic surveys

FIGURE 13-12
A conglomerate may be composed of pebbles of diverse composition and age (see Fig. 13-13). *C. D. Walcott, U.S. Geological Survey.*

even when covered by surface materials. Such surveys plus ground traverses have clearly established the extent of the sediments of the Labrador trough (Fig. 13-11).

The map of Fig. 13-11 also shows radiometric ages determined on micas and other potassium-bearing minerals in the iron formations and their associated rocks. Whereas the mapping definitely shows the iron-bearing rocks to be continuous in the vicinity of Wabush Lake, radiometric dating suggests that there is a marked break near here. Ages of the Labrador trough sediments to the north average about 1.5 billion years, whereas those south of Wabush Lake cluster around 1.0 billion years, a difference of 500 million years. Farther to the west rocks dated at 2.5 billion years north of the line labeled *Grenville front* also exhibit radiometric ages of only 1 billion years south of the front. How can this be?

Mapping in the area has disclosed that the iron formations and associated rocks at Wabush Lake and in the entire region south of the Grenville front are highly recrystallized and metamorphosed. During metamorphism new minerals form from original minerals in response to the pressure-temperature conditions of metamorphism, and this is the answer to the age difference noted above. Imagine a sedimentary rock containing a potassium-bearing mineral that formed at the same time as the rock. Some of the potassium in the mineral would be radioactive potassium 40, which decays to argon 40. In time the potassium mineral would accumulate ^{40}Ar, and the $^{40}Ar/^{40}K$ ratio in the mineral would be a measure of its age and of the age of the rock. However, during metamorphism the potassium, along with other chemical constituents of the rock, forms new minerals. During this recrystallization the argon 40 is lost, and the radioactive clock is thus reset to zero. Of course, argon 40 would again build up in the new potassium minerals formed by metamorphism, but any future radioactive dating would measure the time since the metamorphism and not the time at which the original rock was formed. In our example, therefore, it appears that the ages south of the Grenville front are a measure of the time of metamorphism and not of the time of formation of the rocks.

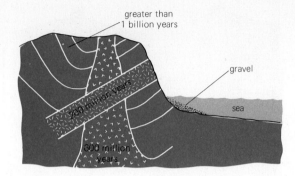

FIGURE 13-13
This gravel may eventually become a hardened conglomerate. If it does, it will contain rock samples differing in age.

The Wabush Lake area in Quebec used to illustrate the need for proper geological interpretation of radiometric dates is not special. It was chosen because iron formation is a sufficiently distinctive rock to be easily traced across the metamorphic boundary. Similar problems involving the interpretation of radiometric ages are common. Without a knowledge of the geology of a region radiometric dates are usually not meaningful because it is difficult to tell what the dates represent.

A simpler example of the need for combining geological information with laboratory dating techniques can be seen in the specimen shown in Fig. 13-12. The rock pictured is a sedimentary rock composed of rounded clastic particles cemented together. It is a lithified, or hardened, gravel called a *conglomerate*. If a uranium-bearing mineral from one of the pebbles in the conglomerate were dated, what would the age mean? Certainly it would not be a measure of the age of the conglomerate. A conglomerate like a sandstone or shale is a clastic sediment. Such rocks represent the accumulation of solids brought to a depositional basin by the erosional agents, as shown in Fig. 13-13. The particles of a clastic sediment are transported from a source area, sometimes hundreds of miles away, to the site where the rock forms. They may have been worn from rocks of diverse age, and thus the mineral age is not related to the age of the conglomerate. The age of a mineral from a pebble tells us only that the conglomerate can be no older.

That the grains in a clastic sedimentary rock do not have the same age as the rock in which they occur has been one of the major difficulties in making quantitative age measurements for the periods of the geologic time scale. We recall that the time scale was developed from the relationships between sedimentary-rock layers. In igneous rocks the situation is quite different. There the minerals and the rock form at the same time, so that the age of a mineral from such a rock is also the age of the rock. Limiting ages for clastic sediments can be determined from their relations with dated igneous rocks, as illustrated in Fig. 13-14. Furthermore, some sedimentary minerals (like calcite $CaCO_3$, in the chemically precipitated sediment limestone) form at the same time and place as the rocks in which

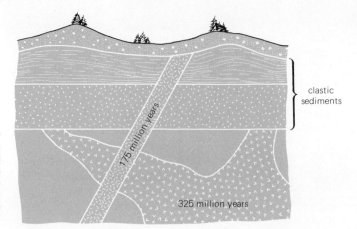

FIGURE 13-14
Although it may not be possible to date clastic sediments directly, their ages can be bracketed by dating associated igneous rocks. These clastic sediments must be younger than 325 million years and older than 175 million years.

they occur. By working with minerals that have grown within sediments and by using the relations between dated igneous rocks and sediments geologists have been able to assign ages to the geologic time scale. Currently new methods and techniques for determining quantitative ages for sedimentary rocks are under investigation.

13-7 THE AGE OF THE EARTH

Ultimately one of the most interesting problems concerned with time is the age of the earth, which has intrigued men for generations. We have seen how early speculations about the earth's age ranged from Bishop Ussher's 6,000 years, to Lord Kelvin's 40 million years, to figures of around 100 million years determined from the annual contribution of salt to the sea. With the development and refinement of radiometric dating it soon became clear that these early estimates for the earth's age were much too low. In fact a limiting figure for the earth's age is the age of the oldest known rock. Radioactive dating of rocks thus far has disclosed ages of up to 3.5 billion years. Some of the oldest dated rocks are sedimentary rocks, and since these rocks had to be laid down on still older rocks, it is clear that the earth must be older than 3.5 billion years.

Earlier in this chapter we saw that uranium 238 decays to lead 206 and that uranium 235 decays to lead 207. Lead 204, or ordinary lead, is always present in crustal materials and is not known to have a radioactive parent. Since lead 206 and 207 are continuously being generated by the decay of radioisotopes, the present $^{206}Pb/^{204}Pb$ or $^{207}Pb/^{204}Pb$ ratio might be used to determine the age of the earth. To compute it in this way one would need to know (1) the decay constant for ^{238}U and ^{235}U, (2) the present abundance of ^{238}U, ^{235}U, ^{206}Pb, and ^{207}Pb, and (3) the original amount of ^{204}Pb, ^{206}Pb, and ^{207}Pb in the earth.

Of the above requirements, the decay constants are accurately known. The average present abundances of the uranium and lead isotopes are difficult to determine accurately, but enough work has been done for these values to be reasonably well established. The original abundance of the lead isotopes offers more of a problem. Evidence for the original composition of lead isotopes on earth comes, strangely enough, from extraterrestrial materials. It is significant that the abundances of the chemical elements in meteorites are very near the average abundances of the same elements in earth materials. Iron meteorites contain practically no uranium. Because there is no uranium to generate lead 206 and 207, we must conclude that the lead in iron meteorites was there when they were formed. Because meteorites are a part of the solar system, it is reasonable to assume that they and the earth originated at the same time. It further follows that the isotopic composition of the lead in meteorites free of radioactive elements is also the isotopic composition of the original lead in the planet earth.

With this information the age of the earth can be computed by determining the present isotopic composition of earth lead, correcting it for the amount of radiogenic lead present when the planet formed, and considering the rates at which the lead isotopes have been generated from the decay constants for the uranium parents. Figure 13-15 shows how the ratios of the lead isotopes must have changed in time. To find the present isotopic composition of lead, scientists have used recent deep-sea sediments, which represent a good sample of the present lead in the earth because lead from all parts of the land is slowly but continually washed into the sea to accumulate in the sediments. The age of the earth determined from such calculations turns out to be at least 4.5 billion years.

A number of independent lines of evidence support this value. The evidence indicates that meteorites and the earth had a common origin. Although iron meteorites contain no uranium, stony meteorites usually have measurable amounts of both uranium and potassium 40. Uranium-lead and potassium-argon dating of materials from these meteorites gives ages that cluster around 4.5 billion years. Recent explorations of the moon, moreover, have shown that some of its rocks are over 4 billion years old as determined by radiometric techniques. The age of the moon also comes out to about 4.5 billion years, which supports the value for the earth's age.

Other evidence that the earth is indeed some 4.5 billion years old comes from its atmosphere. Argon 40 is a fairly abundant constituent of the atmosphere. The presence of argon in the atmosphere is itself not unusual because argon is also a fairly common constituent of the sun and the stars. The argon in the sun, however, is chiefly argon 38. This difference in the isotopic composition of argon in the earth and sun was puzzling until it was suggested that the argon 40 in the earth's atmosphere must have slowly accumulated from the argon 40 generated by the decay of potassium 40. From a consideration of the decay constant of ^{40}K and its concentration in crustal materials, it has been determined that the ^{40}Ar in the atmosphere could indeed have accumulated in this manner over a period of some 4 billion years.

It seems established then that planet earth formed some 4 to 5 billion years ago. The value of 4.5 billion years for the earth's age may change slightly as techniques are refined and as new data are gathered, but there seems to be little likelihood of any major shifts in the value.

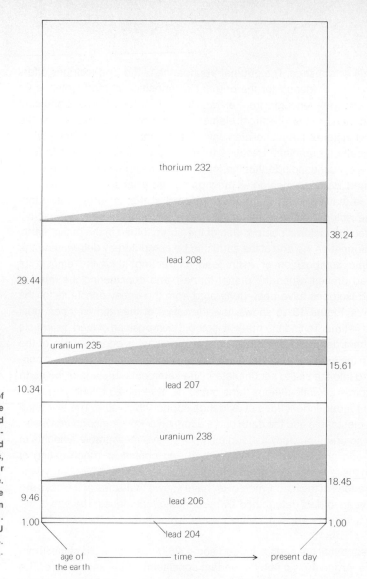

FIGURE 13-15
Evolution of isotopic ratios of lead for the earth as a whole during geologic time. Shaded areas represent radiogenic additions. Because ^{235}U, ^{238}U, and ^{232}Th have different half-lives, the ratio of their daughter products changes with time. Numbers on left represent the abundances of lead isotopes in iron meteorites with ^{204}Pb = 1. The amount of present-day ^{235}U is exaggerated. *From D. L. Eicher, "Geologic Time," Prentice-Hall, 1968.*

SUMMARY

The principles of superposition and original horizontality and the concept of intrusive relations make it possible to arrange the rock units of an area into an order of relative age, but these principles are not useful in correlating relative ages from region to region. Such correlations are made possible by the fossils contained within sedimentary rocks. Because living things have evolved from very primitive life forms over the last 3 billion years, the fossil flora and fauna contained in sedimentary rocks change with time. It is therefore frequently possible to tell the relative age of a rock from its fossils.

The geologic time scale was constructed by applying the principles noted above and by correlating between regions and continents on the basis of fossils. For the most part, names of time periods reflect the localities where rocks of the period are well preserved. As originally conceived, the boundaries between the time periods were set at unconformities, which were thought to represent times of earth revolution. This idea is no longer held, and the boundaries are now recognized as arbitrary. The geologic time scale, however, is a most useful scale for comparing events in earth history throughout the globe.

Many schemes have been proposed to measure the duration of geologic time. Not until the discovery of radioactivity, however, was it possible to measure long time period accurately. The age of a mineral containing a radioactive isotope can be determined from the abundance of the radioisotope and its daughter product when the half-life of the radioisotope is known, provided that neither of these elements has been removed from the mineral or added to it since formation. Because metamorphism often resets the radiometric clocks back to zero, and because the ages of minerals in clastic sediments do not represent the age of the rock, the geology of a region must be known for the proper interpretation of radiometric ages.

That ^{238}U, ^{235}U, and ^{232}Th all yield different isotopes of lead at different rates makes it possible to calculate the age of the earth from the present isotopic composition of its lead. This calculation depends upon knowing the original isotopic composition of lead in the earth, information that is supplied by iron meteorites. The age thus determined works out at about 4.5 billion years. Earth scientists now have confidence in this age because it also turns out to be about the measured age of the moon and the age most often obtained from radiometric dating of stony meteorites.

QUESTIONS

1 Study the cross section shown and arrange the labeled rock units, periods of erosion, faults, and periods of folding in order of relative age.

2 In the diagram for Question 1 radiometric dating shows the granite to be 1 billion years old and the basalt dike to be 500 million years old. What is the age of the sandstone in years? What is the age of the conglomerate?

3 Refer to the diagram of Question 1. Suppose that a $^{40}A/^{40}K$ age for the metamorphic rocks also was 1 billion years, the same as that for the granite. How could you account for this? Would that mean that the rocks were formed at the same time?

4 Why is it not possible to correlate from region to region on the basis of lithology (character of the rocks)?

5 The relative ages of fossils were determined initially from the chronology of the rocks in which they are found. How then can fossils be used to establish the relative ages of rocks? Isn't this circular reasoning?

6 To show that the rocks of one region are of the same relative age as those of another, would it be necessary for both to contain identical fossil assemblages?

7 In what ways can an atomic nucleus undergo radioactive decay?

8 ^{238}U has a half-life of 4.5 billion years. How long would it take for 1 gram of this isotope to decay completely to ^{206}Pb?

9 What is the basis for the conclusion that the isotopic composition of lead on earth has changed in time?

10 Briefly describe several lines of evidence that suggest an age of over 4 billion years for the earth.

REFERENCES

Berry, W. B. N.: "Growth of a Prehistoric Time Scale," W. H. Freeman and Company, San Francisco, 1968.

Eicher, L. Don: "Geologic Time," Prentice-Hall, Inc., Englewood Cliffs, N.J., 1968.

Faul, Henry: "Ages of Rocks, Planets, and Stars," McGraw-Hill Book Company, New York, 1966.

Harbaugh, J. W.: "Stratigraphy and Geologic Time," Wm. C. Brown Company Publishers, Dubuque, Iowa, 1968.

Hurley, P. M.: "How Old Is the Earth?" Anchor Books, Doubleday & Company, Inc., Garden City, N.Y., 1959.

McAlester, A. Lee: "The History of Life," Prentice-Hall, Inc., Englewood Cliffs, N.J., 1968.

14

SEDIMENTARY ROCKS

Now that we have an appreciation of the vastness of geologic time let us return to the subject of Chaps. 11 and 12—erosion. The erosive processes have been abrading, scouring, and dissolving material from the earth's rocky surface for eons. Although their effect during a life-span is insignificant, over the reach of geologic time they have moved immense quantities of material from high to low

Cross-bedding in newly formed sediments of the Vermillion River, Vermillion County, Illinois. Current from left to right. *From F. J. Pettijohn and P. E. Potter, "Atlas and Glossary of Sedimentary Structures," Springer-Verlag, Inc., 1964.*

places on earth. This eroded debris ultimately accumulates to form sedimentary rocks.

Of course, not all the sedimentary rocks formed since the surface processes began are still there. They too have been eroded where they were exposed at the surface, and new sedimentary rocks continued to be formed from them. This does not mean, however, that there are no longer any very old sedimentary rocks. Because of the way in which such rocks form, some very old layers have been buried by overlying layers of younger sedimentary rocks to be preserved from

FIGURE 14-1
Ripple marks and animal trails on thin bedded Mississippian sandstone, Randolph County, Illinois. *Photograph by Illinois Geological Survey, from F. J. Pettijohn and P. E. Potter, "Atlas and Glossary of Sedimentary Structures," Springer-Verlag, Inc., 1964.*

further erosion. We thus have a record of sedimentation that goes back some 3 billion years.

Since each sedimentary rock is the product of weathering and erosion in its source region, a transport history, and the conditions or environment of its depositional basin, we can see that such rocks are particularly important as records of past conditions on earth. Ideally, from the detailed study of a given sedimentary rock it should be possible to deduce the relief or climatic conditions of its source region, to identify the transporting medium and estimate the distance of transport, and to determine whether the rock was deposited on land, along a strand line, or in deep water. Although this ideal is rarely if ever achieved in a single sedimentary rock, these rocks nonetheless are our best record of the past.

Even when the total record of its past is not decipherable, each sedimentary rock usually contains some evidence of its origin. Some sedimentary rocks are good indicators of past climates. Others contain records of current or wind directions that existed when they were formed. Still others reflect the physical or chemical conditions of their sites of deposition.

What should we look for in a sedimentary rock in order to read its history? Figure 14-1 is a photograph of a 300-million-year-old sandstone. The ripple marks and worm burrowings are clear evidence that this sandstone was deposited in water rather than on land. A comparison of the wormholes with those found in modern sands suggests that the water must have been relatively shallow. What else can we read from this sandstone? What should we look for in the rock in order to learn the source of the sand or the vehicle and distance of transport? These are some of the questions that are to be investigated in this chapter.

14-1   THE EARTH'S SURFACE CYCLE TENDS TO SEPARATE THE CHEMICAL ELEMENTS

Before reporting that a rock sample contains a certain percentage of SiO_2, Al_2O_3, FeO, etc., a chemist usually proceeds as follows. First, he powders the rock and dissolves it in acid. Then he changes the conditions of the solution so that only one or two of the constituent chemical elements form insoluble compounds. For example, when the solution is made slightly alkaline, the iron and aluminum precipitate as insoluble oxides, which can be filtered off and thus separated from the calcium, sodium, potassium, magnesium, or other elements that remain in the solution. The filtered solid is further divided into its constituent parts by dissolving the iron in an acid solution that does not affect the aluminum oxide. Step by step the chemist continues until each component had been isolated, identified, and separately weighed.

The surface processes of the earth that produce sedimentary rocks have a certain resemblance to this analytical procedure. Because the chemical elements behave differently during weathering, and because minerals vary in their weathering resistance, the combined effect of weathering, transportation, and deposition at the earth's surface is to separate the chemical elements.

Let us look, for instance, at the weathering and subsequent erosion of an igneous rock. As illustrated in Fig. 14-2, an igneous rock like a granite is composed chiefly of feldspars, which are silicates of potassium, sodium, and aluminum. Quartz, SiO_2, is another prominent constituent, along with one or more dark minerals which are iron magnesium silicates. In igneous rock the eight most abundant elements in the earth's crust (oxygen, silicon, aluminum, iron, calcium, sodium, potassium, and magnesium) are homogeneously distributed.

Chemical weathering proceeds very slowly, and not all the products are formed at once. Imagine, however, that we could collect all the final weathering products of our rock in a pail of water. As we found in Table 10-6, the pail should contain potassium, K, sodium, Na, magnesium, Mg, calcium, Ca, and some silica in solution. In addition, there would be microscopically fine particles of clay minerals and iron oxides formed as a result of the weathering of feldspar and the ferromagnesian minerals. Among the original common minerals only quartz would

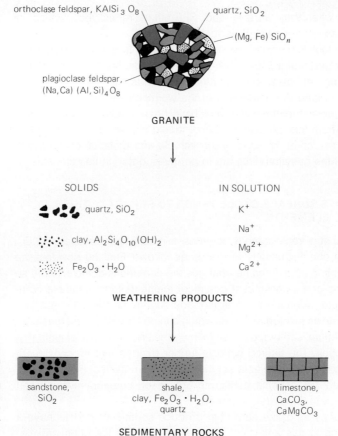

FIGURE 14-2
In a granite the common chemical elements are homogeneously distributed. Weathering tends to separate the elements because some, like silicon, remain in unweathered minerals like quartz while others go into solution or into secondary weathering minerals like clay or iron oxides.

retain its identity and size. The quartz grains in granites have about the same average diameter as those in sandstone, i.e., between $\frac{1}{16}$ and 2 millimeters.

If this imaginary pailful of weathering products were dumped into a river, the ions in solution (K^+, Na^+, Mg^{2+}, Ca^{2+}, $HSiO_4^{3-}$) would move the fastest in the running water. The aluminum-rich clays and the iron oxides would be next, and the comparatively coarse quartz would lag behind in the race to the sea. This tendency of the weathering products to separate would be furthered by the chemical conditions encountered in the moving water. Calcium carbonate is precipitated from calcium-bearing solutions in an alkaline environment; sodium and potassium are not so affected. The overall result is a chemical separation much like that accomplished by the analytical procedures chemists use.

The tendency for the elements to separate in the surface cycle of matter reaches its extreme in the final products of the surface processes, the sedimentary rocks. Whereas in the original igneous rock, the Si, Al, Fe, Ca, Na, K, and Mg were homogeneously distributed, even in a small specimen, the resulting sedimentary rocks tend to have very simple chemical compositions. Thus, the quartz particles, because of their size and resistance to abrasion and decomposition, accumulate as sands, eventually to become sandstones. The clay-sized weathering fraction accumulates as mud, to become the rock known as *shale*. Shale is the most abundant sedimentary rock and is more of a chemical mixture than any of the other common sediments. Sometimes iron oxides become separated and concentrated in rocks called *ironstones*.

Of the dissoved materials, calcium is precipitated as calcite, $CaCO_3$, in parts of the oceans to form limestone. Some limestones are composed of the mineral dolomite, $CaMg(CO_3)_2$. Seawater is enriched in potassium, which is partly removed as it is chemically absorbed by clay minerals. Sodium remains in solution unless a portion of the sea is isolated and the water evaporated, when it accumulates as rock salt.

Man makes good use of the concentrating influence of the surface processes. Most of the iron ore of the world is mined from sedimentary deposits or from concentrations formed by the weathering of such sedimentary rocks. Cement for making concrete is produced from limestone. Rock salt and gypsum are obtained for industry from sedimentary evaporite layers. Even some of the base metals like copper, lead, and zinc are sometimes sufficiently concentrated for mining in sedimentary layers.

14-2   THE KINDS OF SEDIMENTARY ROCK

In our discussion of the sediments of the deep sea (Sec. 9-5) we recognized two main classes of sediments: (*1*) those composed of particles transported to the site of deposition from the source region and (*2*) those composed of minerals formed by chemical or biochemical means at or near the place where the sediment formed. The first group are the clastic sediments. As shown in Table 6-2, clastic sediments are classified or named chiefly on the basis of grain size, the three main types being conglomerates, sandstones, and shales. The second group, known as chemical or biochemical sediments, are named or classified chiefly on the basis of composition. Limestone, the most abundant chemical sediment, is composed of calcium carbonate. Dolostone is composed of the mineral dolomite, a calcium magnesium carbonate. Rock salt is composed of the mineral halite. Chert is made up chiefly of fine-grained quartz, SiO_2.

The two main types of sedimentation are not mutually exclusive. Every sandstone, for example, contains some chemically precipitated minerals. Frequently, the chemically precipitated minerals in sandstones occupy the spaces between the individual sand grains and cement the grains together. Occasionally they make up a significant part of the rock. In the same way, limestones, which are typical chemical sediments, may contain clastic particles the size of sand or clay. We can thus speak of two separate types of mineral constituents of sedimentary rocks: *allogenic* minerals, or those transported to the site of deposition, and *authigenic* minerals, or those formed at the site of deposition by chemical means.

These separate components of sedimentary rocks contribute in different ways toward the total understanding of the rock. The allogenic minerals originated in a region perhaps hundreds of miles from the depositional basin where the sedimentary rock accumulated. Thus they may contain information about the composition of the rocks in the source region and about the conditions that existed there when the sedimentary rock was forming. For example, a sandstone derived from a source region composed of metamorphic rocks would be likely to contain (in addition to quartz) such metamorphic minerals as garnet, kyanite, or andalusite. If other sedimentary rocks acted as the source for a sandstone, these metamorphic minerals would be rare or missing.

By contrast, the authigenic minerals bear no record of their source. It is not possible to distinguish, say, between a calcium ion leached from a grain of feldspar and one dissolved from a piece of calcite or any other calcium-bearing mineral. Authigenic minerals, however, are the best record of the chemical conditions of the depositional basin because they are products of these conditions. If laboratory experiments, for example, reveal that a certain authigenic mineral forms only within a narrow pH range, it may be assumed that this is the pH range that existed in the depositional region at the time this mineral formed.

In succeeding sections we shall investigate some of the information that can be deciphered from sedimentary rocks. The task of deducing ancient environments from the rocks is complicated at best because there are so many variables, and it is made even more difficult by the fact that sedimentary rocks change with time. The compaction brought about by the weight of perhaps thousands of feet of overlying sediment and the exposure to the action of groundwater for hundreds of millions of years bring about changes in sedimentary rocks. In examining a 300-million-year-old sedimentary rock we must recognize that the minerals now in the rock and the texture of the rock may not be exactly the same as those at the time of deposition.

14-3 HOW DOES THE SOURCE REGION AFFECT A SEDIMENTARY ROCK?

A dramatic reconstruction of the source of a sediment was accomplished by the U.S. Geological Survey during World War II, when the Japanese released in Japan a series of incendiary balloons which floated with the prevailing atmospheric circulation to the west coast of North America. The balloons that arrived did little damage, but as they were potentially dangerous, a concerted effort was made to locate and destroy the launch site. Geological personnel were involved because the balloons carried a sand ballast and it was reasoned that there might be some way of establishing the source of this sand. On analyzing the minerals in the sand and checking against a geologic map of the islands of Japan, the geologists were able to pinpoint the source of the sand. Subsequent air missions recognized the balloon launch site at about the predicted position.

The geology of the source area is not its only influence on sedimentary rocks or even the most important one. Climate and topographic relief leave an even more marked imprint. We treat these two factors together, since their effects are similar and overlapping.

We saw in Chap. 10 that chemical weathering proceeds more rapidly, and hence is more likely to be completed, in warm, humid regions than in cold or arid regions. When (Fig. 14-2) we traced the history of an igneous rock through weathering and erosion to the formation of sedimentary rocks, we assumed that the weathering was complete and that minerals like the feldspars were totally decomposed into their weathering products. This is not always the case. Any soil or weathering residuum represents a balance between weathering and erosion. If erosion is more rapid than decomposition, minerals such as feldspar, biotite, or hornblende may be moved to sedimentary basins before they have had time to decompose into their weathering products.

This balance between decomposition and erosion is influenced jointly by climate and topography. When the climatic factors are such that decomposition is very slow, erosion may move rock fragments or grains of undecomposed minerals to the depositional basin. The resulting sediments thus contain minerals that would have been decomposed under ideal weathering conditions. In the same way, rugged topography and high relief in the source area provide the energy for rapid erosion, which also tends to move undecomposed minerals to depositional regions.

When the foregoing ideas are applied in reverse, so to speak, they give us clues about ancient source regions. Our model of what should come out of a source region where decomposition has been complete is a sediment low in sodium (which would have been leached out), low in such decomposable minerals as feldspar and the ferromagnesian silicates, and high in quartz and similar resistant substances. The degree to which an actual sediment approaches this ideal can be measured by its quartz/feldspar ratio or its Al_2O_3/Na_2O ratio. An actual sedimentary rock with a low quartz/feldspar ratio or a low alumina/soda ratio thus points to a source region where a rigorous climate or a high relief, or both, made for incomplete decomposition. Such a sediment is said to be *immature*. On the other hand, a *mature* sediment suggests a source area where conditions promoted complete decomposition.

Again we must note some exceptions. What if the rocks undergoing weathering in the source area were themselves sedimentary rocks? These rocks have already been influenced at least once by the surface cycle. Any sediment formed from a sedimentary rock will have the benefit of two or more trips through the surface cycle and hence, regardless of the climate or relief in the source region, will tend to be mature.

14-4 THE EFFECTS OF TRANSPORTATION AND THE DEPOSITIONAL ENVIRONMENT

In Sec. 12-1 we discussed the transport characteristics of the principal erosional agents—water, wind, and glacial ice. We found that glaciers are unique as sediment transporters: they are not in any way selective in the size of material carried.

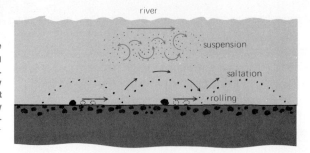

FIGURE 14-3
Methods of river transport. The largest sizes are moved along the bed by rolling and pushing. Intermediate sizes move by bouncing (saltation). Finest sizes are kept in suspension by the water turbulence. In addition ions such as K^+ and Ca^{2+} move in solution.

FIGURE 14-4
Precambrian tillite, near Latchford, Ontario. The smoothed surface is the result of the geologically recent Pleistocene glaciation. *From F. J. Pettijohn and P. E. Potter, "Atlas and Glossary of Sedimentary Structures," Springer-Verlag, Inc., 1964.*

Running water and wind, on the other hand, are selective agents. Of the two, wind is the more selective. Only the finest-grained particles are normally moved by the wind, because of the very low density and viscosity of the air. Running water is able to move coarser sediment than wind, but different sediment sizes are transported in different ways in a river system (Fig. 14-3) and hence tend to become separated and sorted. Although we would normally expect a windblown sediment to be more highly sorted than one transported by water, this is not always the case. The completeness of size sorting depends not only upon the transporting agent but also upon the distance of transport, which is related to how long the sediment is exposed to the sorting action.

In Sec. 12-1 we also found that windblown sand grains tend to be rounded much faster than those carried by water and that they develop frosted surfaces rather than polished ones. Thus it seems as though we might make inferences about the transport history of a sediment quite apart from its depositional environment. In actual practice, however, the depositional and transport history must be considered together.

To illustrate why let us consider the rock shown in Fig. 14-4, a Precambrian (1.6-billion-year-old) sedimentary rock in Ontario that was scraped smooth and scratched by the continental glacier during the Recent Ice Age. The angular cobbles and the extreme range of sizes from fine clay to boulders are convincing evidence that the rock itself is an ancient glacial deposit. The texture of the rock thus tells us not only that the material must have been moved by a glacier but also that the sediment was deposited directly by a glacier (*glacial depositional environment*).

Picture the same unsorted glacial material being deposited at a glacier's terminus, where it is acted upon by rushing meltwaters (*fluvial depositional environment*). The moving water would, of course, separate the particles of varying size, and resulting sediments would be quite different. Lack of sorting no longer could be used as evidence of glacial transport. In fact, some of the material might find its way to a proglacial lake (*lacustrine depositional environment*) or to the ocean (*marine environment*), where the direct record of its glacial transport would be largely erased.

For the remainder of this section, therefore, we shall restrict our discussion to

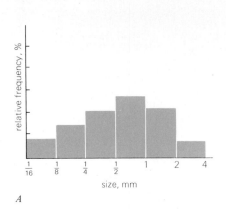

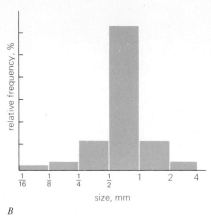

A

B

FIGURE 14-5
Grain-size distributions of two sandstones: (A) poorly sorted; (B) well sorted.

depositional environments, recognizing that for wind and water deposits the degree of sorting (Fig. 14-5) and the rounding of sediment grains are a rough measure of the transport distance.

Figure 14-6 is a photograph of some modern sediments in a bar of the Vermillion River of Indiana. The inclined bedding, or cross-bedding, exhibited by the sand is typical of current deposition. As a moving stream deposits sediment in a delta or in its channel, the structure of the sediment will be somewhat like

FIGURE 14-6
Cross-bedding in newly formed sediments of the Vermillion River, Vermillion County, Illinois. Current from left to right. *From F. J. Pettijohn and P. E. Potter, "Atlas and Glossary of Sedimentary Structures," Springer-Verlag, Inc., 1964.*

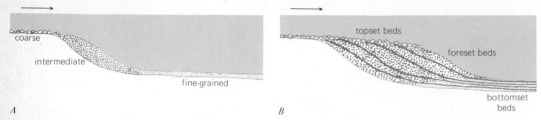

A   *B*

FIGURE 14-7
Current and delta deposits are frequently cross-bedded, as shown by these foreset beds. Sizes coarse, intermediate, and fine-grained are relative. The absolute sizes depend upon the speed of the water.

that depicted in Fig. 14-7. Figure 14-8 is a photograph of a specimen of Mississippian (about 360-million-year-old) sandstone from a location in Maryland. Not only does the cross-bedding in the sandstone tell us that this too is a current-deposited sand, but the attitude of the foreset beds suggests that the current moved from right to left.

The cross-bedding of Fig. 14-9 is unusually steep and erratic. A search of modern sediments shows this unique steep type of cross-bedding to be characteristic of sand-dune deposits. The sedimentary rocks of Fig. 14-9 are thus a record of another type of terrestrial environment, the arid environment. Again the cross-bedded sandstones contain a record of the prevailing currents (wind directions) when the rock was formed.

From observation we know that mud cracks form where water-saturated muds

FIGURE 14-8
Cross-bedding in a specimen of Mississippian sandstone from Washington County, Maryland. The cross beds tell us that the current moved from right to left. *From F. J. Pettijohn and P. E. Potter, "Atlas and Glossary of Sedimentary Structures," Springer-Verlag, Inc., 1964.*

FIGURE 14-9
Wind-deposited cross-bedding is steeper and more erratic than that formed by water currents. Photograph is of the Navajo sandstone near Kanab, Utah. *J. K. Hillers, U.S. Geological Survey.*

are dried by the sun's heat at the surface (Fig. 14-10). We can apply this knowledge in interpreting the depositional conditions of the Silurian (about 420-million-year-old) limestone of Fig. 14-11. This muddy limestone must have formed in very shallow water, so that it was dry during part of its depositional history. A closer look at the limestone reveals the presence of marine fossils, which, together with the mud cracks, suggest deposition in the tidal zone. Thus this limestone outcrop marks the position of a Silurian shoreline.

In Chap. 9 we found that underwater flows of muddy waters (turbidity currents) are effective in moving sediment from the continental shelves to the deeper parts of the ocean basins. Such currents, once started, are able to flow under clear water because turbulence keeps sediment in suspension and makes the currents denser than the surrounding water. When a submarine turbidity current reaches a flat part of the sea, it loses its turbulence and the suspended sediment settles out. The coarsest particles fall to the bottom first, followed by progressively finer

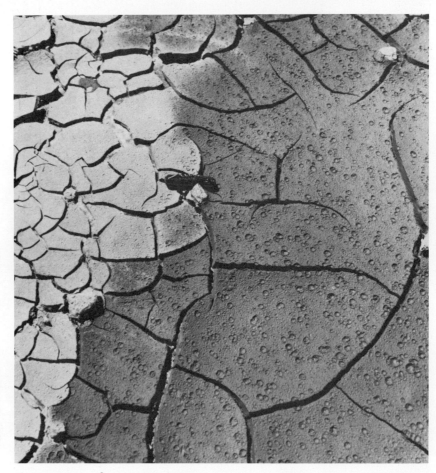

FIGURE 14-10
Modern dessication cracks with rain imprints, Fort Dodge, Iowa. *Photograph by D. M. Baird from F. J. Pettijohn and P. E. Potter, "Atlas and Glossary of Sedimentary Structures," Springer-Verlag, Inc., 1964.*

sizes, to produce a texture called *graded bedding*. A close look at Fig. 14-12 reveals three such graded layers. We might infer, therefore, that the Ordovician shale of the photograph was deposited in a relatively deep and quiet marine environment by turbidity currents.

So far, our examples have illustrated some of the possible physical conditions in the area of deposition. What of the chemical conditions? In Sec. 14-2 we recognized that the chemical or biochemical sediments are the places to look for information about past chemical conditions in the seas. Such sediments form as a result of a particular set of chemical conditions. If we know the conditions presently necessary to precipitate limestone, for example, we can assume that these conditions must have existed where limestone is found.

Two significant chemical variables are pH and the oxidation potential. The pH of a solution is a measure of its hydrogen-ion concentration. More specifically, pH is the negative logarithm of the hydrogen-ion concentration. A solution with a

FIGURE 14-11
Mud cracks in clayey limestone of Silurian age, Washington County, Maryland. *From F. J. Pettijohn and P. E. Potter, "Atlas and Glossary of Sedimentary Structures," Springer-Verlag, Inc., 1964.*

FIGURE 14-12
Graded bedding in an Ordovician shale, Orange County, New York. Three graded units are visible. *Photograph by E. F. McBride. From F. J. Pettijohn and P. E. Potter, "Atlas and Glossary of Sedimentary Structures," Springer-Verlag, Inc., 1964.*

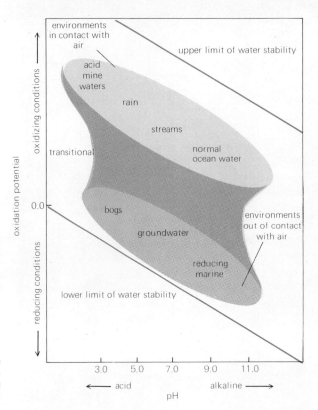

FIGURE 14-13
Approximate positions of some natural environments as characterized by oxidation potential and pH.

hydrogen-ion concentration of 10^{-9} mole per liter has a pH of 9. Distilled water has a pH of 7. Acids have higher hydrogen-ion concentration and thus lower pH numbers. Bases have pH values of over 7. Oxidation potential is a measure of the oxidizing or reducing potential of a solution. In an oxidizing solution, iron is oxidized to the ferric, Fe^{3+}, state, whereas in a reducing environment, iron occurs in minerals in the ferrous, Fe^{2+}, state. Figure 14-13 shows the range of pH and oxidizing potential in surface environments.

In existing depositional basins, these two chemical variables are easily measured. Seawater has an average pH of about 8, whereas the pH of most river waters is around 7. Surface waters in contact with the oxygen of the air are normally strongly oxidizing. Organic debris accumulating in such water becomes oxidized, as does any ferrous iron brought to such an environment. At the other extreme, the bottom water in the Black Sea and some Norwegian fjords is highly reducing. Oxygenated surface waters do not reach these reducing regions, and any organic debris accumulating there remains unoxidized. Such strongly reducing environments frequently contain hydrogen sulfide from the anaerobic decay of plant and animal debris.

Limestone, the sedimentary rock composed of the mineral calcite, $CaCO_3$, is the most abundant chemical sediment. Calcite is relatively insoluble in pure water (pH = 7). Since it does dissolve readily even in weak acids (pH less than 7), we can immediately conclude that where limestones formed the seas could not have been acid. We can be even more specific. The amount of dissolved calcium in the sea is known. At pH 7.8 or higher, calcium normally is precipitated from seawater, whereas at lower pH values, seawater dissolves $CaCO_3$. Whenever calcite is a significant original constituent of a marine rock, we can assume that the pH at the time of deposition must have been higher than about 7.8.

Thus the mineral calcite, as an original constituent of a sedimentary rock, sets a rough limit on the pH of the water at the time the rock formed. In the same way, we can derive from the presence or absence of organic matter in a sediment approximate limits on the oxidation potential of a sedimentary environment. Under oxidizing conditions, plant debris or animal remains slowly oxidize to carbon dioxide. In the absence of oxygen, this reaction cannot proceed, and the organic debris accumulates, becoming incorporated in the sediments. If we find organic matter preserved in a sedimentary rock, we can assume that the sediment must have accumulated in a reducing environment. If there is no organic matter, we conclude either that none was transported to the site of deposition or that the sediment accumulated under oxidizing conditions that caused the destruction of organic matter.

The guides we have just discussed to the pH and oxidation potential of depositional environments are incorporated in Fig. 14-14. The various boundaries, or fences, in the diagram provide a key for reconstructing the chemical conditions that existed when a sediment formed. Two, the *limestone fence* and the *oxide fence* have just been mentioned. The diagram is more a guide to the chemical conditions under which a rock formed than a firm quantitative measure of the exact pH and oxidation potential. A limestone containing primary iron oxide (hematite, limonite), for example, would suggest alkaline and oxidizing depositional conditions. A chert (silica rock) with pyrite would suggest deposition under neutral to slightly alkaline pH and reducing to strongly reducing oxidation potential.

Thus far, we have looked chiefly at the physical and chemical characteristics of sedimentary rocks as guides to the past conditions. Many sedimentary rocks contain fossils (Fig. 14-15), not only invaluable markers of geologic time (Chap. 13) but sources of significant information about ancient environments. For example, coral reefs grow only in the tropical and subtropical regions of the world. Corals thrive in shallow and warm waters. When we look into the past, we find Paleozoic rocks in the Arctic islands of Canada and in Greenland that contain fossil coral reefs. We can infer that these reef-bearing rocks must have formed in at least subtropical waters. Whether the area above the Arctic Circle experienced a tropical climate during the Paleozoic Era or the Arctic islands have moved relative to the earth's poles since the coral reefs formed is a question that we explore in detail in Chap. 16.

Figure 14-16 presents still another technique for reading the conditions of the

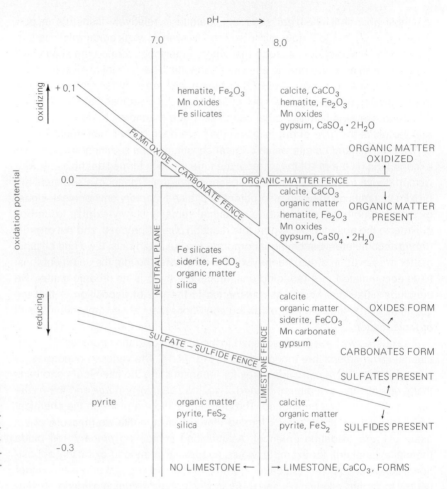

FIGURE 14-14
Sedimentary associations in relation to environmental limitations imposed by pH and oxidation potential. *After W. C. Krumbein and R. M. Garrels, J. Geol., vol. 60, p. 26, 1952.*

past from the rock record. As illustrated by Fig. 14-16*A*, experimental work has revealed a strong correlation between the $^{18}O/^{16}O$ ratio of seawater and the temperature of the water. Any oxygen-bearing mineral forming in water of a given temperature would be expected to exhibit the same $^{18}O/^{16}O$ ratio as the water in which it formed. Thus measurement of the oxygen isotope ratios in authigenic minerals of sedimentary rocks provides a measure of the temperature of formation of the minerals. The oxygen-isotope technique, when combined with the fossil record, permits measurement of ancient annual variations in temperature, as the values for the winter and summer growth rings of the Jurassic (170 million years) belemnite of Fig. 14-16*B* illustrate.

We have reviewed some of the evidence used by earth scientists to decipher past conditions from single sedimentary rocks. Some features of sedimentary rocks are conclusive and easy to read; e.g., a preserved dinosaur footprint in a water-laid sediment is proof of shallow-water deposition. Other properties of sed-

FIGURE 14-15
Fossils like these tell a great deal about the environment in which a sediment formed. *Courtesy of Marc Hult.*

imentary rocks are more difficult to interpret. Careful mineralogic analysis is required to get information about the possible source rocks of a sediment, and even then the information may not be conclusive. Further valuable data come from studying groups or associations of sedimentary rocks.

14-5 GEOSYNCLINES AND THICK SEDIMENTS

James Hall, born in Massachusetts in 1811, graduated from the Rensselaer School, Troy, New York, taught school for several years, and eventually joined the newly formed New York Geological Survey. His work with the survey resulted in a significant discovery about sedimentary basins.

In studying and mapping the Paleozoic rocks of New York, Hall found them to vary tremendously in thickness. In the western parts of the state he discovered these rocks to be at most a few thousand feet thick and to be flat-lying and undeformed. In these rocks Hall detected fossil and structural evidence of deposition in a relatively shallow marine environment. He was able to trace some of the rock series eastward to the Appalachian Mountains. As he followed the layers toward the east, he noted a marked thickening of the beds. In the area of the Appalachians he estimated the total thickness of the Paleozoic sediments to be about 40,000 feet (see Fig. 14-17 for the methods used to measure such thicknesses). Not only was the total thickness in the Appalachian region about 20 times as great as in the west, but the rocks were folded and deformed.

This in itself was a significant feat of mapping, and to think of a basin 40,000

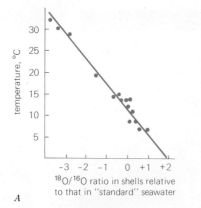

A

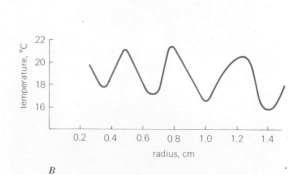

B

FIGURE 14-16

(*A*) **Relation of oxygen isotopes in the calcium carbonate shells of present-day animals to the temperature of the seawater in which the animals grew.** (*B*) **The isotopic temperature scale of** (*A*) **applied to the CaCO₃ of various growth layers of a Jurassic belemnite from the Island of Skye, Scotland. Alternating warm and cool (summer and winter) growth periods are clearly evident.** (*C*) **A cross section of the belemnite used in the investigation. Diameter is approximately 2.5 centimeters.** *W* **and** *S* **indicate winter and summer growth rings.** *After H. C. Urey et al., Bull. Geol. Soc. Am., vol. 62, 1951.*

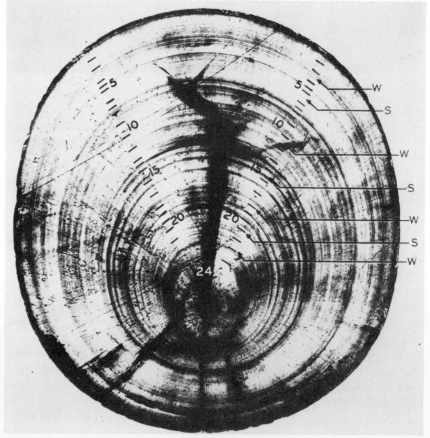

C

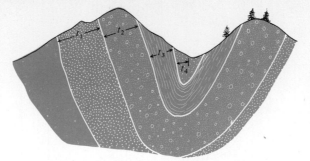

FIGURE 14-17
Sedimentary thicknesses are determined in areas of folded rocks by measuring the true thickness t of each bed and totaling.

feet deep was difficult enough. When Hall examined the thick Paleozoic section of the Appalachian region more carefully, he discovered ample evidence to suggest that these beds, like the thinner beds of western New York, had been deposited in relatively shallow seas. How could this be? Hall reasoned that the basin in which the thick sequence of sediments was deposited must have been actively sinking while sediment deposition was taking place. He attributed the sinking to subsidence due to the increasing load of sediments brought to the basin of deposition.

Since Hall's pioneering work, geologic mapping has disclosed similar thickening of sediments in other mountain systems. The large linear troughs in which great thicknesses of sediments have been accumulated were later named *geosynclines*. Can a shallow depositional basin indeed be depressed 40,000 feet or more merely by the weight of the sediment accumulated in it? To test this notion we return to the concept of isostasy, discussed in Chap. 3, i.e., a state of balance between the major blocks of the earth's crust. Mountain ranges, or even continents, can be thought of as resembling icebergs in a state of flotational balance on a denser subcrust. If this is so, a column of rock from the highest mountain tip to the level of equal pressure in the upper mantle should have the same mass as a column of equal cross-sectional area through an ocean basin to the same level even though the ocean column would be much shorter.

With this idea in mind let us take a more quantitative look at the problem of subsidence in basins of sediment deposition. Figure 14-18 sets up our analysis. If 100 feet of water is displaced by sediment with a density of 2.5 grams per cubic centimeter, how much subsidence would occur in the basin provided isostasy is maintained? For flotational balance the mass of the original column (A) must be the same as the mass of the final column (B). If we let the amount of subsidence of the basin equal h, then we must have a similar subsidence in the denser subcrustal rocks. Using C for crust and S for subcrust, we can thus set up the following relation:

Original column A:
  Weight of water proportional to $100 \times 1 = 100$
  Weight of crust proportional to $C \times 2.7 = 2.7C$
Weight of subcrust proportional to $S \times 3.5 = 3.5S$

Total $100 + 2.7C + 3.5S$

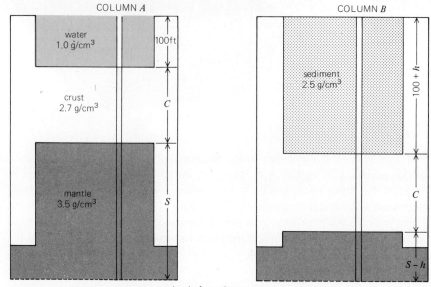

FIGURE 14-18
How much sediment of density 2.5 g/cm³ can accumulate in a basin 100 feet deep if isostasy is maintained? (See text.)

Final column B:

Weight of sediment proportional to $(100 + h)(2.5) = 250 + 2.5h$

Weight of crust proportional to $C \times 2.7 = 2.7C$

Weight of subcrust proportional to $(S - h)(3.5) = 3.5S - 3.5h$

Total $250 + 2.5h + 2.7C + 3.5S - 3.5h$

Equating the two columns gives

$$100 + 2.7C + 3.5S = 250 + 2.5h + 2.7C + 3.5S - 3.5h$$

from which $h = 150$ feet.

The total maximum thickness of sediment that might be expected to accumulate in a basin 100 feet deep by isostatic adjustment is thus $100 + 150$, or 250 feet. The actual numbers would change slightly if we used more accurate figures for rock densities but only by a few percent. A subsidence of 200 feet is a far cry from the 40,000 feet of shallow-water sediments found by Hall in the Appalachian geosyncline.

That very thick geosynclinal sedimentary deposits exist is an established fact. There is also convincing evidence that at least some of the rocks in such thick sedimentary piles were deposited in relatively shallow water. We have just shown that subsidence alone is grossly inadequate to account for such great thicknesses. The only logical conclusion that we can draw, therefore, is that some internal earth forces working against isostasy must be involved in the formation of geosynclines. We return to this question of internal forces in the next chapter.

Geosynclines, then, are the result of internal earth forces; they are products of diastrophism. These mobile belts are frequently places where volcanoes develop, and the relative instability of geosynclinal belts is reflected in the sediments they contain. The Paleozoic rocks of, say, the central part of the Appalachian geosyncline consist of poorly sorted muddy sandstones interlayered with shales and locally with lava flows. Many of the impure sandstones exhibit the characterisitics of those laid down by turbidity currents. The great sediment thicknesses, the poor sorting, and the interlayered volcanics all speak for rapid filling in an unstable basin.

By contrast, rocks of similar age in the upper Mississippi Valley region are chiefly well-sorted pure quartz sandstones, interlayered with limestones. Here the rock layers are relatively thin and undeformed, attesting to the great crustal stability of the region. The completeness of weathering (high degree of maturity) of the sandstones, their excellent sorting, and the presence of limestones, which accumulate very slowly, are further evidence that very stable conditions prevailed while they were formed.

14-6 SEDIMENTARY ASSOCIATIONS AND PALEOGEOGRAPHIC MAPS

In Secs. 14-2 to 14-4 we examined some of the properties of sedimentary rocks that could be used to decipher their history. The distribution of sedimentary rocks and their associations are perhaps equally important guides to the conditions of the past.

The distribution of marine sedimentary rocks provides a key to former positions of the earth's shorelines. We recall from Chap. 13 that rocks deposited during, say, the Cambrian Period are called the Cambrian System. This system is divided into a lower, middle, and upper rock series. Because sedimentary rocks form layer upon layer, Lower Cambrian is the oldest and Upper Cambrian the youngest. Figure 14-19, an outline map of North America, shows the ages of the oldest Cambrian rocks found in various parts of the continent. Such a map is the result of many man-years of mapping, and one must realize that it is not a map of the rocks encountered at the surface in various parts of this continent. In the area where the base of the Cambrian is indicated as Lower Cambrian, for example, the rocks exposed at the surface may be very much younger, but where Cambrian rocks are exposed, as along deep river valleys, the base of the Cambrian is Lower Cambrian.

What information can we read from such a map? In the western part of the continent we can trace the shifting position of the shoreline throughout the Cambrian Period. In the early part of the period, the maximum eastward progression of the shore was along the boundary between the area where the oldest Cambrian rocks are Lower Cambrian and the area where they are the Middle Cambrian. The area to the west of this boundary received sediment and was under water during Lower Cambrian time. The area east of the boundary must have been undergoing erosion because the Lower Cambrian is absent. During the middle part of the

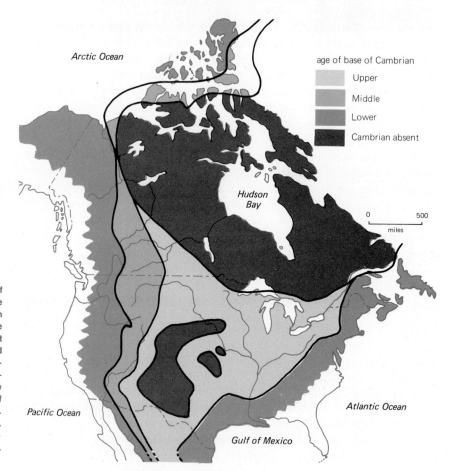

FIGURE 14-19
Outline map showing the age of rocks that lie as the base of the Cambrian System in North America. The areas where Cambrian rocks are absent seem to have remained as land or at least retained no Cambrian sediments. The distributions of Cambrian rocks on the eastern and western margins of the continents are omitted. *After M. Kay and E. H. Colbert, "Stratigraphy and Life History," John Wiley & Sons, Inc., 1964.*

Cambrian Period the margin of the sea moved eastward to the point on the map marking the boundary between Middle and Upper Cambrian. Toward the end of the period, the shoreline moved to about the lines marking the boundaries of the areas where Cambrian rocks are entirely missing. In that part of the continent where there are no Cambrian rocks, we cannot positively say that there never were any. Perhaps Cambrian rocks were deposited in parts of this region and have since been removed by erosion. The probability that the area was once entirely covered by Cambrian is very slim, however, because it is extremely unlikely that erosion would have removed all traces of these beds.

Still another type of paleogeographic map is useful in interpreting the past. Figure 14-20 shows the composition of the Middle Cambrian rocks found in the central part of North America. The term *facies* is used to describe differing compositions of sedimentary rocks that formed during the same time interval. Along modern shorelines we frequently find gravels and coarse sands accumulating near the shore and finer silts and clays accumulating farther offshore. The distribution of the Middle Cambrian facies on the map supports our earlier conclusion of a gradual eastward migration of the sea during the Cambrian. The predominance of sandy sediments along the boundary of the region without Cambrian sediments suggests that this actually is a former shoreline, especially since the sand facies is bounded by a finer-grained silt facies, which, in turn, grades into carbonate deposits characteristic of the deeper portions of the sea.

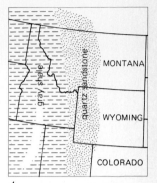

A

14-7 HAS SEDIMENTATION ALWAYS BEEN THE SAME?

Sedimentary rocks are the products of the surface cycle. The fact that ancient marine sediments are now exposed in many parts of the continents is proof that areas of the sea floor are uplifted again to be weathered and eroded to form new sedimentary rocks. Has this cycle gone on in much the same way since the earth first developed a hydrosphere and an atmosphere? Are geologically ancient sediments the same as modern sediments? These are questions currently being explored by sedimentologists.

A first comparison of sedimentary rocks of various ages does not reveal significant differences. A 2-billion-year old sandstone, for example, may be somewhat better cemented and compacted than a recent sandstone because it has been around much longer, but the two might well be identical in composition and in such structural characteristics as cross-bedding or ripple marks. Some ancient sedimentary rocks contain evidence of cold glacial conditions. Others, however, bear the earmarks of tropical formation. There is no clear evidence in the sedimentary record that climate has changed in a uniform way with time.

Are we to conclude then that the earth has remained unchanging (or, rather that it has kept changing in the same way) since the oldest exposed sedimentary rocks were formed some 3 billion years ago? The existence of 3-billion-year-old clastic sediments tells us that the hydrologic cycle has remained unchanged for that time. There might, however, have been changes in the chemical nature of the seas or atmosphere. To detect such chemical evolution, we must look at the chemical sediments.

Differences in the distribution and composition of chemical sediments with time have been discovered, but their interpretation is not always clear. For example, there are fewer limestones in Precambrian sediments than in younger sedimentary rocks. Is this because conditions during the Precambrian were not conducive to the formation of limestone, or is it because the Precambrian limestones, like their recent counterparts, were relatively thin, blanket deposits that long since have been eroded away? Predevonian limestones contain Ca/Mg ratios of about 3.5:2, whereas this same ratio is 12:1 in Carboniferous limestones and from 35:1 to 55:1 in Cretaceous and younger limestones. Does this change in the Ca/Mg ratio with time point to a gradual change in the chemistry of the ocean waters, as has been suggested by some investigators? Or is the lower Ca/Mg ratio of the older limestones simply due to the gradual replacement of calcium by

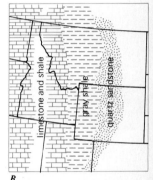

B

FIGURE 14-20
Paleolithologic map showing the distribution of types of sediments on the floors of the oceans in north central United States during the Middle Cambrian. (*A*) Start of the Middle Cambrian; (*B*) later in the same epoch. *C. Lochman, Geol. Soc. America, Memoir 67, 1957.*

FIGURE 14-21
Precambrian iron-rich sedimentary beds (iron formations) in northeastern North America. Areas of iron formation shown dark. *From H. Lepp and S. S. Goldich, Econ. Geol., vol. 59, 1964.*

magnesium with time? (It is known that calcium carbonate is capable of being gradually replaced by magnesium when exposed to magnesium-bearing groundwaters.)

Perhaps the most clear-cut instance of change is found in the iron-rich sediments. In terms of total sediments, those with a sufficient concentration of iron to be of economic interest are rare, but they are widely distributed, both in place and time. Figure 14-21 shows the areas of Precambrian iron-rich sedimentary beds in northeastern North America. Similar old iron formations are found in Brazil, Africa, Australia, India, and in other parts of the world. The iron mines of England, France, and Germany are mainly in sedimentary ironstones of Paleozoic and younger age. It is generally true that iron-rich sediments older than 1.5 billion years (Middle Precambrian) are composed chiefly of chert, SiO_2, and one or more iron-bearing minerals such as magnetite, Fe_3O_4. Iron-rich sediments younger than 600 million years, on the other hand, are chiefly associated with limestones or with clastic beds of sand or shale. Extensive chert beds are known in rocks younger than 600 million years, but these cherts are not normally associated with iron minerals.

This variation in the nature of iron sedimentation has been interpreted as reflecting an evolutionary change in the atmosphere. The association of iron and chert can best be explained by sedimentation in an atmosphere that was oxygen-deficient. We shall see in Chap. 18, where we discuss the origin of the atmosphere, that there is other strong evidence that the earth's early atmosphere was deficient in oxygen. Any change in atmospheric composition should have left its mark on other sediments, but the chemical variations to be expected are small, and the problem is complicated by the fact that sedimentary rocks are known to change after they have been formed. The whole question of evolutionary changes in the nature of sedimentation provides a subject for future research.

SUMMARY

Because surface processes work to separate the chemical materials of the earth's crust, sedimentary rocks have much simpler chemical compositions than igneous rocks. Whereas in the average igneous rock all eight of the common crustal elements are more or less uniformly distributed, in sedimentary rocks one or more of the common elements frequently make up the bulk of a rock.

Any sedimentary rock is a product of a source rock and a set of environmental conditions. The source rock, climate, and relief of the source, the transporting agent, distance of transport, and the depositional environment all leave their marks in the resulting sediment. Although theoretically it is possible to decipher the total history of any sediment, in practice there are too many variables. Clastic sediments offer the best record of source region, transport history, and the physical conditions of deposition. Chemical sediments best reflect the chemical conditions of the depositional region.

The distribution of marine sedimentary rocks can be used to reconstruct past positions of the oceans. Maps showing the type of rock formed during a particular period help locate ancient shorelines because the coarser sediments are normally closest to the shore. The thickest piles of sedimentary rocks are found in long, sinking troughs called geosynclines. Geosynclinal sediments are usually poorly sorted

sandstones and shales, as contrasted with clean, well-sorted sands that accumulate on stable shelves.

The oldest known sedimentary rocks are about 3 billion years old. In most instances the very old sedimentary rocks are nearly identical with their recent counterparts. The only evidence of long-term variation in sedimentary rocks is found in certain chemical characteristics, but even these are difficult to interpret. It now appears that some of the Precambrian sediments reveal the influence of an earlier oxygen-deficient atmosphere.

QUESTIONS

1 Why are sandstones made up chiefly of the mineral quartz?
2 The most abundant dissolved ion in river water is calcium, whereas sodium is the chief ion in seawater. What happens to the calcium in the sea?
3 What evidence would you look for in a sedimentary rock to determine whether it was laid down in water or on land?
4 What would the presence of abundant feldspar in a sandstone tell you about its origin?
5 How would a sand deposited from a turbidity current differ from a normal beach sand?
6 Why is subsidence an inadequate explanation for the great thicknesses of sedimentary rocks found in geosynclines?
7 Folding and faulting are the result of deformation of once-horizontal sedimentary beds after their formation. What would you look for to determine whether a given sequence of sediments formed during a period of crustal unrest?
8 Why are wind-transported sediments usually well sorted?
9 How would you recognize an ancient glacial deposit?
10 Which of the sedimentary rocks is most like igneous rock in terms of chemical composition?
11 What is a chemical sediment?
12 Two sandstones look identical in a hand specimen. How might they differ under detailed examination in the field and in the laboratory?

REFERENCES

Degens, Egan, T.: "Geochemistry of Sediments," Prentice-Hall, Inc., Englewood Cliffs, N.J., 1965.
Krumbein, W., and L. Sloss: "Stratigraphy and Sedimentation," W. H. Freeman and Company, San Francisco, 1963.
LaPorte, L. F.: "Ancient Environments," Prentice-Hall, Inc., Englewood Cliffs, N.J., 1968.
Mason, B.: "Principles of Geochemistry," 3d ed., John Wiley & Sons, Inc., New York, 1966.
Pettijohn, F. J.: "Sedimentary Rocks," 2d ed., Harper & Row, Publishers, Incorporated, New York, 1957.
Woodford, A. O.: "Historical Geology," W. H. Freeman and Company, San Francisco, 1965.

15

INTERNAL EARTH PROCESSES

In Chap. 6 we introduced the concept of a rock cycle. The processes involved in the rock cycle are of two major types—surface and internal. We have examined the surface processes (weathering, erosion, transportation, and deposition) in some detail and have found that they work to level the lands and ultimately to build flat layers of sedimentary rock. Here we examine the other part of the rock cycle, those processes which produce change and form new rocks deep within the earth's crust and upper mantle.

We cannot observe the deep-seated processes that produce metamorphic and igneous rock directly, as we could the surface activity, but continued erosion over eons of time has exposed to view igneous and metamorphic rocks that had formed far beneath the present surface. By studying them we can make some reasonable inferences about the conditions that exist at that depth and the processes operating there.

The surface and internal parts of the rock cycle are not unrelated. Most exposed deep-seated igneous and metamorphic rocks are found in the cores of eroded mountain ranges. Apparently these rocks form in geologically active parts of the earth known as *orogenic belts*. The surface cycle is also highly dependent upon orogeny because erosion is most pronounced in the high regions of the earth. Moreover, were it not for the internally powered earth movements, the continents would have been worn flat and erosion would long since have ceased to produce new surface rocks.

15-1 VOLCANOES AS DIRECT EVIDENCE OF PROCESSES IN THE DEPTHS

In Chap. 5 we found that seismology indicates the earth is solid from the surface to the core. The lava that pours out of volcanoes shows that this conclusion is not completely valid; there must be places in the crust or mantle where the rocks are at least partially fluid. Much more has been learned from volcanoes. For instance, their present distribution establishes clearly that the generation of magma (molten rock) within the crust and upper mantle is not a random process. All of today's active volcanoes are located in three narrow belts, namely the circum-Pacific belt, the belt along the ocean ridge systems, and the Alpine-Himalayan belt. These also are the regions where most earthquakes occur.

Volcanoes provide an opportunity for observing and measuring the properties of magma. The temperature of lavas in volcanic vents generally falls in the range from about 900° to 1200°C, with most measurements clustering around 1100° to 1200°C. These temperatures are well below the dry melting temperatures of the silicates that make up the lava. Studies of volcanic gases show that lava contains

FIGURE 15-1
The 1944 eruption of Mount Vesuvius. Most of the smoke here and in other volcanoes is steam. Water and other volatiles are released from magma under the low pressure at the earth's surface. *Brown Brothers, New York.*

significant amounts of volatiles, which help lower the melting point of the silicate mix. The chief volatile constituent is water (steam), but carbon dioxide, CO_2, fluorine, F, chlorine, Cl, sulfur, S, and boron, B are also present.

We may wonder how a magma could possibly dissolve materials like water. Certainly if a pailful of water were thrown onto a flow of red hot molten lava, it would sputter for a few seconds and be evaporated. However, the situation is quite different deep beneath the surface, where magmas form. There, the high pressures promote solution of volatiles in magma just as pressure makes carbon dioxide dissolve in flavored water, producing carbonated beverages. The large amounts of steam and other gases released by volcanoes is proof that the volatiles are present in magma at depth. Their escape as clouds of billowing steam (Fig. 15-1) is due to the release of pressure.

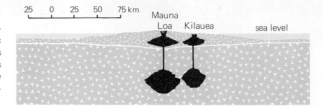

FIGURE 15-2
A cross section of Hawaii showing the shape of this volcanic
cone. The low slope results
because the basaltic lavas
which form the cone are very
fluid. Magma is thought to originate in the earth's mantle.

Figure 15-2 is a cross section of Hawaii drawn to scale. This island is built of lava flows, and we can infer from the gentle slopes that the lava must be quite fluid. Observations of actual extrusions confirm this conclusion. Some flows with temperatures of over 1000°C have been observed to move at speeds of over 20 kilometers per hour. In sharp contrast to the Hawaiian lavas is the material extruded from Mt. Pelee in 1903 (Fig. 15-3). During this eruption, lava at about 600°C squeezed out of the Pelee vent like toothpaste from a tube. It formed a high spire which did not even flow under its own weight.

What causes the great difference in lava fluidity? Temperature plays a role in determining fluidity, but composition is more important. Magmas (or lavas) with relatively high concentrations of magnesium, Mg, and iron, Fe, are *mafic* magmas. Those with abundant silica are *felsic* magmas. When felsic magmas crystallize, the rocks are composed chiefly of feldspar and quartz. Mafic magmas by contrast produce rocks with significant quantities of dark-colored ferromagnesian silicates. Analyses of the Hawaiian lavas disclose a uniform composition with 50 percent silica, SiO_2, 12 to 17 percent alumina, Al_2O_3, 9 to 15 percent iron oxide, FeO and Fe_2O_3, 5 to 9 percent magnesia, MgO, and variable amounts of CaO, Na_2O, and K_2O. The very viscous material extruded at Mt. Pelee, by contrast, contained about 75 percent silica with proportionately lower amounts of the other constituents.

In all the common silicate minerals the silicon ion is surrounded by four oxygen ions, and these silicon-oxygen tetrahedrons frequently join by oxygen-shar-

FIGURE 15-3
In contrast to the very fluid
lavas of Hawaii, the hot material
extruded from Mt. Pelee, Martinique, West Indies, in 1903
was too viscous to flow. Instead
it was ejected as a great spire
of lava that rose almost 1,000
feet in a 2-month period. *After
Lacroix.*

500 ft

Jan. 4   Mar. 9   Mar. 25   Aug. 21

ing to form chains, sheets, or lattices (Chap. 4). Even in molten magma the disordered silicon-oxygen tetrahedrons seek to polymerize, or join, largely explaining why the high-silica felsic lavas tend to be so sticky.

We might conclude that there are all gradations of volcanic extrusions from the very fluid to those which behave more like thick grease. Gradations do indeed exist between these extremes, but not all compositions are equally abundant. In fact, over 90 percent of all lava flows are basaltic. Nor are lavas of varying composition uniformly distributed over the earth. In general the lavas found on the continents and along continental margins tend to be more felsic than those of the ocean basins.

Where does the lava come from? Seismic measurements in Hawaii during periods of volcanic eruption point to a lava source some 70 to 100 kilometers beneath the surface. Similar studies in other parts of the world show lava originating at even greater depths. Such depths, we recall, are well below the base of the earth's crust. Does this then mean that the mantle has the composition of basalt? Not necessarily. In Chap. 5 we found that existing evidence points to an upper earth mantle composed of peridotite, which is a more mafic material than basalt. Because felsic minerals have lower melting points than mafic minerals, partial melting of peridotite could result in a fluid with the composition of basalt. Thus we visualize the source of basaltic lavas not as a large pool of magma but a region of the mantle where the material is only partially melted. Basaltic magmas probably originate in the asthenosphere (Sec. 5-8). This is consistent with seismic evidence, which shows the mantle to be essentially solid.

FIGURE 15-4
Volcanic neck near Albuquerque, New Mexico. Most of the volcano has been eroded away, leaving the feeder plug as an isolated tower. *D. A. Rahm, "Slides for Geology," 1971. Used with permission of McGraw-Hill Book Company.*

15-2 IGNEOUS ACTIVITY AND THE ORIGINAL MAGMAS

Only a part of the magma formed beneath the surface eventually finds its way to a volcanic vent. Magma also solidifies beneath the surface. Igneous rocks that form underground are called intrusive rocks because they cut through or invade other rocks. To form a volcano there must be some underground conduit for magma. A volcanic plug is one example of an intrusive igneous formation (Fig. 15-4). Other types of intrusive bodies were illustrated in Fig. 6-4.

Some intrusive igneous bodies become exposed by continued erosion of the overlying rocks. Whereas the igneous origin of a recent lava is obvious, how is the igneous character of intrusive bodies established? Usually by their texture and the relation they bear to the rocks around them. Texture refers to the size of mineral grains in a rock and the relations between them. Because they form from a melt, the minerals of igneous rocks are tightly intergrown (Fig. 15-5). Grain size depends upon the rate of cooling. Lava flows are usually very fine-grained because they cool relatively quickly. Intrusive igneous rocks cool very slowly because they must lose the heat necessary for crystallization through the overlying layers of rock, which are very poor conductors of heat. Thus intrusive rocks are usually coarse-grained.

The relationship of a rock unit with the surrounding rocks is particularly signif-

FIGURE 15-5
Photomicrograph of a granite.
Magnification 35X. *Courtesy of D. Southwick.*

icant in establishing its igneous character. In Fig. 15-6, for example, we can determine that rock *a* must be an igneous intrusive because:

1 It cuts across other rocks.
2 It is finer-grained near the boundaries where the magma was chilled as it contacted the cool wall rocks.
3 It contains inclusions of the rocks into which it intrudes.
4 It has apparently widened the fracture in which it occurs as evidenced by the displacement of the vein.

We know that the continents consist chiefly of granitic rocks and the ocean basins chiefly of basaltic rocks, and from Table 6-1 we recall that granite and basalt differ in both composition and texture. Basalts are fine-grained, mafic igneous rocks that form either as lava flows or as shallow intrusives. Granites, on

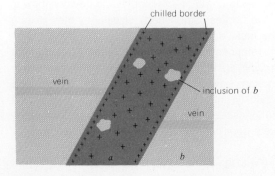

FIGURE 15-6
How can we tell that rock *a* is an intrusive body?

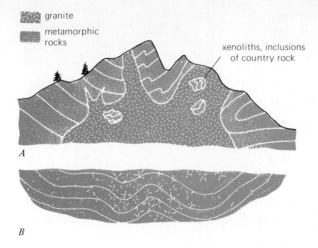

granite

metamorphic
rocks

xenoliths, inclusions
of country rock

A

B

FIGURE 15-7
(A) In young mountains bodies
of granite often exhibit characteristic intrusive features. (B) In
the older shield areas of the
world, where erosion has exposed mountain roots, igneous
and metamorphic rocks usually
grade insensibly into each
other.

the other hand, are coarse-grained felsic rocks that originate by slow cooling
well below the earth's surface. The formation of granite bodies seems to be restricted not only to the continents but more specifically to the mobile continental
mountain belts.

Granites are composed of feldspar, quartz, and minor amounts of dark-
colored biotite or hornblende. Unfortunately, composition is not a definite criterion of an igneous origin for granites because some metamorphic rocks closely
resemble them in mineral content. Metamorphism means change of form. Rocks
exposed to elevated temperatures and pressures and the action of fluids recrystallize to form new minerals, just as soft, pliable clay is changed into hard brick in
a kiln. Although metamorphic rocks do not go through a fluid phase, some metamorphism occurs in approximately the melting-temperature range of rocks. It is
not surprising, therefore, that rocks formed under such conditions contain the
same minerals as igneous rocks and thus cannot be distinguished on the basis
of composition alone.

Both igneous and metamorphic rocks are associated with mountain systems.
We explore the reasons for this association in greater detail in Sec. 15-6, but for
the moment let us simply look at some of the occurrences of these rocks in the
field. In high, young mountain chains granite and other intrusive bodies usually
exhibit textbook criteria for rocks that formed by magma intrusion. They cut
across other rocks, the rocks at their contacts are recrystallized, as would be expected from their proximity to a hot intrusive body, and the granites often contain
inclusions of local rock (Fig. 15-7A).

By contrast, in the Precambrian shield areas, which are the deeply eroded,
oldest parts of the continents, the relation between igneous and metamorphic
rocks is very different. Here there are no mountains left; only the roots of mountains remain. Bodies of granite are widespread in these mountain roots, but their
intrusive and even their igneous character is not always evident. They usually

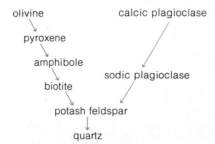

FIGURE 15-8
(Bowen reaction series) The normal order of crystallization of minerals from a melt.

grade insensibly into banded metamorphic rocks of about the same composition (Fig. 15-7B). There is no evidence of chilling or cross-cutting relations at the borders of these granite bodies. Many, in fact, are mixed rocks in which thin layers of granite and of metamorphic material alternate. Geologists working in such terrain question the igneous nature of the granites. If any melting was involved, it was partial at best.

In spite of the controversy over the magmatic or metamorphic origin of some granites, it is still safe to say that most known intrusive igneous rocks are granitic in composition. We also know that most extrusive igneous rocks have basaltic compositions. The question arises: Could these two types of igneous rocks that differ so much in composition have formed from magma sources of the same composition, or are there a number of magma types beneath the earth's surface?

Support for the first hypothesis can be drawn from the fact that the principal silicate minerals crystallize at different temperatures from a rock melt, as specified in the Bowen reaction series (Fig. 15-8). Consequently there is the possibility of forming more than a single compositional rock type from one magma. To see how this so-called magmatic differentiation can take place, let us trace the possible paths in the crystallization of a magma of basaltic composition.

The first minerals to crystallize in the cooling magma are olivine and plagioclase. Olivine, $(Mg, Fe)_2SiO_4$, contains one part of (Mg, Fe) to one of silica. By contrast pyroxene has a ratio of one (Mg, Fe) to two silica, and hornblende and biotite have even smaller (Mg, Fe)-to-silica ratios. Because olivine is rich in magnesium and iron, once it begins to crystallize from the magma, the remaining liquid must become poorer in these elements and therefore enriched in silica. If the crystals and the liquid remain thoroughly mixed as crystallization proceeds to completion, the olivine will react with the remaining liquid to form pyroxene and possibly hornblende. When everything has solidified, the final mineral composition will reflect the composition of the original magma, which in this case was basaltic. On the other hand, if some process were to remove the early crystals from the remaining melt, it would be possible for rocks of diverse composition to form. For example, if the early olivine and plagioclase crystals were to settle to the bottom of the magma chamber before crystallization was completed, the material accumulating at the base would have a composition more mafic than basalt and the remaining liquid would be more silica-rich, or felsic.

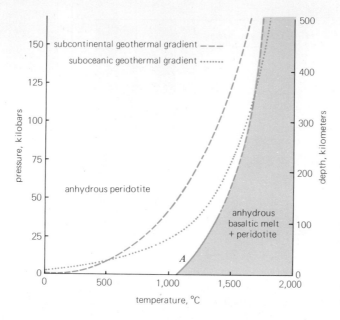

FIGURE 15-9
Calculated geothermal gradients (rate of increase of temperature with depth) under continents and ocean basins and the anhydrous melting of basalt. The melting of basalt has been experimentally investigated only in the PT region shown by the solid line. Since geothermal gradients have been measured directly only in the upper 4 to 7 kilometers of the earth, these curves are speculative. *From W. G. Ernst, "Earth Materials," Prentice-Hall, Inc., 1969.*

Lavas of diverse composition have been observed to erupt from the same volcanic vent, proving that magmatic differentiation does occur. But if it were the sole cause of variability in igneous rocks, we would expect to see a complete spectrum of rock types. Because most rocks are either granitic or basaltic, something besides magmatic differentiation must be involved.

This brings us to our second hypothesis—that of different magmas. Observations described in Sec. 15-1 suggest that perhaps granitic and basaltic magmas arise at different places within the earth. We noted, for instance, that seismic and other evidence points to a magma source of 60 or more kilometers depth for the basaltic lavas of the oceanic islands. This places the source of basaltic magma well within the earth's mantle. The mantle material is generally more mafic than basalt, but it is reasonable to expect basalt to form by the partial melting of such peridotite. We also found that granitic magmas appear to form by the melting or partial melting of the rocks in the roots of mountains; they thus develop within the crust of the earth rather than in its mantle. It appears that we are dealing with two magma types, one mafic and originating in the mantle and the second felsic and originating in the crust. Both principal magma types may differentiate to give rise to the multitude of special varieties of igneous rocks actually encountered in the field. The idea of magma formation by partial melting also helps explain why seismological investigations have not disclosed magma chambers beneath the earth's surface.

Is there any other evidence to support this picture of two magma sources? Figure 15-9 shows the results of some laboratory experiments on the melting temperature of mantle material (peridotite) at various pressures. Curve A

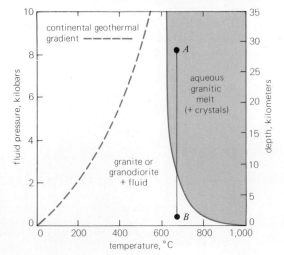

FIGURE 15-10
Calculated "average" continental geothermal gradient (somewhat speculative) and the minimum melting curve for granite in the presence of an aqueous fluid. *After W. G. Ernst, "Earth Materials," Prentice-Hall, Inc., 1969.*

displays the variation in the melting temperature of basalt with depth. Only the solid portion of the curve has been determined experimentally. The two other curves show the estimated geothermal gradients under the oceans and the continents. The graph supports the idea that basalt forms by the partial melting of peridotite at great depths within the mantle. Curve *A* is also consistent with the predominance of basalt in lava flows. Because the melting temperature increases with depth, basaltic liquid with a temperature of say 1500°C at a depth of 200 kilometers might still reach the surface in the liquid state even though it lost considerable heat to surrounding rocks during its upward rise because its surface freezing (or melting) temperature is only about 1050°C.

The melting behavior of granite is quite different. Figure 15-10 shows the minimum melting temperature for granite at various depths and an estimate of the continental geothermal gradient. The two curves almost intersect within the thickness of the crust. Where either the crust is thicker than 35 kilometers or the geothermal gradient is steeper than normal, granite magma would be expected to form by the partial melting of crustal materials.

The slope of the minimum melting curve for granite is opposite that of peridotite. Granitic melt formed at a depth of, say, 35 kilometers tends to rise because it is lighter than the solid rock. As it moves toward the surface, it begins to solidify (even if it does not lose heat to the surrounding rocks) because the minimum melting temperature increases with decreasing depth. This helps explain why most granites are intrusive: they cross the boundary between melt and solid before reaching the surface, as shown by line *AB* in Fig. 15-10. The experimental data shown on these graphs support our earlier conclusion that there are two distinct levels of magma generation. Basaltic magmas originate in the earth's mantle, and their melting temperature decreases as they move upward to regions of lower pressure. Consequently basaltic magmas frequently reach the surface without crystallizing, to pour out as lavas. Granite magmas originate in the lower crust. As they work their way upward, they become solidified because the melting temperature increases with the decrease in pressure.

15-3 KINDS OF METAMORPHIC ROCK

We turn our attention to the second rock-forming process of the depths—metamorphism, i.e., changes induced in rocks beneath the earth's surface by exposure to the elevated temperatures and pressures that exist there. The process of change is aided by pore water, and it involves the recrystallization of old minerals, the replacement of minerals, and sometimes granulation or crushing. Metamorphic changes take place without significant melting (Fig. 15-11). Any rock—igneous, sedimentary, or metamorphic—can be metamorphosed if it is exposed for a long time to a new set of temperature-pressure conditions. Most exposed metamorphic rocks, however, have been formed from sedimentary rocks (metasediments).

It is not difficult to see how conditions at the depths we are discussing can cause metamorphism. Certainly we would expect those rocks adjacent to large igneous intrusives to be strongly heated and thus metamorphosed, as indeed they usually are. This is called *contact metamorphism.* Some of the most extensive areas of exposed metamorphic rocks, however, exhibit no apparent relation to intrusives. If we remember that the temperature in the earth increases downward and that sedimentary and volcanic rocks are known to have reached thicknesses of tens of thousands of feet, the conditions for this *regional metamorphism* become clear. Regionally metamorphosed rocks must be formerly deep-seated rocks that have been exposed by erosion.

Since metamorphism is a response of rocks to elevated temperatures and pressures, and since subterranean temperatures are not uniform, we expect to find considerable variety in metamorphic rocks. Field investigations confirm this expectation. In metasediments there is a complete progression from rocks that are only slightly changed to those which are so intensely metamorphosed that they no longer resemble the originals in any way.

To illustrate this progressive metamorphism, let us follow the changes that have been observed in shale, the most abundant type of sedimentary rock. As originally deposited, a shale is a mudstone. It is soft, pliable, and wet as it accumulates on the sea floor. With burial beneath other sediments and the resulting compaction, the water content and porosity decrease, and in time the sediment becomes hardened, or lithified, into sedimentary rock. The lowest grade of metamorphic rock formed from a shale is slate, a rock which still retains some of the original structures of the parent rock, as illustrated in Fig. 15-12. Slate, however, also has distinctive properties of its own, such as the ability to break along parallel planes. Because of this property it has been widely used for blackboards, roofing, and other building purposes. If we looked at a thin section of a slate under a high-power microscope, we would see that the mineral grains, and

FIGURE 15-11
This gneiss, which has about the same composition as granite, cannot have been completely melted or the foliation would have been destroyed. *Geological Survey of Canada.*

FIGURE 15-12
Although the rocks in this photograph have developed a nearly vertical schistosity, the original sedimentary bedding is still clearly visible. *Maryland Geological Survey.*

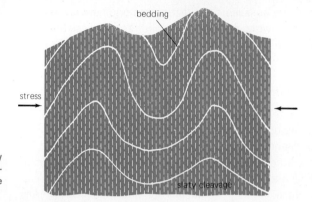

FIGURE 15-13
Slaty cleavage and schistosity form perpendicular to the compressive stresses that produce folding.

particularly grains of platy minerals like the micas, have an orientation that parallels the breakage planes. Since slate occurs mainly in regions where the layered sedimentary rocks have been folded, and since the slaty cleavage is always parallel to the planes of the folds (Fig. 15-13), we conclude that the metamorphism was influenced by the directed stresses that cause the folding.

The minerals in a slate are far too fine-grained to be resolved with the naked eye, but slates do grade into rocks in which the parallel mica grains are large enough to be visible. Such rocks are called *schists* (Fig. 6-13). A schist is a homogeneous foliated (parallel alignment of minerals) metamorphic rock. In a typical schist the sedimentary textures which were still preserved in slates are largely if not completely erased.

When metamorphism is even more intense because of higher temperatures, schists formed from shale may develop crystals of minerals like garnet, kyanite, or sillimanite. Under some conditions banded *gneisses* develop as a result of high-grade metamorphism of shale. The most common type of gneiss has about the same composition as granite.

Thus shale, which begins as soft mud, may be changed with increasing intensity of metamorphism, first to slate, then to schist, and finally to knotty schist, with garnets or other minerals, or to banded gneiss. These changes are caused by long exposure to differing conditions of temperature and pressure. They are the response of the chemical elements in the rock to these changing environmental

TABLE 15-1
Some typical minerals of shale and its metamorphic equivalents

Rock	*Typical minerals*
Shale	Abundant clay minerals (K,Al silicate hydrates) with quartz, SiO_2, and carbonate, $CaCO_3$
Slate	Abundant fine mica, $KAl_2AlSi_3O_{10}(OH)_2$, quartz, SiO_2, carbonate, $CaCO_3$
Schist	Abundant coarse mica, $KAl_2AlSi_3O_{10}(OH)_2$, quartz, SiO_2, wollastonite, $CaSiO_3$, garnet, $Ca_3Al_2(SiO_4)_3$
Gneiss	Abundant feldspar, $KAlSi_3O_8$, quartz, SiO_2, sillimanite, Al_2SiO_5, garnet, $Ca_3Al_2(SiO_4)_3$

conditions. Table 15-1 lists the principal minerals in shale and some of its metamorphic equivalents. It becomes clear from the table how so many different minerals can form from the same original chemical mixture. The various minerals like
clay, mica, feldspar, garnet, and others are all calcium, potassium, and aluminum
silicates. In fact, shale and granite have about the same chemical composition;
the chemical elements are simply combined into different minerals.

Other common sedimentary rocks also undergo metamorphism. An ideal
sandstone is composed almost solely of tiny rounded quartz grains. When such a
rock is metamorphosed, the quartz recrystallizes, destroying the porosity. The
resulting rock is called a *quartzite*. There is no development of new minerals
because the rock is composed only of quartz, SiO_2, and no new minerals can
form from Si and O_2. Similarly a pure limestone when stressed and heated will
change into a coarser-grained rock called *marble*, but the mineral composition
is still calcite, $CaCO_3$. Actually most sandstones and limestones contain some
impurities, so that there are reactions between minerals and consequent mineralogic changes during metamorphism. Such changes are usually not as pervasive
as those observed in shales because the chemical compositions are simpler.

So far we have focused on the metamorphic reactions displayed by sedimentary rocks. Igneous rocks also are metamorphosed. In particular, rocks like basaltic lavas are frequently changed into green chloritic schists or to amphibole-rich
rocks known as *amphibolites*. Basalt is a high-temperature rock to begin with,
and a change to chlorite schist actually is a type of retrogressive metamorphism.
Chlorite, a hydrated magnesium iron silicate, forms at lower temperatures than
the original magnesium iron silicates of basalt, which are anhydrous. The change
from basalt to chlorite schist thus involves the addition of chemically combined
water (hydration).

How do we know that a shale changes first to slate and then to various schists
and gneiss with increasing intensity of metamorphism? George Barrow, a Scottish geologist, was the first to map such progressive metamorphic changes on a
regional basis. Working in the Scottish Highlands, where many of the rocks are
metamorphosed sediments, he was able to trace progressive changes in what
were originally shaly rocks from lightly metamorphosed slate through various
mica schists by noting the first appearance of certain index minerals. He distinguished the following zones of metamorphism in order of increasing intensity:
chlorite zone, biotite zone, garnet zone, staurolite zone, kyanite zone, and
sillimanite zone. Figure 15-14 maps the metamorphic zones in the Scottish
Highlands. The boundaries between Barrow's zones were termed *isograds*
(equal grade).

15-4   HOW ARE THE CONDITIONS OF METAMORPHISM DETERMINED?

We noted in Chap. 4 that minerals are the chief indicators of past environments.
Barrow's index minerals are an example of how the presence of a given mineral
can be used as a guide to the conditions of temperature and pressure that ex-

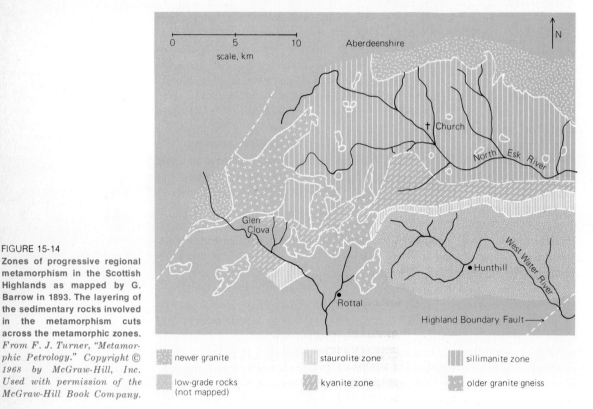

FIGURE 15-14
Zones of progressive regional metamorphism in the Scottish Highlands as mapped by G. Barrow in 1893. The layering of the sedimentary rocks involved in the metamorphism cuts across the metamorphic zones. *From F. J. Turner, "Metamorphic Petrology." Copyright © 1968 by McGraw-Hill, Inc. Used with permission of the McGraw-Hill Book Company.*

newer granite	staurolite zone	sillimanite zone
low-grade rocks (not mapped)	kyanite zone	older granite gneiss

isted when the mineral (and the rock in which the mineral is found) formed. The zones tell us nothing about the absolute conditions of temperature and pressure, but they are useful as a means of determining the relative intensity of metamorphism. Even as a measure of relative intensity, however, the zones cannot be used to compare the conditions of metamorphism on a worldwide basis. To see why let us look more closely at one of Barrow's index minerals, sillimanite, Al_2SiO_5. Since it appears last on the progressive scale of metamorphic intensity, one of the conditions necessary to form sillimanite must be high temperature. But this is not the only condition. For sillimanite to form in a rock the needed chemical elements must be there. Sillimanite gneiss, composed of feldspar, quartz, and sillimanite, forms from mica schist by the reaction

$$KAl_2AlSi_3O_{10}(OH)_2 + SiO_2 \rightarrow KAlSi_3O_8 + Al_2SiO_5 + H_2O$$

Muscovite   Quartz   Feldspar   Sillimanite   Water

If a quartz sandstone, SiO_2, or a limestone, $CaCO_3$, were exposed to the temperature and pressure conditions of the sillimanite zone, sillimanite could not form because the necessary alumina or silica (or both) are lacking. Therefore, the ab-

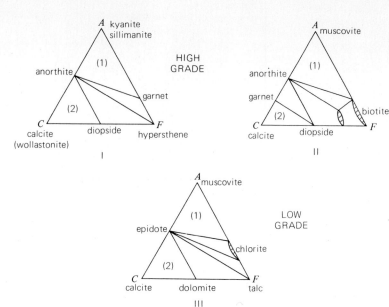

FIGURE 15-15
Equilibrium mineral assemblages for three metamorphic facies. (I) Granulite facies (*after Turner and Verhoogen*); **(II) amphibolite facies (***after Eskola***); (III) greenschist facies (***after Eskola***). Rock composition is given in terms of** $A = Al_2O_3 + Fe_2O_3$; $C = CaO$; $F = MgO + FeO$.

sence of sillimanite in a metamorphic rock does not indicate that the rock has never been exposed to the conditions of the sillimanite zone.

The concept of metamorphic zones provides information on the varying degree of metamorphism at one locality, but, being restricted to a fixed rock composition, it is not useful in comparing region with region or continent with continent. A way of overcoming this deficiency is to find out what minerals formed, say, in limestones under the metamorphic conditions that produced sillimanite in metashales. In Scotland, where Barrow did his pioneer work, the shales used to establish the metamorphic zones are interlayered with limestones. By observing the minerals developed in the limestones within the various metamorphic zones a correlation was established. For example, in the kyanite and sillimanite zones the recrystallized impure limestones contained the indicator minerals garnet and pyroxene.

Limestone and shale are not by any means the only rocks metamorphosed, nor are all limestones and shales exactly alike in chemical composition. Further work with rocks of many compositions finally led the Finnish geologist Pentti Eskola to the concept of *metamorphic facies*, or ideal metamorphic environments. In practice a metamorphic facies is recognized by mineral assemblages that coexist under particular conditions of temperature and pressure. Eskola named the facies after rocks types—greenschist facies, amphibolite facies, granulite facies, hornfels facies, and eclogite facies.

The facies concept applies to rocks of any composition. Figure 15-15 shows some of the metamorphic mineral assemblages for three of the common facies.

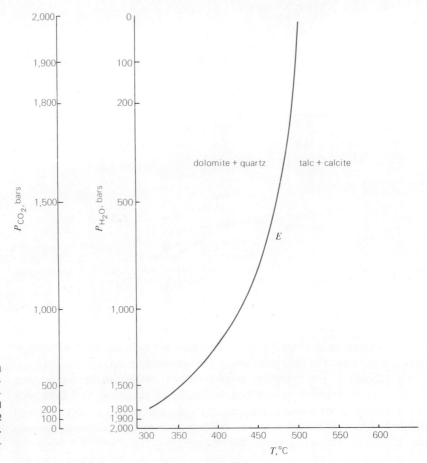

FIGURE 15-16
Experimentally determined curve for the breakdown of dolomite and quartz in the presence of carbon dioxide and water. Total pressure equals 2 kilobars (2,000 atmospheres). *After P. Metz and H. G. F. Winkler.*

The rocks are assumed to have sufficient SiO_2 to form silicates. We can see that a rock of composition 1 would contain muscovite, chlorite, and epidote in the greenschist facies (III), muscovite, anorthite, and biotite in the amphibolite facies (II), and kyanite, anorthite, and garnet in the granulite facies (I). By contrast a rock of composition 2 would be represented by calcite, dolomite, and epidote in the greenschist facies (III).

Even with the facies concept a significant problem remained. What are the actual physical conditions represented by each facies? For example, what temperature and pressure range produced the greenschist facies? This problem is still being attacked, but some significant inroads have been made. In contact metamorphic rocks a knowledge of the temperature of magma, coupled with information on the heat-conducting properties of rocks, makes it possible to infer temperatures at varying distances from the contact. The pressure and temperature of

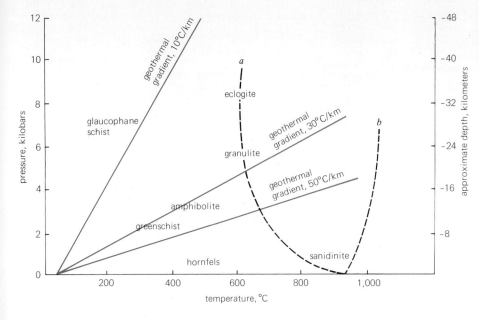

FIGURE 15-17
Approximate pressure-temperature fields of the principal metamorphic facies. Solid lines show the extreme measured values of the geothermal gradient (average is about 30°C per kilometer). Line *a* shows the temperature of incipient melting of granite where the aqueous pressure equals total pressure. Line *b* is the melting curve for granite where the aqueous pressure is 1 atmosphere. Granites are believed to form by partial melting in the region between these two curves. *Modified from K. B. Krauskopf, "Introduction to Geochemistry." Copyright © 1967 by McGraw-Hill, Inc. Used with permission of McGraw-Hill Book Company.*

regional metamorphism can be estimated where there is sufficient information about the thickness of rock eroded to expose the metamorphic rocks. Pressure is given by the weight of the overlying rock that was eroded off, and temperatures can be estimated by extrapolating from measured geothermal gradients.

Laboratory experiments are also useful as guides to the conditions of metamorphism. Dolostones are sometimes changed into the metamorphic rock marble, composed of calcite and talc. The reaction involved in this change must be between quartz impurities and dolomite:

$$3CaMg(CO_3)_2 + 4SiO_2 + H_2O \rightarrow Mg_3Si_4O_{10}(OH)_2 + 3CaCO_3 + 3CO_2$$

| Dolomite | Quartz | Water | Talc | Calcite | Carbon dioxide |

This reaction has been studied experimentally, with the results shown in Fig. 15-16. We can see from the graph that the temperature for the reaction depends upon the fluid pressure (P_{H_2O}), which is related to depth. The graph tells us that the change from dolomite and quartz to talc and calcite occurs in the temperature range from 300° to 500°C. Any information on the fluid pressure narrows down the possible temperature; e.g., if other evidence suggests a fluid pressure of 500 bars, a marble containing talc plus calcite must have formed at about 475°C.

Figure 15-17 is an estimate of the physical conditions encompassed by the principal metamorphic facies. Note the relation of the greenschist, amphibolite, and granulite facies to the projected geothermal gradient. The eclogite facies

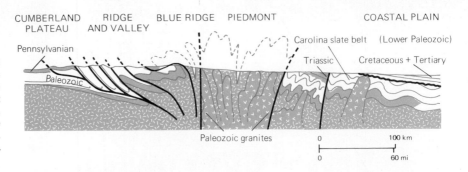

FIGURE 15-18
Diagrammatic section across the Appalachians from Kentucky to South Carolina. As one moves into the mountain belt from the Cumberland Plateau, the sedimentary rocks become highly folded and faulted. *Adapted from P. B. King, Bull. Am. Assoc. Pet. Geol., 1950.*

represents extra high pressures. A high-temperature–low-pressure facies like the hornfels facies would be developed near an igneous intrusion close to the earth's surface.

15-5 PLUTONIC ROCKS AND FOLD MOUNTAIN SYSTEMS

Igneous and metamorphic rocks that form deep within the crust of the earth are named after Pluto, god of the underworld. We have already noted that plutonic rocks are found chiefly in the cores of fold mountain systems. This association is not surprising because it is in the mountain regions that the crust attains its maximum thickness. Only there are the depths sufficiently great to produce the conditions necessary for the formation of high-grade metamorphic rocks and locally to even produce melting to form granites and other continental igneous rocks.

A closer look at fold mountains should provide additional information about the deep processes that produce plutonic rocks. In Chap. 14 we found that fold mountains are related to geosynclines, long troughs holding abnormally great thicknesses of sediment, which eventually were folded and uplifted to become mountains. We have seen that the idea of a relationship between mountain building and sediment accumulation originated with James Hall in New York in the mid-nineteenth century.

Let us examine Hall's Appalachian geosyncline more critically to see how such great crustal thicknesses develop. Figure 15-18 is a cross section through part of the Appalachian mountain system. Beginning in the western part of the region, we find relatively undeformed and unmetamorphosed sedimentary rocks of the Appalachian Plateau. As we move eastward, the sediments become folded and thrust-faulted and the degree of metamorphism increases. Plutonic rocks such as granite and gneiss, together with other metasedimentary rocks, are exposed in the central part of the chain.

Other geosynclinal mountains such as the Rockies or the Alps differ in detail from the Appalachians, but they generally possess the following common traits:

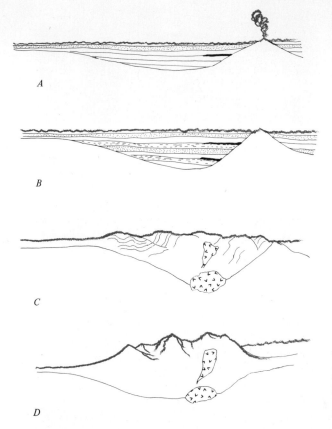

FIGURE 15-19
Inferred history of a geosynclinal mountain range. (A) Sinking basin of deposition. (B) Great thicknesses of sediment and lava accumulate. (C) Orogeny: root may be melted or mobilized. (D) Mountains rise isostatically as downward force diminishes.

1 Sediments are unusually thick.
2 The rocks in the more central portions are tightly folded and thrust-faulted.
3 Plutonic rocks are often found in the axial parts of the mountain ranges.
4 Volcanic lavas are frequently interbedded with the highly folded sediments.

Such observations suggest the following model for the formation of geosynclinal mountain chains. First, as stated in Chap. 14, there must be a sinking linear basin of sediment accumulation to account for the great sediment thicknesses. The sediments are too thick to have built up by subsidence alone (Sec. 14-5): some downward-acting force besides gravity must be in operation at this stage. The crustal shortening evidenced by folding and thrust faulting tells us that this downward force must be compressional.

When the downwarping and folding eventually stop, there is left a tremendous wedge of light sediment or metasediment surrounded by denser rocks. Without some continued force to hold it down this wedge of light rocks is destined to rise isostatically to form a mountainous region. This sequence of events in the history of a geosyncline is diagrammed in Fig. 15-19.

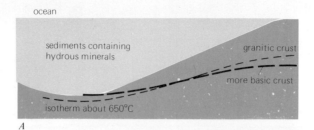

ocean

sediments containing
hydrous minerals

granitic crust

more basic crust

isotherm about 650°C

A

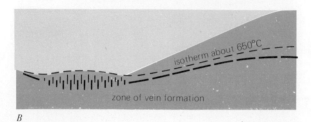

isotherm about 650°C

zone of vein formation

B

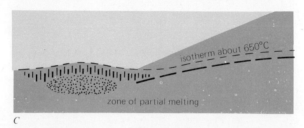

isotherm about 650°C

zone of partial melting

C

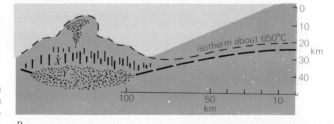

isotherm about 650°C

X
Y
Z

0
10
20 km
30
40

100   50   10
km

FIGURE 15-20
**Formation of a granite intrusion
in a geosyncline.** *From Brian
Bayly, "Introduction to Petrology," Prentice-Hall, Inc., 1968.*

D

The presence of the intrusive granites found in the central parts of fold mountain systems is also explained by this geosynclinal theory. Figure 15-10 showed
the minimum melting temperature for granite in the presence of an aqueous medium, i.e., a few percent of water, which notably lowers the melting point of granitic material. The sediments in a geosyncline contain at least this much pore
water. Moreover, since they are cool, initially their accumulation in the sinking
basin results in lowering the temperatures of the depths. The lines of equal temperature within the earth (isotherms) become depressed in the geosyncline.
Gradually, however, they return to normal, with the result that the material in the

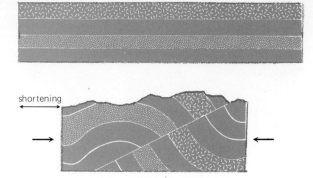

FIGURE 15-21
Folding and thrust faulting involve considerable crustal shortening. This led early earth scientists to speculate that fold mountains were related to a shrinking earth.

base of the geosyncline at a depth of tens of thousands of feet becomes hot enough to begin melting. The granitic magma thus generated, being lighter than solid rock, rises to intrude the rocks in the upper reaches of the sediment pile (Fig. 15-20).

A current relief map of North America shows the highest mountains to be in the cordillera along the western boundary of the continent. The Appalachian mountains are still recognizable as fold mountains though their profile has been subdued by lengthy erosion. Were there once other systems of fold mountains? The answer to this question is a definite *yes*. In many parts of the geologically old Precambrian shield of our continent there are belts of folded metasedimentary rocks intruded by granite that exhibit the characteristics of materials we would expect to find deep within younger geosynclinal mountains. The peaks of these Precambrian mountains have long since been eroded, but their structure shows what the inside of a fold mountain chain is like.

15-6 SPECULATIONS CONCERNING MOUNTAIN BUILDING

What earth forces cause the development of geosynclines and their associated plutonic and volcanic rocks? Subsidence due to sediment load is inadequate as a cause for these sinking basins, and it certainly cannot explain the volcanic rocks associated with geosynclines because they originate in the earth's mantle. Let us review some of the hypotheses proposed to account for the internal forces involved.

Even before James Hall recognized that the sediments of fold mountains are unusually thick, it was known that folding and mountains are related. We have seen that folded structures are formed by compressive stresses and that tensional stresses should create rifting and block faulting (Fig. 15-21). In the nineteenth century since very few large-scale tensional structures were known, it is not surprising that earth scientists were convinced that the earth was shrinking because shrinking and compression should go hand in hand. In a shrinking earth

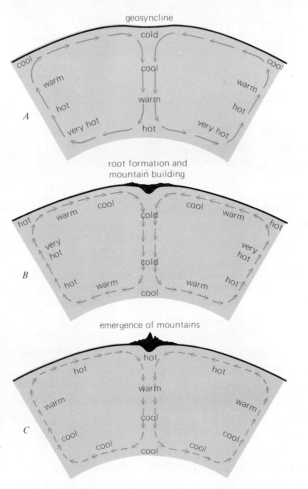

FIGURE 15-22
Sections through the earth's crust and mantle to illustrate the supposed correlation between successive stages of a geosynclinal cycle and those of a hypothetical system of convection currents. (*A*) Stage 1, slowly accelerating currents; (*B*) stage 2, rapid currents; (*C*) stage 3, waning currents. At their peak (stage 1) the converging system of convection cells supplied the downbuckling necessary for the accumulation of great sediment thicknesses. When the cells waned (stage 3), isostasy was reestablished by the slow uplift of the light sediment wedge into a mountain belt. *From A. Holmes, "Principles of Physical Geology," Copyright © 1965, The Ronald Press, New York.*

the outer, rigid shell of fixed dimension would crumple like the skin on a dried-out apple in order to adapt to the decreasing diameter. This idea of a shrinking earth was further strengthened by the view, then accepted, that the earth was cooling.

As knowledge of the earth increased, this simple explanation for mountain building fell into disrepute. In the first place, the analogy with a shrinking apple completely fails to account for the distribution of mountains in linear belts. Moreover, as we have seen, the discovery of radioactivity soon put an end to what had seemed obvious, namely the conclusion that the earth was cooling. It is true that the earth radiates heat into space, but heat is also generated in the rocks of the earth by radioactive decay. The total amount of heat generated within the earth by the decay of uranium, thorium, and radioactive potassium cannot be calculated because the exact abundances of these elements in the entire earth are unknown. However, they are known to be sufficiently large in the crust to suggest that the rate of heat generated by radioactive decay may well equal the rate of heat loss from the earth by radiation. In this case the earth would neither be heating nor cooling at the present time.

With the appearance of the geosynclinal theory of mountain origin pictured in Fig. 15-19 it became clear that the major problem connected with mountain building and plutonism is that of accounting for the downwarping of the geosyncline. A widely accepted theory attributes the downwarping to thermal convection in the solid mantle of the earth. This would seem completely unreasonable if we did not know that solids like glacial ice or deeply buried hot rocks are indeed capable of slow flowage under certain conditions. The basic assumptions of the convection theory are illustrated in Fig. 15-22. Because rocks are very poor conductors of heat, any excess heat generated, say, by radioactive decay in one part of the mantle might be expected to be transferred upward by a slow convective rise. As shown in the diagram, this would generate a system of convection cells. Where two such cells run into each other, conditions would be right for the accumulation of geosynclinal sediments. Since radioactive dating shows the history of a typical geosynclinal mountain system to encompass several hundred million years, there is no need for the convection currents to be fast. It appears that very slow currents in the mantle can account for the downbuckling of the crust along a geosynclinal axis and for the folding of the rocks that ultimately accumulate in the basin thus created.

If opposing convection cells do indeed occur within the earth to produce downwarping, there must also be places on earth where adjacent cells pull away from each other to create crustal tension. When the convection hypothesis was first introduced to explain geosynclines, large tensional earth structures equivalent to the fold mountains were unknown. Their absence was an argument against the convection-current hypothesis. With the discovery of the ocean ridge systems, which are undersea volcanic mountains of tensional origin, this difficulty in the hypothesis was overcome. In fact a diverging system of mantle convection cells helps to explain why the ocean ridges are active centers of volcanic activity. The rising currents bring heat upward from the earth's interior to account for the evolution of basaltic magmas in the upper mantle. Moreover, the pulling apart at the junction of the convection cells creates zones of weakness through which this magma rises, to spill out at the ridges as basaltic lava.

Even with the discovery of these major tensional structures, the simple convection model still failed to account for some important characteristics of major earth structures. One of the unexplained properties is the tendency of fold mountain chains to be shaped like intersecting arcs (Fig. 15-23). This arclike pattern is of particular interest because it suggests that extensive planar fractures are somehow involved for the reason that the intersection of an inclined plane and a sphere (the earth) results in a circular or arclike pattern.

So far we have been looking mainly at fold mountains. Volcanic mountains

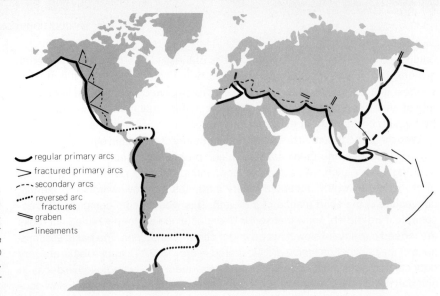

FIGURE 15-23
The major mountain belts (both volcanic and sedimentary) occur in arclike structures. *From J. A. Jacobs, R. D. Russell, and J. T. Wilson, "Physics and Geology." Copyright © 1959 by McGraw-Hill, Inc. Used with permission of Mc-Graw-Hill Book Company.*

regular primary arcs
fractured primary arcs
secondary arcs
reversed arc fractures
graben
lineaments

like the Aleutian chain also occur in arclike patterns. On the convex side of this volcanic-island arc is a deep ocean trench. Similar oceanic trenches are found along the Chilean coast, off Japan, and other places associated with arcs. Records of earthquake foci in the vicinity of such trenches suggests that the arclike structures are indeed related to extensive sloping fracture zones (Fig. 15-24). We recall that earthquakes are caused by the relative slippage between

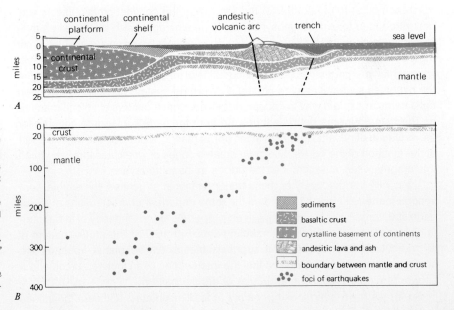

FIGURE 15-24
Cross section of an active island arc. The distribution of earthquake foci along a sloping plane is found in actual arcs, as in Japan or along the west coast of South America. (A) Vertical scale is five times the horizontal scale. (B) No vertical exaggeration. *From J. A. Jacobs, R. D. Russell, and J. T. Wilson, "Physics and Geology." Copyright © 1959 by McGraw-Hill, Inc. Used with permission of McGraw-Hill Book Company.*

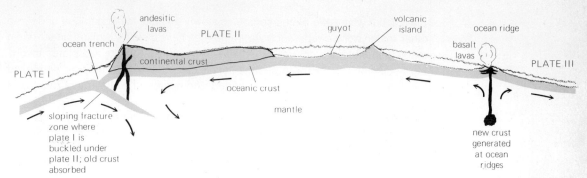

FIGURE 15-25
The new concept of plate tectonics explains many of the formerly puzzling observations of
earth activity. Earthquakes are
rarely experienced within the
plates. Major fracture zones
and their accompanying arcs
are found where one plate
buckles under another. The
lavas found at such junctions
are more silicic (andesite) than
those of the ocean ridges because they are derived in part
from crustal materials.

blocks of the earth. Their distribution as shown in the cross section certainly con-
firms the notion that inclined thrust planes must somehow be worked into any
final hypothesis for mountain building.

The modern view of the earth's internal activity adopted in the mid-1960s in-
corporates thrust planes, as illustrated in Fig. 15-25. According to this interpretation, the earth's outer layer consists of a few large rigid plates, which are set in
motion by convection currents in the underlying mantle. The plates move apart at
the ocean ridges, and the gaps thus created are filled with new basaltic crust by
the lavas extruded there. When two plates collide, major thrust planes develop
wherein one of the plates may be pushed deep into the earth's mantle to be absorbed. Along such lines of collision deep-sea trenches, volcanic-island arcs,
and geosynclines develop. Folding and crumpling accompany the thrusting, and
granitic magma evolves where crustal rocks are pulled into the deeps.

This theory of *plate tectonics*, as it is called, accounts for many of the known
characteristics of the earth's major structures. It explains why earthquakes and
active volcanoes are found only along certain active belts. It provides an explanation for the forces which produce deep ocean trenches, and it explains why
these depressions are arc-shaped. Because the activity associated with colliding plates extends well into the mantle, the association of mantle-derived basaltic lavas and geosynclinal rocks becomes clear. Furthermore, the theory helps to
explain why lavas of the continents are more felsic than their oceanic equivalents. Figure 15-25 shows that lavas associated with colliding plates are more
likely to be mixed with felsic continental crust than the lavas of the ocean ridges.

The relationship between the concept of plate tectonics and the earlier idea of
geosynclines and a geosynclinal cycle is still not completely resolved. In Fig.
15-25 there seems to be no place that completely fulfills James Hall's picture of a
geosyncline. Certainly the part labeled *ocean trench* is a geosyncline in the
sense that it is a sinking trough. However, ocean troughs like the Aleutian Trench
are very deep, and although they could conceivably fill with great thicknesses of
sediment, there would be no evidence of extensive shallow-water deposition. It
has been suggested that shallow sinking troughs and crumpled sedimentary

piles occur where two plates collide so slowly that one is not buckled under the other. Instead of a deep trench we would then have a slowly sinking linear basin marking the line of juncture of the plates. Alternatively, where two plates involving continental blocks with sedimentary rocks collide, they may be squeezed together to produce thick piles of folded and contorted sedimentary rocks and mountains.

The answers to some of these unsolved problems will not be long in coming. The theory of plate tectonics was conceived only during the 1960s. Before then geologists tended to think of the continents as stationary and had no real theory of global tectonics. Many investigators now are reexamining the earth's mountain regions in the light of the new hypothesis.

The idea that the earth's outer shell is composed of moving rigid plates does not depend solely upon its success in explaining the major earth structures. In the next chapter we shall examine some convincing direct evidence for plate tectonics. The theory is so new that many of its details remain to be worked out, but because it ties together so many observations, earth scientists appear to be well on the way to understanding the earth's internal activity.

SUMMARY

Most lavas are basaltic (mafic), whereas most intrusive igneous rocks are granitic (felsic). Although rocks of different composition can arise from a single magma by magmatic differentiation, the evidence indicates that basaltic and granitic magmas originate at different places within the earth. Basaltic lava comes from the earth's mantle, where it originates by the partial melting of peridotite. Granitic magmas form within the crust where it is unusually thick, as in the cores of mountain ranges.

Long exposure to the elevated temperatures and pressures encountered in the depths of the earth causes the chemical elements in rocks to recombine into new minerals that are stable under these conditions. Any rock may be thus metamorphosed. The degree of metamorphism depends mainly upon the temperature. Heat for metamorphism may be supplied by magma, but most frequently it is related to the geothermal gradient. This explains why most high-grade metamorphic rocks are associated with geosynclines; the crust is much thicker there.

The chief problem in explaining the development of geosynclines and their associated igneous intrusives, volcanic lavas, and metamorphic rocks is that of identifying the internal force that causes the downwarping. For several decades now, convection currents in the earth's mantle have been the favored cause of geosynclinal development. Since the mid-1960s it has become evident that mantle convection currents act to move a few large rigid plates that make up the earth's outer shell. Where these plates diverge, basaltic lavas well up to form new oceanic crust. Where two plates collide, the conditions are right for creating linear deeps, crustal thickening, and vulcanism.

QUESTIONS

1 How do mafic and felsic lavas differ in composition?
2 How do they differ in their physical properties?
3 Basaltic lavas supposedly originate by the partial melting of more mafic peridotite in the earth's upper mantle. Would you expect basaltic lava also to form by the partial melting of basaltic crust? Of granitic crust?
4 Contact metamorphism occurs where rocks are in contact with molten rock. Why is there little or no contact metamorphism in the rocks adjacent to lava flows?
5 How much higher are the temperature and pressure at 20 kilometers depth than at the surface? Assume an average thermal gradient of 1°C per 30 meters and an average rock density of 2.8 grams per cubic centimeter.
6 Refer to Fig. 15-15. What minerals would you expect to find in a rock

of composition II in the amphibolite facies? In the granulite facies?

7 What would be the product of high-grade metamorphism of a very pure quartz sandstone?

8 Why is the idea of a shrinking earth no longer acceptable?

9 It has been suggested that the deep sea trenches are a good place for industrial man to dump the vast quantities of solid waste generated by society. How would this solve the waste problem?

10 Refer to the cross section of Hawaii shown. If balance (isostasy) holds for this part of the crust, the column of lava A must have the same mass as the adjacent column of rock B. Calculate the depth to the base of the lava column on the basis of this assumption.

11 What could cause the development of a convection cell in the mantle?

12 List some of the observations that are explained by the theory of plate tectonics.

REFERENCES

Bayly, Brian: "Introduction to Petrology," Prentice-Hall, Inc., Englewood Cliffs, N.J., 1968.

Ernst, W. G.: "Earth Materials," Prentice-Hall, Inc., Englewood Cliffs, N.J., 1969.

Jacobs, J. A., R. D. Russell, and J. T. Wilson: "Physics and Geology," McGraw-Hill Book Company, New York, 1959.

Sumner, John S.: "Geophysics, Geologic Structures and Tectonics," Wm. C. Brown Company Publishers, Dubuque, Iowa, 1969.

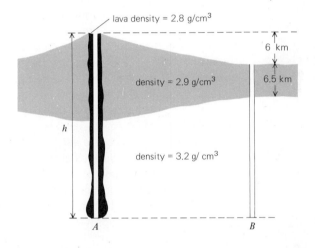

THE DRIFTING CONTINENTS

The newly evolved model of crustal evolution, in which the earth's outer shell is pictured as being made of a few moving, rigid plates, helps answer questions raised by various earth sciences. It is an exciting theory because it brings geology, geophysics, geochemistry, and oceanography closer together. Although there has always been cooperation between these earth sciences, they were never before united by a firm theory of crustal development.

Throughout most of the first half of this century, geologists focused on the problem of mapping and deciphering the record preserved in the rocks of the continents. During the same time geophysicists were busy measuring the earth's magnetic and gravitational fields and developing adequate models of the earth's interior. It is true that these and other earth investigations did not proceed completely independently of one another, but the trend was for each discipline to develop its own theories of the earth.

Direct evidence for the idea of spreading sea floors and moving crustal plates comes, in large part, from the ocean floors. Because the ocean basins are hidden under thousands of meters of water, scientists must use every avenue to gain information about this hidden crust. Through the combined attack of all of the earth sciences the ocean deeps were forced to give up their secrets. Continued exploration of the ocean basins is exposing a great segment of the earth that was previously hidden. Information obtained from these studies will help to sharpen our present views and perhaps modify them.

One of the problems that plate tectonics helps clarify is continental drifting. Were the continents ever joined together as shown in Fig. 16-1? That is one of the questions we hope to answer in this chapter.

16-1 DO THE CONTINENTS MOVE LIKE HUGE ICEBERGS?

The idea of continental drifting is not new. As world mapping unfolded the shapes of the continents several centuries ago, some men were intrigued by the fact that the Americas, if pushed eastward, almost fit into the coast of Africa and Europe. An obvious interpretation was that these continents had once been joined, but this view was not widely accepted because the idea of whole continents moving was too drastic.

Early in the present century a German meteorolgist, Alfred Wegener, placed the concept of continental drift on a firmer scientific basis. He used the fit between the continents as one argument for drift, but he mustered considerable other evidence for his theory. Wegener postulated that the continents were joined during the Paleozoic Era and that they began moving in the Mesozoic to their

Gemini XI photograph showing Africa (lower landmass) being separated from Arabia by a widening rupture along the Red Sea. *NASA.*

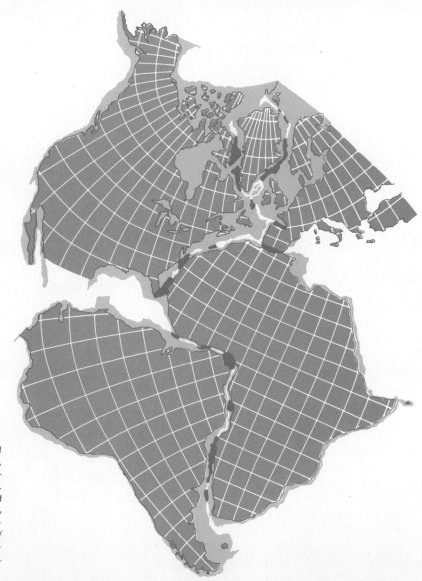

FIGURE 16-1
A statistically determined fit of North America, South America, Europe, and Africa at the 900-meter depth level in the ocean. Dark areas along the line of juncture represent overlap, light areas are gaps. *From Edward Bullard et al., The Fit of the Continents around the Atlantic, Phil. Trans. Roy. Soc. London, 1088, 1965.*

present positions. Believing that the Americas moved westward, he pointed to the Rocky Mountains and the Andes as evidence of crumpling along the advancing edge of these continents.

If the continents were indeed joined together during the Paleozoic, there should be a continuity of Paleozoic rock types between North America and Europe and between South America and Africa. Figure 16-2 shows Wegener's

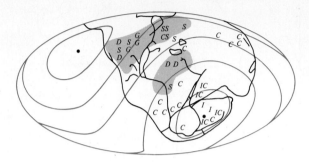

FIGURE 16-2
Wegener's evidence for the existence of a single continent in Permian time. D = desert sandstones; G = gypsum deposits; S = salt deposits; C = coal beds; I = glacial deposits. *After Köppen and Wegener.*

reconstruction of the climatic zones of the late Paleozoic as read from the rocks of that time. The belt of former hot, dry climates marked by desert sands and evaporite deposits of gypsum and salt lines up nicely from North America to Europe. The distribution of areas on the map where there is evidence for late Paleozoic glaciation suggests a single continental mass with the South Pole in Australia.

According to Wegener's reconstruction of continental positions, Greenland became separated from Europe some 50,000 to 100,000 years ago. This means that Greenland was moving westward at the rate of 10 to 20 meters per year. Measurements of longitude on Greenland made in the late nineteenth and early twentieth centuries apparently revealed a change of this order of magnitude, to lend strong support for Wegener's idea. We should note, however, that these measurements were later discredited and that modern longitude determinations do not reveal any measurable changes with time.

In spite of Wegener's strong geologic, paleoclimatologic, and paleontologic evidence for the existence of a single continent in the Paleozoic Era, his ideas were not widely accepted, particularly by American geologists. Part of the reason was that in addition to marshaling evidence for continental drift, Wegener also suggested a probable mechanism. He proposed that North and South America had moved westward from Europe and Africa as a result of tidal forces, and he pointed to the crumpled Andean and Rocky Mountain chains as evidence. When Sir Harold Jeffreys, a prominent English geophysicist, quantitatively evaluated the forces necessary to move these continental masses as distinct blocks, he found the minimum force required to be many orders of magnitude greater than the weak tidal forces invoked by Wegener.

Although Wegener's idea that continental drifting was caused by tidal forces seemed improbable, his evidence for drift was nonetheless intriguing and led some scientists to continue the search for additional evidence that might settle the question one way or another. Figure 16-3 is a reconstruction of late Paleozoic glaciation based on glacial deposits and erosional features. With the continents in their present positions the direction of movement of glaciers in South Africa, India, and South America during the Paleozoic Era makes little sense. When the

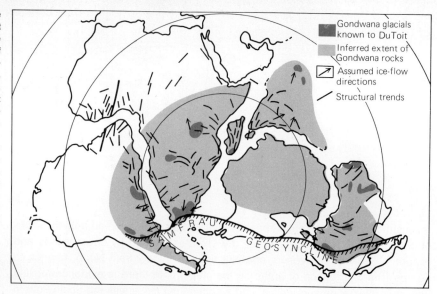

FIGURE 16-3

DuToit's reconstruction of the Gondwanaland supercontinent during late Paleozoic time based upon congruence of shorelines, matching of structural features in ancient rocks, and late Paleozoic mobile belts, here combined in what DuToit called the Samfrau geosyncline (from South America, Africa, and Australia). The glacial directions and structural trends appear far more intelligible when the continents are thus joined than when they are moved to their existing positions. *Adapted from A. L. Du-Toit, from R. H. Dott, Jr., and R. L. Batten, "Evolution of the Earth." Copyright © 1971 by McGraw-Hill, Inc. Used with permission of McGraw-Hill Book Company.*

Gondwana glacials known to DuToit

Inferred extent of Gondwana rocks

Assumed ice-flow directions

Structural trends

continents are brought together as they are on the map, the Paleozoic glacial deposits and directions become meaningful. This new evidence, however, also failed to convince the skeptics. The map is based on sparse data which are open to question and could be interpreted in other ways.

Still further evidence for drift was found in the distribution of certain fossils, especially those of small fernlike plants named *Glossopteris.* Fossils of the glossopteris flora are widespread in late Paleozoic rocks of the world. Remains are found in rocks of India, Australia, South Africa, South America, and Antarctica. The glossopteris flora is not found in rocks of the Northern Hemisphere. How did this plant spread throughout the Southern Hemisphere? Could it have done so with the present distribution of continents?

From the present distribution of living things we know that similar evolution requires intermixing. For instance, the present flora and fauna of Australia and Africa are different. We would expect them to be different because these continents are separated by a wide expanse of ocean, which precludes mixing between plant or animal groups on the two land masses. Because the glossopteris flora is found in the late Paleozoic rocks of both of these continents, we must assume that they were somehow connected during the Paleozoic Era. Of course there is the remote possibility that plant spores could have traveled over the intervening oceans, but the fact that glossopteris is restricted to the Southern Hemisphere speaks against this possibility. If the seed of glossopteris was transported over the great distances separating India, Africa, Australia, and South America, why was it not also implanted in the northern continents? Certainly it seems that the most logical solution to the glossopteris puzzle is to assume that the land masses containing the glossopteris rocks must once have been joined.

Other paleontologic evidence also speaks for the past junction of continents.

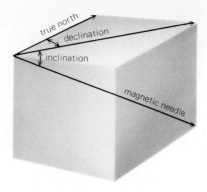

FIGURE 16-4
Magnetic declination and inclination.

Fossils of the early Mesozoic reptile *Mesosaurus* are found in rocks of Africa and Brazil. Again we must ask how this land dweller or its ancestors got from one continent to the other. It could perhaps have migrated over land bridges, but the fact that similar fossils are not found elsewhere makes this interpretation doubtful. However, the absence of fossils along probable migration routes could be an accident of preservation, and most geologists were willing to accept such an interpretation until recently.

16-2 THE EARTH'S MAGNETIC FIELD

Even as recently as 1950 the question of continental drift was not definitively settled. Most American earth scientists believed then that the continental positions were fixed and that the evidence in favor of drift could be explained in other ways. The evidence for continental movement was too strong to be ignored completely, however, and the search for new data continued.

Thus far we have been looking at evidence on the continents that suggests that they were once joined. Is there another way to tell whether the continents have moved? In 1925, R. Chevallier of France demonstrated that the magnetic direction of lava flows on Mt. Etna are parallel to the earth's magnetic field measured at the same locality. If rocks contain a record of the magnetic directions existing at the time and the place where they were formed, it should be possible to reconstruct past positions of the earth's poles from a study of magnetic directions in rocks.

Most paleomagnetic work has been done during the past two decades. Before we review the results of this work it would be wise to look at the basic principles upon which the work is founded. A magnetized needle weighted to swing horizontally in a compass points toward the earth's north magnetic pole in this hemisphere. If the magnetized needle were suspended so that it could swing freely both sideways and up and down, it would orient itself parallel to the earth's magnetic field. As shown by Fig. 16-4, the angle between true north and magnetic

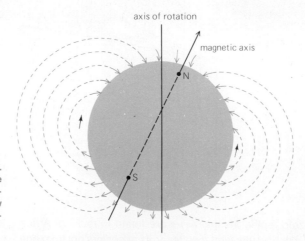

FIGURE 16-5
The earth's magnetic field.
Solid lines with arrows show the
orientation of the magnetic needle at various places; the arrow
marks the direction of the north-
seeking pole of the needle.

north is known as the *declination* at a place, and the angle the needle makes with the horizontal is the magnetic *inclination*. By noting the attitude of such free-swinging magnetized needles at many points on earth, the simple idealized dipole model of the earth's magnetic field shown in Fig. 16-5 was developed.

The earth's magnetic field is not static. Not only are short-term changes in field intensity observed, but the declination also changes at the rate of about 1 second of arc per year. Moreover, the present magnetic poles are many miles from the geographic poles of the earth. Is it of any use, therefore, to attempt to determine the pole positions of the distant past from magnetic directions preserved in rocks?

Figure 16-6 shows the position of the earth's north magnetic pole during the recent geologic past. These measurements indicate that the magnetic and the axial poles of the earth do indeed coincide on the average over periods of 1,000 to 2,000 years. Coincidence between the geographic and magnetic poles is also predicted by the accepted dynamo theory of the earth's magnetism, which attributes the magnetic field to relative movements between the earth's partially fluid metallic core and its stony mantle. If this is the cause of the magnetic field, we can expect the axis of rotation and the magnetic axis to coincide at least approximately.

The earth's present magnetic poles can be located by recording compass directions at many places over the globe. Just as iron filings form converging lines toward the poles of a bar magnet, so too would the compass directions tend to merge toward the earth's magnetic poles. Our problem is to find a way of locating the position of the earth's magnetic poles in the past. To solve this question we must ask why the magnetic directions of modern lava flows are parallel to the earth's field at the place where the flow formed.

Most, if not all, igneous rocks, including lava flows, contain small quantities of

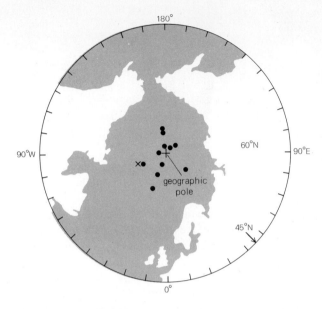

FIGURE 16-6
The position of the north magnetic pole during the past 7,000 years as indicated by the remnant magnetism of various materials. Although the magnetic pole (X) is now at a considerable distance from the geographic pole, paleomagnetic studies indicate that the two poles do coincide when the position of the magnetic pole is averaged over periods of a few thousand years. *After E. Irving, "Paleomagnetism and Its Application to Geological and Geophysical Problems," John Wiley & Sons, Inc., 1964.*

the ferromagnetic mineral magnetite. A grain of magnetite suspended freely behaves like a compass needle. The fact that the modern lava flows at Mt. Etna have magnetic directions parallel to those of the earth's magnetic field means that the polarities of the magnetite grains in the lava must be aligned parallel to the earth's field. How did they develop this parallelism? Experiments have shown that a magnetic material loses its magnetic properties at a certain temperature known as its *Curie point*. The Curie point for magnetite is 578°C. When it is heated above this temperature, it loses its magnetic properties, and when it cools to below the Curie point, it becomes magnetic again. Since lavas crystallize at a temperature higher than 578°C, the magnetite grains within a lava must acquire their magnetic direction during the cooling stage. We also know from experiments that a magnetic substance cooled below its Curie temperature in a magnetic field adopts the magnetic directions of that field. Thus the magnetite grains in a lava would be expected to have the orientation of the earth's magnetic field at the place where the lava formed.

Herein lies a way of reconstructing past directions of the earth's magnetic field. The magnetic direction as determined by the polarities of magnetite grains in a 100-million-year-old lava flow should be parallel to the direction of the earth's field at that time. Likewise, the tiny magnetite grains in sandstones are also possible indicators of paleomagnetism. As such grains fall through water to become incorporated in a sandstone, we would expect them to align themselves in the direction of the earth's magnetic field.

With the instruments now available it is not difficult to determine the magnetic direction of a rock, but such measurements must be treated with caution. Many

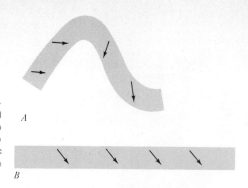

FIGURE 16-7
Measurements of paleomagnetism in specimens of folded rocks (A) must first be rotated to the prefolding position (B) to indicate the earth's magnetic field at the time the rocks were formed.

FIGURE 16-8
(A) Because the pebbles and boulders in gravel are too heavy to be affected by the earth's magnetic field during deposition, the magnetic directions of individual pebbles are randomly distributed. (B) Where the magnetic directions of pebbles in ancient conglomerates exhibit parallel orientations, it and the surrounding rocks must have been heated above the Curie temperature for magnetite after deposition.

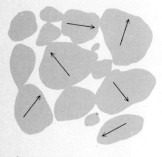

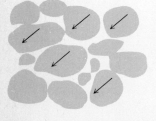

old rocks have been folded, and their present magnetic directions are meaningless until they are corrected for the folding, as illustrated in Fig. 16-7. Investigators of paleomagnetism must also be alert to the possibility that the rocks under study may have been heated above their Curie temperature and remagnetized since the time of their formation. One test for this is to study magnetic directions in conglomerates, as shown in Fig. 16-8. In modern conglomerates the magnetic directions of the individual pebbles are erratic. This is just what one would expect of a rock made up of many pebbles and cobbles that had acquired their magnetic characteristics in the source area. If a number of randomly chosen pebbles in a geologically old conglomerate all showed the same magnetic direction, there would be no question that this magnetism must have been acquired after the rock was laid down. Paleomagnetic measurements in such an area would not tell us where the earth's magnetic poles were when the rock formed.

16-3 PALEOMAGNETIC AND PALEOCLIMATOLOGIC DATA

Now that we have examined the basis of paleomagnetism, let us look at some of the results. The inferred positions of the earth's north magnetic pole, based upon many measurements of magnetic direction in rocks of known age, are shown in Fig. 16-9. From the map it is clear that the apparent position of the magnetic pole has shifted significantly with time. This shift can be explained either by assuming that the magnetic pole itself has moved or that the pole has remained more or less stationary while the continents have shifted. We noted earlier that the earth's magnetic field is believed to be due to differential motion between its partially fluid core and solid mantle. If so, the magnetic poles should correspond, on the average, with the axial poles; and they have during the recent geologic past. Thus, if we interpret Fig. 16-9 to mean an actual motion of the magnetic pole, we must also assume motion of the earth's axial pole. This is a highly unlikely if not impossible solution. The earth is a giant gyroscope, and it would take a catastrophic force to produce such changes in the direction of its spin axis.

It is far more reasonable to interpret the paleomagnetic data to mean that the shell of the earth has moved relative to the axis. This does not necessarily imply continental drift in the sense proposed by Wegener, because the entire crustal layer could shift without any relative displacement of the continents. The term

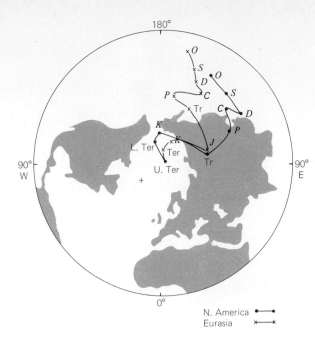

FIGURE 16-9
Polar-wandering paths for Europe and North America. The paths for the two continents are roughly parallel from the Ordovician (*O*) to the Permian (*P*), where they begin to converge. This is further evidence that these continents were joined, becoming separated during the Mesozoic Era. *From D. W. Strangway, "History of the Earth's Magnetic Field." Copyright © 1970 by McGraw-Hill, Inc. Used with permission of McGraw-Hill Book Company.*

N. America ●——●
Eurasia ×——×

polar wandering is used to describe the worldwide shifting of the earth's entire outer shell, whereas *continental drift* refers to relative motion between continents.

If we reexamine Fig. 16-9 for possible evidence of a continental drift, we find that although the magnetic pole as located from paleomagnetic studies in Eurasia is in about the same position as that determined from North American studies for the Tertiary (*Ter*), the poles determined for the Permian in the two regions are several thousand kilometers apart. From the Permian (*P*) to the Ordovician (*O*) the polar wandering paths for Eurasia and North America are roughly parallel. We would, of course, expect the poles for any two regions to coincide for a given time period. The fact that the polar wandering paths diverge from the Tertiary to the Permian suggests that this was indeed a time of continental separation. The parallelism of the paths during the Paleozoic Era (Ordovician through Permian) supports the conclusion that the continents were then joined into one supercontinent which split apart about 225 million years ago, at the end of the Paleozoic Era.

We have already seen how Wegener used climatic indicators in rocks as evidence that North and South America were once joined to Europe and Africa. Much new information on the distribution of rock types has been acquired since Wegener's time. The mapping of geologically ancient climatic zones from evidence preserved in the rocks is called *paleoclimatology*. Let us see how the study of paleoclimates has contributed toward the question of past pole positions.

Existing coral reefs are known to be restricted to the belt between 30°N and 30°S latitude. Consequently, a map showing all coral reefs today could be used

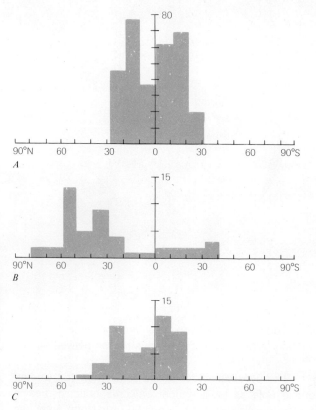

FIGURE 16-10
The distribution of coral reefs as a function of latitude: (A) present distribution; (B) distribution of fossil reefs; (C) distribution of fossil reefs when they are restored to their original latitudes using continental positions as determined from paleomagnetic measurements. *From Edward Irving, "Paleomagnetism," John Wiley & Sons, Inc., 1964.*

to define the equator roughly by drawing a line through the center of the reef belt. Since the earth's axial poles are on a line perpendicular to the equator, by locating the equator we would also have fixed the poles. This method should work equally well for any past time period provided a sufficient number of fossil reefs are preserved in the rocks of that period. Thus from the distribution of ancient reefs, laterites, coral beds, or other climate-sensitive deposits geologists should be able to reconstruct the approximate past positions of the earth's equator and its axial poles.

Because much of the sedimentary record is either covered by other sedimentary rocks or has been eroded away, it has been difficult to map the climates of the past in sufficient detail to locate past pole positions with confidence. The rather sparse data do suggest, however, that the apparent position of the equator has shifted with time. While there are insufficient data to allow a comparison of the paleomagnetic and paleoclimatologic poles period for period, there is a strong suggestion that data from the two techniques support each other. Figure 16-10 graphs the distribution of existing and fossil coral reefs with latitude. Had there been no polar wandering or continental drifting, these graphs would be alike. When the fossil reefs are assigned latitudes based on pole positions at the time of their formation determined by paleomagnetic studies, we find a pattern much closer to that existing today. Because we expect the reefs to exhibit roughly the same latitudinal distribution in the past as now, their corrected distribution lends strong support to the magnetic data.

The paleomagnetic and paleoclimatologic data acquired during the 1950s left little doubt that the earth's poles had wandered in time. The discovery that former pole positions on different continents were not the same led many earth scientists of the early 1960s to view continental drift with more favor than they had for several decades. The problem of a drift mechanism, however, remained troublesome, and the data were not conclusive enough to overcome this difficulty completely.

16-4 MAGNETIC REVERSALS

Some of the early students of rock magnetism noted that the magnetic polarity in certain rocks was completely reversed. In a sequence of relatively closely spaced samples, where the magnetic directions should be roughly parallel, some were found to be turned by 180°. If rocks do indeed acquire the magnetic direction of the earth's field at the time and place where they form, such reversals must mean that the earth's magnetic poles have switched positions in the past. The first scientists to discover these reversals were loath to accept so drastic an explanation and sought other possible causes.

At first it seemed that rock specimens with reversed magnetic polarity were erratically distributed and that the reversals might be the result of local effects. Magnetic studies conducted on a series of lava flows in the 1950s showed that entire flows were either normal or reversed in magnetic polarity. A decade later, investigations of accurately dated lava flows from many parts of the world revealed the magnetic reversals to be restricted not only to certain lava flows but to flows formed during specific periods of time.

Figure 16-11 shows the results of magnetic measurements made on specimens of lava flows dated by the potassium-argon method. From the diagram we can see, for example, that all flows younger than 0.7 million years exhibit normal polarity, regardless of whether they are in the continental United States, Hawaii, Europe, or Africa. On the other hand, all flows ranging in age from about 1 to 2 million years exhibit reversed polarity, regardless of where they occur. It seems clear, therefore, that the magnetic reversals cannot be attributed to local effects. Since the flows of a given period the world over show the same polarity, there remains no doubt that the measured reversals must indeed be the result of complete reversals of the earth's magnetic poles.

Figure 16-11 thus becomes a time scale for the reversals in polarity of the earth's magnetic field. Epochs of normal and reversed polarity have been given

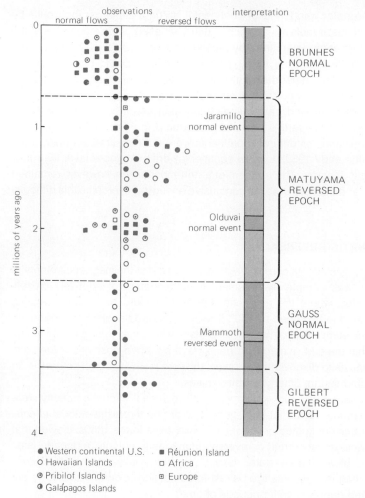

names such as Brunhes normal and Matuyama reversed. Short reversals within a normal or reversed epoch have been termed events like the Jaramillo and Olduvai events of the Matuyama epoch.

If the magnetic reversals found in the lava flows truly reflect reversals in polarity of the earth's magnetic field, similar reversals should occur in other rocks. We found in Chap. 9 that sedimentation in the deep sea proceeds very slowly. Our expectation, therefore, is that the record of the past 3 to 4 million years of sedimentation in the deep sea should be contained in a few meters of sediment. In 1966 N. D. Opdyke and his associates discovered a magnetic-reversal pattern in the very feeble magnetism of some deep-sea sediments. Figure 16-12 illustrates the relationship between depth and magnetic direction in one of

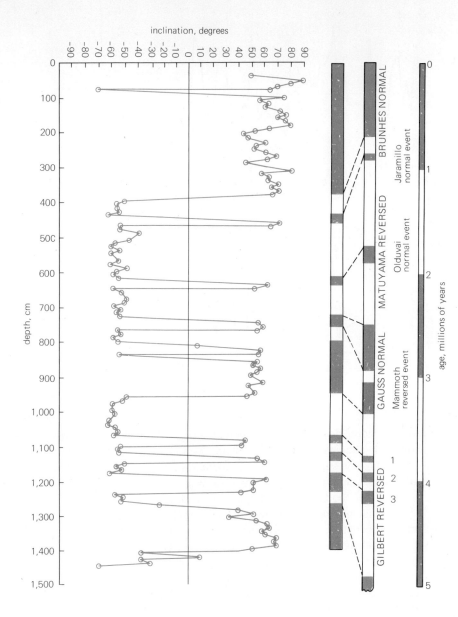

inclination, degrees

BRUNHES NORMAL

Jaramillo normal event

MATUYAMA REVERSED

Olduvai normal event

GAUSS NORMAL

Mammoth reversed event

age, millions of years

GILBERT REVERSED

depth, cm

FIGURE 16-12
Magnetic stratigraphy of a deep-sea core from the Western Pacific. The Brunhes normal, Matuyama reversed, Gauss normal, and Gilbert reversed periods of the magnetic-reversal time scale are clearly reflected in the core. *From N. D. Opdyke, fig. 7, p. 79, in R. A. Phinney (ed.), "The History of the Earth's Crust." Copyright © 1968 by Princeton University Press. Used with permission of Princeton University Press.*

their deep-sea cores from the western Pacific. The first bar graph in the diagram shows the periods of normal and reversed magnetic polarity found in the core, and we can see that this indeed matches the magnetic-reversal time scale derived from dated lava flows, displayed in the second bar graph.

Recent work on deep-sea cores has contributed to the refinement and extension of the magnetic-reversal time scale and to our knowledge of the time in-

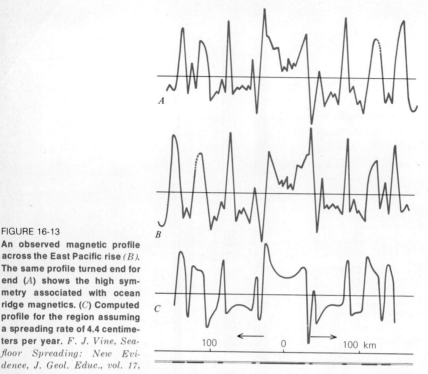

FIGURE 16-13

An observed magnetic profile across the East Pacific rise (*B*). **The same profile turned end for end** (*A*) **shows the high symmetry associated with ocean ridge magnetics.** (*C*) **Computed profile for the region assuming a spreading rate of 4.4 centimeters per year.** *F. J. Vine, Sea-floor Spreading: New Evidence, J. Geol. Educ., vol. 17, 1969.*

volved in a magnetic reversal. Considering the depth dimension of Fig. 16-12 as approximately equivalent to time, the sharp swings from periods of positive to negative inclination suggest that the magnetic reversals took place suddenly. It appears that the time involved in a reversal was of the order of 1,000 to 2,000 years, which is indeed sudden in a geologic scale of time.

The recognition of magnetic reversals in deep-sea sediments had some important side benefits for oceanographers. From Fig. 16-12 we can determine that about 950 centimeters of sediment accumulated since the beginning of the Gauss normal magnetic epoch. The time scale shows that the Gauss normal began about 3.3 million years ago. From these values we can calculate the average net sedimentation rate at the place where the core was taken. The rate of sedimentation here turns out to be

$$\frac{950 \text{ cm}}{3,300,000 \text{ y}} = 0.0003 \text{ cm/y}$$

Another type of magnetic measurement, when related to the magnetic-reversal time scale, provides the most startling information of all. Before we consider it, however, let us briefly review the picture of deep-sea topography presented in Chap. 9. The ocean ridges discovered during the 1950s are the most extensive structural features on the earth. Most of the earthquakes that occur in the ocean basins are restricted to the ridge systems and their associated cross faults. Volcanic activity in the oceans also is largely isolated along the ridges.

Measurements of magnetic intensity made over parts of the ridge system in the early 1960s disclosed an interesting pattern of magnetic anomalies. Figure 16-13 is a magnetic profile across the east Pacific rise. The profile is marked by a series of peaks and valleys in magnetic intensity representing values higher than normal (positive anomaly) and lower than expected (negative anomaly). The positive and negative anomalies are clearly symmetrically distributed with respect to the ridge axis, as we can see by comparing the measured and reversed profiles of Fig. 16-13. We saw in Fig. 1-6 the pattern produced along a section of the mid-Atlantic ridge when the positive (dark) and negative (light) anomalies from many such magnetic profiles are joined together. Again, a high degree of bilateral symmetry is evident.

When first discovered, this parallelism of magnetic anomalies along the ocean ridge systems was puzzling, but the explanation was not long in coming. In 1963, F. J. Vine and D. H. Matthews suggested that the parallel magnetic bands may be the result of a gradual spreading of the sea floor outward from the ridge. Lavas formed at the ridge would adopt the polarity of the earth's field at the time that they cooled. As the sea floor spread (Fig. 16-14), the normal and reversed magnetic periods would be recorded in the lavas like a giant tape recorder. Lavas which crystallized at the ridge axis when the earth's magnetic field was normal would have normal polarity, whereas those formed during a reversed period would exhibit reversed polarity.

Vine and Matthews proposed the idea of sea-floor spreading before the magnetic-reversal time scale had been developed. When the reversal time scale was established, it became evident that the spacings of the positive and negative magnetic anomalies along the ocean ridges displayed the same basic pattern as the reversal time scale. Not only did the magnetic anomalies paralleling the ocean ridge systems show that the ocean basins are spreading apart; they also provided a means of measuring the spreading rates.

To see how, study Fig. 16-15, which contains a magnetic profile across the East Pacific rise measured by the U.S.N.S. *Eltanin* in 1965. The observed magnetic profile is also shown turned end for end in the reversed position. By comparing the measured and reversed profiles, we can see the striking symmetry of the magnetic pattern that exists over the 400 kilometers on either side of the ridge axis. The bar graph at the bottom of the profiles has the peaks (normal magnetics) shaded in color and the troughs (reversed magnetics) in white. It is not difficult to see the similarity between this bar graph and the magnetic-reversal time scale shown in the lower part of the figure. We can see, for example,

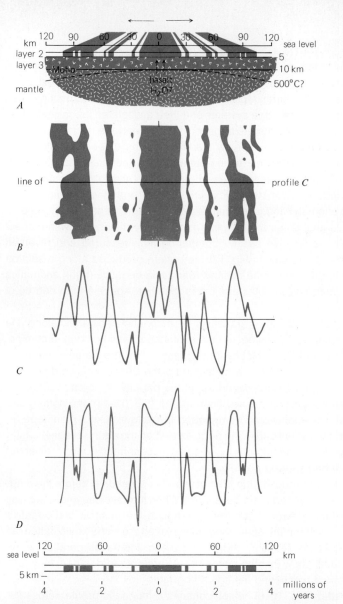

FIGURE 16-14

(*A*) **Schematic representation of the crustal model that accounts for the ocean ridge magnetics as applied to the Juan de Fuca Ridge, southwest of Vancouver Island. Shaded layer is normally magnetized; unshaded reversely magnetized.** (*B*) **Part of summary map of magnetic anomalies actually recorded over the ridge. Dark areas represent positive anomalies; light areas negative anomalies.** (*C*) **A single profile along the line indicated in** (*B*). (*D*) **Computed profile assuming the model in** (*A*) **and the reversal time scale of Fig. 16-11.** *From F. J. Vine, fig. 1, p. 75, in R. A. Phinney (ed.), "The History of the Earth's Crust." Copyright © 1968 by Princeton University Press. Used with permission of Princeton University Press.*

that the Mammoth reversed event in the Gauss normal epoch, which occurred about 3 million years ago, is recorded in the lavas that are now about 140 kilometers from the ridge axis. The spreading rate on a single side must, therefore, be about

$$\frac{140 \times 10^5 \text{ cm}}{3 \times 10^6 \text{ y}} = 4.7 \text{ cm/y}$$

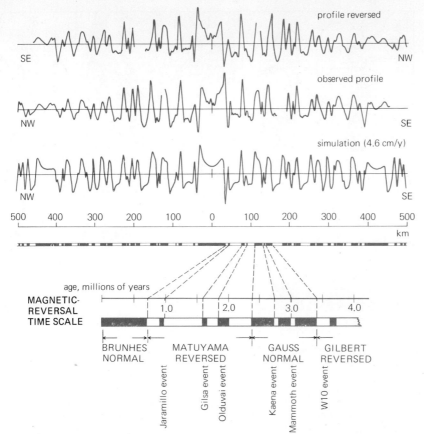

FIGURE 16-15
A magnetic profile across the East Pacific rise, made on U.S.N.S. *Eltanin*, matched with the magnetic-reversal time scale. See text for explanation.

The total spreading rate at the ridge would be twice this, or 9.4 centimeters per year. A better but more complicated way of determining average spreading rates is to compute the magnetic profile across an ocean ridge system from the magnetic-reversal time scale at various spreading rates. The graph of Fig. 16-15 labeled *simulation* was calculated in this way by accepting the spreading model and assuming a spreading rate of 4.6 centimeters per year. Its match with the observed magnetic profile is truly remarkable.

Little question remains in the minds of most earth scientists that the sea floors are spreading. Measured rates of spreading vary from about 2 centimeters per year for the Atlantic to 12 or more centimeters per year for parts of the Pacific. Figure 16-16 illustrates the amount of new oceanic crust created by sea-floor spreading during the past 65 million years (within the Cenozoic) as determined from measured spreading rates. From the diagram it becomes clear that the entire Atlantic basin, for example, must have formed within the past 150 million years. Here then is another way of testing this idea. If spreading had actually oc-

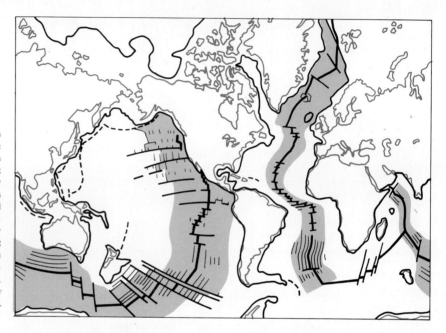

FIGURE 16-16

Provisional delineation of areas of continental and oceanic crust. Within the ocean basins trenches are indicated by thick dashed lines, ridge crests by thick solid lines, and fractures (transverse to ridge crests) and correlatable magnetic anomalies (parallel to ridge crests) by thin solid lines. Oceanic crust believed to have formed within the last 65 million years (Cenozoic) is shaded. *From F. J. Vine, Sea-floor Spreading: New Evidence, J. Geol. Educ., vol. 17, 1969.*

curred as indicated, we would not expect to find any geologically old rocks in the ocean basins. Many rocks from oceanic islands and many specimens dredged from the sea floor have been dated by radiometric methods. So far, the oldest rocks found are only about 200 million years old, which strongly supports the idea that the oceanic crust is continually renewed. The oceans are truly unique in that their water is many times older than the floor upon which it rests.

16-5 FURTHER EVIDENCE FOR PLATE TECTONICS

In Chap. 5 we discussed the instruments and methods used to locate and monitor earthquakes. Records of seismic activity have been kept for many decades, and it is well known that earthquakes are not randomly distributed but occur in a few narrow linear belts. The major seismic zones on earth are the circum-Pacific belt, which follows a series of ocean trenches and young fold mountain ranges, the Alpine-Himalayan fold mountain belt, and the belt along the ocean ridge systems. Most earthquakes occur in the circum-Pacific belt.

The mere regional distribution of earthquakes does not tell the entire story. Figure 16-17 is a summary map of the earth's seismicity on which earthquakes of varying focal depth are plotted separately. The earthquakes associated with the ocean ridge systems are all shallow quakes. Deep-focus earthquakes are restricted to parts of the circum-Pacific belt.

The localization of seismic activity to distinct narrow belts demands an expla-

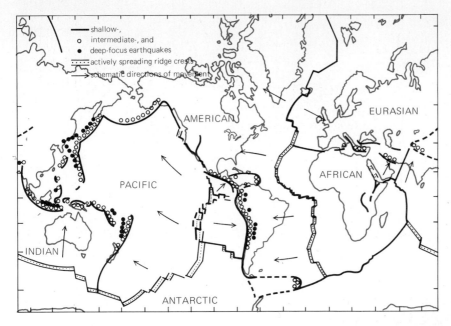

FIGURE 16-17
Summary of the seismicity of the earth and hence the extent of crustal plates bounded by active ridge crests, faults, trench systems, and zones of compression. The six major crustal blocks assumed by Le Pichon are named. Spreading rates at ridge crests are indicated schematically and vary from 1 centimeter per year in the vicinity of Iceland to 6 centimeters per year in the equatorial Pacific Ocean. *After Gutenberg and Richter, from F. J. Vine, Proc. Am. Phil. Soc., vol. 112, no. 5, 1968.*

nation. Why are such great areas of the earth essentially earthquake-free? What causes the localization of earthquakes in a few narrow belts? The only logical answer to these questions is the model for the earth's outer sphere (Chap. 15) that assumes the existence of several large stable plates, as outlined on Fig. 16-17. Along the ocean ridge systems these plates move apart as new oceanic crust is generated at the axes of the ridges. Where two plates come together, e.g., at the west coast of South America, we find much earthquake activity of the shallow-, intermediate-, and deep-focus types. The deepest earthquakes occur the farthest inland, indicating a model like that illustrated in Fig. 16-18, where one plate is being forced down into the mantle. While new crustal material is generated along the ocean ridges causing a spreading of the sea floors, old crust is absorbed in the mantle to maintain material balance where one plate rides over another.

Figure 16-17 summarizes the inferred motion of continental plates. Although the interpretation shown involves continental motion, there is a significant difference between this interpretation and the older ideas of continental drift. Early drift theorists thought that the continents themselves moved over the subcrust. It was hard to believe that there were forces strong enough to overcome the friction between the granitic continents and the basaltic subcrust. According to the plate theory, the continents ride on the moving rigid plates like boulders trapped on a glacier. The motion occurs not in the crust but in the weak asthenosphere (Chap. 5).

Additional evidence for sea-floor spreading is found in the extensive cross

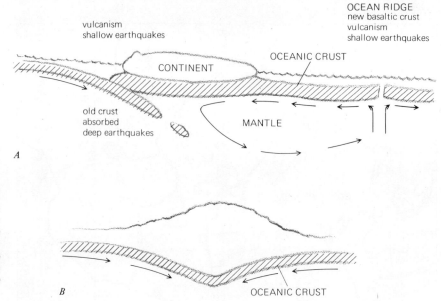

FIGURE 16-18
Different ways in which crustal plates behave in collision. (*A*) One plate is buckled under another to be absorbed in the mantle. (*B*) Slow collision involving continental masses which because of their low density resist being pulled into the dense mantle.

FIGURE 16-19
Two possible interpretations of the large cross faults that displace the ocean ridge systems: (*A*) transverse faulting and (*B*) transform faulting. Interpretation *B* is correct (see Fig. 16-20).

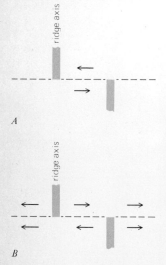

fractures that offset the ocean ridge systems. Figure 16-19 is a schematic drawing of one of these cross faults. Normally we would infer that the motion along the fault was that of Fig. 16-19*A*. If we recognize that the ocean floors at the ridges are spreading, a transform motion like that illustrated by Fig. 16-19*B* is suggested. Studies of earthquakes along these fractures shows them to be restricted to the portions of the fractures between the ridges (Fig. 16-20), which is just what one would expect to be the case in transform faults.

If most volcanoes begin near the ocean ridges and move outward as the sea floor spreads, the volcanic islands in the oceans should increase in age with distance from the ridge. Actual age determinations show this to be so. For example, islands on or near the mid-Atlantic ridge are all relatively young. Iceland, the Azores, and Nightingale Island all are less than 20 million years old. Farther from the ridge the ages increase. The Bahamas, on the western margin, and Fernando Po, on the eastern margin of the Atlantic, both show ages of 120 million years. The speed of spreading deduced from the ages of islands (assuming they started at the ridges and moved outward) is of the same order of magnitude as that determined from the magnetic-reversal pattern, namely a few centimeters per year.

Recently many new data have been obtained on sediment thicknesses in the deep sea. With instruments called *subbottom profilers* oceanographers get pictures of the ocean bottom like that reproduced in Fig. 16-21. These profilers work like the echo sounders used to measure water depth, but they use a much more powerful noise source that penetrates the bottom materials. Such measurements have confirmed that the thickness of sediment in the deep sea is almost insignificant compared with that along some continental margins. The rate of

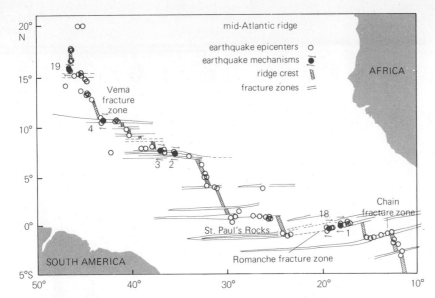

FIGURE 16-20
Earthquake epicenters along the mid-Atlantic Ridge (1955-1965) with direction of motion shown for six earthquakes. Both the earthquake mechanisms and the restriction of earthquakes to the parts of the fracture zones between the ridges tell us that the situation in Fig. 16-19B pertains. *From Lynn R. Sykes, fig. 10, p. 131, in R. A. Phinney (ed.), "The History of the Earth's Crust." Copyright © 1968 by Princeton University Press. Used with permission of Princeton University Press.*

sedimentation in the deep sea is admittedly very small, but even if it averaged only $\frac{1}{1,000}$ centimeter per year for the 3 to 4 billion years since erosion began, we still would expect to find much more sediment than is there now. Some process must have been operating through much of geologic time to take sediments away from the deep sea. Detailed measurements of sediment thicknesses in the deep seas generally reveal an increase in thickness away from the ocean ridges, which is just what one would expect if the sea floors are spreading.

A recent estimate by J. Gilluly and his associates showed the volume of sediments off the Atlantic Coast of the United States to be at least six times that of the sediments off the Pacific Coast. Referring to our moving-plate model, we can see that the Atlantic sediments are enjoying a free ride on the lee side of the continent whereas sediments on the Pacific side may well be drawn into the depths along the continental margin.

We found in Chap. 15 that geologists have long invoked subcrustal convection currents as the driving mechanism for the crustal shortening associated with mountain chains. More recently they have found that convection currents in the mantle provide the best explanation for the spreading sea floors and the moving crustal plates. Although such currents can well account for the observed plate movements, is there any independent evidence for their existence? The idea of convection currents is supported by measurements of heat flow in the earth's crust. In boreholes and mines the temperature of the rock always increases with depth. This means that heat is flowing outward from inside the earth. Because continental rocks contain more of the radioactive heat-producing elements uranium, thorium, and potassium 40, one would expect the rate of heat flow in the continents to be higher than that measured in the oceans. This, however, is not

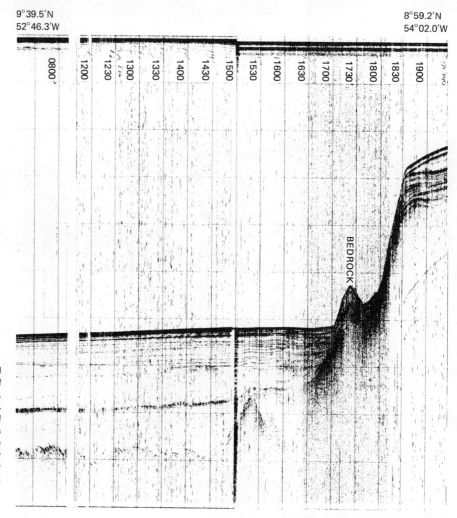

FIGURE 16-21
Seismic profiles (this page and next page) of the sea botton off the northeastern coast of Brazil, obtained aboard the U.S.N.S. *Kane* **in 1968. The blanket of geologically recent sediment is easily distinguished from the hardened bedrock. Notice how the sedimentary layers obey the rule of original horizontality.** *U. S. Naval Oceanographic Office.*

the case. Some of the highest values for heat flow are found over the ocean ridge systems.

Several interpretations for the unusually high heat flows measured in the oceanic crust are possible. The mantle under the oceans could contain more heat-producing radioactive elements than the mantle under the continents. This is not a satisfying explanation, however, because there is no reason to suspect such an unequal distribution of radioactive elements. More probably the differences in heat flow between continents and ocean basins are related to the manner in which heat is transferred outward from the earth's interior. Recall that heat can be transferred from one place to another by radiation, conduction, or convection.

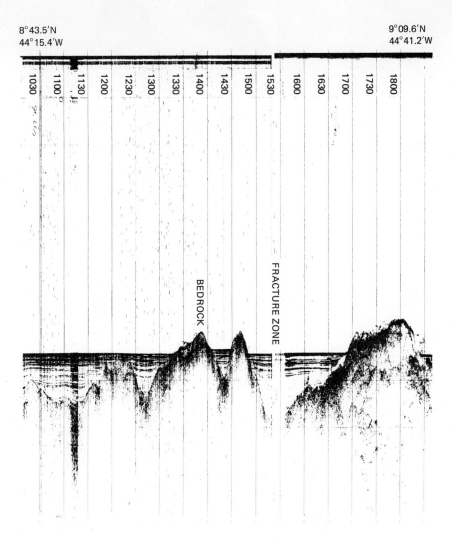

Normally the heat coming from inside the earth is transferred by conduction. Since rocks are poor conductors, a possible explanation for the higher heat flow of the ocean basins and in particular for the unusually high heat flow along the ocean ridges is that more efficient heat transfer by convection is taking place there.

16-6 SOME UNSOLVED PROBLEMS

In view of existing evidence there no longer can be much doubt that the sea floors are spreading apart and that the continents have indeed moved. It turns out that Wegener was right in proposing that the Atlantic basin evolved since the

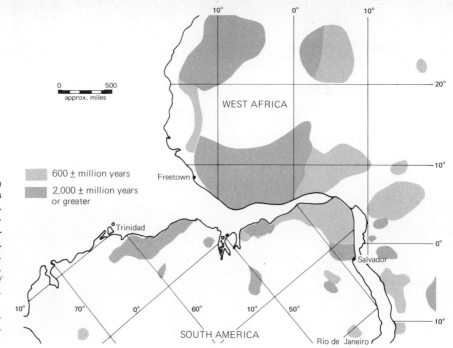

FIGURE 16-22
West Africa and northern South America according to Bullard's predrift reconstruction (Fig. 16-1), showing regional distribution of ±2,000- and ±600-million-year age provinces. *From P. M. Hurley and R. R. Rand, fig. 1, p. 154, in R. A. Phinney (ed), "The History of the Earth's Crust." Copyright © 1968 by Princeton University Press. Used with permission of Princeton University Press.*

In figure:
- 600 ± million years
- 2,000 ± million years or greater
- WEST AFRICA
- Freetown
- Trinidad
- Salvador
- SOUTH AMERICA
- Rio de Janeiro
- 0 — 500 approx. miles

FIGURE 16-23
Gemini XI **photograph showing Africa (lower landmass) being separated from Arabia by a widening rupture along the Red Sea. See Fig. 16-24.**

beginning of the Mesozoic Era and that before then the continents were joined together. Only his mechanism for drift was wrong. Instead of drifting as discrete blocks, the continents are riding on much larger rigid plates that move over the asthenosphere. Radiometric dating of rocks in Africa and South America provides further proof that these continents were once joined. Figure 16-22 shows the remarkable fit between them and the continuity of rock-age provinces. A similar fit in rock ages occurs between Australia and eastern South Africa.

It does not take much imagination to infer from the satellite photograph of Fig. 16-23 that the Red Sea and the Gulf of Aden are a recent example of continental rifting. The floors of these bodies of water consist of typical oceanic basalts that exhibit the parallel magnetic pattern characteristic of the ocean ridge systems. Dating shows that Africa began to be torn away from Arabia about 30 million years ago. As we can see from Fig. 16-24, the predrift fit here is again excellent, the only discrepancy being in the small area called the Afar triangle. This little triangle of land turns out to exhibit the oceanic magnetic pattern, which, together with the presence of young evaporite deposits, testifies that it is actually part of the recently formed sea floor.

It might appear, therefore, that little remains to be learned about sea-floor spreading and plate tectonics. This sort of activity appears to be going on today, and it has been active since the Atlantic basin opened up some 200 million years ago. When we look earlier into the earth's long history, however, the picture becomes much less clear.

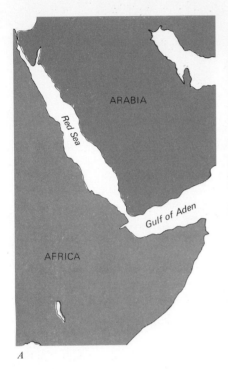

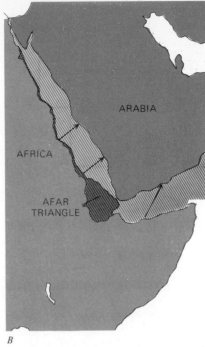

A

B

FIGURE 16-24
Continental rifting caused by the widening of the Red Sea and the Gulf of Aden. Some 20 million years ago the Arabian Peninsula and Africa were joined, as evidenced by the remarkable fit between the shorelines. The best fit (*B*) is obtained if Africa is left intact and the Arabian coast is superposed in two sections. In this reconstruction a corner of Arabia overlaps the Afar triangle, which now has some characteristics of an ocean floor. *From Sir Edward Bullard, in "The Ocean," A Scientific American Book, W. H. Freeman and Company, 1969.*

Figure 16-25 is a reconstruction of the continental blocks in the positions they occupied before they began to separate in the Mesozoic. The shaded portions of the map are continental areas with rocks older than 1.7 billion years. It is easy to see that these areas of old rocks line up very nicely on the predrift reconstruction. Does this mean that continental drifting did not take place during the long span of time before the Mesozoic? Some earth scientists interpret the data to mean that there was essentially a single growing continental mass prior to about 200 million years ago. Others contend that such an interpretation is unreasonable because drifting then would be a unique event in earth history.

It is possible to have sea-floor spreading and renewal without continental drift. In Fig. 16-26*A* the new oceanic crust generated at the ridge is continually pushed back down into the mantle, and thus the light continental mass need not be moving. By contrast, the situation in Fig. 16-26*B* shows the material absorbed into the mantle to be from another plate. Generation of new crust along this ocean ridge must be accompanied by continental motion. In both the possibilities the major activity in terms of downwarping, vulcanism, and earthquake activity should occur along a continental margin.

Returning to the idea of a single continental mass in the Premesozoic we can appreciate some of the unsolved problems. If the continents were indeed joined

FIGURE 16-25
A predrift reconstruction in which the continental blocks having apparent ages greater than 1,700 million years (shaded areas) appear to be in a coherent grouping within two restricted regions. These blocks are transected and circumscribed by belts of younger rocks. It seems unlikely that during the time between 1,700 and 200 million years ago the continents were scattered and drifting, only to be reassembled with this degree of ordering when the Atlantic opened up some 200 million years ago. *From P. M. Hurley and J. R. Rand, Pre-drift Continental Nuclei, Science, June 13, 1969, pp. 1229–1242, fig. 9; vol. 164, no. 3885, copyright 1969 by The American Association for the Advancement of Science.*

during the Paleozoic, how did the Appalachian geosyncline develop? According to the plate model, one would expect downwarping and geosynclinal development to occur along the line of collision of two plates. Does this mean that North America and Europe bumped against each other during the Paleozoic only to be torn apart during the Mesozoic? Much work remains to be done to settle the puzzling question of continental motions early in the earth's history. If it turns out that drifting is an event unique to the last 200 million years of earth history, we must explain how fold mountains and volcanoes grew in the central portions of the continental mass.

Working out a mechanism for plate movement still remains to be done. Although there is strong evidence for mantle convection, the exact cause of convection cells and the factors determining their locations and shapes are largely unknown. A particularly puzzling problem is the rough equality of heat flow in the continents and ocean basins. The rocks of the continents contain more radioac-

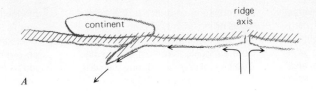

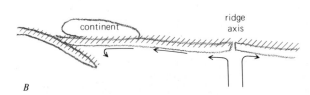

FIGURE 16-26
(*A*) **Sea-floor spreading at the ridge axis need not involve continental motion because the oceanic crust generated is absorbed.** (*B*) **The continent must be moving with the plate being pushed to the left from the ridge axis.**

tive elements than the rocks of the oceanic crust. A logical explanation for the equality of heat flow is that the mantle under the continents contains less of the heat-producing radioisotopes. If the continents move, however, this explanation does not hold because the continents would soon find themselves over oceanic mantle, where they should exhibit greater heat flows.

The 1960s marked a dramatic change in the earth sciences. With the convincing evidence from the ocean floors it became clear that the old ideas of fixed continents and ocean basins were wrong. The earth turned out to be a much more dynamic and mobile planet than had previously been guessed. Although details of the picture of crustal evolution will doubtless change as new information is acquired and new hypotheses tested, it is safe to conclude that the days of immobile continents are over.

SUMMARY

The concept of continental drift was proposed by Alfred Wegener at the beginning of this century. Although he presented strong arguments for the existence of a single continent in the early Mesozoic, most scientists rejected the drift hypothesis because there seemed to be no known forces strong enough to move the continents as blocks.

Paleomagnetism provided an independent method of detecting pos-

sible continental movement. Volcanic lavas tend to adopt the magnetic orientation of the earth's magnetic field where they formed. By making measurements of magnetic direction in specimens of lava of known age, scientists were able to trace the apparent shifting position of earth's magnetic poles. Such polar-wandering paths for North America and Europe are roughly parallel for most of the span of geologic time except for the most recent 200-

million-year period, when they converge, as would be the case if the continents had drifted apart during that time span.

Three distinct types of magnetic measurements made during the 1960s drastically changed man's view of crustal evolution. One involved the measurement of magnetic polarity in lavas of known age, which disclosed a series of complete reversals of the earth's magnetic field within the past few million years and led to the development of a reversal time scale. Measurements of magnetic polarity at varying depths in cores of deep-sea sediments were found to contain the same reversal pattern. The determination of magnetic intensity over the ocean ridge systems showed parallel and symmetrical bands of positive and negative anomalies on either side of the ridges. These anomalies, with widths measured in hundreds of kilometers, again exhibited the same proportional spacing as the magnetic-reversal time scale.

The magnetic anomalies of the ocean ridges are interpreted as the result of sea-floor spreading. As volcanic rocks form along the ocean ridges, they adopt the magnetic direction of the earth's field where they crystallize. Spreading of the sea floor outward from the ridge thus results in a series of positive or negative strips of crust, depending upon whether the earth's field was normal or reversed when the lavas erupted. A comparison of the spacings between these magnetic anomalies with the magnetic-reversal time scale gives the rates of spreading, which vary between 1 and 16 centimeters per year.

Most earthquakes occur in the circum-Pacific belt, in the Alpine-Himalayan region, or along the ocean ridge systems. Compared to these belts, the rest of the world is essentially earthquake-free. This earthquake distribution led to the suggestion that the outer layer of the earth consists of a series of rigid plates which move apart at the ocean ridges and collide in other areas, e.g., along the west coast of South America or along the Aleutian arc. The new crust generated along the ocean ridges is balanced by crustal material absorbed by the mantle at places where plates collide.

There now is little doubt that the continents are drifting. The present interpretation of drift has the continents riding on crustal plates moving over the asthenosphere. Evidence to date suggests that most continental drift has taken place during the past 200 million years. Further work is needed to decipher the geotectonic pattern prior to that time.

QUESTIONS

1 Why were Wegener's ideas on continental drift not widely accepted?

2 Magnetic declination of a place arises because the geographic and magnetic poles are not at exactly the same position. Are there places on earth where magnetic north and true north are in the same direction?

3 A 400-million-year-old lava flow cools through the Curie temperature for magnetite and adopts a magnetic direction parallel to the earth's field at the time and place where the lava formed. If one took an oriented sample of this lava today and determined its magnetic direction, would it necessarily be the same as it was 400 million years ago? If not, why?

4 Let us say that paleomagnetic measurements indicate a marked shift in the position of the poles with time. Does this mean that the continents have drifted relative to one another?

5 What is the evidence for complete reversals of the earth's magnetic field?

6 The diagram shows the magnetic pattern of sediments in a drill core from the deep sea. Using the reversal time scale of Fig. 16-11, calculate the average rate of sedimentation (in centimeters per year) over the past 2 million years.

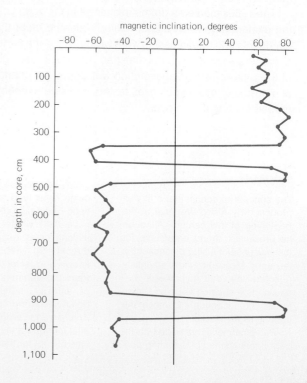

7 The diagram shows a cross section of the Atlantic from the mid-Atlantic ridge to Africa. If the spreading rate shown has remained constant, what is the oldest rock that you would expect to find in the Atlantic basin?

8 The magnetic inclination at the equator is roughly 0°, whereas at the poles it is about 90°. Is the inclination also a rough measure of the latitude at places between the equator and the poles? (See Fig. 16-5.)

9 Why do scientists believe that the earth's outer shell consists of a few large rigid plates?

10 How do transform faults support the idea of sea-floor spreading?

11 In parts of the deep sea oceanographers have found flat-topped volcanic mountains called guyots. They seem to have been planated by wave erosion, which means that they were once at the sea surface; yet many are now under thousands of feet of water. How may guyots have become so submerged?

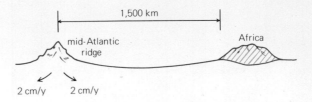

REFERENCES

"Continents Adrift: Readings from Scientific American," W. H. Freeman and Company, San Francisco, 1972.

Gondwanaland Revisted: New Evidence for Continental Drift, *Proc. Am. Phil. Soc.*, vol. 112, no. 5, 1968, pp. 303–353.

"The Ocean," A Scientific American Book, W. H. Freeman and Company, San Francisco, 1969.

Phinney, Robert A. (ed.): "The History of the Earth's Crust," Princeton University Press, Princeton, N.J., 1968.

Strangway, D. W.: "History of the Earth's Magnetic Field," McGraw-Hill Book Company, New York, 1970.

Takuchi, H., S. Vyeda, and H. Kanamori: "Debate about the Earth," W. H. Freeman and Company, San Francisco, 1967.

17 THE EARTH IN SPACE

In this chapter we leave the earth, its planetary neighbors, and our private star, the sun, to explore the worlds of other stars, galaxies, and nebulae that together make up the universe. As we found in Chap. 2, man's picture of the universe has changed dramatically with time. To someone of several thousand years ago the universe was a small patch of flat ground upon which he lived out his life. The sky above was dotted with spots of light that seemed not too far away. With increasing knowledge this picture changed. The ground underfoot turned out to be curved rather than flat. Telescopic studies of the friendly stars eventually revealed them to be separated by unimaginable stretches of dark empty space. Even the distances between stars turned out to be small compared to the distances between galaxies. In this evolving view the universe constantly became larger, and the earth by comparison shrank into insignificance.

Yet infinitesimal as it may be in the overall scheme of things, the earth and its satellite moon are still the only objects we have been able to observe at first hand. They are the platforms from which man has looked outward to construct, through reason, the picture of the universe he sees today.

In our study of the earth it is important to look at the big picture so that we see our planet in proper perspective. In extending our gaze beyond the planets we ask: How far away are the stars? How can their distances be measured? What are they made of? Are they moving or still? How do they differ? Where does the earth fit into our picture of the universe?

17-1 HOW FAR TO THE STARS?

In Chap. 2 we reviewed the picture of the universe seen by the Greek philosopher Ptolemy some 1,800 years ago. According to Ptolemy, the earth was at the center of things. Around it the sun and planets circled in complicated orbits. Surrounding the system of planets was a giant sphere, on which the fixed stars were somehow suspended and which rotated slowly without disturbing the stellar patterns. This imaginary sphere was believed to be not much farther away than the planets. Thus in those days the entire universe was thought to lie within the confines of the planetary system.

The Horsehead Nebula. This dark nebula blots out the luminous nebula behind it. The Horsehead is merely a protrusion of a larger dark gaseous mass. Notice the higher density of stars in the right-hand part of the picture. *Hale Observatories.*

FIGURE 17-1
Nearby stars should appear to shift against the more distant stellar background as the earth orbits around the sun. The parallax angle is half the angular displacement from opposite sides of the earth's orbit.

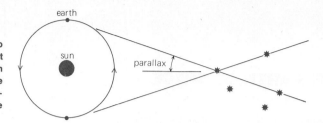

With the work of Tycho Brahe, Copernicus, Kepler, and others it became evident by the sixteenth century that the sun is at the center of our planetary system. The idea of a heliocentric solar system worked well in explaining the regular but intricate observed motions of the sun and planets. Moreover, the idea of a rotating earth accounted for the observed motions of the stars and planets in the night sky. But the steadfastness of the stars was a definite stumbling block to the sun-centered scheme.

Let us consider the solar system as it was viewed by scientists of the sixteenth century to see why the stars were a problem. As shown in Fig. 17-1, if the earth actually moved around the sun, and if the stars were spread throughout space, one would surely expect the observed positions of the stars to change with the seasons as the earth occupied different orbital positions. Yet the relative positions of the stars remained fixed, month after month and year after year. The apparent shift of an object against a more distant background when viewed from different positions is called its *parallax*. Failure of the stars to exhibit the expected parallactic displacement was a strong argument against the heliocentric system in the sixteenth century.

We now know that the failure to detect stellar parallax was due to the tremendous distances to the stars and to the limitations of the instruments of that time. Had we lived then, however, this explanation would not have been so convincing. An equally valid way out of the *parallax* dilemma for scientists of that day was to accept the view of the ancient Greeks and assume that all the stars were at an equal distance from the earth on a great sphere. Parallax occurs only if a near object is viewed against a more distant object, and if all stars were equidistant, there would be no parallax. Were the stars all on a great sphere surrounding the solar system? Was the solar system with its encompassing wall of stars the whole universe?

A look into the night sky reveals stars of varying brightness. This fact has been known throughout history, and the Greek Hipparchus was the first to classify stars according to their brightness into orders of magnitude. He assigned first magnitude to the brightest stars, second magnitude to the next brightest, and so forth to the sixth magnitude. The observed brightness of stars is clearly related to the question of distance. If the universe were surrounded by a vault of stars all at about equal distance, any differences in brightness would have to be due to in-

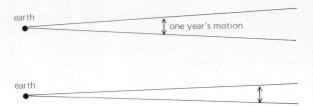

trinisic differences in the stars. On the other hand, the stars could conceivably all possess the same intrinsic brightness, in which case the observed variation in brightness or magnitude must be due to their varying distances from us. Seventeenth-century astronomers thus had to wrestle with the question whether some stars truly possess a greater intrinsic brightness or merely appear brighter because they are closer.

Until the eighteenth century the stars were considered to be immobile. They traced out their circles in the night sky due to the rotation of the earth, but each seemed to keep its own exact place. In 1718 the English astronomer Edmund Halley discovered that several bright stars were not in exactly the same positions allocated to them by the Greeks 1,500 years earlier. With further work it became evident that some stars at least do exhibit small proper motions. Observed stellar motions are very small compared to the motions of the planets, and so it was not at all surprising that they were not discovered earlier. Barnard's star, which displays the largest proper motion, moves at the rate of only 10.3 seconds of arc per year.

The discovery of stellar motions was a strong argument against the view of stars fixed upon a great encompassing sphere. Continued research on stellar motion soon disclosed that generally the greatest motions were displayed by the brightest stars. Figure 17-2 shows the relationship between stellar motion and distance from an observation point. Since the brightest stars seemed to possess the greatest motion, it appeared reasonable to conclude that the stars were indeed at different distances from earth. Variations in apparent brightness must then be at least partly due to differing distances.

Thus the model of the universe in which the stars were assumed to be at an equal distance from the earth fell into disrepute. With the realization that the stars are indeed spread throughout the vastness of space the search for parallactic shift in those closest to the earth was continued with renewed vigor. The development of new astronomic instruments and measuring techniques spurred the searchers on.

The discovery that stars do move complicated the search for stellar parallax. A shift in the position of a star with time was no longer necessarily due to parallax. As more careful stellar observations were made, other motions of the stars were detected to compound the problem further. The aberration of starlight,

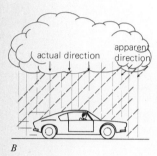

FIGURE 17-3

The aberration of starlight illustrated by analogy with the apparent direction of raindrops for (*A*) a stationary and (*B*) a moving observer.

discovered in the early eighteenth century, is one such motion. It is an apparent shift in the position of a star because of the speed of the earth in its orbit (Fig. 17-3). The analogy is often made to a rainstorm in which the raindrops fall vertically. A man standing still sees the rain coming straight down, but to someone in a moving car the rain appears to be angling toward the windshield because of the forward motion of the vehicle. In the same way the earth moves through a rain of starlight, and the apparent direction of the light is influenced by the earth's motion.

In the search for parallax, astronomers paid particular attention to stars that appeared very close together in the sky. If one of such a pair of stars were actually trillions of miles further than the other, the situation would be ideal for detecting parallax. Detailed studies of such pairs of stars showed that some exhibit relative movement, but the observed period of motion was different from the annual period expected for parallactic shift. Analysis revealed that some pairs were truly double, or binary, stars revolving about a common center of gravity.

Figure 17-4 shows photographs of Barnard's star taken 22 years apart. It has the largest proper motion of any star, and the photographs give us some idea of the minuteness of stellar motions. By now, astronomers had some appreciation of the distances to the stars, and they knew that the parallax of even the closest stars would be only a tiny fraction of the proper motion shown in Fig. 17-4. Moreover, they realized that stellar parallax could be recognized only after the proper motion of a star, the aberration of its light, the binary motion (if it was a multiple star), and other motions were subtracted or accounted for.

How could parallax ever be identified amongst these many variables? The expected parallactic shift of stars against a more distant background is illustrated in Fig. 17-5. A star located perpendicular to the plane of the earth's orbit should describe a very small circle each year. A star in the plane of the earth's orbit should shift back and forth along a line, while all other stars should trace out tiny annual ellipses due to parallactic shift.

Three astronomers—Thomas Henderson, of Scotland, Friedrich von Struve, a German-Russian, and Friedrich W. Bessel, a German—almost simultaneously detected the parallax of three different stars in the period 1838–1840. Henderson's study of Alpha Centauri, the third brightest star, disclosed a parallax of 0.726 second of arc, the largest parallax ever discovered. This, therefore, is the closest known star to our solar system. It is about 19 trillion miles, or 30 trillion kilometers, away from us.

If even the nearest star is 19 trillion miles away, it is clear that miles or kilometers are not good units of measure for solar distances. To avoid large numbers astronomers employ two other units, the light-year and the parsec. A light-year is the distance traveled by light during one year (since light travels at 2.998×10^5 kilometers per second, a light year is 9.461×10^{12} kilometers). Alpha Centauri is 4.29 light-years from us. Parsec is an abbreviation for parallax-second. A star's distance in parsecs is the reciprocal of its parallax. Since Alpha Centauri's

AUG. 24, 1894

MAY 30, 1916

FIGURE 17-4
The proper motion of Barnard's star in two photographs taken 22 years apart. *Yerkes Observatory.*

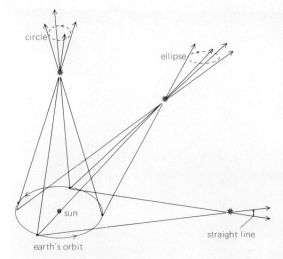

FIGURE 17-5
The parallactic shift of a star depends upon where the star is with respect to the plane of the earth's orbit.

parallax is 0.76 second, it is 1/0.76 = 1.32 parsecs distant. Table 17-1 lists the distances to some of the nearest stars.

There are severe limitations to the parallax method of distance measurement. Even with modern instrumentation about the smallest angle that can be measured with precision is 0.05 second of arc. This is only 1/0.05 = 20 parsecs, or 65 light-years. Small wonder that parallax measurements are available for only a tiny fraction of the total number of visible stars when we consider that some stars are now believed to be billions of light-years from us.

Fortunately, there are several other, less direct means of estimating the distances to stars, of which one is related to a class of variable stars known as the Cepheids. The Cepheid stars vary in brightness with time. Each variable star has a characteristic period during which it passes through a cycle of bright to dim to bright. In the early 1900s Henrietta Leavitt (1868–1921), an American astronomer, located and examined hundreds of Cepheid variables in a star cluster known as the Small Magellanic Cloud. She found that the period of any Cepheid in the cloud was related to its brightness. The brighter the Cepheid the longer its period of changing from bright to dim.

The relationship between brightness and period of Cepheids observed in the

TABLE 17-1
Distance to some of the nearest stars

Star	Distance	
	Light-years	*Parsecs*
Alpha Centauri	4.29	1.32
Barnard's star	5.97	1.84
Sirius	8.7	2.67
61 Cygni	11.1	3.42
Altair	15.7	4.82

Magellanic Cloud did not hold for other variable stars in our own neighborhood. The reason soon became obvious when it was realized that the Cepheids studied are all essentially at the same distance from us. Although the Magellanic Cloud is large, it is so far away that we can consider all its stars to be at an equal distance from us, just as all the people on Long Island can be considered to be at an equal distance from the South Pole. The brightness-period relationship of the Cepheids thus turned out to be a relation between intrinsic brightness, or luminosity, and period rather than between measured or apparent brightness and period.

Unfortunately, even the nearest Cepheid is so far away that its distance cannot be directly determined by parallax measurement. Initially, therefore, the Cepheid distance scale could be used only to determine the relative distances between stars or groups of stars. To see how the scale works let us consider two Cepheids; both have a 12-day period, and one appears only one-fourth as bright as the other. Since the stars have the same period, we assume that they are equally luminous. One must be dimmer because it is farther away. Because the intensity of light varies inversely as the square of the distance from the source, we can see that one of the stars must be twice as far away as the other ($1/2^2 = \frac{1}{4}$) in order to appear only one-fourth as bright. Although we do not know the distance to either star, we can estimate their relative distances using the period-luminosity relationship.

Ultimately statistical studies of the relation between proper motion and distance led to information on the absolute distances to some Cepheids. These pulsating stars could thus be used as yardsticks to the distant star systems. We should note that the task of plumbing stellar distances is more complicated than this brief survey suggests. Minute concentrations of dust and gas are found in interstellar space. Light from a distant star travels through billions of miles of space, so that even infinitesimal concentrations of dust tend to dim its light. If proper corrections for this dimming effect were not made, distance estimates would be too large.

17-2 HOW BIG ARE THE STARS?

Even with the best available telescopes the stars appear only as points of light. Information about the size or temperature of stars must somehow be inferred from the intensity and nature of the light coming from them. We have already referred to the brightness classes, or magnitudes, of stars. Modern astronomers are able to measure the brightnesses of individual stars, and they have devised a numerical magnitude scale. A difference of one magnitude is defined as a ratio of 2.512. A star of magnitude 1 is thus 100 times (2.512^5) brighter than one of magnitude 6.

Since stars are located at widely different distances from the earth, measured magnitudes clearly do not represent intrinsic brightnesses because the intensity of light reaching the earth from a star is related to the distance traveled. To compare stellar magnitudes the differences in their distances must first be accounted for. This can be done for stars whose distances are known by applying the inverse-square law to calculate what their brightness would be if they were equidistant. By convention the absolute magnitude of a star is defined as the magnitude it would have if it were at a distance of 10 parsecs. Table 17-2 shows some absolute magnitudes for stars. Notice that the sun, which appears so very bright because it is so close, would not be a particularly bright star if it were moved to a distance comparable to that of other stars.

If all stars emitted light with the same intensity, there should be a simple relationship between their size and their absolute magnitude. Even with the naked eye (or at least with a set of binoculars) we can see that not all stars emit the same kind of light. Some appear red, others yellow, and still others blue. The colors represent varying temperatures—another factor to be accounted for in estimating the size of stars.

We return here to the radiation laws discussed in Chap. 7 in the study of the sun, the only star close enough to look like a sphere. Imagine a radiator used to heat a room. As the name implies, a radiator radiates energy. Its warmth is easily felt although the radiation cannot be seen in a darkened room. If a bar of iron similar to the material the radiator is made of were heated to a higher temperature, it would eventually turn cherry red and thus become visible by its own light. At still higher temperatures the color would change to yellow and finally to blue.

The German physicist Wilhelm Wien studied the relationship between the wavelength of radiation and temperature of radiating bodies, and in 1893 he proposed what is known as *Wien's law*. He discovered that for any given temperature there is a particular wavelength of maximum radiation. Mathematically his law can be written

$$\lambda_{max} = \frac{0.2897}{T}$$

where λ_{max} = wavelength of maximum radiation
T = temperature, kelvins
0.2897 = constant

TABLE 17-2
Absolute magnitude of some well-known stars

Star	Absolute magnitude	Absolute luminosity
Sun	4.9	1.0*
Altair	2.3	10.9
Sirius	1.4	25.0
Vega	0.5	57.5
Capella	−0.3	120
Antares	−5.4	13,000
Deneb	−7.1	25,000

*By definition.

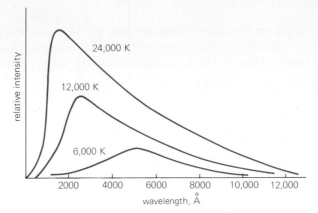

FIGURE 17-6
The relative intensity of radiation at various temperatures.
The area under each curve is a
measure of the total radiation.
As the temperature increases,
the total radiation increases
(Stefan's law) and the wavelength of maximum radiation
(peak of curve) shifts to shorter
wavelengths (Wien's law).

With this relation and with instruments capable of measuring the intensity of
radiation at various wavelengths, the surface temperatures of stars can be determined. By applying Wien's Law to the sun in Chap. 2 we found its surface temperature to be about 6000°C. Some stars, like Betelguese, exhibit surface temperatures that are less than 3500°C. The surface temperature of Sirius is 11,000°C,
and some stars have surface temperatures over 25,000°C.

Figure 17-6 shows the energy emitted at different wavelengths by a perfect radiator at various temperatures. We can see from the graph that the wavelength of
maximum radiation changes with temperature, as predicted by Wien's law. This,
however, is not the only change. The area under each of the graphs is a measure
of the total intensity of radiation at the particular temperature. It is clear that the
rate of energy emission climbs rapidly with temperature. The relationship between the rate of emission of radiant energy and temperature is expressed by the
following equation, known as *Stefan's law*:

$$E = aT^4$$

where E = energy radiated per unit of time from a unit of surface area
   a = constant
   T = absolute temperature

The value of the constant a has been determined from laboratory experiments by
measuring the energy emitted per square centimeter of surface at various temperatures. When T is in kelvins and E is in ergs per square centimeter per second, the value for a becomes 5.672×10^{-5} and Stefan's law can be written

$$E = 5.672 \times 10^{-5} T^4$$

Let us see how the radiation laws can be put to work to determine the size of a
star. A star's temperature can be calculated by applying Wien's law. A star's total
energy output per unit of time can be evaluated from the radiation arriving at the
earth, provided its distance is known. The surface area of a sphere of radius R is
$4\pi R^2$. Therefore, if the overall rate of energy radiation is e, the rate per unit of sur-

face area E is $e/4\pi R^2$. Now we have the information necessary to compute the radius of a star whose absolute surface temperature T and whose total rate of energy radiation e are known. According to Stefan's law,

$$E = 5.672 \times 10^{-5} T^4$$

Substituting $e/4\pi R^2$ for E gives

$$\frac{e}{4\pi R^2} = 5.672 \times 10^{-5} T^4 \qquad \text{or} \qquad R^2 = \frac{e}{4\pi(5.672 \times 10^{-5} T^4)}$$

Since e and T are known, the relation can be solved for R.

To illustrate with a specific example, let us consider a star whose temperature has been determined to be 3000 K, about half the temperature of our sun. Let us also suppose that the luminosity of this star (overall rate of energy radiation) is twice as large as the sun's. How big is the star? It must be quite a bit larger than the sun because since it is only half as hot as the sun, each square centimeter of its surface radiates only $1/2^4 = \frac{1}{16}$ as much energy as an equivalent area on the sun according to Stefan's law. In order for the star to be twice as luminous as the sun it must therefore have $2 \times 16 = 32$ times as much surface area. Since surface area is related to the square of the radius, the star in question must have 5.6 times the radius of the sun. This follows because

$$\frac{4\pi(R_{\text{star}})^2}{4\pi(R_{\text{sun}})^2} = \frac{32}{1} \qquad \text{or} \qquad \frac{R_{\text{star}}}{R_{\text{sun}}} = \sqrt{32} = 5.6$$

In using the radiation laws to determine stellar radii, we have assumed that the stars are perfect radiators. How do we know that this assumption is at all reasonable? Fortunately the sun is close enough for its size to be measured directly. Its radius can also be calculated from the intensity and nature of its radiant energy. The measured and computed values for the solar radius are almost the same, which suggests that the sun behaves almost like a perfect radiator, and there is no reason to suppose that other stars are different. Actually the small difference between the measured and calculated values for the sun's radius are used as a correction factor for other stars.

Even though the nearest stars are so far that they appear only as points of light in modern telescopes, the dimensions of some can be measured more directly by a very sensitive instrument called an *interferometer*. The rays of light that reach a telescope from a star do not all come from the same point on the star. Thus two rays, one from the top and one from the bottom edge of a star, will reach the telescope at a small angle to each other. This causes the rays to interfere, and the angle at which the rays come together can be determined from the nature of the interference provided the star is not too far away. The diameters of a number of nearby stars have been measured by this method.

Stellar dimensions measured by an interferometer prove to be in fair agreement with those determined from the radiation laws. Astronomers thus had reason to be confident in their measurements even though the values were as-

1908   1915   1920

FIGURE 17-7
The double star in the upper left-hand portion of these photographs is Kruger 60. This system is made up of two stars that revolve around each other. *Yerkes Observatory.*

tonishing. The diameter of Alpha Scorpii, for example, turned out to be about 300 times the sun's diameter. Its diameter is 260 million miles, which means that if it were in the sun's place, it would extend all the way to Mars. This is by no means the largest star. The diameters of some stars are 2,000 times as great as the sun's, whereas others are only $\frac{3}{1,000}$ as large.

17-3 STELLAR MASSES

In Chap. 6, we determined the mass of the sun by applying Newton's laws to the characteristics of the earth-sun orbit. We found the sun to be very massive indeed, about 330,000 times as massive as the earth. How does it compare in mass with stars? We have seen that some stars are several thousand times bigger than the sun, but are they also that much more massive?

To answer these questions astronomers obviously needed some means of measuring stellar masses. The mass of the sun was determined from its gravitational effect upon the earth and other planets, but the stars are so far away that even if they had planets, the best telescopes could not see them. Fortunately, the discovery that many stars occur in pairs as *binary stars* revolving about a common center of mass provided the means of measuring some stellar masses. Figure 17-7 shows photographs of one such binary-star system taken over a 12-year period. From such photographs the periods of revolution of binary stars can be determined. When distances to the stars involved are known from parallactic measurements, their distance of separation can be determined from the angular distance between them.

For some binary stars, therefore, the period of orbit, the distance between them, and the center of mass (center of rotation) of the system are known. The masses of such stars can be calculated from Kepler's third law. In its original form his third law, which states that the square of the time of revolution of a planet around the sun is proportional to the cube of its mean distance from the sun, seems to have little application to the problem at hand because Kepler's laws were written for the special case of the planets. Newton was able to derive Kepler's empirical laws from his laws of motion and gravitation. He recognized that the planetary system was a special case, and he restated Kepler's third law to apply to any pair of mutually revolving bodies in space. His more general form

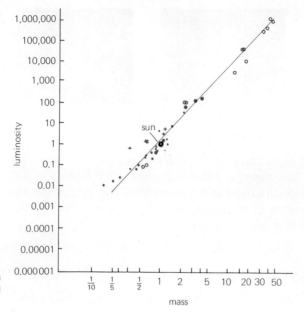

states that when two bodies revolve about each other, the sum of their masses times the square of their period of mutual revolution is proportional to the cube of the semimajor axis of orbit of one about the other.

If the period of revolution P is measured in years, the masses M_1, M_2 of the binary stars in multiples of the sun's mass and the distance A between the stars in astronomical units (distance between the earth and sun), the law can be written

$$(M_1 + M_2)P^2 = A^3$$

The binary system Sirius A and Sirius B has a period of revolution of 50 years. The two stars are 20.25 astronomical units apart. Their combined mass, therefore, must be

$$M_1 + M_2 = \frac{(20.25)^3}{50^2} = 3.2 \text{ solar masses}$$

To find the masses of each star requires consideration of their respective distances from the center of mass (barycenter) of the system. Sirius B is about twice as far from the barycenter as Sirius A. For the system to balance, therefore, Sirius B must contain twice the mass of Sirius A, or about two times the sun's mass, since together the two stars make up three solar masses.

With increasing data it became possible for astronomers to study the relationship between stellar masses and luminosities. Figure 17-8, in which each point represents a star of known mass and luminosity, shows this relationship.

We can see from the graph that most stars (about 90 percent) plot along a narrow band, showing a close relation between mass and luminosity. It is interesting to note also that the range of stellar luminosities is much greater than their range of masses. Most stars have masses ranging from one-fifth to five times the sun's mass. On the other hand, luminosities range from 0.01 to 100,000 times that of the sun.

Because the binary stars whose masses can be determined exhibit a strong correlation between mass and luminosity, it seems reasonable to assume that single stars also conform to this relation. Thus Fig. 17-8 can be used for estimating masses of single stars. According to the diagram, a star with a luminosity equal to that of the sun should have the same mass as the sun. One with a luminosity of 100 solar units should be about four times as massive as the sun.

17-4 TYPES OF STARS

Spectroscopy was first applied to the study of stars during the mid-nineteenth century. As light from an increasing number of stars was analyzed spectroscopically, it became apparent that there are distinct differences in stellar spectra. In 1897 an Italian astronomer, Pietro Secchi, subdivided stellar spectra into four classes. Later work resulted in a finer subdivision of nine classes, each named after a letter of the alphabet. The sun, for instance, was assigned to class G. Ultimately these classes were each further broken down into 10 subclasses so that the sun is now assigned to class G-2.

When spectral differences first were discovered, the reason for them was not completely understood. One obvious explanation was that the spectra are different because the stars are made of different elements. This explanation, however, was inadequate for several reasons, and it was soon abandoned. In the first place, it seemed much more reasonable to assume that the stars are all powered by the same basic energy source and thus that they are all made of basically the same stuff. Moreover, the fact that adjacent spectral classes graded into each other was not at all what one would expect if the spectral differences were indeed due to differences in composition.

With further research it became clear that spectral differences are related to temperature. As it is in the sun, hydrogen is the most abundant element in all the stars. In stars with the highest temperatures, however, the hydrogen is almost completely ionized, so that there are no hydrogen absorption lines in their spectra. In somewhat cooler stars the hydrogen atoms are not ionized, and hydrogen absorption lines are prominent. Every other element also has a characteristic temperature at which it passes into its possible ionization stages. Table 17-3 describes the characteristics of the chief spectral classes and their relation to stellar temperatures.

Early in this century Ejnar Hertzsprung, of Denmark, and Henry Russell, of the United States, independently discovered a relationship between the luminosity

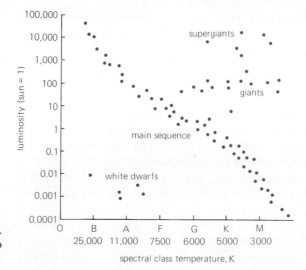

FIGURE 17-9
H-R diagram showing the distribution of stars according to spectral type and luminosity.

and the spectral class (temperature) of stars. Graphs like that of Fig. 17-9, in which stars are plotted in terms of these two variables, are known as Hertzsprung-Russell (H-R) diagrams.

The H-R diagram shows that most stars plot along a diagonal line through the middle of the graph. This is just what one would expect; the hottest stars plot near the top of the graph because they are brightest, while the cooler stars plot progressively lower because they are dimmer. Over 95 percent of all stars investigated fall onto the diagonal band; they are called the *main-sequence stars*.

Some stars, however, are anomalous. For example, those in the upper right-hand corner of the diagram labeled *giants* are relatively cool stars according to their spectral class. How then can they be near the upper part of the graph, which is the position for very bright stars? The only logical explanation for the brightness of these stars is to assume that they are very large. A single match does not light up a room, but a thousand matches can. Measurements of stellar radii confirm that the stars in the upper right of the H-R diagram are truly giants.

The stars near the bottom of the diagram labeled *dwarfs* present just the op-

TABLE 17-3
Spectral classes of stars

Class	Temperature, kelvins	Spectral characteristics
O	25,000–50,000	Lines of highly ionized atoms
B	11,000–25,000	Lines of hydrogen and neutral helium strongest
A	7,500–11,000	Hydrogen lines at maximum; ionized metals weak; helium nearly absent
F	6,000–7,500	Hydrogen weaker and ionized metals stronger than in class A
G	5,100–6,000	Sun is in this class; neutral and singly ionized metals dominate; some molecular bands of CH
K	3,600–5,100	Neutral metals strong; molecular bands stronger than in class K
M	3,000–3,600	Molecular bands of CN, CH, and C_2 strong

posite problem. According to their spectra they are relatively hot. Their luminosities, however, are significantly lower than those of average stars of the same temperature. They must therefore be much smaller than normal.

When the first H-R diagrams were constructed, ideas about energy sources in
the stars were still unsettled. Many astronomers still believed that stellar energy
was due to contraction. In Chap. 6 we found why contraction is inadequate as an
energy source for the sun and stars. To one convinced that contraction was the
major energy source, however, the H-R diagram suggested a logical evolutionary
sequence for stars. According to this theory of stellar evolution, stars began their
lives in the upper right-hand corner of the diagram as relatively cool giants. As
such a star contracted, it became hotter and bluer until it reached the upper left-
hand part of the main sequence. Once it arrived on the main sequence, it slowly
slid down the sequence by gradual cooling until it arrived at the lower right-hand
end. From there it finally shrank to become a dwarf.

This theory of stellar evolution did not long survive. For one thing it was based
on incomplete knowledge of the principal energy source within the stars. When it
became known that nuclear processes and not contraction provide stellar
energy, a major argument for this theory vanished. Moreover, the theory failed to
account for the mass-luminosity relationship discussed in Sec. 17-3. It attributes
the position of a star on the main sequence to the star's age. Actually the sphere
occupied by a star represents a balance between gravitational contraction,
which tends to shrink the star, and internal nuclear heating, which works to expand it. The more massive the star the greater the gravitational compression and
the higher the temperature it can maintain. This being the case, it follows that the
spectral class and hence the position of the H-R diagram are related to mass.

The luminosity of a star is a measure of the amount of energy being produced
by nuclear processes. We have noted that the more massive stars are very much
more luminous than their less massive counterparts. To be more luminous they
must be using up their supplies of hydrogen much faster. Being more massive,
however, they have more hydrogen to begin with, but the rate at which they radiate energy is so great that the extra supply does not mean much. Astronomers
have calculated the time required for stars of various luminosities to use up their
fuel. The results show that the most luminous stars can last only a fraction of the
time of their less luminous neighbors (Table 17-4). A remarkable thing about
these star life-expectancy estimates is that the bright stars visible today must be

TABLE 17-4
**Estimates of lifetimes of stars of
varying mass based upon rates
of energy radiated**

Spectral type	Luminosity	Mass	Lifetime, millions of years
O	100,000	14	10
B	1,000	10	400
A	10	2.5	5,000
F	2.5	1.3	20,000
G (sun)	1*	1*	40,000

*By definition.

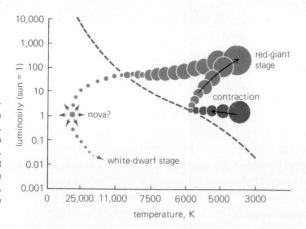

FIGURE 17-10
Inferred path of stellar evolution on the H-R diagram for a star of about the sun's mass. The rate of evolution depends upon the star's initial mass. Evolutionary path is from dust and gaseous nebula to main sequence star, to giant star, and then by stages to white dwarf.

very much younger than our sun. Although the sun is only about one-fourth of the way through its hydrogen supply, massive stars of the type O class must have been formed since the age of the dinosaurs.

What happens to a star when it has used up the hydrogen in its core? Obviously this question cannot be answered from direct observation because the length of a human life and even the entire history of astronomy are woefully short compared to the history of even the shortest-lived star, but we can approach the problem in another way. Assuming that the stars visible today are in different stages of development, it should be possible to arrange them into an evolutionary sequence based upon a theory of stellar evolution.

Let us see what sort of a future astronomers predict for a star on the main sequence that has used up the hydrogen in its core. Such a star should first contract, because the inward thrust of gravitational attraction would begin to exceed the outward pressure due to heat generated by internal nuclear reactions. The resulting contraction would cause the interior temperature to increase, which eventually would make possible nuclear reactions involving elements heavier than hydrogen. Once started, these reactions would pour out energy at a prodigious rate, and the star would expand in response to this pressure to become a giant. Whereas its total energy output or luminosity would increase, the star would become so large that the energy radiated per unit of surface would be much reduced. The star thus would have changed into a relatively cool giant.

Nuclear reactions involving the heavier elements are much less efficient than hydrogen fusion; and the giants soon run out of nuclear steam. Again, we would expect them to contract and with possible explosive spasms move toward the main sequence. With their fuel gone, they must slowly shrink and cool to become white dwarfs, small spheres of matter so dense that 1 cubic centimeter weighs 1 million times as much as a similar volume of water.

It now appears that a typical star has the following life history. It begins as a cool mass of gas and dust that contracts in response to gravitational forces. The

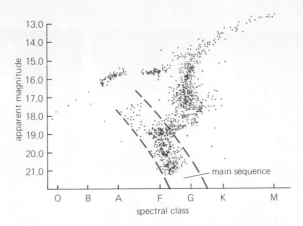

FIGURE 17-11
H-R diagram of the globular star cluster M3.

contraction causes the internal temperature to rise, and when this reaches about 1 million degrees, the nuclear reaction involving the conversion of hydrogen into helium begins. The star is now on the main sequence, where it remains most of its life. Once the hydrogen has nearly been used up, nuclear reactions involving the heavier elements come into play. They proceed at tremendous rates, causing the star to expand into a giant. Soon this internal energy source is used up, and the star again contracts. This time contraction continues to the dwarf stage. Figure 17-10 illustrates the probable evolutionary paths of stars to and from the main sequence.

Is there any way of verifying this model of stellar evolution, or is it based solely on theory? One method of observationally checking the stellar-evolution model is to examine a coherent group of stars all of the same chronological age. Some stars occur in great clusters. Because the stars of the cluster are all about the same distance from us, it seems reasonable to assume that they must have formed at about the same time.

Although all the stars in a cluster might be of the same chronological age, we would expect them to be in different stages of development, depending upon their masses. Thus an H-R diagram of such a cluster ought to reflect the stages of development of the stars within it. Figure 17-11 is such a diagram. It is very different from the H-R diagram for all stars, but it closely resembles our predicted evolutionary paths over the fixed time span shown in Fig. 17-10. Thus star clusters provide independent observational evidence for our view of stellar evolution.

17-5   THE STRUCTURE OF THE UNIVERSE

Figure 17-12 is a photograph of the Andromeda galaxy with a smaller companion galaxy. On the enlargements we can see that these galaxies contain countless stars. A galaxy is an island universe consisting of billions and billions of stars.

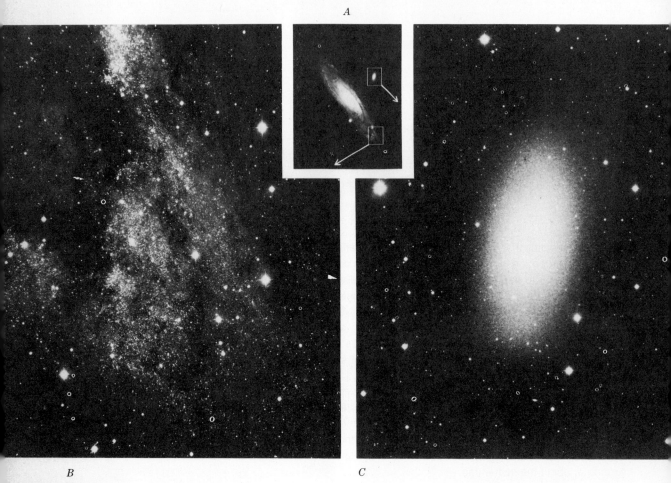

FIGURE 17-12
The Andromeda galaxy (A) and an enlargement (B) of one of its arms, together with (C) a smaller companion galaxy and its enlargement. In (B) and (C) the brightest stars are foreground stars belonging in our own Milky Way galaxy. *Hale Observatories.*

From studies of the Cepheid variables in the arms of the Andromeda galaxy its distance from us is found to be about 2 million light-years. This is one of our near-neighbor galaxies. When our largest telescopes are pointed spaceward, they see billions of galaxies. The number within telescope range is so large that they cannot be counted. From actual counts in small samples of the sky astronomers conclude that there are about 100 billion galaxies within the range of their telescopes. The total number of galaxies in the universe is, of course, likely to be infinitely larger.

The Andromeda galaxy is notable because it is the farthest object that can be seen in the night sky with the unaided eye. Without a telescope it appears as a very faint, hazy patch of light that is somewhat smaller than the disk of the full moon. It is only when the galaxy is photographed with large telescopes using

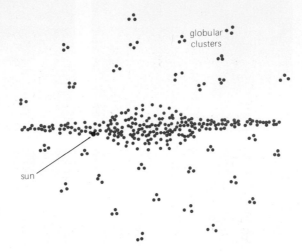

FIGURE 17-13
Diagrammatic sketch of our Milky Way galaxy; its diameter is about 100,000 light-years.

long time exposures that its spiral shape becomes evident. Such photographs show that the galaxy occupies a segment of the sky that extends for nearly 5° (the moon subtends an angle of only 0.5°). To fill an angle this large when it is nearly 2 million light-years distance means that the galaxy must itself be very big. Its diameter is estimated to be about 130,000 light-years.

The Andromeda galaxy belongs in a cluster of galaxies that includes our own, known as the Milky Way galaxy. In fact, the Milky Way and Andromeda galaxies are thought to look alike. Although we cannot see our own galaxy from the outside, counts of star densities in different space directions indicate that it appears rather like the diagram of Fig. 17-13.

If the Andromeda galaxy is 2 million light-years away, then the galaxies that appear only as fuzzy patches of light in even the largest telescopes must be thousands of times as far away. By assuming that the faint galaxies photographed by the largest telescopes are intrinsically as bright as Andromeda, it can be shown that some must be billions of light-years away from us in order to appear so dim. Light from the most distant galaxies must have started its journey toward us as the earth was being formed.

Our picture of the universe is one in which the stars occur in island universes called galaxies. Most of the galaxies studied (about 75 percent) exhibit some type of spiral structure. About 20 percent of the galaxies are elliptical and lack the spiral arms, and about 5 percent appear irregular in outline. Figure 17-14 shows some of the principal types.

The picture of the universe in which the stars are grouped into galaxies separated by millions of light-years of relatively empty space is not difficult to accept when we look at photographs like those in Fig. 17-15. This, however, was not always the case. Only after the installation of the 100-inch telescope on Mt. Wilson in 1917 were individual stars first detected in the arms of the Andromeda galaxy

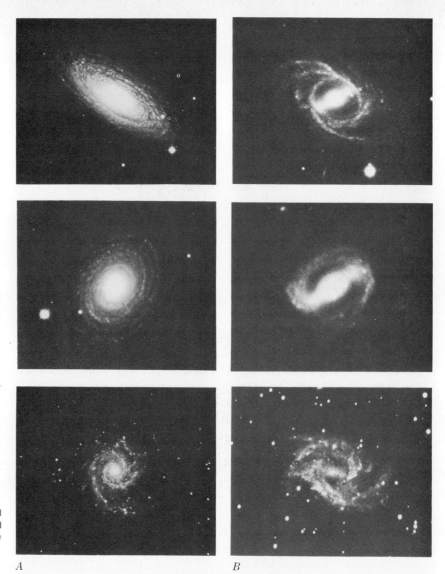

FIGURE 17-14
Different varieties of (*A*) **normal spiral and** (*B*) **barred spiral galaxies.** *Hale Observatories photographs.*

A   *B*

FIGURE 17-15
A galaxy as seen edge on by the 200-inch telescope. *Hale Observatories photograph.*

by the American astronomer Edwin Hubble. Before Hubble took his famous pictures with the then new 100-inch telescope, a heated debate had raged among astronomers for almost a century over the nature of fuzzy objects like Andromeda.

Picture for a moment the predicament of an astronomer of the last century equipped with telescopes incapable of resolving the stars in even the closest galaxy. From the earth platform he looked outward to try to unravel the nature of the universe. He saw countless millions of stars whose numbers kept increasing with each new and better telescope. Some of the stars occurred in clusters or globules (Fig. 17-16). In addition to the stars, clouds of gas and dust called nebulae were observed (Fig. 17-17). Some of these gas clouds were hot and shining; others blocked out the view of more distant stars. Then there were also the fuzzy objects like Andromeda that obviously were not stars. Because the telescopes could not resolve individual stars in these fuzzy masses, they too were thought to be clouds of glowing gas or nebulae. There was no known way of determining the distances to such objects, and most astronomers assumed that they were part of our galaxy. Thus to an astronomer of the last century our galaxy seemed to be the entire universe. Star counts in different regions of the sky disclosed a picture of this galaxy or universe like that in Fig. 17-13.

The discovery that objects like Andromeda actually are galaxies of stars far away from our own galaxy had some significant cosmological implications. For many years it had appeared that the universe might indeed be finite and limited to what we now consider our own galaxy. Now, no end could be seen. At the farthest depth of observable space today we can see only the galactic giants. These giants appear as dim points of light. We can only guess at their total luminosities and thus at their distances from us, but it appears safe to conclude that the farthest are of the order of 5 billion light-years away. Large radio telescopes have detected sources of radio waves where even the best optical telescopes see nothing. These may be even more distant galaxies. Truly there now appears to be no prospect of an end to the universe.

FIGURE 17-16
The globular cluster M13, which appears to contain over 50,000 stars. *Hale Observatories photograph.*

FIGURE 17-17
The Horsehead Nebula. This dark nebula blots out the luminous nebula behind it. The Horsehead is merely a protrusion of a larger dark gaseous mass. Notice the higher density of stars in the right-hand part of the picture. *Hale Observatories photograph.*

17-6 OLBERS' PARADOX

We have seen how the development of new instruments continued to extend the universe. Is the universe truly infinite? Does it extend forever, so that no matter what observing systems are invented in the future, we shall never see the end?

At first it might seem that these questions are merely philosophical speculations and that there is no way of answering them. However, these are questions that the German astronomer Heinrich Olbers asked himself in 1826, and he proposed a means by which they might be investigated.

Olbers began by making certain assumptions about the universe:

1 The universe is infinite in extent.

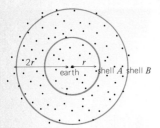

FIGURE 17-18
In a universe that is uniformly populated with stars, the number of stars in a spherical shell will vary as the square of its distance.

2 There are an infinite number of stars, and if taken on a large enough scale, the stars are uniformly distributed throughout space.

3 The universe is not only uniform in space but also in time.

4 The laws of physics apply throughout this infinite space.

What are the implications of these assumptions? Imagine our solar system within such an infinite universe and picture the universe as being divided up into many concentric shells (like those in an onion) with us at the center. The thickness of each shell is the same, and so the volumes of the shells are proportional to the square of their distances from us. If the universe is uniformly populated, therefore, (assumption 2) shell B of Fig. 17-18 should contain $2^2 = 4$ times as many stars as shell A because it is twice as far away. On the other hand, the light from a star in shell B will have spread out over a very large sphere by the time that it reaches us. Light intensity decreases as the square of the distance from the source. Each star in shell B thus contributes only $(\frac{1}{2})^2 = \frac{1}{4}$ the light of an equivalent star in shell A. The total light contribution of shell B is thus $4 \times \frac{1}{4} = 1$ times the contribution of shell A.

Similar computations with any other shells would show that all contribute the same amount of light. If the universe is truly infinite, there must be an infinite number of such shells. Since each shell contributes the same amount of light, there should be infinite light at night. Even allowing for the fact that one star may shield the light of others behind it, the nighttime sky should still be as bright as day if the assumptions hold true. We know, of course that it is dark at night, and herein lies Olbers' paradox. Why is it dark at night?

We must remember that Olbers suggested this line of reasoning in 1826, well before the universe of galaxies described in Sec. 17-5 was discovered. Because the sky is not bright at night, he reasoned that something must be wrong with the original assumptions. Either the universe was not infinite or if it was, there must be a finite number of stars. Some contemporaries of Olbers were busy counting the numbers of stars in different patches of the sky at about the time he proposed his approach to the problem of the extent of the universe. They found that the stars are not uniformly distributed in space. As illustrated in Fig. 17-13, many more stars are visible in the direction of the Milky Way than are visible perpendicular to that direction. Both Olbers' reasoning and actual star counts thus seemed to point to the conclusion that the universe was finite. Not only was it finite, but the star counts showed it to have a lenslike, or elliptical, shape. Small wonder then that for almost a century the idea of a finite universe limited to what we now know as the Milky Way galaxy prevailed.

With the discovery of distant galaxies early in this century, Olbers' paradox arose again. Counts of galaxies showed them to be more or less uniformly distributed in space. Therefore, if we assume the number of galaxies to be infinite, we find ourselves with the same situation pictured in Fig. 17-18, only this time the points on the diagram represent galaxies instead of individual stars.

In Chap. 3 we noted that light from a receding object should appear reddened

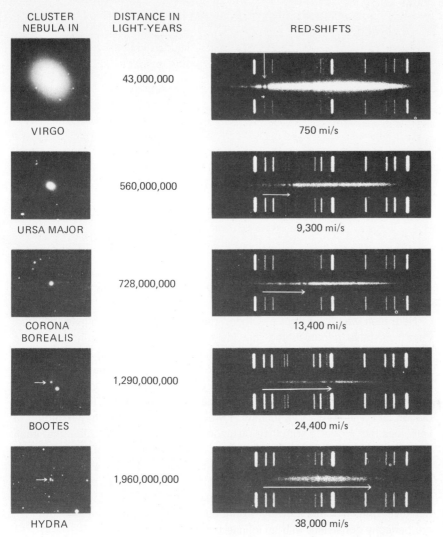

CLUSTER NEBULA IN	DISTANCE IN LIGHT-YEARS	RED-SHIFTS
VIRGO	43,000,000	750 mi/s
URSA MAJOR	560,000,000	9,300 mi/s
CORONA BOREALIS	728,000,000	13,400 mi/s
BOOTES	1,290,000,000	24,400 mi/s
HYDRA	1,960,000,000	38,000 mi/s

FIGURE 17-19
Actual spectrograms of five galaxies showing the extent of red shift in the H and K lines of calcium. The galaxies appear smaller and smaller with increasing distance. *Hale Observatories photographs.*

whereas that from an approaching source should be bluer, and we found that this Doppler effect for light can be measured with sensitive spectrographs. During the mid-1920s, shortly after Hubble demonstrated that many of the objects astronomers had considered as gaseous nebulae were actually stellar galaxies, he and his associates began to study the problem of galactic motions as revealed by the Doppler shift. They discovered that light from all the distant galaxies was reddened or in other words that all the galaxies are receding from us (Fig. 17-19). Even more startling was the discovery that their recession velocities are proportional to their distance. A galaxy twice as far away as another shows twice the

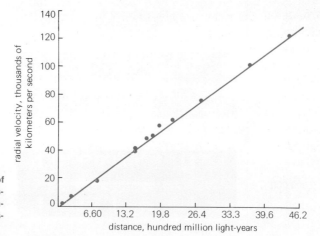

FIGURE 17-20
The velocity of recession of galaxies increases with distance. It was from such measurements that Hubble established his law of red shifts.

recession velocity; one four times as far away recedes with four times the velocity.

Here then was a way out of Olbers' paradox, even for an infinite universe. Physicists have demonstrated that the radiation from a receding source is weakened and that the degree of weakening is a function of its radial velocity. With this in mind let us return to Fig. 17-18 and our original analysis of Olbers' paradox. There we showed that each shell of stars contributes an equal amount of radiation. If the radiation from an individual layer is taken as 1, then the total radiation is $1 + 1 + 1 + \cdots$ to infinity. However, if galaxies are truly receding at velocities that increase with their distance from us, it becomes clear that each layer cannot be contributing the same amount of light. Instead of $1 + 1 + 1 + \cdots$ to infinity we are dealing here with a situation like $1 + \frac{1}{2} + \frac{1}{4} + \frac{1}{8} + \cdots$ to infinity. Even though there are an infinite number of layers, such a series does not add up to infinity. In fact, the series chosen for illustration $(1 + \frac{1}{2} + \frac{1}{4} + \cdots)$ approaches but never quite reaches 2 even if extended indefinitely. Dark skies at night then are perfectly consistent with an infinite but expanding universe.

17-7 COSMOLOGICAL MODELS

Let us examine Hubble's discovery that galaxies move away from us with speeds that are proportional to their distance. Figure 17-20 is a plot of the radial velocities of galaxies, as determined from the Doppler shift, against distance. It illustrates the law of red shifts, which can be written $V = Hr$, where V is the radial velocity, r is the distance to the galactic cluster, and H is Hubble's constant.

Does the measured recession of the galaxies as viewed from earth mean that the earth after all is at the center of things? Not at all. There is no reason for believing that our little part of the universe is really different from any other part. A more logical explanation for the observed radial velocities of galaxies is that the entire universe is expanding. We can liken such an expanding universe to dots on a balloon being inflated. No matter which dot is chosen as an observation site, all others appear to be moving away from it (Fig. 17-21).

Let us carry our balloon analogy a little further and see what would happen if the air were let out. Then, of course, the dots would approach each other until the whole thing shrank to nearly nothing. It seems logical to speculate that the universe also might once have been in such a deflated condition. This being the case, it follows that the material of an expanding universe might once have been concentrated in a single glob. In fact, if the present rate of recession of the galaxies is assumed to have remained constant, it is easy to calculate time zero when all matter of the universe was concentrated in one monstrous mass. For any galaxy this time would be equal to its distance divided by its velocity r/V. We saw earlier that $V = Hr$, and so r/V is simply the reciprocal of Hubble's constant H. Depending upon the value adopted for Hubble's constant, the age of the universe turns out to be somewhere in the range of 7 to 15 billion years.

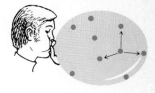

FIGURE 17-21
No matter which dot we choose as a reference, all others move away from it as the balloon is inflated.

The idea that the universe began by the explosion of a single mass is frequently referred to as the *big-bang* theory of cosmology. Abbé Lemaître, a Belgian cosmologist, proposed a version of this theory in the 1920s, and it was championed and refined by the late American physicist George Gamow. The big-bang theory is an evolutionary model of the universe. According to this theory, the universe had a finite starting time and has been expanding (evolving) ever since.

Just as the concept of a universe of fixed dimensions was bothersome to some astronomers, so too was the thought of a universe of finite age. According to the big-bang theory, the primordial explosion marked the beginning. It was then that most of the elements were supposedly formed and the universe as we know it began. Several British astronomers (F. Hoyle, H. Bondi, and T. Gold) proposed a cosmological theory in the 1940s that managed to avoid the troublesome question of a finite age. Their theory is known as the *steady-state theory*. It assumes that the universe is infinite in both space and time and that it is unchanging. To account for the fact that the galaxies are moving apart Hoyle and his colleagues made the startling assumption that new matter is created continuously in space at just the rate necessary to compensate for the expansion. The new matter is in the form of the simplest element, hydrogen, which eventually concentrates to form new stars and galaxies to keep their distribution in space forever the same in spite of the expansion.

The idea of matter being continuously created at first seems to violate the principles of science, and one might thus be led to favor the big-bang theory. However, even if the universe started by the explosion of a giant ball of matter, there is still the problem of explaining how the cosmic egg was created in the first place.

What evidence might help test these two cosmological models? Figure 17-22 diagrammatically portrays the universe at two points in time according to the big-bang and the steady-state interpretations. According to the evolutionary model, the galaxies became more widely separated with time, whereas there is

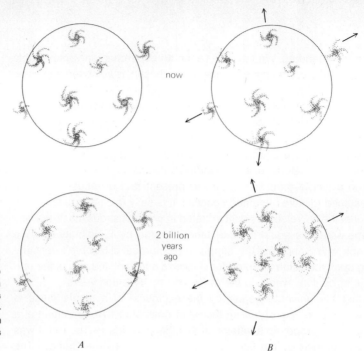

FIGURE 17-22

The steady-state (*A*) and evolutionary (*B*) universes at two points in time. Whereas a steady-state universe remains uniformly populated with galaxies, the galactic density in the big-bang situation changes with time.

no change in spacing with the continuous-creation model. In looking at a galaxy that is today a billion light years away we are seeing it as it was a billion years ago. According to the big-bang theory, the galaxies were closer together a billion years ago and furthermore they were a billion years younger. The steady-state model, on the other hand, sees the universe as constant in time and space. It would predict that the galaxies a billion light years from us should be of the same average age and possess the same spacing as those near to us.

It would seem then that astronomers should be able to decide between the two cosmological models by comparing the very distant galaxies with those near to us. If galaxies that are several billion light years away turn out to be closer together or if they are markedly different (younger) than the nearby galaxies, the big-bang theory would fit best. Conversely, if the distant galaxies turned out to possess the same spacing and the same general characteristics as their nearer counterparts, the steady-state theory would provide a better explanation.

It is very difficult to estimate the spacings and the properties of the distant galaxies that appear only as fuzzy patches of light on even the biggest telescopes. There are presently no reliable yardsticks for measuring distances in the billion-light-year range, and moreover it is impossible even to resolve individual stars at that distance, let alone to estimate their age. In spite of these difficulties the evidence seems to favor the big-bang model. The more distant galaxies appear to be receding a little slower than they should according to the law of red shifts. This observation favors the evolutionary model. However, much more remains to be done, and new theories will doubtless be forthcoming before scientists settle on a particular cosmological model.

SUMMARY

Interstellar distances are very great and are measured in light-years or in parsecs. Distances to the nearby stars can be determined from their parallax, whereas Cepheid variables, a type of pulsating star, are used in estimating distances to far-away stars.

Some stars are thousands of times as big as the sun, whereas others are only about the size of our moon. Some are blue and very hot; others red and relatively cool. Although stars vary greatly in diameter and temperature, most have masses within the range from one-fifth to 5 times the sun's mass. Mass is an important stellar property because stellar temperatures, spectral classes, and expected lifetimes all seem related to it.

A typical star is thought to begin as a contracting diffuse mass of gas and dust. Contraction raises the internal temperature to the point where hydrogen fusion begins. The new star thus formed spends most of its time on the main sequence of the H-R diagram. When the hydrogen of the interior is nearly depleted, another period of contraction further increases the internal temperature, eventually to trigger nuclear reactions involving the heavy elements. This new-found energy causes the star to expand into a red giant. The heavy elements are not nearly so abundant as the original hydrogen, and the star soon runs out of fuel and contracts into a tiny dwarf.

Galaxies contain countless billions of stars. Most are elliptical in shape with spiral arms. The nearest galaxy, Andromeda, is 2 billion light-years from us; others have been estimated to be 5 billion light-years away. They seem to be uniformly distributed in space.

Spectral studies of light from galaxies show a progressive shift toward the red with distance. This red shift suggests that the galaxies are moving apart with recession rates directly proportional to distance. The universe thus appears to be expanding. Two main cosmic models have been proposed to account for the observed expansion. The big-bang theory supposes that the universe began with a large explosion which threw matter outward from a central cosmic egg. The steady-state theory proposes that matter is continuously created in intergalactic space and that the universe, although expanding, is constant in its properties.

QUESTIONS

1 Why did it take astronomers so long to detect stellar parallax?
2 Two Cepheid variables are found to have the same period, yet one is only one-sixteenth as bright as the other. What are their relative distances?
3 Why is the parallax method of determining distances to the stars restricted to about 100 light-years?
4 Two stars are found to have the same magnitude. Does this mean that they are equidistant? Can we infer that they are the same size? Explain.
5 A star is found to radiate most intensely at a wavelength of 6.8×10^{-5} centimeter. What is its surface temperature?
6 Consider two stars, one of which is twice as luminous as the other yet both belong to the same spectral class and both have the same parallax. How are the two related in diameter?
7 How do we know the shape of our galaxy when we are situated within it?
8 Briefly describe the predicted life history of a typical star.
9 How are distances to faraway galaxies estimated?
10 How do the big-bang and the continuous-creation hypotheses differ in regard to the size and age of the universe?

REFERENCES

Abell, G. O.: "Exploration of the Universe," 2d ed., Holt, Rinehart and Winston, Inc., New York, 1969.

Asimov, Isaac: "The Universe: From Flat Earth to Quasar," Walker Publishing Company, Inc., New York, 1966.

Gamow, G.: "The Creation of the Universe," rev. ed., The Viking Press, Inc., New York, 1961.

Hoyle, Fred: "Frontiers of Astronomy," The New American Library, New York, 1963.

Hynek, J. A., and N. D. Anderson: "A Challenge of the Universe," McGraw-Hill Book Company, New York, 1963.

Lovell, Sir Bernard: "Our Present Knowledge of the Universe," Harvard University Press, Cambridge, Mass., 1967.

Mehlin, Theodore G.: "Astronomy and the Origin of the Earth," Wm. C. Brown Company Publishers, Dubuque, Iowa, 1968.

Struve, Otto, B. Lunds, and H. Pillans: "Elementary Astronomy," Oxford University Press, New York, 1959.

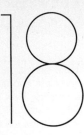

THE EARTH'S ORIGIN

It may seem strange to find a chapter on the earth's beginning at the end of a book about the earth, but there is good reason for this arrangement. Man has probably speculated about the origin of his planet since he first began to think. Until the end of the sixteenth century, however, most speculations attributed the earth's birth to some form of divine creation. These early stories were simple compared to modern cosmological explanations because they had to account for only a few observations. Moreover, they differed from scientific explanations of the earth's beginning because they were incapable of being tested by further observations.

With the growth of knowledge about the solar system, it was recognized that the order observed in the system cannot have been the result of some chance event. Consequently hypotheses of origin that could logically account for the observed characteristics of the system were developed. Like the model earth we constructed in Chap. 5, the best hypothesis of origin for the earth and the solar system is one which explains the largest number of observations and stays within the limits set by the laws governing the behavior of matter and energy.

Now we can see why the earth's beginning is discussed at the end. It is only with the background knowledge of such topics as the motion of the planets, the age of the earth and its rocks, the structure of the earth, the compositions of the planets and stars, etc., that we can truly assess any hypothesis of origin for the earth. Perhaps even more important, such knowledge suggests other observations by which theories of origin can be tested by further observations.

18-1 ASTRONOMICAL LIMITS AND EARLY HYPOTHESES FOR THE ORIGIN OF THE SOLAR SYSTEM

In Chap. 15 we looked into the question of radioactive dating of earth materials. We found that there is good reason for concluding that the earth formed some 4.5

FIGURE 18-1
In the eighteenth century objects like this spiral galaxy were thought to be whirling gaseous nebulae because telescopes then could not resolve individual stars. The Kant-Laplace nebular hypothesis arose from observations of such objects. *Hale Observatories photograph.*

billion years ago and that the oldest exposed rocks are of the order of 3 billion years old. There is no direct record on earth, therefore, of the events or conditions of its birth, a lack which obviously complicates the problem of deciphering the earth's origin.

The best that can be done, therefore, is to put together a picture of the origin of the earth, planets, and sun that accounts for the observed characteristics of the solar system. Before proceeding to some of the early speculations, we briefly review what is known about the system. Any hypothesis of origin must account for the following observations:

1 The sun, planets, satellites, and meteorites all appear to have been made from the same mixture of chemical elements.
2 Over 99.8 percent of the mass of the solar system is in the sun.
3 The planets all revolve about the sun in the same direction in nearly circular orbits, and they lie roughly in the same plane.
4 The planets exhibit a regularity of spacing expressed by Bode's law (Table 18-1) and form two distinct groups, the inner, small terrestrial planets (Mercury, Venus, Earth, and Mars) and the outer, large planets (Jupiter, Saturn, Uranus, and Neptune).
5 Although 99.8 percent of the mass of the solar system is in the sun, over 98 percent of the angular momentum of the system resides in the planets.

Many hypotheses have been proposed to account for the regularity of the solar system thus summarized. The most widely recognized of these fall into two groups, those which visualize the planets as evolving slowly along with the sun and those which invoke some catastrophic event to account for the development of the planetary system.

The idea that the planets evolved along with the sun from a large, hot, rotating mass of gas and dust was first suggested by Immanuel Kant in 1755. Pierre de Laplace amplified Kant's nebular hypothesis in 1796. The Kant-Laplace explanation for the formation of the solar system was influenced by objects in the sky like

TABLE 18-1
Bode's law*

	Planets									
	Mercury	Venus	Earth	Mars	Asteroids	Jupiter	Saturn	Uranus	Neptune	Pluto
Constant	0.4	0.4	0.4	0.4	0.4	0.4	0.4	0.4	0.4	0.4
$+0x, x, 2x, 4x, \ldots$	0.0	0.3	0.6	1.2	2.4	4.8	9.6	19.2	38.4	76.8
	—	—	—	—	—	—	—	—	—	—
Total = distance predicted by Bode's law	0.4	0.7	1.0	1.6	2.8	5.2	10.0	19.6	38.8	77.2
Actual distance	0.4	0.7	1.0†	1.5	(2.8)	5.2	9.5	19.2	30.1	39.5

*This empirical scheme was suggested by Bode in 1772; distances are in astronomical units.
†By definition

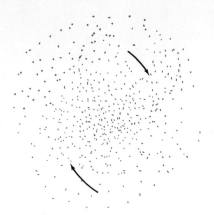 

FIGURE 18-2
The Laplace hypothesis begins with a rotating hot gaseous nebula. As the nebula shrinks, it turns faster and faster, sloughing off rings of gas to condense into planets. The central core forms the sun.

that in Fig. 18-1. In the eighteenth century such galaxies of stars were mistakenly thought to be gaseous nebulae.

Kant proposed that the solar system origninated from a contracting gaseous nebula in the following manner. As the gaseous cloud contracted, its rotational velocity increased according to the law of conservation of angular momentum. We can think of angular momentum as the product mvr, where m is mass, v is rotational velocity, and r is the distance from the center of rotation. For any small part of a nebula of constant m, therefore, v must increase with decreasing r (contraction) in order to keep mvr constant. According to Laplace, this rotational speed finally reached a point where rings of gas and dust sloughed off from the main mass, and these rings ultimately condensed to form the planets (Fig. 18-2).

The Kant-Laplace hypothesis explains much of the known regularity of the solar system. According to their model, the planets should lie in roughly the same plane and should rotate in the same direction about the central sun. Consequently this hypothesis dominated the scene for over a century.

The nebular hypothesis was not without faults, however. According to Laplace's theory, most of the angular momentum of the system should be in the sun because that is where the mass is. As we have noted, the reverse is actually true. By 1900 it became clear that the original nebular hypothesis completely failed to account for the distribution of angular momentum in the solar system. Moreover, it was shown that a rotating cloud of gas and dust would be more likely to continue developing spiral arms than to slough off a series of rings. Accordingly the Laplace interpretation lost favor.

Early in the twentieth century two Americans, T. C. Chamberlin, a geologist, and F. R. Moulton, an astronomer, proposed that the planets had been formed from material torn out of the sun by a passing star. As the gases drawn from the sun by such a near collision cooled in space, they supposedly formed vast numbers of solid particles, which Chamberlin and Moulton called *plane-tesimals.* According to this hypothesis, the attraction of the passing star im-

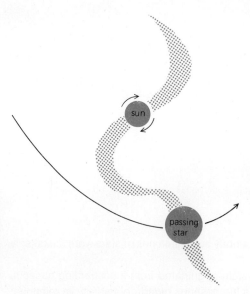

FIGURE 18-3
Chamberlin and Moulton hypothesized a near miss between the sun and a passing star. Solid particles called planetesimals condensed from the eruptions thus produced and slowly accreted to form the planets.

parted strong rotational motion to the material pulled from the sun, thus accounting for the high momentum of the planets, which supposedly condensed through collisions of the planetesimals (Fig. 18-3).

Whereas the Chamberlin-Moulton hypothesis solved the dilemma of angular momentum according to its proposers, it suffered from some serious defects. Although variants of such a dynamic-encounter hypothesis persisted until the 1950s, they became less and less popular, as it was recognized that such an encounter between stars was extremely improbable. Measurements made during the early part of this century revealed the distances between stars to be so great that it was safe to predict that only a few such near misses could have occurred among the 100 billion stars of our galaxy within the past 2 to 3 billion years. Admittedly our sun could have been one of the unlucky stars, but to base a theory on such an unlikely event is unsatisfactory. To overcome the extreme improbability of a near collision a variation of the explosion hypothesis evolved which suggested that our sun was originally a double star and that the planets were formed from material left behind when the double exploded.

Even more damaging to the encounter or explosion hypotheses was the analysis of the fate of material that might have been drawn from the sun by a near collision or an explosion. We know that the sun is very hot and that its gases are under tremendous pressure. If enough white-hot compressed gas had been pulled from the sun by a passing star, it should explode violently in the cold vacuum of space instead of condensing to form planetesimals. So it was back to some form of the evolutionary or nebular hypothesis.

In the mid 1940s a German physicist, C. von Weizsäcker, studied the problem

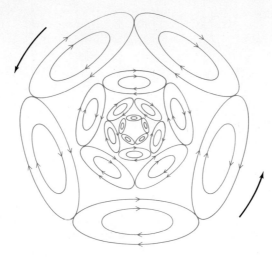

FIGURE 18-4
Weizsäcker pictured the planets as condensing from vortices in a rotating mantle of gas and dust surrounding the sun. According to this interpretation, planets form at boundaries between vortices, which accounts for their direction of rotation and revolution and spacing.

of motion in a large cloud of gas and dust rotating about a central body. From theory and laboratory experience with rotating fluids he was able to demonstrate that such a cloud would develop vortices, or eddies. The eddies closer to the center of mass should be small and fast whereas those in the outskirts should be large. While much of the gas of such a system would escape to outer space as the central sun started to radiate, some of it, together with the dust particles, would slowly accrete to form the planets. Weizsäcker's scheme (Fig. 18-4) not only explains the regular motions of the planets and satellites but also accounts for the spacings between the planets as expressed by Bode's law. His model forms the basis of the currently accepted theory for the origin of the solar system discussed in the next section.

18-2 THE PROTOPLANET HYPOTHESIS

The most widely held model for the evolution of the solar system today was suggested by G. P. Kuiper, of the Yerkes Observatory, University of Chicago. Like the Kant-Laplace hypothesis, the Kuiper model begins with a vast nebulous mass of gas and dust similar to the material observed in the arms of the Milky Way. Contrary to some of the earlier ideas, the temperature of the original gaseous body must have been near absolute zero. At this temperature even a very slight gravitational attraction would overcome the velocity of the individual particles or molecules.

As the cloud condensed, it began to develop an ordered rotation at the expense of its initial turbulence. At first its density must have been about that of a laboratory vacuum. Slowly the density increased, along with a corresponding rise in rotational velocity. The equatorial regions, of course, must have shrunken

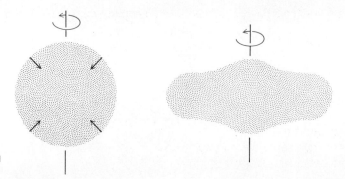

FIGURE 18-5
**Formation of a disk of gas and
dust in a condensing nebula.**

slower than the polar regions because of the centrifugal effect of rotation, and a
lens shape ultimately developed around the protosun (Fig. 18-5). Within this
equatorial web the ordered type of turbulence shown in Fig. 18-4 evolved.

How dense was the web of gas and dust out of which the planets grew? We
cannot go back to that time in the distant past to get a sample of the nebula as
the planets were forming, but it is possible to set limits on the density. Suppose
that we have two small, temporary spherical condensations in space. Would the
two stick together by mutual gravitational attraction? The force of attraction between such particles according to Newton is

$$F = \frac{Gm_1 m_2}{(2r)^2}$$

or if they had equal mass,

$$F = \frac{Gm^2}{4r^2}$$

However, as we found in our discussion of tides, the sun would attract the nearer
one (Fig. 18-6) more than the distant one. If the difference in the sun's gravitational attraction for the two particles was greater than their own mutual attraction,
they would be pulled apart instead of sticking together. Certainly their mutual
gravitational attraction must be at least as great as the sun's tidal effect for them
to stick together and ultimately grow to form larger fragments.

condensations
m m

$2r$

d

sun

FIGURE 18-6
**The sun's tidal effect on two
condensations in the nebula at
distance d.**

According to Fig. 18-6, the sun's attraction on the nearer particle is

Nearer particle: $\qquad \dfrac{GMm}{(d-r)^2} \qquad$ dynes

More distant particle: $\qquad \dfrac{GMm}{(d+r)^2} \qquad$ dynes

where M = mass of sun

$\qquad m$ = mass of particle

$\qquad d - r$ = distance from sun of nearer particle

$\qquad d + r$ = distance from sun of farther particle

The difference in attraction thus is

$$GMm\left[\frac{1}{(d-r)^2} - \frac{1}{(d+r)^2}\right] \qquad \text{dynes}$$

which reduces to

$$\frac{4GMmr}{d^3} \qquad \text{(approx)}$$

because d is very much larger than r.

We have already noted that for the particles to stick together the absolute minimum of their mutual attraction must at least equal this value, and so

$$\frac{Gm^2}{4r^2} = 4\frac{GMmr}{d^3} \qquad \text{or} \qquad \frac{m}{r^3} = \frac{16M}{d^3}$$

The mass of each of the particles if they are spherical is $m = 4\pi r^3 \rho/3$, where ρ is the density. Substituting this for m in the above equation, we get

$$\frac{4\pi r^3 \rho}{3r^3} = \frac{16M}{d^3} \qquad \text{or} \qquad \rho = \frac{4M}{d^3} \qquad \text{(approx)}$$

To put this into more meaningful form let us calculate the minimum density of the gaseous web from which the planets supposedly formed. The distance from the sun to the middle of the solar system is 1.5×10^{14} centimeters. Since the mass of the sun is 2×10^{33} grams, the average density of the solar nebula at the time that the planets condensed must have been

$$\frac{4(2 \times 10^{33})\,\text{g}}{(1.5 \times 10^{14})^3\,\text{cm}^3} = 2 \times 10^{-9}\,\text{g/cm}^3$$

By itself this figure does not tell us much. But let us see how it compares with another value for the density of the nebula out of which the planets grew according to our model. We have said that all the planets revolve about the sun in a plane. This is not exactly true. Mercury's orbit deviates by 6.6° from the average plane of the planets, and Jupiter moves in a plane slanting 0.3° from the average

FIGURE 18-7
The orbits of the inner planets seen edge on. The orbits of the outer planets deviate by comparable distances from the plane of the ecliptic (except for Pluto, whose path is clearly anomalous). This view establishes a minimum thickness for the initial planetary web.

minimum thickness
of planetary web

Mars   Venus   Mercury

Earth   Sun

(Fig. 18-7). These deviations give us a minimum estimate of the thickness of the nebula from which the planets must have condensed. From Fig. 18-7 we can see that the nebula must have been at least 0.1 astronomical unit thick. The radius of the nebula was at least 30 astronomical units, the distance from the sun to Neptune (neglecting Pluto, which may well be a captured satellite), and its volume was therefore about 10^{42} cubic centimeters. If the total mass of the planets as they exist today (2×10^{30} grams) were distributed in this volume, the average density would be about 2×10^{-12} gram per cubic centimeter. This is only one-thousandth of the value we determined earlier as the minimum density for the particles to begin to stick together by mutual gravitational attraction.

Now we can see why the Kuiper hypothesis is called the *protoplanet hypothesis*. A nebula containing only the same amount of material now present in the planets would have been far too tenuous to develop condensations. However, in one that was considerably denser and at a very low temperature condensations of gas, ice, and dust could form. These would collide and grow to ultimately form the protoplanets, which must have had the same composition as the original nebula—mainly hydrogen and helium, with only minor amounts of the heavy elements. These original planets must have been much larger than the present planets. Protoearth, for example, has been estimated to have been 1,000 times as massive as the earth is today.

During growth each of the protoplanets would have trapped its own disk of gas and dust, and within such planetary disks the satellite moons ultimately condensed. The protoplanet hypothesis thus explains not only the regularities of spacing and motions of the planets but also those of their satellites. Because the planets condensed from rapidly whirling eddies, the protoplanet scheme offers a better explanation for the distribution of angular momentum within the solar system. By itself, however, the hypothesis still fails to explain the exceptionally high concentration of angular momentum in the planets. Recent studies have demonstrated that the magnetic field of the protosun may have played a significant role in transferring angular momentum from this central body to the less dense part of the nebular disk where the planets were forming.

So far we have focused on the planetary part of the nebula. Now we turn our attention to the central mass, the protosun. As it slowly evolved, the protosun must eventually have acquired an internal density and temperature high enough to trigger the nuclear reactions described in Chap. 17. Radiation from the newly emerging sun would have markedly affected the protoplanets, particularly those closest to it. The temperatures of these planets would be expected to rise to the point where the light gases would attain their escape velocities, to be driven off into space by the solar radiation, just as the materials in a comet are today driven away by the sun's corpuscular radiation (Fig. 18-8).

The effect of the growing sun was to drive most of the original light elements away from the inner group of protoplanets. Today these planets contain very little hydrogen and helium, and their densities are between 3.8 and 5.5 times the density of water. The more massive outer protoplanets were able to hold onto a large portion of their initial gases both because of their large mass and because they are so far from the warming sun. As a result Jupiter, Saturn, Uranus, and Neptune still consist largely of the original light elements. The present densities of these planets range from 0.7 to 1.6 times that of water.

The protoplanet hypothesis does provide an adequate explanation for the regularities of the solar system listed in Sec. 18-1, but it is not necessarily the last word on the subject of origin. So far, for instance, there is no acceptable explanation for the belt of asteroids between Mars and Jupiter. Are these objects chunks of a former planet? If so, it must have been quite small because the total number of known asteroids would together only make a planet one-tenth the size of the earth. Our moon presents another problem. The ratio of the earth mass to moon mass is far greater than any other planet-satellite mass ratio in the solar system. With new data that are coming out of our space explorations these and other puzzling questions may soon be answered.

18-3 ORIGIN OF THE HYDROSPHERE AND ATMOSPHERE

What was the earth like when it formed some 4.5 billion years ago? We have already seen that it had already lost an early atmosphere of hydrogen and helium. Did it immediately develop the present hydrosphere and atmosphere after the light gases of protoearth were swept away, or have these spheres evolved slowly since the earth solidified to its present form?

We must again take an indirect approach in looking for an answer to these questions. Since the oldest known rocks are about a billion years younger than the earth itself, they cannot tell us about the conditions on our planet in the beginning. Some of the oldest known rocks, however, are water-deposited sediments, and so we do know that the hydrologic cycle was in operation at least 3 billion years ago. The question remains whether the water and air necessary for a surface cycle represent an initial condensation or whether they gradually accumulated on the earth's surface.

Even today the earth is losing hydrogen and helium to space in the upper atmosphere. As we saw back in Fig. 6-29, these light molecules are lost because some have speeds greater than their escape velocities. The reason that nitrogen or oxygen molecules are not now escaping from the atmosphere is that their maximum velocities are too low. The average velocity of a gas molecule is proportional to the square root of the absolute temperature divided by its mass. At the

FIGURE 18-8
The tail of a comet always points away from the sun. The force of repulsion of the sun's radiation drives the tenuous gases of the tail spaceward.
Courtesy of Sherman Schultz.

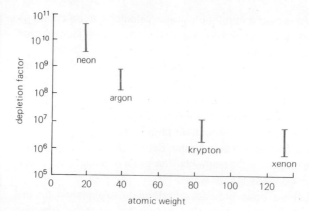

FIGURE 18-9
Depletion of the noble gases on earth relative to the sun and stars. Lighter gases are more highly depleted than heavier ones. *After H. Brown.*

existing temperature of the outer atmosphere only some of the low-mass molecules of hydrogen and helium attain velocities high enough to permit their escape from the earth's gravitational attraction. But what if the temperature of the earth had been significantly higher in the distant past? Then nitrogen, oxygen, and water vapor would also have escaped, and the earth could not possibly have retained a primitive atmosphere.

Our question seems to reduce to one of deciphering the earth's thermal history. Was the temperature of the earth ever sufficiently high to drive off any primitive nitrogen or water vapor? It seems evident that protoearth must have been very cold, otherwise the rapid motions of the gas particles from which it grew would have precluded any condensations. At the same time, however, the present layering of the earth into core, mantle, and crust plus the fact that most of the core even now is molten suggests that out planet must once have been quite hot.

A better clue to the earth's thermal history comes from a study of its rare gases, i.e., helium, neon, argon, krypton, and xenon, which are also called *noble* gases because they do not combine chemically with other elements easily. Unlike hydrogen and oxygen, for example, which may be bound up chemically as OH in solids such as the mineral hornblende, the rare gases are always in the gaseous state at the earth's temperature and must therefore always have been part of the atmosphere. This is one of the reasons why hydrogen is now many thousands of times more abundant than helium on earth.

The nebula from which the earth and other planets condensed must have had about the same composition as the sun because the sun still contains most of the mass of the system. To see how the earth has fared with respect to its rare gases, therefore, we can compare their abundances on earth with those in the sun. A direct comparison of weight percentages of these gases in the sun and earth would not be useful because the sun is composed mainly of hydrogen and helium and the earth has lost most of these elements. To get around this we can compare the ratios of the rare gases to an element that the earth has not lost, namely silicon, which is tied up in its solid rocks. A comparison of the silicon/noble gas ratios of the sun with those of the earth should show whether or not these gases have escaped from earth.

Harrison Brown, an American geochemist, investigated the relative abundances of the noble gases, and his results (Fig. 18-9) reveal that all the rare gases are highly depleted on earth relative to the sun and moreover that the degree of depletion is a function of their atomic weight. This is exactly what one would expect if the earth had sometime been heated sufficiently to promote the escape of the rare gases. Neon, for example is only 100 billionth as abundant relative to silicon on earth as it is in the sun. This means that if the earth started with the same neon/silicon ratio as the sun, and if silicon has not been lost, only 1 of every 100 billion molecules of neon originally in the earth's atmosphere is still there.

It certainly seems that the earth must have been much hotter than it is now in order to have lost these gases. And if, as the figures indicate, it lost most of its original argon (atomic weight = 40), it must also have lost most of any original water vapor (molecular weight = 18), nitrogen (molecular weight = 28), and oxygen (molecular weight = 32) from its primitive atmosphere.

Then where did all the hydrogen and oxygen now in water of the hydrosphere and all the nitrogen and oxygen in the present atmosphere come from? These elements, together with other constituents of the hydrosphere and atmosphere, are known to be chemically combined in some rock-forming minerals. Those hydrogen, oxygen, or nitrogen atoms which were chemically bound up in minerals in the primitive earth would not have been in the atmosphere when the original gases were lost and thus would have been retained in the earth. The present hydrosphere and atmosphere must have grown by a gradual degassing of the solid earth. Vulcanism releases large quantities of volatiles at the earth's surface. It is from such outpourings of volatiles over billions of years that the present atmosphere and hydrosphere are believed to have grown.

18-4 EVOLUTION OF THE HYDROSPHERE AND ATMOSPHERE

We have been led to the conclusion that the water and air now present at the earth's surface must have emanated from its interior since the solid earth formed 4.5 billion years ago. Is there any other evidence to support the interpretation that the vast quantities of water in the world's oceans are indeed a product of degassing?

Additional support comes from studies of geochemical balances at the earth's surface. In Chap. 14 we discussed the surface cycle of matter, which involves the breakdown of rocks by weathering, the transportation of the weathered

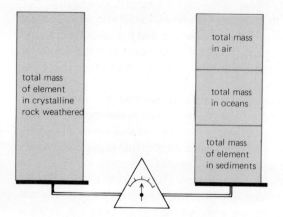

FIGURE 18-10
Since nothing is lost during weathering, the total mass of an element released by weathering must equal its total mass in sediments plus its total mass in the oceans and its total mass in the atmosphere.

debris, and the deposition of sedimentary rocks. In studying element distributions at the earth's surface geochemists have drawn up balance sheets for the elements. Since nothing is lost during this cycle, the balance shown in Fig. 18-10 must pertain. Taking sodium as an example, the average sodium content of igneous rocks times the total mass of igneous rock weathered since weathering began must equal the average sodium content of sedimentary rocks times the total mass of these rocks plus the average concentration of sodium in the sea times the total mass of seawater plus the average sodium content of the atmosphere times its total mass. Some of the items in this conservation-of-mass equation are difficult to evaluate. Fortunately, most of the sodium released by weathering ends up in the sea. Since the total mass of seawater and its sodium content are well known, as are the average concentrations of sodium in igneous rocks and sediments, we can use the sodium balance to estimate the total amount of igneous rock that has been weathered.

TABLE 18-2
Geochemical balance sheets for the excess volatiles, 10^{20} grams*

	Water	Carbon as CO_2	Chlorine	Nitrogen	Sulfur
In atmosphere and hydrosphere	14,600	1.5	276	39	13
In sedimentary rock	2,100	920	30	4	15
Total	16,700	922	306	43	28
From weathering of igneous rocks	130	11	5	0.6	6
Excess	16,570	911	301	42	22

*Data from W. W. Rubey, Geologist History of Seawater: An Attempt to State the Problem, *Geol. Soc. Am. Bull.,* vol. 62, 1962.

By using this estimate of the total amount of igneous rock weathered since the beginning, other geochemical balances have been computed for many elements. It would be wrong to suggest that they all balance perfectly, because there are too many variables. The surprising thing is that most investigators do achieve a rough agreement for most elements. Some elements found at the earth's surface, however, are way out of balance. These elements could not possibly have been generated by the weathering of rock. They have been called the *excess volatiles* by W. W. Rubey because they are chiefly volatile at the earth's surface. Table 18-2 reveals the imbalance that exists for some of these excess volatiles.

So far this exercise has merely identified the excess volatiles and demonstrated that they could not have been released by weathering. It is significant, however, that these are exactly the materials that are brought to the earth's surface by volcanoes, fumaroles, and hot springs. Furthermore, analyses of small bubbles (Fig. 18-11) of fluid trapped in igneous rocks at the time of their formation also show a composition corresponding to that of the excess volatiles (Table 18-2). Compositionally then it seems reasonable to infer that the volatiles of the hydrosphere and atmosphere have indeed been brought to the surface from the interior by vulcanism.

Volcanic emanations seem able to account for the compositions of the hydrosphere and atmosphere, but are they an adequate source for all the earth's water and air? If the present rate of flow of hot springs and volcanic steam had persisted throughout geologic time, it would have filled the present ocean basins several hundred times over. This does not mean that our source is necessarily too large because only a fraction of the water exuded by hot springs and volcanoes is new water. Much of it is simply surface water that is recirculated.

We can further see that degassing of the interior is indeed an adequate source for the water of the oceans by examining the composition of the earth's mantle. Although the mantle has not been sampled directly, analyses of stony meteorites and of rock inclusions believed to have been brought up from the mantle show a water content of about 0.5 percent. The mantle has a mass of about 4×10^{27} grams. The water of the oceans amounts to 1.4×10^{24} grams, or $1.4 \times 10^{24}/4 \times 10^{27} \times 100 = 0.035$ percent of the mass of the mantle. Certainly the mantle appears to be an adequate source for all of the water in the oceans.

So far no reliable method has been devised of estimating ocean volumes in the geologic past. As a result some students of the problem propose that degassing of the interior was much more rapid during the first billion years of the earth's history and that there have only been slight additions of new volatiles during the past 3 billion years. The favored alternate view is that vulcanism has continually added to the earth's hydrosphere and atmosphere since the beginning 4.5 billion years ago.

One would expect evidence in the geologic record if the total volume of seawater had increased gradually through the ages. Unfortunately a slow

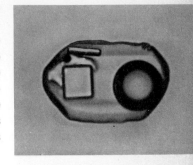

FIGURE 18-11

Inclusion of fluid trapped in a quartz crystal as it grew. The inclusion is only $\frac{2}{1000}$ inch long. It originally was filled with a homogeneous liquid, but at the low temperatures on the earth's surface it contracted to form the vapor bubble, and it has deposited tiny crystals. Analyses of such inclusions provide information on the composition of volatiles coming from the depths of the earth. *Courtesy of E. Roedder.*

increase in the total volume of seawater does not necessarily imply a change in the surface area of the seas. As we found in Chap. 3, the heights of the continents and the depths of the oceans are dictated by isostasy. There is good reason to believe that light continental crust, which makes the continents ride high, evolved slowly in time by weathering, sedimentation, and mountain building (Chap. 15). Isostasy demands that the higher the light continents the deeper the ocean basins. Thus although water may have been added continually to the oceans throughout geologic time, the surface areas of the seas might not have changed significantly during the past 3 billion years. In fact the processes of continental development and the filling of the seas might well be interrelated.

18-5 LIFE AND THE ATMOSPHERE

If the materials of the atmosphere did indeed arise from a gradual degassing of the earth's interior, as discussed in Sec. 18-3, we are faced with the problem of accounting for its present composition. The volatiles brought to the earth's surface by volcanoes are chiefly H_2O, CO_2, HCl, N_2, H_2S, and SO_2. Of these constituents the chlorine and sulfur would have accumulated with the water in the seas, leaving the carbon oxides, nitrogen, and hydrogen for the atmosphere. These constituents would probably have occurred in reduced compounds such as ammonia, NH_4, and methane, CH_4.

The presence of hydrogen and other reduced gases in volcanic emanations tells us that a primitive atmosphere formed from volcanic emanations could not have contained free oxygen, as any free oxygen in such a mix would have reacted with methane or hydrogen to form carbon dioxide and water. Additional evidence for this conclusion comes from the valence state of iron in volcanic rocks. Iron in these rocks is largely in the ferrous state, Fe^{2+}. If there had been free oxygen in volcanic gases, it would have oxidized the ferrous iron to ferric, (Fe^{3+}), iron. How then can we reconcile our present oxygen-rich atmosphere with the oxygen-free atmosphere expected from degassing?

It is known that some water vapor decomposes in the upper atmosphere under the sun's ultraviolet radiation into hydrogen and oxygen. We have also seen that hydrogen can escape from the earth's gravitational attraction; here is a means whereby free oxygen can be generated. There is no doubt that some of the free oxygen of the atmosphere evolved in this way. However, this slow process seems entirely inadequate to account for the present 20 percent oxygen, especially when we consider that any initial free oxygen would have been quickly used up in the oxidation of surface materials.

Oxygen is effectively generated by plant life. By the process of photosynthesis plants are able to utilize sunlight to change water and atmospheric carbon dioxide into organic matter with the release of oxygen. Of course in the present atmosphere the reverse process also occurs. Organic debris, like leaves and trees that fall to the ground, is quickly oxidized to return carbon dioxide to

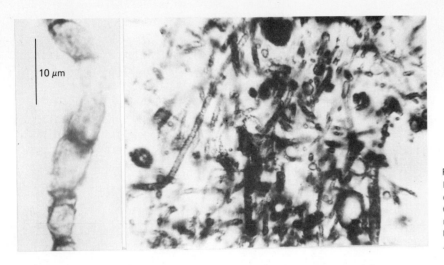

FIGURE 18-12
Plant fragments 2 billion years old from the Gunflint chert of Ontario, Canada. These forms resemble modern bacteria and blue-green algae. *Courtesy of Elso Barghoorn.*

the air just as surely as if it were burned. Otherwise the continents would be choked with dead organic debris. Today there is a close tie between the atmosphere and life activity.

The present relationship between living things and air cannot always have been the same. The fossil record clearly reveals that animals which require oxygen for survival first became abundant at the beginning of the Paleozoic Era, some 600 million years ago. Land plants became widespread only during the Devonian Period, some 200 million years later. Therefore, if the composition of the atmosphere is somehow related to life, as seems to be the case, we must conclude that its composition, like the abundance and diversity of life forms, has also evolved in time.

Although the first evidence of abundant life is found in the rocks of the Cambrian System, remains of simple life forms have been detected in much older rocks. In fact within the past two decades the earliest evidences of life observed in the rocks has been pushed farther back into the geologic record. Figure 18-12 shows some plant fragments from the 2-billion-year-old Gunflint chert of Ontario. Recently similar specimens of blue-green algae and bacterialike objects were discovered in 3-billion-year-old rocks. There is now no question that life in its simplest forms is traceable to the beginning of geologic history. However, it is equally well established that an explosion in animal populations occurred somewhere around 600 million years ago.

So far then we have been led to conclude that life must have started in an atmosphere that was very different from the present one. Although no one has yet been able to create life artificially, students of the problem are convinced that life could only have developed from inorganic matter in an oxygen-free environment. Had there been free oxygen in the primitive atmosphere, the organic compounds

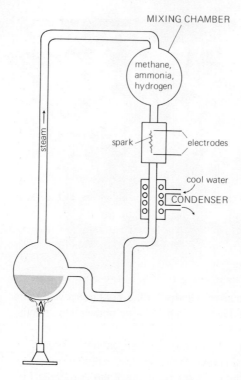

MIXING CHAMBER

methane,
ammonia,
hydrogen

steam

spark — electrodes

cool water

CONDENSER

FIGURE 18-13
S. L. Miller's apparatus for re-
producing primitive earth conditions. Continued operation of
the cycle results in the formation of amino acids, the basic
building blocks of proteins and
living things.

from which life potentially developed would have been quickly oxidized. Without oxygen, however, in an atmosphere of carbon dioxide, CO_2, methane, CH_4, and ammonia, NH_3, organic compounds would have been able to accumulate in seas and lakes. It is in local thick soups of such carbon compounds that life is believed to have originated on earth.

Support for this speculation was supplied by S. L. Miller, of the University of Chicago, in the 1950s. He circulated a mixture of methane, ammonia, water vapor, and hydrogen through a series of electric discharges (Fig. 18-13); after a time the water in the bottom of the closed apparatus was found to contain amino acids, which are the basic units of proteins and thus of life forms.

Let us suppose that life did indeed begin as we have indicated and try to see how the atmosphere might have changed in time. By 3 billion years ago we know that there already were simple algae capable of photosynthesis. This does not mean that the envelope of air immediately changed to one with free oxygen. All the free oxygen produced by the few early Precambrian plants must have quickly reacted with iron in solution or with the gases methane and ammonia. Gradually carbon dioxide and water vapor would replace methane and ammonia in the atmosphere ($CH_4 + 2O_2 \rightarrow CO_2 + 2H_2O$).

The conclusion that most of the oxygen produced by plants must have been tied up in reactions with other elements is not based on theory alone. It has been estimated that there are now some 6×10^{20} moles of carbon buried in sediments. This includes all the coal and oil deposits of the world plus lesser concentrations of organic carbon in sedimentary rocks. Each carbon atom taken as CO_2 from the atmosphere by plants results in the release of one molecule (O_2) of oxygen. Thus the total net oxygen production since photosynthesis began must be 6×10^{20} moles. The atmosphere now contains 0.38×10^{20} moles of oxygen, which is only about 6 percent of the total net oxygen production; 94 percent of the net oxygen generated by plants must have been involved in the oxidation of mineral matter and atmospheric gases at the earth's surface.

When did the free oxygen produced by photosynthesis finally reach the point where it began to accumulate in the atmosphere? In 1964 two atmospheric physicists, L. V. Berkener and L. C. Marshall, suggested that the great expansion of animal life around 600 million years ago marked the point where free oxygen first became a significant constituent of the atmosphere. Although their hypothesis is not without shortcomings, it is appealing because it explains the striking absence of life on land and in the shallow seas during the Precambrian. Today the sun's deadly ultraviolet radiation is absorbed by a layer of ozone, O_3, in the upper atmosphere. Without oxygen there could be no ozone layer and thus no life on land or in the shallow seas. Only under rocks and in the protected deeper waters could life have existed if ultraviolet rays were not screened out. According to Berkener and Marshall, the explosion of shallow marine life in the Cambrian marks the point where free oxygen in the atmosphere reached one-hundredth of its present value. The appearance of land organisms in the Devonian represents an oxygen concentration of one-tenth of the present value.

Although the details of atmospheric evolution remain a subject for continuing research, scientists are generally convinced that the earth's atmosphere was devoid of free oxygen throughout most of the long Precambrian Era. Just what the exact composition of the atmosphere was is still debated. Much present thinking envisions an initial atmosphere of CH_4, NH_3, and H_2, like the atmospheres of Jupiter and Saturn. This atmosphere changed by oxidation to one of N_2 and CO_2, like the probable present atmospheres of Venus and Mars. Finally, chiefly through photosynthetic activity, the N_2 and CO_2 became N_2 and O_2, the earth's present atmosphere.

18-6   NEW DATA FROM THE MOON

In our discussion of the earth's origin we noted that there are no exposed rocks for the first billion years or so of its history. This is one of the reasons why lunar exploration is of such great interest to scientists. Rocks older than any exposed on earth have already been returned for study from the moon, and it now appears certain that in the moon's highland areas man will be able to sample and study rocks dating back to the beginning of the solar system.

When *Apollo 11* rocketed moonward on July 16, 1969, scientists were not sure that the samples returned would be as old as they hoped. Until the late 1950s the prevailing view was that the moon's evolution had ceased eons ago. The moon was generally considered to be a dead and inactive planet. According to this cold-moon interpretation lunar rocks would, of course, be expected to date back to the earliest stages of the planetary system.

Not all investigators agreed, however, that the moon is cold and inactive. For centuries there had been sporadic reports of telescopic sightings of bright objects on the lunar surface. In 1958 a Russian astronomer reported seeing a reddish cloudlike object in the crater Alphonsus. Photographs of the same crater relayed to earth by *Ranger IX* several years later revealed darkened patches around some of the smaller craters in Alphonsus that were suggestive of volcanic outpourings. Such observations indicated that the moon is not dead but still losing heat by vulcanism at its surface. Furthermore, calculations made in the late 1950s based upon the expected concentrations of radioactive elements in lunar materials tended to confirm the view that the moon had once been molten and might still be losing internal heat. We can easily see that the activity of the moon would make quite a difference in the age of its rocks. If the moon were as active internally as the earth, its rocks too would have melted and reformed many times since its beginning and there would be no record of the initial events. Hence the ages of the first lunar rocks brought back to earth were awaited with great interest. The *Apollo 11* rocks from the Mare Tranquillitatis turned out to be around 3.7 billion years old. One erratic piece gave a radiometric age of 4.4 billion years, which is close to the expected age of the solar system.

These ages do not necessarily favor the cold-moon interpretation. In fact scientists are now convinced that the reverse is true and that the moon may even now be undergoing slight internal changes. The samples from *Apollo 12* gave ages of around 2.7 billion years. Like the first lunar rocks, they are chiefly volcanic in nature and exhibit features that suggest formation by melting within the lunar interior rather than by impact. Rocks collected on the *Apollo 14* and the *Apollo 15* missions also showed ages in the range of from 3 to over 4 billion years. It appears established that lunar vulcanism did indeed span a considerable period of time, and future missions may even reveal that it is still continuing locally.

Since some of the lunar samples so far studied are older than any rocks on earth, we might wonder if they have helped clarify the picture of the early history of the earth and solar system. As with most scientific studies, the first assault on the newly acquired lunar materials has raised about as many new questions as it has answered. To date samples have been collected from only a tiny fraction of the moon's surface, and although they already have shown that the surface rocks are variable in both age and composition, any far-reaching conclusions must await further sampling.

The moon samples have provided some significant insights into the question of lunar history. Previous speculations on the origin of the moon supposed *(1)* that the moon had originally split off from the earth or *(2)* that the moon was a captured planet or *(3)* that the moon and earth had a common origin. While it is still not possible to make a definitive choice between these alternatives on the basis of the new information, there are now some significant new constraints on theories of lunar origin. If the moon did indeed separate from the earth, we now know that it must have done so sometime prior to 4.4 billion years ago. Moreover proponents of possibilities 1 and 3 must now account for small but significant differences in chemical composition between the moon and earth.

The lunar rocks provide samples of gases blown from the sun by the solar wind. Continuing studies of the abundances of the noble gases in lunar materials will provide a better estimate of the concentration of these gases in the sun, and, as we saw in Sec. 18-5, this will contribute to our understanding of the evolution of the earth's atmosphere. It will also help astronomers sharpen their models of solar evolution.

18-7 WHAT DOES THE FUTURE HOLD?

It seems fitting to end this book with a brief look at the earth's probable future. We have said that our planet, like a living thing, has a "physiology," and much of our discussion has been devoted to the processes now acting and interacting on and in the earth. On the basis of our knowledge of these processes what prognosis can we make for the ultimate fate of this dynamic planet?

The picture we get from our overview of the earth is that it is constantly changing and yet seems somehow changeless. On the surface, weathering and erosion continually act to move material from high to low areas. These processes break down and decompose existing rocks while at the same time forming new sedimentary rocks. They work to redistribute the chemical elements, increasing the amounts of some in the oceans, some in sedimentary rocks, and still others in soils or weathering residue. That these processes have been operative for a long, long time is evident from the existence of sedimentary rocks at least 3 billion years old.

This surface activity of the earth is balanced by equally active internal processes. Land that is eroded away is constantly replaced by new land generated by vulcanism or by upheavals resulting from forces acting beneath the surface. Great mountain chains are known to have risen from areas formerly covered by seas. The sedimentary rocks of the surface processes are locally remelted. The crust buckles and crumples where moving rigid plates driven by internal convection currents collide. Again we know from the dating of volcanic rocks and structures that these internal processes have been active throughout the expanse of geologic time.

These then are the processes that change and rechange our planet today. Let us now speculate on their future activity, focusing first on the internal processes. We know that the energy for the internal processes comes chiefly from the radioactive decay of isotopes of potassium, uranium, and thorium. These isotopes have half-lives measurable in billions of years. Consequently a marked slowing of the internal activity would not be expected for at least 10 to 15 billion years. At that time, however, most of the internal activity would cease.

Without the internal forces to create new crust, gradation would gradually flatten the continents as long as the sun continued to shine. For a time the continental regions would continue to rise by isostatic rebound, but ultimately the surface processes would win the battle. The continental areas would be worn flat. Our earth would be completely covered by water. Although the sites of former continents would still be recognizable as shallow portions of the seas, the earth would become a water planet.

This, however, is not likely to be earth's ultimate fate. In making the above prediction we assumed that the surface processes would continue unchanged. These processes are powered by the sun, and astronomers tell us that the sun already has spent about half its time on the main sequence. Available evidence suggests that long before the earth runs out of internal steam, the sun will leave the main sequence and evolve into a red giant. It is not possible to predict just how big the sun will get, but from experience with other giant stars it seems likely that it will reach the orbit of Mercury. This will have some dire effects on the planet earth. The waters of the oceans will boil, and any life that might then remain will be destroyed. A thick cloud of steam and other gases will completely surround our planet.

Eventually the sun will leave the giant stage and slowly evolve into a cold dwarf. The waters which will have again condensed to fill the oceans slowly will freeze over. From this icy planet the dwarf sun will appear as a tiny spot of dim light.

SUMMARY

Available evidence suggests that the solar system grew out of a flat disk of gas and dust whirling about the protosun. Initially the terrestrial planets were much larger than they are today. Heat from the newly evolving sun stripped these planets of their light gases, leaving them with about their present compositions some 4.5 to 5 billion years ago.

The primitive earth was different from the earth we know today. Chemical evidence strongly supports the view that the water and air that now encircle our globe were missing when the earth first became a stony planet. The materials of the hydrosphere and atmosphere are believed to have been added to the earth's surface by a gradual degassing of its interior.

For the first several billion years of its history the earth's atmosphere almost certainly was devoid of free oxygen. With the appearance of simple life forms some 3 billion years ago, plants began to manufacture oxygen from carbon dioxide by photosynthesis. At first this oxygen was quickly used up in chemical reactions with elements in the water and in the air. Gradually free oxygen began to appear in the atmosphere, and along with it animal life evolved sharply. The exact dates of the atmospheric changes are not known with certainty, but it appears likely that free oxygen did not become abundant until the beginning of the Paleozoic, some 600 million years ago.

The earth's ultimate fate will probably be determined by the sun. Before the earth runs out of internal fuel, the sun will evolve into a red giant. As our sun grows increasingly larger, the waters of the oceans will boil and all life on our planet will cease.

QUESTIONS

1 What are the principal characteristics of the solar system that any hypothesis of origin must explain?

2 Why are the catastrophic-encounter theories of origin for the solar system not widely accepted today?

3 If the earth and planets had depended upon the near collision of two stars, what could you say about the probability of finding other planetary systems in the universe?

4 What is Bode's law?

5 Why does Kuiper's protoplanet hypothesis assume that the planets were once much larger than now?

6 The escape velocities of Mars and Mercury are only slightly different. How then do you account for the fact that Mars has an atmosphere whereas Mercury does not?

7 If the planets evolved from a rotating disk of gas around the protosun, the satellites must have grown from disks of gas and dust surrounding the planets. Would the gaseous disks from which the satellites grew have been more or less dense than the solar nebula? Why?

8 On what evidence do we conclude that the earth must have lost any primitive atmosphere?

9 Jupiter and Saturn have ammonia, NH_3, in their atmosphere. On earth free nitrogen, N_2, makes up the bulk of the atmosphere, and there is no ammonia. Why the difference?

10 Why does it now appear evident that the moon is not completely cold and inactive but has internal processes?

11 It has been estimated that there are 6×10^{17} moles of carbon tied up in fossil fuel deposits. If all this coal, oil, and gas were burned, what fraction of our atmospheric storehouse of oxygen would be used up? (One mole of carbon combines with one mole of oxygen during burning. The atmosphere contains 0.38×10^{20} moles of oxygen.)

REFERENCES

Abell, G. O.: "Exploration of the Universe," 2d ed., Holt, Rinehart and Winston, Inc., New York, 1969.

Krauskopf, Konrad: "Introduction to Geochemistry," McGraw-Hill Book Company, New York, 1967.

Mason, Brian: "Principles of Geochemistry," John Wiley & Sons, Inc., New York, 1966.

Mehlin, Theodore G.: "Astronomy and the Origin of the Earth," Wm. C. Brown Company Publishers, Dubuque, Iowa, 1968.

Page, T., and L. W. Page (eds.): "The Origin of the Solar System," The Macmillan Company, New York, 1966.

APPENDIX

POWERS OF TEN, UNITS OF MEASURE, AND SOME CONVERSION FACTORS

A-1 POWERS OF TEN

In studying something as large as the earth and its place in the solar system and universe it is often necessary to use very large numbers. By contrast, investigations of the atomic composition of earth materials are concerned with very small numbers. To simplify the problem of making calculations with very large or very small numbers scientists commonly use powers of 10 to indicate the number of zeros. The number 4,500,000,000 is easier to work with when it is written 4.5×10^9. Some examples of this type of notation follow.

$$1,000,000,000 = 10^9 = \text{one billion}$$
$$1,000,000 = 10^6 = \text{one million}$$
$$1,000 = 10^3 = \text{one thousand}$$
$$10 = 10^1 = \text{ten}$$
$$0.001 = 10^{-3} = \text{one-thousandth}$$
$$0.000001 = 10^{-6} = \text{one-millionth}$$
$$0.000000001 = 10^{-9} = \text{one-billionth}$$

Powers of 10 are *multiplied* by adding the exponents. For example $2,000 \times 60,000 = 120,000,000$ can be written $(2 \times 10^3) \times (6 \times 10^4) = 12 \times 10^7$. In *division* the exponent of the divisor is subtracted from the exponent of the dividend. For example, $2,000/100 = 20$ can be written $(2 \times 10^3)/(1 \times 10^2) = 2 \times 10^1$.

A-2 UNITS OF MEASURE

Length

1 kilometer (km) $= 10^3$ meters $= 0.621$ mile (1 mi $= 1.610$ km)

1 meter (m) $= 10^2$ centimeters $= 39.4$ inches $= 3.28$ feet (1 ft $= 0.305$ m)

1 centimeter (cm) $= 10$ millimeters (mm) $= 0.394$ inch (1 in $= 2.54$ cm)

1 micrometer (μm) $= 10^{-3}$ millimeter $= 0.000394$ inch

1 angstrom (Å) $= 10^{-8}$ centimeter

Distance

1 astronomical unit (a.u.) $= 149.6 \times 10^6$ kilometers (mean distance between earth and sun)

1 light-year $= 9.46 \times 10^{12}$ kilometers $= 5.88 \times 10^{12}$ miles

1 parsec $= 3.26$ light-years

Area

1 square centimeter (cm²) $= 0.155$ square inch

1 square meter (m²) $= 10.7$ square feet

1 square kilometer (km²) $= 0.386$ square mile

Volume

1 cubic kilometer (km³) $= 10^9$ cubic meters $= 0.24$ cubic mile

1 cubic meter (m³) $= 10^6$ cubic centimeters $= 35.3$ cubic feet $= 264$ U.S. gallons

1 cubic centimeter (cm³) $= 0.061$ cubic inch

Mass

1 kilogram $= 10^3$ grams $= 2.205$ pounds (1 lb $= 0.45$ kg)

1 metric ton $= 10^6$ grams $= 2,205$ pounds $= 1.1$ U.S. tons (0.909 metric ton)

Temperature

To change degrees Fahrenheit (°F) to degrees Celsius (C°):

$$°C = \frac{°F - 32}{1.8}$$

To change Celsius to Fahrenheit:

$$°F = 1.8C° + 32$$

Force

One dyne is the force that will produce an acceleration of one centimeter per second per second when applied to a one-gram mass.

Pressure

1 bar $= 10^6$ dynes/cm² $= 14.5$ lb/in² (approximately 1 atmosphere)

1 millibar $= 10^{-3}$ bar

NAMES, SYMBOLS, AND ATOMIC NUMBERS OF THE NATURALLY OCCURRING ELEMENTS

Element	Symbol	Atomic number	Element	Symbol	Atomic number
Actinium	Ac	89	Neodymium	Nd	60
Aluminum	Al	13	Neon	Ne	10
Antimony	Sb	51	Nickel	Ni	28
Argon	Ar	18	Niobium	Nb	41
Arsenic	As	33	Nitrogen	N	7
Barium	Ba	56	Osmium	Os	76
Beryllium	Be	4	Oxygen	O	8
Bismuth	Bi	83	Palladium	Pd	46
Boron	B	5	Phosphorous	P	15
Bromine	Br	35	Platinum	Pt	78
Cadmium	Cd	48	Polonium	Po	84
Calcium	Ca	20	Potassium	K	19
Carbon	C	6	Praseodymium	Pr	59
Cerium	Ce	58	Protactinium	Pa	91
Cesium	Cs	55	Radium	Ra	88
Chlorine	Cl	17	Radon	Rn	86
Chromium	Cr	24	Rhenium	Re	75
Cobalt	Co	27	Rhodium	Rh	45
Copper	Cu	29	Rubidium	Rb	37
Dysprosium	Dy	66	Ruthenium	Ru	44
Erbium	Er	68	Samarium	Sm	62
Europium	Eu	63	Scandium	Sc	21
Fluorine	F	9	Selenium	Se	34
Gadolinium	Gd	64	Silicon	Si	14
Gallium	Ga	31	Silver	Ag	47
Germanium	Ge	32	Sodium	Na	11
Gold	Au	79	Strontium	Sr	38
Hafnium	Hf	72	Sulfur	S	16
Helium	He	2	Tantalum	Ta	73
Holmium	Ho	67	Tellurium	Te	52
Hydrogen	H	1	Terbium	Tb	65
Indium	In	49	Thallium	Tl	81
Iodine	I	53	Thorium	Th	90
Iridium	Ir	77	Thulium	Tm	69
Iron	Fe	26	Tin	Sn	50
Krypton	Kr	36	Titanium	Ti	22
Lanthanum	La	57	Tungsten	W	74
Lead	Pb	82	Uranium	U	92
Lithium	Li	3	Vanadium	V	23
Lutetium	Lu	71	Xenon	Xe	54
Magnesium	Mg	12	Ytterbium	Yb	70
Manganese	Mn	25	Yttrium	Y	39
Mercury	Hg	80	Zinc	Zn	30
Molybdenum	Mo	42	Zirconium	Zr	40

APPENDIX

C

PROPERTIES AND IDENTIFICATION OF MINERALS

In Chap. 4 we found that the physical properties of a mineral are determined chiefly by its internal atomic structure and to a lesser degree by its chemical composition. Because atomic structure and composition are what make one mineral different from another, the ultimate method of identification is to determine these basic characteristics. Internal atomic structures are found by x-ray analysis, which involves expensive and sophisticated instrumentation and considerable training in mathematics and crystal chemistry. Clearly this is not a process for day-to-day mineral identification.

Some important optical properties of minerals can be measured with precision by means of a polarizing (petrographic) microscope, and this is a common means of positive mineral identification. While not as costly as x-ray analysis, microscopic identification can be properly carried out only in the laboratory. Other techniques involving measurement of some physical property also depend upon laboratory facilities and cannot be used for routine identification in the field.

Fortunately, the 2,000 or so known mineral species are not equally abundant. The feldspars alone account for over half of all the minerals in the crust. Adding some 20 to 30 other minerals like quartz, pyroxene, and calcite to feldspar accounts for well over 90 percent of the total minerals in the crust. Usually the more common minerals can be identified by physical properties that are detectable by the senses or with simple tools. These properties are luster, color, streak, hardness, cleavage, fracture, and specific gravity.

C-1 PHYSICAL PROPERTIES OF MINERALS

Luster
This is the appearance of a mineral in reflected light. Minerals are grouped into two main classes on the basis of luster: (1) those whose luster is metallic (opaque and reflecting like polished metal) and (2) those with a nonmetallic luster. Nonmetallic lusters are further subdivided and described as glassy, adamantine or diamondlike, waxy, greasy, pearly, resinous, silky, etc.

Color
Although color is the most obvious physical property of a mineral, unfortunately few minerals have a constant color, and the color of a single species may not be

uniform from specimen to specimen. Quartz may be colorless and transparent, or it may occur in almost any shade from white, rose, blue, purple, yellow to black. The color of most minerals is not a diagnostic feature alone. Taken together, all the light-dependent properties (color, luster, and streak) are often diagnostic.

Streak

The color displayed by a mineral when powdered, streak may or may not be the same as the color of the mineral. The streak of a mineral is usually obtained by rubbing a specimen firmly against a small piece of unglazed porcelain. Streak is a fairly constant property; it can be used to good advantage in the identification of sulfide and oxide minerals, but it is not so useful for silicate or carbonate minerals because they all have white or gray streaks.

Hardness

One of the most helpful properties for identifying minerals, hardness is a measure of the mineral's resistance to being scratched or abraded by another substance. Talc, which can be scratched easily with the fingernail, if the softest mineral, and the diamond the hardest. All other minerals represent stages or degrees of hardness between or equal to these two. On this basis a hardness scale ranging from 1 (talc) to 10 (diamond) has been devised. The scale is as follows:

1	Talc	*6*	Orthoclase
2	Gypsum	*7*	Quartz
3	Calcite	*8*	Topaz
4	Fluorite	*9*	Corundum
5	Apatite	*10*	Diamond

The number associated with the name of each mineral in the scale is an expression of its degree of hardness. An unknown mineral that can scratch calcite but is itself scratched by fluorite thus has a hardness of between 3 and 4. For routine mineral identification it is usually sufficient to subdivide minerals into three hardness classes. Those scratched by the fingernail (hardness $2\frac{1}{2}$) are soft; those not scratched by the fingernail but scratched by a knife (hardness $5\frac{1}{2}$) are of medium hardness; and those not scratched by a knife are hard.

Fracture

Fracture refers to the manner in which a mineral breaks. The fractured surface of a mineral may be uneven, splintery, earthy, or conchoidal (smooth, very often concave, concentrically marked surface).

Cleavage

The tendency of some minerals to break along innumerable parallel planes is called cleavage. The easier such breaking or splitting takes place, the smoother and more brilliant the resulting cleavage. (Cleavage is in a sense a special type of fracture.) Cleavage directions reveal themselves in (*1*) straight edges; (*2*) smooth, reflecting planes; (*3*) numerous straight cracks lying parallel to one another. A mineral may not have any cleavage or it may have one, two, three, or more directions of cleavage. Cleavage is recorded with reference to the number of cleavage directions, the degree of perfection of development (excellent, good, poor), and the angle of intersection between adjacent cleavage faces.

Specific gravity

The weight of a substance relative to the weight of an equal volume of water is its specific gravity. Most minerals have specific gravities of about 2.7. The simplest way to determine this property when no great degree of accuracy is required is to compare the "heft" of pieces of different minerals (the pieces should be approximately the same size).

Other properties

Also useful in hand-specimen identification are crystal form, magnetism, ductility or lack of it, feel, and sometimes taste.

C-2 MINERAL IDENTIFICATION

The identification of an unknown mineral specimen from its physical properties is essentially an elimination procedure. Suppose that we wanted to identify a mineral that is known to be one of the 39 minerals listed in Table C-1. Initially our problem is that of picking one name out of 39. As soon as we observe that the unknown specimen has a metallic luster, the task reduces to choosing one name out of six because only chalcopyrite, galena, graphite, hematite, magnetite, and pyrite in the attached list exhibit metallic lusters. If our unknown has a brassy color, it must be either chalcopyrite or pyrite because of the metallic minerals only these are brassy yellow. The problem then reduces to looking for differences in these two look-alikes. It turns out that chalcopyrite is more yellow than pyrite and considerably softer. Usually this will suffice to distinguish between the two. If that is not enough, the fact that pyrite is frequently found in equidimensional cubic crystals may lead to a positive identification.

Table C-1 of minerals and their properties includes the most common minerals together with some selected minerals that have appeared elsewhere in this book. More extensive listings of mineral properties with identification keys are found in the mineralogy textbooks cited in the references for Chap. 4.

TABLE C-1
Properties of some common minerals

Mineral	Formula	Color	Hardness	Number of cleavage directions	Specific gravity	Observations
Actinolite (an amphibole)	$Ca_2(Mg, Fe)_5Si_8O_{22}(OH)_2$	White to light green	5–6	2 at about 60°	3.0–3.3	Commonly found in low- to medium-grade metamorphic rocks
Amphibole family	See actinolite, hornblende, tremolite			2 at about 60°		A group of rock-forming silicates with the double-chain configuration; hornblende is the most important
Apatite	$Ca_5(F, Cl)(PO_4)_3$	Green, brown, white	5	None	3.1–3.2	Commonly in six-sided (hexagonal) crystals
Andalusite	Al_2SiO_4	White, gray, brown	$7\frac{1}{2}$	2; good	3.15	Occurs in metamorphic rocks
Augite (a pyroxene)	$Ca(Mg, Fe, Al)(Al, Si)_2O_6$	Dark green, black	5–6	2 at about 90°	3.2–3.4	Important mineral of mafic igneous rocks; distinguished from hornblende by cleavage directions
Beryl	$Be_3Al_2Si_6O_{18}$	Transparent green, pink, white	$7\frac{1}{2}$–8	1; imperfect	2.8	Emerald, aquamarine, and morganite are gem varieties of beryl
Biotite (a mica)	$K(Mg, Fe)_3AlSi_3O_{10}(OH)_2$	Black, brown	$2\frac{1}{2}$–3	1; perfect	2.8–3.2	Common mineral in igneous and metamorphic rocks
Calcite	$CaCO_3$	White, clear	3	3; perfect; rhombohedral	2.71	Effervesces in cold dilute HCl; principal or only mineral in limestone
Chalcopyrite	$CuFeS_2$	Brass-yellow	$3\frac{1}{2}$–4	None	4.2	Metallic luster; softer and yellower than pyrite; ore of copper
Chlorite	$(Mg, Fe)_6(Al, Si)_4O_{10}(OH)_8$	Green	2	1; perfect	2.4–2.6	Common in low-grade metamorphic rock
Corundum	Al_2O_3	Transparent, blue, brown, red	9	None	4.0	Gemstones ruby (red) and sapphire (blue) are corundum
Diamond	C	Colorless	10	4; perfect	3.5	Occurs in ultramafic igneous rocks
Diopside (a pyroxene)	$CaMgSi_2O_6$	Light green	5–6	2 at nearly 90°	3.2	Occurs chiefly in metamorphosed dolostones

Mineral	Formula	Color	Hardness	Cleavage	Specific gravity	Remarks
Dolomite	$CaMg(CO_3)_2$	White, gray, pink	$3\frac{1}{2}$–4	3; perfect; rhombohedral	3.5	Unlike calcite, which it resembles, dolomite effervesces in cold dilute HCl only when powdered
Enstatite (a pyroxene)	$(Mg, Fe)_2Si_2O_6$	Gray, yellow, white	$5\frac{1}{2}$	2 at nearly 90°	3.2–3.5	Occurs in mafic igneous rocks, meteorites, and high-grade metamorphic rocks
Fluorite	CaF_2	Purple, clear, green	4	4; perfect	3.18	Cubic crystals common
Galena	PbS	Lead gray	$2\frac{1}{2}$	3; perfect; cubic	7.6	Metallic luster, cubic crystals; chief ore mineral of lead
Garnet group	$R_3''R_2'''(SiO_4)_3$ where R'' may be Ca, Mg, Fe, or Mn, and R''' may be Al, Fe, Ti, or Cr	Dark red, brown, green	7–$7\frac{1}{2}$	None	3.85–4.32	Occur chiefly in metamorphic rocks; often in 12-sided crystals
Goethite	$Fe_2O_3 \cdot H_2O$	Brown, yellow	3–$5\frac{1}{2}$	1; fair	4.2	Usually earthy with brown streak; an ore of iron
Graphite	C	Black	1	1; perfect	2.23	Frequently found in metamorphic rocks; used in lead pencils
Gypsum	$CaSO_4 \cdot 2H_2O$	Clear, white, pink	2	1; perfect 2; imperfect	2.32	In evaporite deposits; used in making plaster
Halite	$NaCl$	White, clear	$2\frac{1}{2}$	3; perfect; cubic	2.16	Salty taste; often in cubic crystal
Hematite	Fe_2O_3	Red, blue-gray	5–6	None	5.26	Luster earthy or metallic; red streak; ore of iron
Hornblende (an amphibole)	$Ca_2(Mg, Fe, Al)(Al,Si)_8O_{22}(OH)_2$	Dark green, black	6	2 at about 60°	3.0–3.4	Common dark mineral in igneous and metamorphic rocks
Kaolinite	$Al_2Si_2O_5(OH)_4$	White	2	1; perfect	2.6	Very fine-grained clay mineral; slippery feel; occurs in soils and sedimentary rocks
Lepidolite (a mica)	$K_2Li_3Al_3(AlSi_3O_{10})(OH)_2$	Lavender, pink	$2\frac{1}{2}$–4	1; perfect	2.8–3.0	Lithium mica; comparatively rare mineral found in pegmatites
Magnetite	Fe_3O_4	Black	6	None	5.18	Metallic luster, strongly magnetic; an ore of iron
Muscovite (a mica)	$KAl_2AlSi_3O_{10}(OH)_2$	Transparent, white	$2\frac{1}{2}$–3	1; perfect	2.8	Common mineral in metamorphic and granitic igneous rocks

TABLE C-1
Properties of some common minerals (*Continued*)

Mineral	Formula	Color	Hardness	Number of cleavage directions	Specific gravity	Observations
Olivine	$(Mg, Fe)_2SiO_4$	Light green	$6\frac{1}{2}$	None	3.3–3.6	Occurs chiefly in mafic igneous rocks
Orthoclase feldspar	$KAlSi_3O_8$	White, pink	6	1; perfect 1; good	2.56	The feldspars make up about 60 percent of igneous rocks and are common in metamorphic rocks
Plagioclase feldspar	$(Na, Ca)(Al, Si)_4O_8$	Gray, white	6	1; perfect 1; good	2.62–2.76	Differs from orthoclase in having striations on its cleavage surfaces
Pyroxene family	See augite, diopside, enstatite			2 at about 90°		A widespread group of rock-forming silicates with the single-chain configuration; augite is most important
Pyrite	FeS_2	Brassy yellow	6–$6\frac{1}{2}$	None	5.1	Frequently in cubic crystals
Quartz	SiO_2	Transparent, white, pink, gray	7	None	2.65	In igneous, sedimentary, and metamorphic rocks
Siderite	$FeCO_3$	Brown, buff	$3\frac{1}{2}$–4	3; perfect; rhombohedral	3.85	Same cleavage as calcite but denser; ore of iron
Sillimanite	Al_2SiO_5	White, brown, gray	7	1; good	3.24	Usually in needlelike crystals; occurs in high-grade metamorphic rocks
Talc	$Mg_3Si_4O_{10}(OH)_2$	Gray-white, green	1	1; perfect	2.7	Occurs in low-grade metamorphic rocks
Topaz	$Al_2SiO_4(OH, F)_2$	Colorless, blue, yellow, white, brown	8	1; good	3.5	Massive forms look like quartz; distinguished by its cleavage
Tremolite (an amphibole)	$Ca_2Mg_5Si_8O_{22}(OH)_2$	White	6	2 at about 60°	3.0	Occurs chiefly in metamorphic rocks
Wollastonite	$CaSiO_3$	White	5–6	2 at nearly 90°	3.1	Occurs in metamorphosed limestones
Zircon	$ZrSiO_4$	Brown, gray, green	$7\frac{1}{2}$	None	4.68	Transparent variety is used as gemstone; important accessory mineral in igneous rocks

INDEX